# 2009
# Senior
# *Biology 1*

## *Student Workbook*

 BIOZONE

# Senior *Biology 1 2009*
## *Student Workbook*

Previous annual editions 2002-2008
Eighth Edition 2009

**ISBN  978-1-877462-21-4**

Copyright © **2008** Richard Allan
Published by **BIOZONE International Ltd**

Printed by REPLIKA PRESS PVT LTD using paper
produced from renewable and waste materials

## About the Writing Team

Tracey Greenwood joined the staff of Biozone at the beginning of
1993. She has a Ph.D in biology, specialising in lake ecology, and
taught undergraduate and graduate biology at the University of
Waikato for four years.

Lissa Bainbridge-Smith worked in industry in a research and
development capacity for eight years before joining Biozone as an
author in 2007. Lissa has an M.Sc from Waikato University.

Richard Allan has had 11 years experience teaching senior biology
at Hillcrest High School in Hamilton, New Zealand. He attained a
Masters degree in biology at Waikato University, New Zealand.

Purchases of this workbook may be made direct from the publisher:

# www.thebiozone.com

**UNITED KINGDOM:**

BIOZONE Learning Media (UK) Ltd.
P.O. Box 23698, Edinburgh  EH5 2WX,
**Scotland**
Telephone:   +44 (131) 557 5060
FAX:            +44 (131) 557 5030
E-mail:         sales@biozone.co.uk

**ASIA & AUSTRALIA:**

BIOZONE Learning Media Australia
P.O. Box 7523,  GCMC 4217  QLD
**Australia**
Telephone:   +61 (7) 5575 4615
FAX:            +61 (7) 5572 0161
E-mail:          info@biozone.com.au

**NORTH & SOUTH AMERICA, AFRICA:**

BIOZONE International Ltd.
P.O. Box 13-034, Hamilton 3251, **New Zealand**
Telephone:   +64 (7) 856 8104
FREE Fax:    1-800-717-8751 (USA-Canada)
FAX:            +64 (7) 856 9243
E-mail:         sales@biozone.co.nz

## Preface to the 2009 Edition

This is the eighth edition of **Senior Biology 1**. It is designed to meet the needs of students in biology programs at grades 11 and 12 or equivalent. It is particularly well suited to students taking **International Baccalaureate** (IB) **Biology**, **Advanced Placement** (AP) **Biology**, or **Honors Biology**. Biozone's Senior Biology 1 and 2 workbooks cater for a wide audience and may contain more material than is required by any one particular biology program. The two compact softback volumes provide the ideal supplement to a compete biology program without the inconvenience of a single, large workbook. However, we would recommend purchasing both workbooks at the commencement of the teaching program to provide full flexibility and access to content. Previous editions have received very favorable reviews; see our web site: **www.thebiozone.com** for details.

There have been some changes to the content of this edition of Senior Biology 1. A new chapter, "*Cell Division and Organization*", has been included in this edition. It contains some of the material formerly located in "*Cell Structure*", as well as some new material on apoptosis and tissue types. Several pages from Senior Biology 2, mainly relating to gene technology and the production of human proteins, have been moved into the "*Gene Technology*" chapter. This edition also sees a small amount of material move into "*Microbes and Biotechnology*" in Senior Biology 2. Other new or updated activities can be found throughout the book and are clearly marked in the contents for easy reference. We have continued with the use of page tabs identifying "**Related activities**" in the workbook and "**Web links**". The tabs provide a simple way for students to locate related material within the workbook or additional information and activities (including animations) on the web to enhance their understanding of the topic. See page 11 to find out more about these. Supplementary material and extension activities continue to be available with a limited photocopy licence on Biozone's **Teacher Resource CD-ROM**. In addition, we continue to update all our lists of resources. These annual revisions are in keeping with our ongoing commitment to providing up-to-date, relevant, interesting, and accurate information to students and teachers.

## A Note to the Teacher

This workbook has been produced as a student-centered resource, and benefits students by facilitating independent learning and critical thinking. Biozone's workbooks motivate and challenge a wide range of students by providing a highly visual format, a clear map through the course, and a synopsis of available supplemental resources. In modern biology, a single textbook may no longer provide all the information a student needs to grasp a topic. This workbook is a generic resource and **not a textbook**, and we make a point of referencing texts from other publishers. Above all, we are committed to continually revising and improving this resource **every year**. The price, at only US$19.95 for students, is a reflection of our commitment to providing high-quality, cost effective resources for biology. Please **do not photocopy** from this workbook. We cannot afford to supply single copies to schools and still provide annual updates as we intend. If you think it is worth using, then we recommend that the students themselves own this resource and keep it for their own use. A free model answer book is supplied with your **first order** of 5 or more workbooks.

## How Teachers May Use This Workbook

This workbook may be used in the classroom to guide students through each topic. Some activities may be used to introduce topics while others may be used to consolidate and test concepts already covered by other means. The workbook may be used as the primary tool in teaching some topics, but it should not be at the expense of good, 'hands-on' biology. Students may attempt the activities on their own or in groups. The latter provides opportunities for healthy discussion and peer-to-peer learning. Many of the activities may be set as homework exercises. Each page is perforated, allowing for easy removal of pages to be submitted for marking. This has been facilitated this year by the back-to-back format of two page activities. Teachers may prescribe the activities to be attempted by the students (using the check boxes next to the objectives for each topic), or they may allow students a degree of freedom with respect to the activities they attempt. The objectives for each topic will allow students to keep up to date even if they miss lessons and teachers who are away from class may set work easily in their absence. I thank you for your support.

**Richard Allan**

## Acknowledgements

We would like to thank the people who have contributed to this edition: • Stacey Farmer and Greg Baillie, Waikato DNA Sequencing Facility, University of Waikato, for their assistance with material on PCR, DNA sequencing, and genetic profiling • Jan Morrison for her diagrams • Mary McDougall, Sue Fitzgerald and Gwen Gilbert for their efficient handling of the office • TechPool Studios, for their clipart collection of human anatomy: Copyright ©1994, TechPool Studios Corp. USA (some of these images were modified by R. Allan and T. Greenwood) • Totem Graphics, for their clipart collection • Corel Corporation, for vector clipart from the Corel MEGAGALLERY collection • 3D artwork created using Poser IV, Curious Labs and Bryce.

## Photo Credits

Royalty free images, purchased by Biozone International Ltd, are used throughout this workbook and have been obtained from the following sources: **Corel** Corporation from various titles in their Professional Photos CD-ROM collection; **IMSI** (International Microcomputer Software Inc.) images from IMSI's MasterClips® and MasterPhotosTM Collection, 1895 Francisco Blvd. East, San Rafael, CA 94901-5506, USA; ©1996 **Digital Stock**, Medicine and Health Care collection; ©Hemera Technologies Inc, 1997-2001; © 2005 JupiterImages Corporation www.clipart.com; ©1994., ©**Digital Vision**; Gazelle Technologies Inc.; **PhotoDisc®**, Inc. USA, www.photodisc.com • 3D modeling software, Poser IV (Curious Labs) and Bryce.

The writing team would like to thank the following individuals and institutions who kindly provided photographs: • Sam Banks for his photograph of wombat scat • Dena Borchardt at HGSI for photos of large scale DNA sequencing • Campus Photography at the Uni. of Waikato (NZ) for photographs of monitoring equipment • Dept. of Natural Resources, Illinois, for the photograph of the threatened prairie chicken • Genesis Research & Development Corp. Auckland (NZ), for the photo used on the HGP activity • Kurchatov Inst., for the photo of Chornobyl • Stephen Moore, for his photos of stream invertebrates • PASCO for their photographs of probeware (available for students of biology in the USA) • Marc King for photographs of comb types in poultry • Pharmacia (Aust) Ltd. for providing the photographs of DNA gel sequencing • The Roslin Institute, for their photographs of Dolly • Dr. Nita Scobie, Cytogenetics Department, Waikato Hospital (NZ) for chromosome photographs • Jane Ussher, for her photo of the albatross bycatch • Dr. David Wells, AgResearch, NZ, for his photos on livestock cloning, Alan Sheldon Sheldon's Nature Photography, Wisconsin for the photo of the lizard without its tail • Adam Luckenbach and the North Carolina State University for use of the poster image on sex determination in flounder. • The three-spined stickleback image was originally prepared by Ellen Edmonson as part of the 1927-1940 New York Biological Survey. Permission for use granted by the New York State Department of Environmental Conservation.

Contributors identified by coded credits are as follows: **BF**: Brian Finerran (Uni. of Canterbury), **BH**: Brendan Hicks (Uni. of Waikato), **BOB**: Barry O'Brien (Uni. of Waikato), **CDC**: Centers for Disease Control and Prevention, Atlanta, USA, **COD**: Colin O'Donnell, **DEQ**: Dept of Environment Queensland Ltd., **DOC**: Dept of Conservation (NZ), **DNRI**: Dept of Natural Resources, Illinois, **EII**: Education Interactive Imaging, **EW**: Environment Waikato, **FRI**: Forest Research Institute, **GT**: ©1994 Gazelle Technologies Inc., **GU**: Graham Ussher, **GW**: Graham Walker, **HGSI**: Human Genome Sciences Inc., **IF**: I. Flux (DoC), **JB-BU**: Jason Biggerstaff, Brandeis University, **JDG**: John Green (Uni. of Waikato), **MPI**: Max Planck Institute for Developmental Biology, Germany; **NASA**: National Aeronautics and Space Administration, **NOAA**: National Oceanic and Atmospheric Administration www.photolib.noaa.gov **RA**: Richard Allan, **RCN**: Ralph Cocklin, **TG**: Tracey Greenwood, **VM**: Villa Maria Wines, **WBS**: Warwick Silvester (Uni. of Waikato), **WMU**: Waikato Microscope Unit.

Special thanks to all the partners of the Biozone team for their support.

## Cover Photographs

**Main photograph**: The red eyed tree frog (*Agalychnis callidryas*) is a slender, delicate frog found in the neotropical forests of central America. This species is nocturnal and completely arboreal (tree-dwelling). Bright markings along the sides of the body and on the limbs startle and distract predators with a bright flash of color as the frog moves away. PHOTO: Carol Farneti Foster-/OSF/hedgehoghouse.com

**Background photograph**: Autumn leaves, Image ©2005 JupiterImages Corporation www.clipart.com

# Contents

---

**CODES:** Δ **Upgraded** this edition   ☆ **New** this edition   **Activity** is marked: ⦁ to be done; ☑ when completed

# CONTENTS *(continued)*

**CODES:**  △  **Upgraded** this edition  ☆  **New** this edition   **Activity** is marked:  • to be done;  ✓ when completed

# CONTENTS (continued)

---

**CODES:**   △   **Upgraded** this edition    ☆   **New** this edition     **Activity** is marked:   ☐ to be done;   ☑ when completed

# How to Use this Workbook

This workbook is designed to provide you with a resource that will make the study of biology more enjoyable. While this workbook meets the needs of most general biology courses, it also provides specific keyed objectives for the **International Baccalaureate** (IB) and **Advanced Placement** (AP) courses. Consult the Syllabus Guides on pages 12-14 of this workbook to establish where material for your syllabus is covered. It is hoped that this workbook will reinforce and extend the ideas developed by your teacher. It must be emphasized that this workbook is **not a textbook**. It is designed to complement the biology textbooks provided for your course. For each topic the workbook provides the following useful resources:

## Guidance Provided for Each Topic

**Learning objectives**:

These provide a map of the topic content. Completing the relevant learning objectives will help you to satisfy the knowledge requirements of your course. Your teacher may add to or omit points from this list.

**Topic outcomes**:

This panel identifies the learning objectives relevant to the topic for each designated course. Attempt only those objectives that relate to your course. See pages 12-14 for a listing of your syllabus requirements.

**Key words**:

Key words are displayed in **bold** type in the learning objectives and should be used to create a glossary as you study each topic. From your own reading and your teacher's descriptions, write your own definition for each word. Only the terms relevant to your learning objectives should be used to create your glossary. Free glossary worksheets are also available from our web site.

Use the check boxes to mark objectives to be completed.
Use a **dot** to be done (•).
Use a **tick** when completed (✓).

**Comprehensive textbooks**

The **Textbook Reference Grid** on pages 8-9 lists the major comprehensive textbooks available for your course (these are texts providing coverage of the majority of course topics). The grid provides the page numbers from each text relevant to each topic in the workbook.

**Internet addresses**:

Access our database of links to more than **800** web sites relevant to the topics covered. These are updated regularly. Go to **www.thebiozone.com** and link directly to these sites using the *BioLinks* button.

**Supplementary texts**:

References to supplementary texts, which have only a restricted topic coverage, are provided as appropriate in each topic.

**Periodical articles**:

Ideal for those seeking more depth or the latest research on a specific topic. Articles are sorted according to their suitability for student or teacher reference. Visit your school, public, or university library for these articles.

**Supplementary resources from Biozone:** Supporting **Presentation MEDIA** are noted where appropriate. Additional activities, spreadsheeting exercises and references to multimedia resources for each topic are provided on the **Teacher Resource CD-ROM** (which may be purchased separately). See page 7 for details.

# Activity Pages

The activities and exercises make up most of the content of this book. They are designed to reinforce the concepts you have learned about in the topic. Your teacher may use the activity pages to introduce a topic for the first time, or you may use them to revise ideas already covered. They are excellent for use in the classroom, and as homework exercises and revision. In most cases, the activities should not be attempted until you have carried out the necessary background reading from your textbook. Your teacher should have a model answer book with the answers to each activity. This workbook caters for the needs of more than one syllabus, and you will find some activities or even whole topics that may not be relevant to your course. Although you may miss out these pages, you will still find our workbooks to be exceptional value.

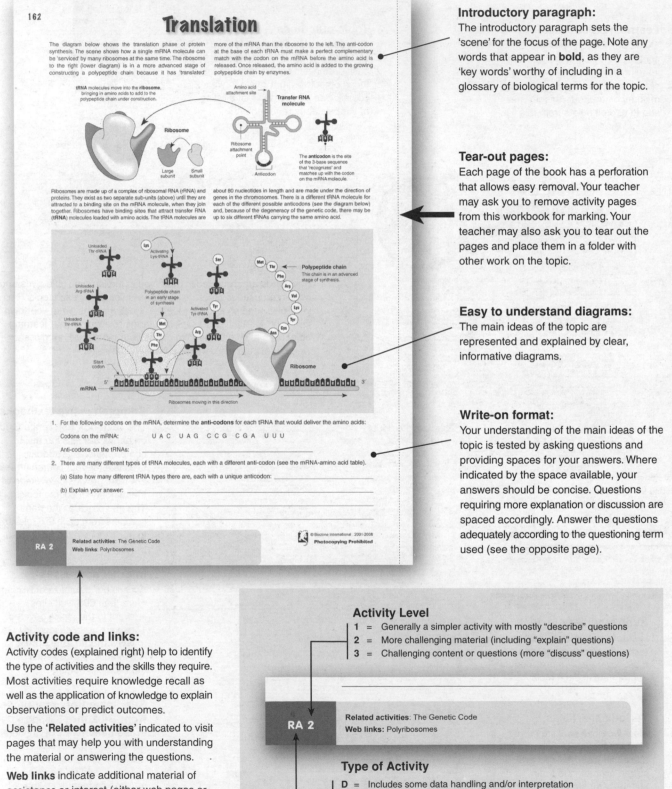

**Introductory paragraph:**
The introductory paragraph sets the 'scene' for the focus of the page. Note any words that appear in **bold**, as they are 'key words' worthy of including in a glossary of biological terms for the topic.

**Tear-out pages:**
Each page of the book has a perforation that allows easy removal. Your teacher may ask you to remove activity pages from this workbook for marking. Your teacher may also ask you to tear out the pages and place them in a folder with other work on the topic.

**Easy to understand diagrams:**
The main ideas of the topic are represented and explained by clear, informative diagrams.

**Write-on format:**
Your understanding of the main ideas of the topic is tested by asking questions and providing spaces for your answers. Where indicated by the space available, your answers should be concise. Questions requiring more explanation or discussion are spaced accordingly. Answer the questions adequately according to the questioning term used (see the opposite page).

**Activity code and links:**
Activity codes (explained right) help to identify the type of activities and the skills they require. Most activities require knowledge recall as well as the application of knowledge to explain observations or predict outcomes.

Use the '**Related activities**' indicated to visit pages that may help you with understanding the material or answering the questions.

**Web links** indicate additional material of assistance or interest (either web pages or pdf activities). You can access these from: *www.thebiozone.com/weblink/SB1-2214.html*

**Activity Level**
1 = Generally a simpler activity with mostly "describe" questions
2 = More challenging material (including "explain" questions)
3 = Challenging content or questions (more "discuss" questions)

RA 2    **Related activities**: The Genetic Code
        **Web links**: Polyribosomes

**Type of Activity**
D = Includes some data handling and/or interpretation
P = includes a paper practical
R = May require research outside the page
A = Includes application of knowledge to solve a problem
E = Extension material

# Explanation of Terms

Questions come in a variety of forms. Whether you are studying for an exam, or writing an essay, it is important to understand exactly what the question is asking. A question has two parts to it: one part of the question will provide you with information, the second part of the question will provide you with instructions as to how to answer the question. Following these instructions is most important.

Often students in examinations know the material but fail to follow instructions and, as a consequence, do not answer the question appropriately. Examiners often use certain key words to introduce questions. Look out for them and be absolutely clear as to what they mean. Below is a list of commonly used terms that you will come across and a brief explanation of each.

## Commonly used Terms in Biology

The following terms are frequently used when asking questions in examinations and assessments. Most of these are listed in the IB syllabus document as action verbs indicating the depth of treatment required for a given statement. Students should have a clear understanding of each of the following terms and use this understanding to answer questions appropriately.

**Account for**: Provide a satisfactory explanation or reason for an observation.

**Analyze**: Interpret data to reach stated conclusions.

**Annotate**: Add **brief** notes to a diagram, drawing or graph.

**Apply**: Use an idea, equation, principle, theory, or law in a new situation.

**Appreciate**: To understand the meaning or relevance of a particular situation.

**Calculate**: Find an answer using mathematical methods. Show the working unless instructed not to.

**Compare**: Give an account of similarities and differences between two or more items, referring to both (or all) of them throughout. Comparisons can be given using a table. Comparisons generally ask for similarities more than differences (see contrast).

**Construct**: Represent or develop in graphical form.

**Contrast**: Show differences. Set in opposition.

**Deduce**: Reach a conclusion from information given.

**Define**: Give the precise meaning of a word or phrase as concisely as possible.

**Derive**: Manipulate a mathematical equation to give a new equation or result.

**Describe**: Give an account, including all the relevant information.

**Design**: Produce a plan, object, simulation or model.

**Determine**: Find the only possible answer.

**Discuss**: Give an account including, where possible, a range of arguments, assessments of the relative importance of various factors, or comparison of alternative hypotheses.

**Distinguish**: Give the difference(s) between two or more different items.

**Draw**: Represent by means of pencil lines. Add labels unless told not to do so.

**Estimate**: Find an approximate value for an unknown quantity, based on the information provided and application of scientific knowledge.

**Evaluate**: Assess the implications and limitations.

**Explain**: Give a clear account including causes, reasons, or mechanisms.

**Identify**: Find an answer from a number of possibilities.

**Illustrate**: Give concrete examples. Explain clearly by using comparisons or examples.

**Interpret**: Comment upon, give examples, describe relationships. Describe, then evaluate.

**List**: Give a sequence of names or other brief answers with no elaboration. Each one should be clearly distinguishable from the others.

**Measure**: Find a value for a quantity.

**Outline**: Give a brief account or summary. Include essential information only.

**Predict**: Give an expected result.

**Solve**: Obtain an answer using algebraic and/or numerical methods.

**State**: Give a specific name, value, or other answer. No supporting argument or calculation is necessary.

**Suggest**: Propose a hypothesis or other possible explanation.

**Summarize**: Give a brief, condensed account. Include conclusions and avoid unnecessary details.

## In Conclusion

Students should familiarize themselves with this list of terms and, where necessary throughout the course, they should refer back to them when answering questions. The list of terms mentioned above is not exhaustive and students should compare this list with past examination papers and essays etc. and add any new terms (and their meaning) to the list above. The aim is to become familiar with interpreting the question and answering it appropriately.

# Resources Information

Your set textbook should always be a starting point for information. There are also many other resources available, including scientific journals, magazine and newspaper articles, supplementary texts covering restricted topic areas, dictionaries, computer software and videos, and the internet. A synopsis of currently available resources is provided below. Access to the publishers of these resources can be made directly from Biozone's web site through our resources hub: **www.thebiozone.com/resource-hub.html** or by typing in the relevant addresses provided below. Most titles are also available through www.amazon.com. Please note that our listing any product in this workbook does not, in any way, denote Biozone's endorsement of that product.

## Comprehensive Biology Texts Referenced

Appropriate texts for this course are referenced in this workbook. Page or chapter references for each text are provided in the text reference grid on pages 8-9. These will enable you to identify the relevant reading as you progress through the activities in this workbook. Publication details of texts referenced in the grid are provided below and opposite. For further details of text content, or to make purchases, link to the relevant publisher via Biozone's resources hub by going to:

**www.thebiozone.com > Resources > Textbooks > International**

Allott, Andrew, 2007
**Biology for the IB Diploma - Standard and Higher Level** 2 edn
**Publisher**: Oxford University Press
**Pages**: 192
**ISBN**: 978-0199151431
**Comments**: *Updated edition to meet the IB Diploma programme from 2007. Includes core and option material.*

Bloom, M. and J. Greenberg, 2006
**Biological Science: A Molecular Approach**, (BSCS Blue Version), 9 edn
**Publisher**: Glencoe/McGraw Hill
**Pages**: 820+ including glossary
**ISBN**: 0-078-66427-6 (student edition)
**Comments**: *Aimed at gifted and honors biology students. A teacher's annotated edition, resource book, and overhead transparency booklet are also available.*

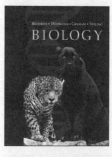

Brooker, R.J., Widmaier, E.P. L. Graham, and P. Stiling, 2008
**Biology**, 1 edn
**Publisher**: McGraw Hill
**Pages**: 1488
**ISBN**: 978-0073268071
**Comments**: *A comprehensive, modern text featuring an evolutionary focus with an emphasis on scientific inquiry, and especially critical thinking. Various electronic resources accompany the text.*

Campbell, N. A. and J.B. Reece, 2008
**Biology**, 8 edn
**Publisher**: Benjamin Cummings
**Pages**: 1393
**ISBN**: 978-0321543257
**Comments**: *Provides good coverage of a wide range of biological principles, and has CD-ROM and website support. Reviews are included for each chapter. A wide range of supplemental materials are also available for instructors and students. Graphics have been updated this edition.*

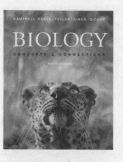

Campbell, N. A., J.B. Reece, M.R. Taylor, E.J. Simon, and L. Mitchell 2009
**Biology: Concepts and Connections**, 6 edn
**Publisher**: Benjamin Cummings
**Pages**: 728
**ISBN**: 978-032489845
**Comments**: *Extensively revised edition. This text takes a modular approach and uses key concepts help the student focus on major concepts throughout the book.*

Clegg, C.J., 2007
**Biology for the IB Diploma**
**Publisher**: Hodder Murray
**Pages**: 448
**ISBN**: 978-0340926529
**Comments**: *This new text has been specifically written to cater for the IB diploma course. The content covers the core topics, and options are provided on the accompanying CD-ROM.*

Freeman, S., 2008
**Biological Science**
**Publisher**: Benjamin Cummings
**Pages**: 1392
**ISBN**: 978-0321543271
**Comments**: *Aimed at Biology majors, particularly the AP course. This text has an introductory chapter, and nine units covering core themes. Key themes of evolution and molecular biology run throughout the book.*

Mader, Sylvia, 2007
**Biology**, 9 edn
**Publisher**: McGraw Hill
**Pages**: 1040 including appendices
**ISBN**: 978-0072464634
**Comments**: *A revised edition, with updated content, covering concepts and principles of biology. An evolutionary theme continues to be central to its approach and modern ecological problems are stressed throughout.*

Raven, P.H., G.B. Johnson, K.A. Mason, and J. Losos, 2008
**Biology**, 8 edn
**Publisher**: McGraw-Hill
**Pages**: 1376 plus appendices
**ISBN**: 978-0072965810
**Comments**: *An authoritative majors text with a strong emphasis on evolution as a unifying theme. Content revision focuses on inheritance and evolution. A range of ancillary resources are also available.*

Russell, P.J., S.L. Wolfe, P.E. Hertz, and C. Starr 2008
**Biology: The Dynamic Science**, 1 edn
**Publisher**: Brooks/Cole
**Pages**: 1456
**ISBN**: 978-0534249663
**Comments**: *A well illustrated new text for AP students. Study plans at the start of each chapter keep the major themes in focus while a chapter summary and questions review student knowledge.*

Sadava, D., H.C. Heller, G.H. Orians, W.K. Purves, and D. Hillis 2007
**Life: The Science of Biology**, 8 edn
**Publisher**: W.H. Freeman/Sinauer
**Pages**: 1121 plus appendices
**ISBN**: 978-0716776710
**Comments**: *Revised to include new content in key areas, with new illustrations and support resources. Also available in three softback volumes.*

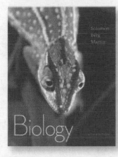

Solomon, E., L. Berg, and D.W. Martin, 2008
**Biology**, 8 edn
**Publisher**: Brooks/Cole
**Pages**: 1376
**ISBN**: 978-0495317142
**Comments**: *A popular introductory majors text which has been substantially revised in key areas, including cell communication and genetics. Accompanied by online and multimedia resources.*

Starr, C., 2008
**Biology: Concepts and Applications**, 7 edn
**Publisher**: Brooks/Cole
**Pages**: 799
**ISBN**: 978-0495119814
**Comments**: *An introductory, issue-oriented approach for honors students, this text encourages critical thinking and includes overviews, chapter outlines, and multiple choice questions.*

Starr, C. and R. Taggart, 2006
**Biology: The Unity & Diversity of Life**, 11 edn
**Publisher**: Brooks/Cole
**Pages**: 1056
**ISBN**: 0-495-01599-7
**Comments**: *A well illustrated, engaging majors text. As with earlier editions, this one emphasizes the interconnectedness between structure, function, and evolution. Includes an interactive CD-ROM.*

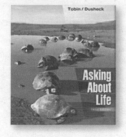

Tobin, A.J. and J. Dusheck, 2005
**Asking About Life**, 3edn
**Publisher**: Brooks/Cole
**Pages**: 960
**ISBN**: 0-53-440653-X
**Comments**: *An important revision featuring streamlined coverage (this is a smaller text) and numerous examples. Evolution is the unifying theme throughout.*

## Supplementary Texts

For further details or to make purchases, link to the publisher via Biozone's resources hub by going to: **www.thebiozone.com > Resources > Supplementary > International**
All titles are available in North America unless indicated by (§).

Barnard, C., F. Gilbert, F., and P. McGregor, 2007
**Asking Questions in Biology: Key Skills for Practical Assessments & Project Work**, 256 pp.
**Publisher**: Benjamin Cummings
**ISBN**: 978-0132224352
**Comments**: *Covers many aspects of design, analysis and presentation of practical work in senior level biology. Available in June 2007.*

Barnum, S.R., 2nd edn 2005
**Biotechnology: An Introduction**, 336 pp.
**Publisher**: Thomson Brooks/Cole
**ISBN**: 978-0495112051
**Comments**: *A broad view of biotechnology, integrating historical and modern topics. Processes and methods are described, and numerous examples describe applications.*

Cadogan, A. and Ingram, M., 2002
**Maths for Advanced Biology**
**Publisher**: NelsonThornes
**ISBN**: 0-7487-6506-9
**Comments**: *Provides coverage of basic mathematics requirements for biology at grades 11 and 12 (UK AS/A2). It includes worked examples.*

Helms, D.R., C.W. Helms, R.J. Kosinski, and J.C. Cummings, 3rd edn 1998
**Biology in the Laboratory**, 500 pp (paperback)
**Publisher**: W.H. Freeman
**ISBN**: 0-7167-3146-0
**Comments**: *A full lab program is covered in this text. Activities (#0-#45) are also available for purchase individually.*

Indge, B., 2003 (§)
**Data and Data Handling for AS and A Level Biology**, 128 pp.
**Publisher**: Hodder Arnold H&S
**ISBN**: 1340856475
**Comments**: *Examples and practice exercises to improve skills in data interpretation and analysis.*

Jones, A., R. Reed, and J. Weyers, 4th edn, 2007
**Practical Skills in Biology**, 496 pp.
**Publisher**: Benjamin Cummings
**ISBN**: 978-0131755093
**Comments**: *Excellent, accurate guidance on study design, implementation, and data analysis. This edition includes several new chapters.*

Knisely, K., 2 edn, 2005
**A Student Handbook for Writing in Biology**, 224 pp.
**Publisher**: W.H. Freeman/Sinauer
**ISBN**: 0-7167-6709-0
**Comments**: *Practical advice covering writing, referencing, preparing lab reports, and poster and oral presentations. Includes appendices.*

Miller, G.T. Jr., 4th edn, 2007
**Essentials of Ecology**, 384 pp.
**Publisher**: Thomson Brooks/Cole
**ISBN**: 978-0495125440
**Comments**: *A new edition of this succinct introduction to ecology. It uses straightforward language and provides a sound foundation for understanding ecological issues.*

Introduction

Morgan, S., 2002
**Advanced Level Practical Work for Biology**,
128 pp.
**Publisher**: Hodder and Stoughton
**ISBN**: 0-340-84712-3
**Comments**: *Caters for the practical and investigative requirements of biology at this level: experimental design, observations and measurement, and interpretation and analysis.*

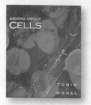

Tobin, A.J. and R.E Morel, 1997
**Asking About Cells**, 698 pp (paperback)
**Publisher**: Thomson Brooks/Cole
**ISBN**: 0-030-98018-6
**Comments**: *An introduction to cell biology, cellular processes and specialization, DNA and gene expression, and inheritance. The focus is on presenting material through inquiry.*

**Advanced Biology Readers** (John Murray Publishers)
*Designed as supplementary resources to support a range of specific topics in biology. Advanced Biology Readers are useful as both teacher reference and student extension. There are a number of titles in the series.*

Jones, N., A. Karp., & G. Giddings, 2001.
**Essentials of Genetics**, 224 pp.
**ISBN**: 0-7195-8611-9
*Thorough supplemental for genetics and evolution. Comprehensive coverage of cell division, molecular genetics, and genetic engineering. The application of new gene technologies to humans is also discussed.*

**Illustrated Advanced Biology** (John Murray Publishers)
*One title in a series aimed as supplementary resources for biology students at grades 11 and 12. These are slim, well illustrated, and well written volumes. Others in the series cover mammalian structure and physiology, plant biology, and microbiology.*

Clegg, C.J., 1999.
**Genetics and Evolution**, 96 pp.
**ISBN**: 0-7195-7552-4
*Concise but thorough coverage of molecular genetics, genetic engineering, inheritance, and evolution. An historical perspective is included by way of introduction, and a glossary and a list of abbreviations used are included.*

**Nelson Advanced Sciences** (NelsonThornes)
*Modular-style texts suitable as teacher reference and student extension reading for specific topics in grades 9-12 biology.*

Adds, J., E. Larkcom & R. Miller, 2004.
**Exchange and Transport, Energy and Ecosystems**, revised edition 240 pp.
**ISBN**: 0-7487-7487-4
*Includes exchange processes (gas exchanges, digestion, absorption), transport systems, adaptation, sexual reproduction, energy and the environment, and human impact.*

Adds, J., E. Larkcom & R. Miller, 2003.
**Molecules and Cells**, revised edition 112 pp.
**ISBN**: 0-7487-7484-X
*Includes coverage of the basic types of biological molecules, with extra detail on the structure and function of nucleic acids and enzymes, cellular organization, and cell division. Practical activities are also provided.*

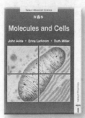

Adds, J., E. Larkcom & R. Miller, 2004.
**Genetics, Evolution, and Biodiversity**,
revised edition, 200 pp.
**ISBN**: 0-7487-7492-0
*A range of topics including photosynthesis, classification, quantitative field ecology, populations and pest control, conservation, genetics and evolution, and gene technology.*

Adds, J., E. Larkcom, R. Miller, & R. Sutton,
1999. **Tools, Techniques and Assessment in Biology**, 160 pp.
**ISBN**: 0-17-448273-6
*A guide to basic lab protocols, microscopy, quantitative lab and field techniques, DNA techniques and tissue culture, data handling and statistical tests, and exam preparation.*

---

# Periodicals, Magazines, and Journals

Periodical articles can be of great value in providing current information on specific topics. Periodicals may be accessed in your school, local, public, and university libraries. The periodicals referenced in this workbook are listed below. For general enquiries and further details regarding subscriptions, link to the relevant publisher via Biozone's resources hub or type: **www. thebiozone.com > Resources > Journals**

**Biological Sciences Review** (Biol. Sci. Rev.)
*An excellent quarterly publication for teachers and students of biology. The content is current and the language is accessible.* Subscriptions available from Philip Allan Publishers, Market Place, Deddington, Oxfordshire OX 15 OSE.
**Tel.** 01869 338652
**Fax**: 01869 338803
**E-mail**: sales@philipallan.co.uk

**New Scientist**: *Published weekly and found in many libraries. It often summarizes the findings published in other journals. Articles range from news releases to features.*
Subscription enquiries:
**Tel.** (UK and international): +44 (0)1444 475636. (US & Canada) 1 888 822 3242.
**E-mail**: ns.subs@qss-uk.com

**Scientific American**: *A monthly magazine containing mostly specialist feature articles. Articles range in level of reading difficulty and assumed knowledge.*
Subscription enquiries:
**Tel.** (US & Canada) 800-333-1199.
**Tel.** (outside North America): 515-247-7631
**Web**: www.sciam.com

**The American Biology Teacher**: *The official, peer-reviewed journal of the National Association of Biology Teachers. Published nine times a year and containing information and activities relevant to the teaching of biology in the US and elsewhere.* Enquiries:
NABT, 12030 Sunrise Valley Drive, #110, Reston, VA 20191-3409
**Web**: www.nabt.org

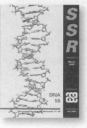

**School Science Review**: *A quarterly journal published by the ASE for science teachers in 11-19 education. SSR includes articles, reviews, and news on current research and curriculum development. Free to all Ordinary Members of the ASE or available on subscription.* Subscription enquiries:
**Tel**: 01707 28300
**Email**: info@ase.org.uk *or visit their web site.*

# Biology Dictionaries

Access to a good biology dictionary is of great value when dealing with the technical terms used in biology. Below are some biology dictionaries that you may wish to locate or purchase. They can usually be obtained directly from the publisher or they are all available (at the time of printing) from www.amazon.com. For further details of text content, or to make purchases, link to the relevant publisher via Biozone's resources hub or by typing:
**www.thebiozone.com > Resources > Dictionaries**

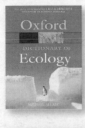

Allaby, M. (ed)
**A Dictionary of Ecology**, 2004, 440 pp. Oxford University Press
**ISBN**: 0198609442
*A revised edition, with 5000 entries fully updated to incorporate developments in this rapidly evolving field. Covers plant and animal physiology, behavior, evolution, and all aspects of ecology and conservation biology.*

Clamp, A.
**AS/A-Level Biology. Essential Word Dictionary**, 2000, 161 pp. Philip Allan Updates.
**ISBN**: 0-86003-372-4.
*Carefully selected essential words for AS and A2. Concise definitions are supported by further explanation and illustrations where required.*

Collin, P.H
**A Dictionary of Ecology and Environment** 4 ed., 2001, 560 pp. Peter Collin Publishers Ltd
**ISBN**: 1901659615
*A revised edition, with 8500 entries. All main entries include pronunciation guides. A special feature is the frequent concise comment or quotation at the end of each entry.*

Hale, W.G. **Collins: Dictionary of Biology** 4 ed. 2005, 528 pp. Collins.
**ISBN**: 0-00-720734-4.
*Updated to take in the latest developments in biology and now internet-linked. (§ This latest edition is currently available only in the UK. The earlier edition, ISBN: 0-00-714709-0, is available though amazon.com in North America).*

Henderson, I.F, W.D. Henderson, and E. Lawrence. **Henderson's Dictionary of Biological Terms**, 1999, 736 pp. Prentice Hall.
**ISBN**: 0582414989
*This edition has been updated, rewritten for clarity, and reorganized for ease of use. An essential reference and the dictionary of choice for many.*

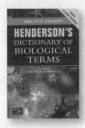

King, R.C. and W.D. Stansfield
**A Dictionary of Genetics**, 6 ed., 2002, 544 pp. Oxford University Press.
**ISBN**: 0195143256
*A good source for the specialized terminology associated with genetics and related disciplines. Genera and species important to genetics are included, cross linked to an appendix.*

Lincoln, R.J., G.A. Boxshall, & P.F. Clark.
**A Dictionary of Ecology, Evolution, and Systematics**, 2 ed., 1998, 371 pp. Cambridge Uni. Press.
**ISBN**: 052143842X
*6500 entries covering all major fields within biology, and recently expanded to reflect recent developments in the science. There are no pronunciation guidelines provided.*

Market House Books (compiled by).
**Oxford Dictionary of Biology** 5 ed., 2004, 698 pp. Oxford University Press.
**ISBN**: 0198609175. Includes biographical entries on key scientists.
*Revised and updated, with many new entries. This edition contains biographical entries on key scientists and comprehensive coverage of terms in biology, biophysics, and biochemistry.*

McGraw-Hill (ed). **McGraw-Hill Dictionary of Bioscience**, 2 ed., 2002, 662 pp. McGraw-Hill.
**ISBN**: 0-07-141043-0
*22 000 entries encompassing more than 20 areas of the life sciences. It includes synonyms, acronyms, abbreviations, and pronunciations for all terms. Accessible, yet comprehensive.*

Rudin, N.
**Dictionary of Modern Biology** (1997), 504 pp. Barron's Educational Series Inc
**ISBN**: 0812095162.
*More than 6000 terms in biosciences defined for college level students. Includes extensive cross referencing and several useful appendices.*

Thain, M. and M. Hickman.
**Penguin Dictionary of Biology** 10/c (2000), 704 pp. Penguin (USA).
**ISBN**: 0140513590
*Pocket sized reference with definitions to more than 7500 terms, including more than 400 new entries. It includes explanations of fundamental concepts ad explorations of some of the more recent discoveries and developments in biology.*

## Internet Resources

The internet is a powerful tool for locating information. See pages 10-11 for details of how to access internet resources.

## Teacher Resource CD-ROM

Biozone's **Teacher Resource CD-ROM** supports the content of the Senior Biology 1 and 2 workbooks with supplementary material and extension activities, worked statistical examples and worksheets, and comprehensive lists of available resources. The CD-ROM also includes glossary worksheets, crosswords and digital copies of the model answers for both workbooks. Contact Biozone for further details.

# AP Textbook Reference Grid

**Guide to use:** Chapters in the grid refer to the material in each text relevant to the stated topic in the workbook.

| TOPIC IN WORKBOOK | Brooker et al. 2008 | Campbell & Reece 2008 | Freeman 2008 | Mader 2007 | Raven & Johnson 2008 | Russell et al. 2008 | Sadava et al. 2007 | Solomon et al. 2008 | Starr & Taggart 2006 |
|---|---|---|---|---|---|---|---|---|---|
| Skills in Biology | N/A | N/A | See CD-Rom | N/A | N/A | N/A | N/A | N/A | Chpt. 1 |
| The Chemistry of Life | Chpt. 2 & 3 | Chpt. 2-5 | Unit 1 as reqd | Chpt. 2 & 3 | Chpt. 2 & 3 | Chpt. 2-4 | Chpt. 2 & 3 | Chpt. 1-3 | Chpt. 2-3, 6 |
| Cell Structure | Chpt. 4 | Chpt. 6 | Chpt. 7 & 8 | Chpt. 4 | Chpt. 4 | Chpt. 5 | Chpt. 4 | Chpt. 4 | Chpt. 4 |
| Cell Membranes | Chpt. 5 | Chpt. 7 | Chpt. 6 | Chpt. 5 | Chpt. 5 | Chpt. 6 & 7 | Chpt. 5 | Chpt. 5-6 | Chpt. 4 & 5 |
| Cell Division and Organization | Chpt. 6 & 15 | Chpt. 12 | Chpt. 8 & 11 | Chpt. 9 | Chpt. 10 | Chpt. 5 & 10 | Chpt. 9 | Chpt. 4 & 10 | Chpt. 9 |
| Cellular Energetics | Chpt. 7 & 8 | Chpt. 8-10 | Chpt. 9 & 10 | Chpt. 6-8 | Chpt. 6-8 | Chpt. 8 & 9 | Chpt. 6-8 | Chpt. 7-9 | Chpt. 6-8 |
| Molecular Genetics | Chpt. 11-13 | Chpt. 16-18 | Chpt. 14-18 | Chpt. 13-15 | Chpt. 14-16 | Chpt. 14-16 | Chpt. 11-14 | Chpt. 12-14 | Chpt. 3 &13-15 |
| Genes and Chromosomes | Chpt. 14-15 | Chpt. 14-15, & 21 | Chpt. 12 & 13 | Chpt. 14-15 | Chpt. 11-13 | Chpt. 11-13 | Chpt. 9 & 14 | Chpt. 10-12 | Chpt. 10-12, 14 |
| Inheritance | Chpt. 16-17 | Chpt. 14 & 15 | Chpt. 13 & 15 | Chpt. 11 & 12 | Chpt. 12-13 | Chpt. 12 & 13 | Chpt. 10 & 11 | Chpt. 11 | Chpt. 11-12 |
| Aspects of Biotechnology | Chpt. 20 & 21 | Chpt. 20 | Chpt. 19 & 20 | Chpt. 16 | Chpt. 17 & 18 | Chpt. 17 & 18 | Chpt. 16 & 17 | Chpt. 15-17 | Chpt. 16 |
| Ecosystems | Chpt. 54 & 59 | Chpt. 52 & 55 | Chpt. 50 & 54 | Chpt. 47 & 49 | Chpt. 58 | Chpt. 51 & 52 | Chpt. 52, 55 & 56 | Chpt. 54 & 55 | Chpt. 46-49 |
| Energy Flow and Nutrient Cycles | Chpt. 54 | Chpt. 52 & 55 | Chpt. 50 & 54 | Chpt. 46 | Chpt. 57 | Chpt. 50 & 51 | Chpt. 56 | Chpt. 54 | Chpt. 47 & 48 |
| Populations | Chpt. 56-59 | Chpt. 53 | Chpt. 52 | Chpt. 46 | Chpt. 55 & 59 | Chpt. 50 | Chpt. 54 & 55 | Chpt. 52 & 53 | Chpt. 45 |
| Classification | Chpt. 26 | Chpt. 26-33 | Chpt. 1 & 27 | Chpt. 20 | Chpt. 26 | Chpt. 23 | Chpt. 25-27 | Appendix B | Chpt. 21-27 |
| Practical Ecology | N/A | N/A | N/A | N/A | N/A | N/A | N/A | N/A | N/A |
| Human Impact and Conservation | Chpt. 60 | Chpt. 56 | Chpt. 55 | Chpt. 48 & 50 | Chpt. 58 & 59 | Chpt. 53 | Chpt. 57 | Chpt. 56 | Chpt. 45-49 |

# IB & Honors Textbook Reference Grid

**Guide to use:** Chapters in the grid refer to the material in each text relevant to the stated topic in the workbook.

| TOPIC IN WORKBOOK | Allott 2007 | Bloom & Greenberg 2006 | Campbell et al. 2009 | Clegg 2009 | Starr 2008 | Tobin & Dusheck 2005 |
|---|---|---|---|---|---|---|
| Skills in Biology | N/A | Integral | N/A | Chapter 21 | Appendix 2 | Chapter 1 |
| The Chemistry of Life | Chapter 3 | Chapter 1 & 2 | Chapter 2 & 3 | Chapter 2 | Chapter 1 & 2 | Chapter 2 & 3 |
| Cell Structure | Chapter 2 | Chapter 6 | Chapter 4 & 5 | Chapter 1 | Chapter 4 | Chapter 4 |
| Cell Membranes | Chapter 2 | Chapter 3 | Chapter 5 | Chapter 1 | Chapter 4 & 5 | Chapter 5 |
| Cell Division and Organization | Chapter 2 | Chapter 8 | Chapter 8 | Chapter 1 | Chapter 8 | Chapter 4 & 8 |
| Cellular Energetics | Chapter 3 & 8 | Chapter 2, 4 & 5 | Chapter 6 & 7 | Chapter 3, 9 & 15 | Chapter 5-7 | Chapter 6 & 7 |
| Molecular Genetics | Chapter 3 & 7 | Chapter 1, 8 & 9 | Chapter 10 & 11 | Chapter 2 & 8 | Chapter 3, 12-14 | Chapter 10 & 11 |
| Genes and Chromosomes | Chapter 4 & 10 | Chapter 13 & 15 | Chapter 8 - 10 | Chapter 4 & 11 | Chapter 9-11 | Chapter 9 |
| Inheritance | Chapter 4 & 10 | Chapter 13 & 14 | Chapter 9 | Chapter 4 & 11 | Chapter 10 & 11 | Chapter 9 |
| Aspects of Biotechnology | Chapter 17 | Chapter 15 | Chapter 12 | Chapter 5 | Chapter 15 | Chapter 13 |
| Ecosystems | Chapter 18 | Chapter 24 & 25 | Chapter 34 & 37 | Chapter 6 & 19 | Chapter 42 & 43 | Chapter 25 & 26 |
| Energy Flow and Nutrient Cycles | Chapter 5 & 18 | Chapter 2 & 24 | Chapter 37 | Chapter 6 & 19 | Chapter 41 & 42 | Chapter 27 |
| Populations | Chapter 5 | Chapter 24 | Chapter 36 | Chapter 6 & 19 | Chapter 40 | Chapter 27 & 28 |
| Classification | Chapter 5 | Chapter 18 | N/A | Chapter 6 | Appendix 1 | Chapter 19 |
| Practical Ecology | N/A | N/A | N/A | N/A | N/A | N/A |
| Human Impact and Conservation | Chapter 18 | Chapter 25 | Chapter 38 | Chapter 6 & 19 | Chapter 40-43 as reqd | N/A |

# Using the Internet

The internet is a powerful resource for locating information. There are several key areas of Biozone's web site that may be of interest to you. Go to the **BioLinks** area to browse through the hundreds of web sites hosted by other organizations. These sites provide a supplement to the activities provided in our workbooks and have been selected on the basis of their accurate, current, and relevant content. We have also provided links to biology-related **podcasts** and **RSS newsfeeds**. These provide regularly updated information about new discoveries in biology; perfect for those wanting to keep abreast of changes in this dynamic field.

## The BIOZONE website: www.thebiozone.com

The current internet address (URL) for the web site is displayed here. You can type a new address directly into this space.

Use Google to search for web sites of interest. The more precise your search words are, the better the list of results. EXAMPLE: If you type in "biotechnology", your search will return an overwhelmingly large number of sites, many of which will not be useful to you. Be more specific, e.g. "biotechnology medicine DNA uses".

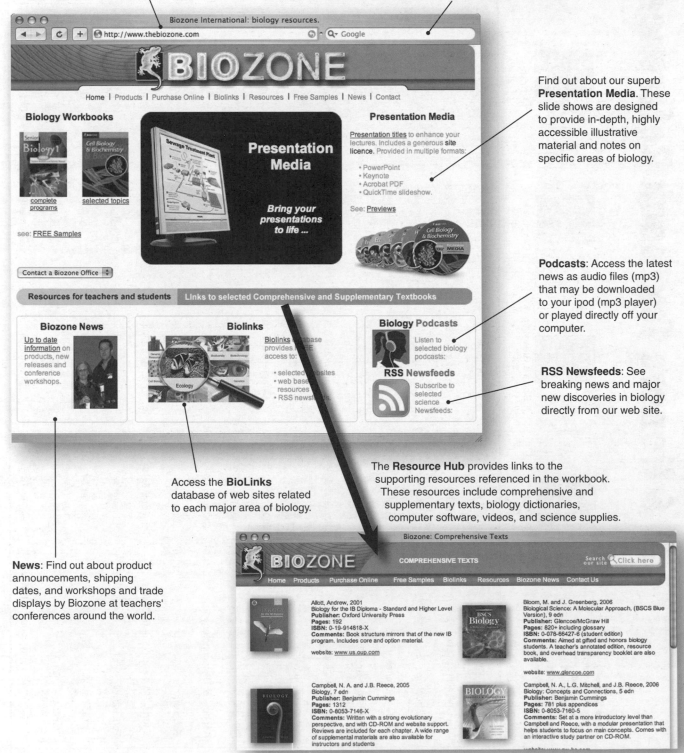

Find out about our superb **Presentation Media**. These slide shows are designed to provide in-depth, highly accessible illustrative material and notes on specific areas of biology.

**Podcasts**: Access the latest news as audio files (mp3) that may be downloaded to your ipod (mp3 player) or played directly off your computer.

**RSS Newsfeeds**: See breaking news and major new discoveries in biology directly from our web site.

The **Resource Hub** provides links to the supporting resources referenced in the workbook. These resources include comprehensive and supplementary texts, biology dictionaries, computer software, videos, and science supplies.

Access the **BioLinks** database of web sites related to each major area of biology.

**News**: Find out about product announcements, shipping dates, and workshops and trade displays by Biozone at teachers' conferences around the world.

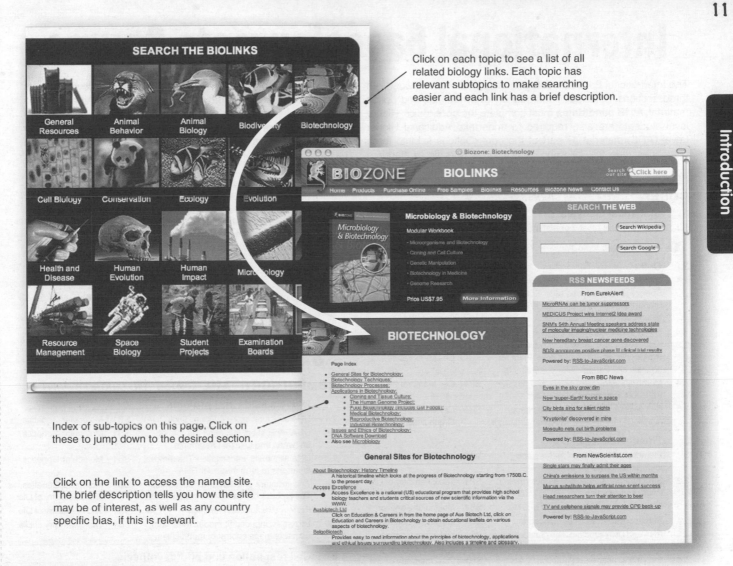

Click on each topic to see a list of all related biology links. Each topic has relevant subtopics to make searching easier and each link has a brief description.

Index of sub-topics on this page. Click on these to jump down to the desired section.

Click on the link to access the named site. The brief description tells you how the site may be of interest, as well as any country specific bias, if this is relevant.

# Weblinks:

Go to: **www.thebiozone.com/weblink/SB1-2214.html**

Throughout this workbook, some pages make reference to additional or alternative activities, as well as web sites that have particular relevance to the activity. See example of page reference below:

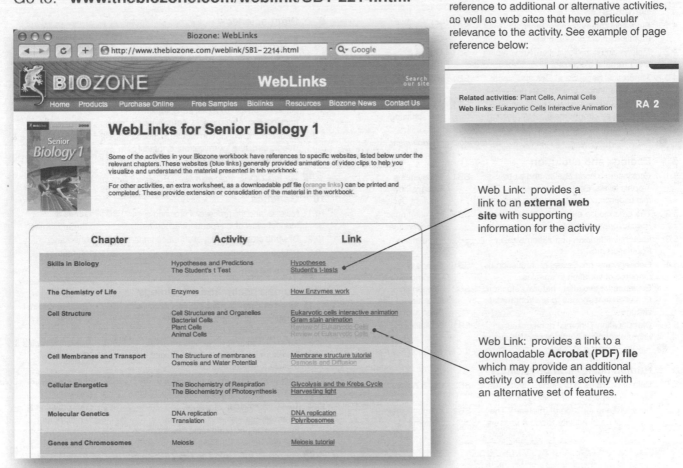

Related activities: Plant Cells, Animal Cells
Web links: Eukaryotic Cells Interactive Animation    **RA 2**

Web Link: provides a link to an **external web site** with supporting information for the activity

Web Link: provides a link to a downloadable **Acrobat (PDF) file** which may provide an additional activity or a different activity with an alternative set of features.

# International Baccalaureate Course

The International Baccalaureate (IB) biology course is divided into three sections: core, additional higher level material, and option material. All **IB candidates** must complete the **core** topics. Higher level students are also required to undertake Additional Higher Level **(AHL)** material as part of the core. Options fall into three categories (see the following page): those specific to standard level students **(OPT-SL)**, one only specific to higher level students **(OPT-HL)** and those offered to both **(OPT-SL/HL)**. All candidates are required to study two options. All candidates must also carry out **practical work** and must participate in **the group 4 project**. In the guide below, we have indicated where the relevant material can be found: SB1 for Senior Biology 1 and SB2 for Senior Biology 2.

| Topic | | See workbook | |
|---|---|---|---|

## CORE: (All students)

### 1 Statistical analysis
| | | | |
|---|---|---|---|
| 1.1 | Mean and SD, t-test, correlation. | SB1 | Skills in Biology |

● *For this CORE topic also see TRC: Statistical Tests Supplement*

### 2 Cells
| | | | |
|---|---|---|---|
| 2.1 | Cell theory. Cell and organelle sizes. Surface area to volume ratio. Emergent properties. Cell specialization and differentiation. Stem cells. | SB1 | Cell Structure, Cell Membranes Cell Division & Organization |
| 2.2 | Prokaryotic cells: ultrastructure & function. | SB1 | Cell Structure |
| 2.3 | Eukaryotic cells: ultrastructure & function. Prokaryotic vs eukaryotic cells. Plant vs animal cells. Extracellular components. | SB1 | Cell Structure, Cell Membranes |
| 2.4 | Membrane structure. Active and passive transport. Diffusion and osmosis. | SB1 | Cell Membranes |
| 2.5 | Cell division and the origins of cancer. | SB1 | Cell Division & Organization |

### 3 The chemistry of life
| | | | |
|---|---|---|---|
| 3.1 | Elements of life. The properties and importance of water. | SB1 | The Chemistry of Life |
| 3.2 | Structure and function of carbohydrates, lipids, and proteins. | SB1 | The Chemistry of Life |
| 3.3 | Nucleotides and the structure of DNA. | SB1 | Molecular Genetics |
| 3.4 | Semi-conservative DNA replication. | SB1 | Molecular Genetics |
| 3.5 | RNA and DNA structure. The genetic code. Transcription. Translation. | SB1 | Molecular Genetics |
| 3.6 | Enzyme structure and function. | SB1 | The Chemistry of Life |
| 3.7 | Cellular respiration and ATP production. | SB1 | Cellular Energetics |
| 3.8 | Biochemistry of photosynthesis. Factors affecting photosynthetic rates. | SB1 | Cellular Energetics |

### 4 Genetics
| | | | |
|---|---|---|---|
| 4.1 | Eukaryote chromosomes. Genomes. Gene mutations and consequences. | SB1 | Genes & Chromosomes |
| 4.2 | Meiosis and non-disjunction. Karyotyping and pre-natal diagnosis. | SB1 | Genes & Chromosomes |
| 4.3 | Theoretical genetics: alleles and single gene inheritance, sex linkage, pedigrees. | SB1 | Inheritance |
| 4.4 | Genetic engineering and biotechnology: PCR, gel electrophoresis, DNA profiling. HGP. Transformation. GMOs. Cloning. | SB1 | Aspects of Biotechnology |

● *For this CORE topic also see TRC: Biotechnology Supplement*

### 5 Ecology and evolution
| | | | |
|---|---|---|---|
| 5.1 | Ecosystems. Food chains and webs. Trophic levels. Ecological pyramids. The role of decomposers in recycling nutrients. | SB1 | Ecosystems, Energy Flow & Nutrient Cycles |
| 5.2 | The greenhouse effect. The carbon cycle. Precautionary principle. Global warming. | SB1 | Human Impact & Conservation |
| 5.3 | Factors influencing population size. Population growth. | SB1 | Populations |
| 5.4 | Genetic variation. Sexual reproduction as a source of variation in species. Evidence for evolution: natural selection. Evolution in response to environmental change. | SB1 SB2 | Genes & Chromosomes, The Origin & Evolution of Life, Speciation |
| 5.5 | Classification. Binomial nomenclature. Features of plant & animal phyla. Keys. | SB1 | Classification |

● *For this CORE topic also see TRC: Ecology & Classification Supplement*

### 6 Human health and physiology
| | | | |
|---|---|---|---|
| 6.1 | Role of enzymes in digestion. Structure and function of the digestive system. | SB2 | Diet & Animal Nutrition |
| 6.2 | Structure and function of the heart. The control of heart activity. Blood & vessels. | SB2 | Animal Transport Systems |

| Topic | | See workbook | |
|---|---|---|---|
| 6.3 | Pathogens and their transmission. Antibiotics. Role of skin as a barrier to infection. Role of phagocytic leucocytes. Antigens & antibody production. HIV/AIDS. | SB2 | Pathogens & Disease, Defense Against Disease |
| 6.4 | Gas exchange. Ventilation systems. Control of breathing. | SB2 | Gas Exchange in Animals |
| 6.5 | Principles of homeostasis. Control of body temperature and blood glucose. Diabetes. Role of the nervous and endocrine systems in homeostasis. Nervous system. | SB2 | Homeostasis & Excretion, Nerves, Muscles & Movement |
| 6.6 | Human reproduction and the role of hormones. Reproductive technologies and ethical issues. | SB2 | Reproduction & Development |

● *For this CORE topic also see TRC: Animal Biology Supplement*

## COMPULSORY: AHL Topics *(HL students only)*

### 7 Nucleic acids and proteins
| | | | |
|---|---|---|---|
| 7.1 | DNA structure, exons & introns (junk DNA) | SB1 | Molecular Genetics |
| 7.2 | DNA replication, including the role of enzymes and Okazaki fragments. | SB1 | Molecular Genetics |
| 7.3 | DNA alignment, transcription. The removal of introns to form mature mRNA. | SB1 | Molecular Genetics |
| 7.4 | The structure of tRNA and ribosomes. The process of translation. Peptide bonds. | SB1 | Molecular Genetics, The Chemistry of Life |
| 7.5 | Protein structure and function. | SB1 | The Chemistry of Life |
| 7.6 | Enzymes: induced fit model. Inhibition. Allostery in the control of metabolism. | SB1 | The Chemistry of Life |

### 8 Cell respiration and photosynthesis
| | | | |
|---|---|---|---|
| 8.1 | Structure and function of mitochondria. Biochemistry of cellular respiration. | SB1 | Cellular Energetics |
| 8.2 | Chloroplasts, the biochemistry and control of photosynthesis, chemiosmosis. | SB1 | Cellular Energetics |

### 9 Plant science
| | | | |
|---|---|---|---|
| 9.1 | Structure and growth of a dicot plant. Function and distribution of tissues in leaves. Dicots vs monocots. Plant modifications. Auxins. | SB2 | Plant Structure & Adaptation, Plant Responses & Reproduction |
| 9.2 | Support in terrestrial plants. Transport in angiosperms: ion movement through soil, active ion uptake by roots, transpiration, translocation. Abscisic acid. Xerophytes. | SB2 | Plant Structure & Adaptation |
| 9.3 | Dicot flowers. Pollination and fertilization. Seeds: structure, germination, dispersal. Flowering and phytochrome. | SB2 | Plant Responses & Reproduction |

● *For this CORE topic also see TRC: Plant Biology Supplement*

### 10 Genetics
| | | | |
|---|---|---|---|
| 10.1 | Meiosis, and the process of crossing over. Mendel's law of independent assortment. | SB1 | Genes & Chromosomes |
| 10.2 | Dihybrid crosses. Types of chromosomes. | SB1 | Inheritance |
| 10.3 | Polygenic inheritance. | SB1 | Inheritance |

● *For this CORE topic also see TRC: Genetics Supplement*

### 11 Human health and physiology
| | | | |
|---|---|---|---|
| 11.1 | Blood clotting. Clonal selection. Acquired immunity. Antibodies and monoclonal antibodies. Vaccination. | SB2 | Defense Against Disease |
| 11.2 | Animal Locomotion. Nerves, muscles, bones and movement. Joints. Skeletal muscle and contraction. | SB2 | Nerves, Muscles & Movement |
| 11.3 | Excretion. Structure and function of the human kidney. Urine production. Diabetes. | SB2 | Homeostasis & Excretion |
| 11.4 | Testis and ovarian structure. Spermatogenesis and oogenesis. Fertilization and embryonic development. The placenta. Birth. Role of hormones. | SB2 | Reproduction & Development |

● *For this CORE topic also see TRC: Animal Biology Supplement*

# International Baccalaureate Course *continued*

| Topic | | See workbook | |
|---|---|---|---|

## OPTIONS: OPT - SL *(SL students only)*

### A Human nutrition and health

| | | | |
|---|---|---|---|
| A.1 | Main constituents of diet. Balanced diet. Malnutrition. Deficiency & supplements. PKU. | SB2<br>SB1 | Diet & Animal Nutrition<br>Molecular Genetics |
| A.2 | Energy content of food types. BMI. Obesity and anorexia. Appetite control centre. | SB2 | Diet & Animal Nutrition |
| A.3 | Special diet issues, breastfeeding vs bottle-feeding, type II diabetes, cholesterol. | SB2 | Aspects covered in Diet & Animal Nutrition |

### B Physiology of exercise

| | | | |
|---|---|---|---|
| B.1 | Locomotion in animals. Roles of nerves, muscles, and bones in movement. Joints. Skeletal muscle and contraction. | SB2 | Nerves, Muscles & Movement |
| B.2 | Training and the pulmonary system. | SB2 | Gas Exchange |
| B.3 | Training and the cardiovascular system. | SB2 | Transport Systems |
| B.4 | Respiration and exercise intensity. Roles of myoglobin and adrenaline. Oxygen debt and lactate in muscle fatigue. | SB2 | Nerve, Muscles & Movement, Gas Exchange |
| B.5 | Exercise induced injuries and treatment. | | *Not yet covered* |

● *For this OPTION topic also see TRC: Animal Biology Supplement*

### C Cells and energy

| | | | |
|---|---|---|---|
| C.1 | Protein structure and function. Fibrous and globular proteins. | SB1 | The Chemistry of Life |
| C.2 | Enzymes: induced fit model. Inhibition. Allostery in the control of metabolism. | SB1 | The Chemistry of Life |
| C.3 | Biochemistry of cellular respiration. | SB1 | Cellular Energetics |
| C.4 | The biochemistry of photosynthesis including chemiosmosis. Action and absorption spectra. Limiting factors. | SB1 | Cellular Energetics |

## OPTIONS: OPT - SL/HL *(SL and HL students)*

### D Evolution

| | | | |
|---|---|---|---|
| D.1 | Prebiotic experiments. Comets. Protobionts and prokaryotes. Endosymbiotic theory. | SB2 | The Origin & Evolution of Life |
| D.2 | Species, gene pools, speciation. Types and pace of evolution. Transient vs balanced polymorphism. | SB2 | Speciation, Patterns of Evolution |
| D.3 | Fossil dating. Primate features. Hominid features. Diet and brain size correlation. Genetic and cultural evolution. | SB2 | Patterns of Evolution Human Evolution |

#### D.4-D.5 is extension for HL only

| | | | |
|---|---|---|---|
| D.4 | The Hardy-Weinberg principle. | SB2 | Speciation |
| D.5 | Classification. Biochemical evidence for evolution. Biochemical variations indicating phylogeny. Cladistics and cladograms. | SB1<br>SB2 | Classification<br>The Origin & Evolution of Life |

● *For this OPTION topic also see TRC: Human Evolution Supplement, Primate Supplement, Evolution Supplement*

### E Neurobiology and behavior

| | | | |
|---|---|---|---|
| E.1 | Stimuli, responses and reflexes in the context of animal behavior. Animal responses and natural selection. | SB2 | Nerves, Muscles & Movement, Animal Behavior |
| E.2 | Sensory receptors. Structure and function of the human eye and ear. | SB2 | Nerves, Muscles & Movement |
| E.3 | Innate vs learned behavior and its role in survival. Learned behavior and birdsong. | SB2 | Animal Behavior |
| E.4 | Presynaptic neurons at synapses. Examples of excitatory and inhibitory psychoactive drugs. Effects of drugs on synaptic transmission. Causes of addiction. | SB2 | Aspects covered in Nerves, Muscles & Movement |

#### E.5-E.6 is extension for HL only

| | | | |
|---|---|---|---|
| E.5 | Structure and function of the human brain. ANS control. Pupil reflex and its use in testing for death. Hormones as painkillers. | SB2 | Aspects covered in Nerves, Muscles & Movement |
| E.6 | Social behavior and organization. The role of altruism in sociality. Foraging behavior. Mate selection. Rhythmical behavior. | SB2 | Animal Behavior |

● *For this OPTION topic also see TRC: Behavior Supplement, Sensory Supplement*

### F Microbes and Biotechnology

| | | | |
|---|---|---|---|
| F.1 | Classification. Diversity of Archaea and Eubacteria. Diversity of viruses. Diversity of microscopic eukaryotes. | SB1 | Classification, Cell Structure |
| F.2 | Roles of microbes in ecosystems. Details of the nitrogen cycle including the role of bacteria. Sewage treatment. Biofuels. | SB1 | Energy Flow & Nutrient Cycles, Human Impact & Conservation |
| F.3 | Reverse transcription. Somatic vs germline. gene therapy. Viral vectors. | SB1 | Aspects of Biotechnology |
| F.4 | Microbes involved in food production of beer, wine, bread, and soy sauce. Food preservation. Food poisoning. | SB1<br>SB2 | Aspects of Biotechnology,<br>Pathogens and Disease |

#### F.5-F.6 is extension for HL only

| | | | |
|---|---|---|---|
| F.5 | Metabolism of microbes. Modes of nutrition. Cyanobacterium. Bioremediation. | SB2 | Diet & Animal Nutrition |
| F.6 | Pathogens and disease: influenza virus, malaria, bacterial infections. Controlling microbes. Epidemiology. Prion hypothesis. | SB2 | Pathogens & Disease, Defense Against Disease |

● *For this OPTION topic also see TRC: Biotechnology Supplement*

### G Ecology and conservation

| | | | |
|---|---|---|---|
| G.1 | Factors affecting plant and animal distribution. Sampling. Ecological niche and the competitive exclusion principle. Species interactions. Measuring biomass. | SB1 | Ecosystems, Populations, Practical Ecology |
| G.2 | Trophic levels. Ecological pyramids. Primary vs secondary succession. Biome vs biosphere. | SB1 | Ecosystems, Energy Flow & Nutrient Cycles |
| | Plant productivity (includes calculating gross and net production, and biomass). | SB2 | Plant Structure & Adaptation |
| G.3 | Conservation of biodiversity. Diversity index. Human impact on ecosystems: alien species. Biological control. Effect of CFCs on ozone layer. UV radiation absorption. | SB1 | Ecosystems, Human Impact & Conservation |

#### G.4-G.5 is extension for HL only

| | | | |
|---|---|---|---|
| G.4 | Monitoring environmental change. Biodiversity. Endangered species. Conservation strategies. | SB1 | Human Impact & Conservation |
| | Extinction. | SB2 | Patterns of Evolution |
| G.5 | r-strategies and K-strategies. Mark-and-recapture sampling. Fisheries conservation. | SB1 | Populations, Practical Ecology, Human Impact & Conservation |

● *For this OPTION topic also see TRC: Human Impact Supplement, Evolution Supplement, Ecology and Classification Supplement*

## OPTION: OPT - HL *(HL students only)*

### H Further human physiology

| | | | |
|---|---|---|---|
| H.1 | Hormones and their modes of action. Hypothalamus and pituitary gland. Control of ADH secretion. | SB2 | Homeostasis & Excretion |
| H.2 | Digestion and digestive juices. Stomach ulcers and stomach cancers. Role of bile. | SB2 | Diet & Animal Nutrition |
| H.3 | Structure of villi. Absorption of nutrients and transport of digested food. | SB2 | Diet & Animal Nutrition |
| H.4 | The structure and function of the liver (including role in nutrient processing and detoxification). Liver damage from alcohol. | SB2 | Homeostasis & Excretion, Diet & Animal Nutrition |
| H.5 | The cardiac cycle and control of heart rhythm. Atherosclerosis, coronary thrombosis and coronary heart disease. | SB2 | Animal Transport System |
| H.6 | Gas exchange: oxygen dissociation curves and the Bohr shift. Ventilation rate and exercise. Breathing at high altitude. | SB2 | Gas Exchange in Animals |
| | Causes and effects of asthma. | SB2 | Defense Against Disease |

● *For this OPTION topic also see TRC: Health & Disease Supplement, Animal Biology Supplement*

## Practical Work *(All students)*

Practical work consists of short and long term investigations, and an interdisciplinary project (The Group 4 project). Also see the "Guide to Practical Work" on the last page of this introductory section.

### Short and long term investigations

Investigations should reflect the breadth and depth of the subjects taught at each level, and include a spread of content material from the core, options, and AHL material, where relevant.

### The Group 4 project

All candidates must participate in the group 4 project. In this project it is intended that students analyze a topic or problem suitable for investigation in each of the science disciplines offered by the school (not just in biology). This project emphasizes the processes involved in scientific investigations rather than the products of an investigation.

# Advanced Placement Course

The Advanced Placement (AP) biology course is designed to be equivalent to a college introductory biology course. It is to be taken by students after successful completion of first courses in high school biology and chemistry. In the guide below, we have indicated where the relevant material can be found: SB1 for Senior Biology 1 and SB2 for Senior Biology 2. Because of the general nature of the AP curriculum document, the detail given here is based on the content in the workbooks.

| Topic | | See workbook |
|---|---|---|
| **Topic I:** | **Molecules and Cells** | |

**A    Chemistry of life**

| 1 | The chemical & physical properties of water. The importance of water to life. | SB1 | The Chemistry of Life |
| 2 | The role of carbon. Structure and function of carbohydrates, lipids, nucleic acids, and proteins. The synthesis and breakdown of macromolecules. | SB1 | The Chemistry of Life, Molecular Genetics, Cell Membranes |
| 3 | The laws of thermodynamics and their relationship to biochemical processes. Free energy changes. | SB1 | The Chemistry of Life |
| 4 | The action of enzymes and their role in the regulation of metabolism. Enzyme specificity. Factors affecting enzyme activity. Applications of enzymes. | SB1 | The Chemistry of Life |

**B    Cells**

| 1 | Comparison of prokaryotic and eukaryotic cells, including evolutionary relationships. | SB1 SB2 | Cell Structure, The Origin & Evolution of Life |
| 2 | Membrane structure: fluid mosaic model. Active and passive transport. | SB1 | Cell Membranes |
| 3 | Structure and function of organelles. Comparison of plant and animal cells. Cell size and surface area: volume ratio. Organization of cell function. | SB1 | Cell Structure, Cell Membranes Cell Division & Organization |
| 4 | Mitosis and the cell cycle. Mechanisms of cytokinesis. Cancer (tumour formation) as the result of uncontrolled cell division. | SB1 | Cell Division & Organization |

**C    Cellular energetics**

| 1 | Nature and role of ATP. Anabolic and catabolic processes. Chemiosmosis. | SB1 | Cellular Energetics |
| 2 | Structure and function of mitochondria. Biochemistry of cellular respiration, including the role of oxygen in energy yielding pathways. Anaerobic systems. | SB1 | Cellular Energetics |
| 3 | Structure and function of chloroplasts. Biochemistry of photosynthesis. Adaptations for photosynthesis in different environments. | SB1 | Cellular Energetics |

| **Topic II:** | **Heredity and Evolution** | |

**A    Heredity**

| 1 | The importance of meiosis in heredity. Gametogenesis. Similarities and differences between gametogenesis in animals and plants. | SB1 SB2 | Genes & Chromosomes Reproduction & Development, Plant Responses & Reproduction |
| 2 | Structure of eukaryotic chromosomes. Heredity of genetic information. | SB1 | Genes & Chromosomes |
| 3 | Mendel's laws. Inheritance patterns. | SB1 | Inheritance |

◉ *For this topic also see TRC: Genetics Supplement*

**B    Molecular genetics**

| 1 | RNA and DNA structure and function. Eukaryotic and prokaryotic genomes. | SB1 | Molecular Genetics |
| 2 | Gene expression in prokaryotes and eukaryotes. The *Lac* operon model. | SB1 | Molecular Genetics |
| 3 | Causes of mutations. Gene mutations (e.g. sickle cell disease). Chromosomal mutations (e.g. Down syndrome). | SB1 | Genes & Chromosomes |
| 4 | Viral structure and replication. | SB2 | Pathogens & Disease |
| 5 | Nucleic acid technology and applications. legal and ethical issues. | SB1 | Aspects of Biotechnology |

◉ *For this topic also see TRC: Genetics Supplement, Biotechnology Supplement, Replication in Bacteriophage*

**C    Evolutionary biology**

| 1 | The origins of life on Earth. Prebiotic experiments. Origins of prokaryotic cells. Endosymbiotic theory. | SB2 | The Origin & Evolution of Life |
| 2 | Evidence for evolution. Dating of fossils. | SB2 | The Origin & Evolution of Life |
| 3 | Mechanisms of evolution: natural selection, speciation, macroevolution. The species concept. | SB2 SB1 | Speciation, Patterns of Evolution Classification |

◉ *For this topic also see TRC: Evolution Supplement, Ecology and Classification Supplement*

| **Topic III:** | **Organisms and Populations** | |

**A    Diversity of organisms**

| 1 | Evolutionary patterns: major body plans of plants and animals. | SB1 | Classification |
| 2 | Diversity of life: representative members from the five kingdoms Monera (=Prokaryotae), Fungi, Protista (=Protoctista), Animalia and Plantae. | SB1 | Classification |
| 3 | Phylogenetic classification. Binomial nomenclature. Five kingdom classification. Use of dichotomous keys. | SB1 | Classification |
| 4 | Evolutionary relationships: genetic and morphological characters. Phylogenies. | SB1 SB2 | Classification The Origin & Evolution of Life |

◉ *For this topic also see TRC: Animal Biology Supplement, Ecology and Classification Supplement*

**B    Structure and function of plants and animals**

| 1 | Plant and animal reproduction and development (includes humans). Adaptive significance of reproductive features and their regulation. | SB2 | Reproduction & Development, Plant Responses & Reproduction |
| 2 | Organization of cells, tissues & organs. | SB1 | Cell Division & Organization |
| | The structure and function of animal and plant organ systems. Adaptive features that have contributed to the success of plants and animals in occupying particular terrestrial niches. | SB2 | Plant Structure & Adaptation, Diet & Animal Nutrition, Animal Transport Systems, Homeostasis & Excretion, Gas Exchange in Animals |
| 3 | Plant and animal responses to environmental cues. The role of hormones in these responses. | SB2 | Animal Behavior, Plant Responses and Reproduction |

◉ *For this topic also see TRC: Animal Biology Supplement, Plant Biology Supplement, Behavior Supplement*

**C    Ecology**

| 1 | Factors influencing population size. Population growth curves. | SB1 | Populations |
| 2 | Abiotic and biotic factors: effects on community structure and ecosystem function. Trophic levels: energy flows through ecosystems and relationship to trophic structure. Nutrient cycles. | SB1 | Ecosystems, Energy Flow & Nutrient Cycles |
| 3 | Human influence on biogeochemical cycles: (e.g. use of fertilizers). | SB1 | Human Impact & Conservation |

◉ *For this topic also see TRC: Human Impact Supplement, Ecology and Classification Supplement*

**Practical Work**

Integrated practicals as appropriate: see Senior Biology 1: Skills in Biology. Also see the page "Guide to Practical Work" in this introductory section.

# Guide to Practical Work

A practical or laboratory component is an essential part of any biology course, especially at senior level. It is through your practical sessions that you are challenged to carry out experiments drawn from many areas within modern biology. Both AP and IB courses have a strong practical component, aimed at providing a framework for your laboratory experience. Well executed laboratory and field sessions will help you to understand problems, observe accurately, make hypotheses, design and implement controlled experiments, collect and analyze data, think analytically, and communicate your findings in an appropriate way using tables and graphs. The outline below provides some guidelines for AP and IB students undertaking their practical work. Be sure to follow required safety procedures at all times during practical work.

## International Baccalaureate Practical Work

The practical work carried out by IB biology students should reflect the depth and breadth of the subject syllabus, although there may not be an investigation for every syllabus topic. All candidates must participate in the group 4 project, and the internal assessment (IA) requirements should be met via a spread of content from the core, options and, where relevant, AHL material. A wide range of IA investigations is possible: short laboratory practicals and longer term practicals or projects, computer simulations, data gathering and analysis exercises, and general laboratory and field work.

Suitable material, or background preparation, for this component can be found in this workbook and its companion title, Senior Biology 2.

## College Board's AP® Biology Lab Topics

Each of the 12 set laboratory sessions in the AP course is designed to complement a particular topic area within the course. The basic structure of the lab course is outlined below:

**LAB 1: Diffusion and osmosis**
Overview: To investigate diffusion and osmosis in dialysis tubing. To investigate the effect of solute concentration on water potential ($\psi$) in plant tissues.
Aims: An understanding of passive transport mechanisms in cells, and an understanding of the concept of water potential, solute potential, and pressure potential, and how these are measured.

**LAB 2: Enzyme catalysis**
Overview: To investigate the conversion of hydrogen peroxide to water and oxygen gas by catalase.
Aims: An understanding of the effects of environmental factors on the rate of enzyme catalyzed reactions.

**LAB 3: Mitosis and meiosis**
Overview: To use prepared slides of onion root tips to study plant mitosis. To simulate the phases of meiosis by using chromosome models.
Aims: Recognition of stages in mitosis in plant cells and calculation of relative duration of cell cycle stages. An understanding of chromosome activity during meiosis and an ability to calculate map distances for genes.

**LAB 4: Plant pigments and photosynthesis**
Overview: To separate plant pigments using chromatography. To measure photosynthetic rate in chloroplasts.
Aims: An understanding of Rf values. An understanding of the techniques used to determine photosynthetic rates. An ability to explain variations in photosynthetic rate under different environmental conditions.

**LAB 5: Cell(ular) respiration**
Overview: To investigate oxygen consumption during germination (including the effect of temperature).
Aims: An understanding of how cell respiration rates can be calculated from experimental data. An understanding of the relationship between gas production and respiration rate, and the effect of temperature on this.

**LAB 6: Molecular biology**
Overview: To investigate the basic principles of molecular biology through the transformation of E.coli cells. To investigate the use of restriction digestion and gel electrophoresis.
Aims: An understanding of the role of plasmids as vectors, and the use of gel electrophoresis to separate DNA fragments of varying size. An ability to design appropriate experimental procedures and use multiple experimental controls.

**LAB 7: Genetics of organisms**
Overview: Use Drosophila to perform genetic crosses. To collect and analyze the data from these crosses.
Aims: An understanding of the independent assortment of two genes and an ability to determine if genes are autosomal or sex linked from the analysis of the results of multigeneration genetic crosses.

**LAB 8: Population genetics and evolution**
Overview: To learn about the Hardy-Weinberg law of genetic equilibrium and study the relationship between evolution and changes in allele frequency.
Aims: An ability to calculate allele and genotype frequencies using the Hardy-Weinberg formula. An understanding of natural selection and other causes of microevolution.

**LAB 9: Transpiration**
Overview: To investigate transpiration in plants under controlled conditions. To examine the organization of plant stems and leaves as they relate to this.
Aims: An understanding of the effects of environmental variables on transpiration rates. An understanding of the relationship between the structure and function of the tissues involved.

**LAB 10: Physiology of the circulatory system**
Overview: To measure (human) blood pressure and pulse rate under different conditions. To analyze these variables and relate them to an index of fitness. To investigate the effect of temperature on heart rate in Daphnia.
Aims: An understanding of blood pressure and pulse rate, and their measurement and significance with respect to fitness. An understanding of the relationship between heart rate and temperature in a poikilotherm.

**LAB 11: Animal behavior**
Overview: To investigate responses in pillbugs (woodlice). To investigate mating behavior in fruit flies.
Aims: To understand and describe aspects of animal behavior. To understand the adaptiveness of appropriate behaviors.

**LAB 12: Dissolved oxygen & aquatic primary productivity**
Overview: To measure & analyze dissolved oxygen concentration in water samples. To measure and analyze the primary productivity of natural waters or lab cultures.
Aims: An understanding of primary productivity and its measurement. To use a controlled experiment to investigate the effect of changing light intensity on primary productivity.

# Skills in Biology

| IB SL | IB HL | IB Options | AP Biology |
|-------|-------|------------|------------|
| Complete:<br>*1-22, 28* | Complete:<br>*1-28* | Complete:<br>Option G: *23-27* | Complete:<br>*1-28* |

*Teachers may wish to make some points extension as appropriate*

## Learning Objectives

□ 1. Compile your own glossary from the **KEY WORDS** displayed in **bold type** in the learning objectives below.

□ 2. Demonstrate an understanding of the meaning of the following terms: **compare**, **contrast**, **define**, **describe**, **discuss**, **explain** (or account for), **evaluate**, **identify**, **illustrate**, **list**, **outline**, **state**, **suggest**, **summarize**. A correct understanding of these terms will enable you to answer questions appropriately *(see page 3 for help)*.

### Planning an Investigation  *(pages 18-26)*

Guidelines for planning and executing practical studies in the field are provided in the topic *Practical Ecology*.

□ 3. Recall the role of **observation** as a prelude to forming a **hypothesis**. Appreciate that your study design will be determined by the nature of the investigation, i.e. a controlled experiment vs a population study in the field. Some of the following objectives apply specifically to controlled experiments. They will also apply, with modification if necessary, to field studies.

□ 4. Formulate a **hypothesis** from which you can generate testable **predictions** about the outcome of your investigation. Consider a **pilot study**, to test the experimental procedure you have in mind.

□ 5. Define and explain the purpose of each of the following variables in a controlled experiment:
  • **Independent variable** (manipulated variable)
  • **Dependent variable** (response variable)
  • **Controlled variables** (to control nuisance factors)

□ 6. For your own investigation distinguish clearly between:
  • A **data value** for a particular **variable**, e.g. height.
  • The individual sampling unit, e.g. a test-tube with an enzyme at a particular pH.
  • The sample size, e.g. the number of test-tubes in each treatment.

□ 7. Determine the amount of data that you need to collect in order to reasonably test your hypothesis.
  • For lab based investigations, determine the **sample size** (e.g. the number of samples within each treatment) and the number of **treatments** (the range of the independent variable).
  • For field based investigations, determine the size of the sampling unit (it may be an individual organism or a quadrat size) and the sample size (e.g. the number of organisms or quadrats).

□ 8. Determine the type of data that you will collect (e.g. counts, measurements) and how you will collect it. Have a clear idea about how you are going to analyze your data before you start and appreciate why this is important. Appreciate why it is desirable to collect **quantitative** rather than **qualitative** data.

□ 9. Describe any **controls** in your investigation and identify any assumptions made in the investigation.

□ 10. Identify different methods for systematically recording data: tables, spreadsheets, and software linked to **dataloggers**. Decide on the method by which you will **systematically record** the data as they are collected.

□ 11. Identify **sources of error** in your experimental design and explain how you will minimize these.

□ 12. Recognise that all biological investigations should be carried out with appropriate regard for safety and the well-being of living organisms and their environment.

### Dealing with Data  *(pages 25-40)*

□ 13. Critically evaluate the **accuracy** of your methods for data collection (#10), any **measurement errors**, and the repeatability (**precision**) of any measurements.

□ 14. Demonstrate an ability to perform simple and appropriate **data transformations**, e.g. totals, percentages, increments, reciprocals, rates, and log.

□ 15. Demonstrate an ability to use **SI units** and an appropriate number of **significant figures**.

□ 16. Describe the benefits of graphing data. Recognize the **x axis** and **y axis** of graphs and identify which variable (dependent or independent) is plotted on each.

□ 17. Demonstrate an ability to plot data appropriately using different methods: **scatter plots**, **kite graphs**, **line graphs**, **pie charts**, **bar graphs**, and **histograms**.

□ 18. Explain what is meant by a **line of best fit** and when it is appropriate. Draw lines of best fit to graphs with plotted points. Use **error bars** to place your line or try a computer generated fit (see #24).

□ 19. Where appropriate to your investigation, record information in **biological drawings**.

### Descriptive Statistics  *(pages 41-42, 45-47)*

□ 20. Distinguish between a **statistic** and a **parameter**. Demonstrate an understanding of the calculation and use of the following **descriptive statistics**:
  (a) Sample **mean** and **standard deviation**. Identify when the use of these statistics is appropriate.
  (b) **Median** and **mode** (calculated from your own, or second hand, data). Explain what each statistic summarizes and when its use is appropriate.

□ 21. Calculate measures of dispersion for your data, related to the true population parameters. Consider:
  (a) The **standard error** of the mean.
  (b) The **95% confidence intervals** and the **95% confidence limits**.

□ 22. Identify **trends** in your data for further analysis and discussion. Evaluate unexpected results and outlying data points and be prepared to discuss them.

## Statistical Tests *(pages 43-44 and the TRC)*

Use the information in this topic, and the guidelines below, to help you decide on the appropriate analysis for your data.

### Tests for a trend

Recognize tests for trends (relationships) in data.

☐ 23. **Correlation**: Data are **correlated** when there is a relationship between the two variables in question, but neither is assumed to be dependent on the other. A test for correlation can demonstrate that two measures are associated; it cannot establish cause and effect.

☐ 24. **Regression**: A regression is appropriate when the magnitude of the dependent variable is determined by the magnitude of the independent variable. Recognize:

**Linear regression**: This is the simplest functional relationship of one variable to another and is indicated by a straight line relationship on a scatter plot. Generate a **line of best fit** for plotted data and comment on the fit of the data to the line. Discuss the **predictive** nature of linear regression analyses. See the *TRC: Linear regression*.

**Non-linear regression**: Many relationships between an independent variable and its corresponding biological response are not linear (e.g. change in respiration rate with changes in salinity). If your data plot in a non-linear scatter, consider a non-linear regression to test the relationship. See the *TRC: Non-linear regression*.

### Tests for a difference *(pages 47, 222 & the TRC)*

Recognise tests for difference between groups.

☐ 25. **Chi-squared** is a test for difference between two groups where the observed result is compared to an expected outcome. It is often used in ecology and for testing the outcome of simple genetic crosses.

☐ 26. **Student's *t* test** is a test for difference between two means, and can be used even when sample sizes are small. It is often used to test differences in a variable between two populations. See the *TRC: Student's t Test Exercise*.

☐ 27. **ANOVA** (analysis of variance) is a test for difference between more than two means. It is an appropriate test for investigations involving a biological response to specific treatments (*TRC: Analysis of Variance* is available as extension).

## Writing a Report *(pages 48-54)*

☐ 28. Write up your report. Give it a concise, descriptive title, and organize it into the following sections:

(a) **Introduction**: Describe the aim, hypothesis, and the current state of knowledge in the topic area.

(b) **Materials and methods**: Describe how you carried out your investigation in a way that allows the method to be reproduced by others.

(c) **Results**: Use text, graphs, and tables to describe your results; do not discuss them at this stage.

(d) **Discussion**: Discuss your results, including a critical evaluation of any discrepancies in your results. Include reference to published work.

(e) **Conclusion**: Summarize your findings with respect to your original hypothesis. Draw conclusions *only* about the variable that you planned to investigate.

(f) **Reference list**: Distinguish between a bibliography and a reference list, and use whichever meets your requirements. List all sources of information, including personal communications.

---

 See the 'Textbook Reference Grid' on pages 8-9 for textbook page references relating to material in this topic.

### Supplementary Texts

See pages 5-6 for additional details of these texts:

■ Adds, J. *et al.*, 1999. **Tools, Techniques and Assessment in Biology** (NelsonThornes).

■ Barnard, C., *et al.*, 2007. **Asking Questions in Biology**, 3 edn (Prentice Hall).

■ Cadogan, A. and Sutton, R., 2002. **Maths for Advanced Biology** (NelsonThornes).

■ Helms, D.R. *et al.*, 1998. **Biology in the Laboratory** (W.H. Freeman), #0-#2, & appendices.

■ Indge, B., 2003. **Data and Data Handling for AS and A Level Biology** (Hodder Arnold H&S).

■ Jones, A., *et al.*, 2007. **Practical Skills in Biology** (Prentice-Hall).

■ Knisely, K., 2005. **A Student Handbook for Writing in Biology** (Freeman/Sinauer).

■ Morgan, S., 2002. **Advanced Level Practical Work for Biology** (Hodder and Stoughton).

See page 6 for details of publishers of periodicals:

### STUDENT'S REFERENCE

■ **Correlation** Biol. Sci. Rev., 14(3) February 2002, pp. 38-41. *An examination of the relationship between variables. An excellent synopsis.*

■ **Experiments** Biol. Sci. Rev., 14(3) February 2002, pp. 11-13. *The basics of experimental design and execution: determining variables, measuring them, and establishing a control.*

■ **Descriptive Statistics** Biol. Sci. Rev., 13 (5) May 2001, pp. 36-37. *A synopsis of descriptive statistics. The appropriate use of standard error and standard deviation is discussed.*

■ **Testing Hypotheses** New Scientist, 4 Dec. 1993 (Inside Science). *Scientific method, statistical analyses, and hypothesis testing.*

■ **Statistical Modelling** New Scientist, 17 Sept. 1994 (Inside Science). *Useful presentation of data; distributions, normal curves, and histograms.*

■ **Statistical Sampling** New Scientist, 10 June 1995 (Inside Science). *An excellent account of hypothesis testing, sampling methodology and accuracy, significance, & the central limit theorem.*

■ **The Truth is Out There** New Scientist, 26 Feb. 2000 (Inside Science). *The philosophy of scientific method: starting with an idea, formulating a hypothesis, and following through to theory.*

■ **Estimating the Mean and Standard Deviation** Biol. Sci. Rev., 13(3) January 2001, pp. 40-41. *Simple statistical analysis. Includes formulae for calculating sample mean and standard deviation.*

■ **The Variability of Samples** Biol. Sci. Rev., 13(4) March 2001, pp. 34-35. *The variability of sample data and the use of sample statistics as estimators for population parameters.*

■ **Drawing Graphs** Biol. Sci. Rev., 19(3) Feb. 2007, pp. 10-13. *A guide to creating graphs.*

■ **Percentages** Biol. Sci. Rev., 17(2) Nov. 2004, pp. 28-29. *The calculation of percentage and the appropriate uses of this important transformation.*

### TEACHER'S REFERENCE

■ **Illustrating probability** The Am. Biology Teacher, 69(9), Nov 2007, pp. 544-551. *Illustrating probability with hands on learning.*

■ **Which Scientific Method Should We Teach and When?** The Am. Biology Teacher, 67(5), May 2005, pp. 262-264. *The different ways in which the Scientific Method is taught between disciplines.*

■ **Detecting Mold in School Buildings: An Exercise in Biodiversity** The Am. Biology Teacher 67(6), Aug. 2005, pp. 401-410. *An experiment designed to teach students about fungal biodiversity but includes many skills such as experimental design and laboratory techniques.*

■ **Biology Statistics made Simple using *Excel*** SSR 83(303), Dec. 2001, pp. 29. *An instructional account on the use of spreadsheets for statistics in A level science (excellent).*

■ **Teaching and Learning the Scientific Method** The Am. Biology Teacher 63(4), April 2001, pp. 242-245. *The nature of biological investigations.*

■ **The Generality of Hypothetico-Deductive Reasoning...** The Am. Biology Teacher, 62(7), Sept. 2000, pp. 482-495. *The application of the hypothetico-deductive method in science.*

See pages 10-11 for details of how to access **Bio Links** from our web site: **www.thebiozone.com** From Bio Links, access sites under the topics:

**STUDENT PROJECTS > General:** • AP Biology training • Mr Knight's AP lab activities • StudyZones.com **> Skills in Biology:** • A scientific report • Scientific investigation • Study skills - biology • The scientific method • Tree lupins • Woodlice online **> Statistics:** • Chi-square lesson • What is a P value? *... and others*

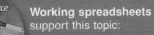

**Working spreadsheets** support this topic:

**Teacher Resource CD-ROM** • **Statistics spreadsheets**

# Terms and Notation

The definitions for some commonly encountered terms related to making biological investigations are provided below. Use these as you would use a biology dictionary when planning your investigation and writing up your report. It is important to be consistent with the use of terms i.e. use the same term for the same procedure or unit throughout your study. Be sure, when using a term with a specific statistical meaning, such as sample, that you are using the term correctly.

## General Terms

**Data**: Facts collected for analysis.

**Qualitative**: Not quantitative. Described in words or terms rather than by numbers. Includes subjective descriptions in terms of variables such as color or shape.

**Quantitative**: Able to be expressed in numbers. Numerical values derived from counts or measurements.

## The Design of Investigations

**Hypothesis**: A tentative explanation of an observation, capable of being tested by experimentation. Hypotheses are written as clear statements, not as questions.

**Control treatment (control)**: A standard (reference) treatment that helps to ensure that responses to other treatments can be reliably interpreted. There may be more than one control in an investigation.

**Dependent variable**: A variable whose values are determined by another variable (the independent variable). In practice, the dependent variable is the variable representing the biological response.

**Independent variable:** A variable whose values are set, or systematically altered, by the investigator.

**Controlled variables:** Variables that may take on different values in different situations, but are controlled (fixed) as part of the design of the investigation.

**Experiment**: A contrived situation designed to test (one or more) hypotheses and their predictions. It is good practice to use sample sizes that are as large as possible for experiments.

**Investigation**: A very broad term applied to scientific studies; investigations may be controlled experiments or field based studies involving population sampling.

**Parameter**: A numerical value that describes a characteristic of a population (e.g. the mean height of all 17 year-old males).

**Prediction**: The prediction of the response (Y) variable on the basis of changes in the independent (X) variable.

**Random sample**: A method of choosing a sample from a population that avoids any subjective element. It is the equivalent to drawing numbers out of a hat, but using random number tables. For field based studies involving quadrats or transects, random numbers can be used to determine the positioning of the sampling unit.

**Repeat / Trial**: The entire investigation is carried out again at a different time. This ensures that the results are reproducible. Note that repeats or trials are not **replicates** in the true sense unless they are run at the same time.

**Replicate**: A duplication of the entire experimental design run at the same time.

**Sample**: A sub-set of a whole used to estimate the values that might have been obtained if every individual or response was measured. A sample is made up of **sampling units**, In lab based investigations, the sampling unit might be a test-tube, while in field based studies, the sampling unit might be an individual organism or a quadrat.

**Sample size** ($n$): The number of samples taken. In a field study, a typical sample size may involve 20-50 individuals or 20 quadrats. In a lab based investigation, a typical sample size may be two to three sampling units, e.g. two test-tubes held at 10°C.

**Sampling unit**: Sampling units make up the sample size. Examples of sampling units in different investigations are an individual organism, a test tube undergoing a particular treatment, an area (e.g. quadrat size), or a volume. The size of the sampling unit is an important consideration in studies where the area or volume of a habitat is being sampled.

**Statistic**: An estimate of a parameter obtained from a sample (e.g. the mean height of all 17 year-old males in your class). A precise (reliable) statistic will be close to the value of the parameter being estimated.

**Treatments**: Well defined conditions applied to the sample units. The response of sample units to a treatment is intended to shed light on the hypothesis under investigation. What is often of most interest is the comparison of the responses to different treatments.

**Variable**: A factor in an experiment that is subject to change. Variables may be controlled (fixed), manipulated (systematically altered), or represent a biological response.

## Precision and Significance

**Accuracy**: The correctness of the measurement (the closeness of the measured value to the true value). Accuracy is often a function of the calibration of the instrument used for measuring.

**Measurement errors**: When measuring or setting the value of a variable, there may be some difference between your answer and the 'right' answer. These errors are often as a result of poor technique or poorly set up equipment.

**Objective measurement**: Measurement not significantly involving subjective (or personal) judgment. If a second person repeats the measurement they should get the same answer.

**Precision** (of a measurement): The repeatability of the measurement. As there is usually no reason to suspect that a piece of equipment is giving inaccurate measures, making precise measurements is usually the most important consideration. You can assess or quantify the precision of any measurement system by taking repeated measurements from individual samples.

**Precision** (of a statistic): How close the statistic is to the value of the parameter being estimated. Also called **reliability**.

### The Expression of Units

The value of a variable must be written with its units where possible. Common ways of recording measurements in biology are: volume in liters, mass in grams, length in meters, time in seconds. The following example shows different ways to express the same term. Note that ml and $cm^3$ are equivalent.

**Oxygen consumption** (milliliters per gram per hour)

**Oxygen consumption** ($ml\,g^{-1}h^{-1}$) or ($mL\,g^{-1}h^{-1}$)

**Oxygen consumption** ($ml/g/h$) or ($mL/g/h$)

**Oxygen consumption**/$cm^3 g^{-1}h^{-1}$

**Statistical significance**: An assigned value that is used to establish the probability that an observed trend or difference represents a true difference that is not due to chance alone. If a level of significance is less than the chosen value (usually 1-10%), the difference is regarded as statistically significant. Remember that in rigorous science, it is the hypothesis of no difference or no effect (the null hypothesis, $H_0$) that is tested. The alternative hypothesis (your tentative explanation for an observation) can only be accepted through statistical rejection of $H_0$.

**Validity**: Whether or not you are truly measuring the right thing.

# Hypotheses and Predictions

Scientific knowledge grows through a process called the **scientific method**. This process involves observation and measurement, hypothesizing and predicting, and planning and executing investigations designed to test formulated **hypotheses**. A scientific hypothesis is a tentative explanation for an observation, which is capable of being tested by experimentation. Hypotheses lead to **predictions** about the system involved and they are accepted or rejected on the basis of findings arising from the investigation. Rejection of the hypothesis may lead to new, alternative explanations (hypotheses) for the observations. Acceptance of the hypothesis as a valid explanation is not necessarily permanent: explanations may be rejected at a later date in light of new findings. This process eventually leads to new knowledge (theory, laws, or models).

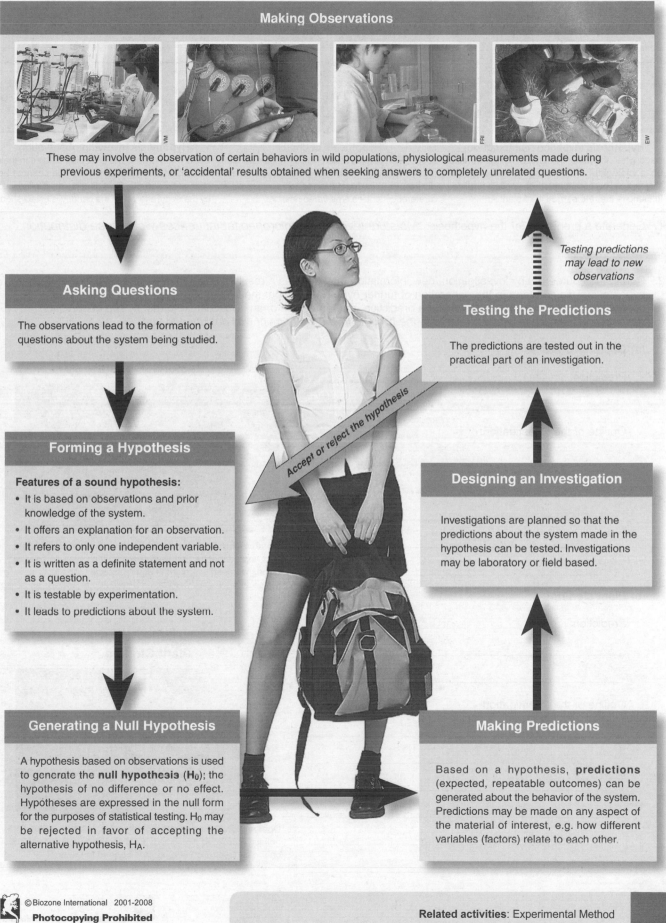

### Making Observations

These may involve the observation of certain behaviors in wild populations, physiological measurements made during previous experiments, or 'accidental' results obtained when seeking answers to completely unrelated questions.

### Asking Questions

The observations lead to the formation of questions about the system being studied.

### Forming a Hypothesis

**Features of a sound hypothesis:**
- It is based on observations and prior knowledge of the system.
- It offers an explanation for an observation.
- It refers to only one independent variable.
- It is written as a definite statement and not as a question.
- It is testable by experimentation.
- It leads to predictions about the system.

### Generating a Null Hypothesis

A hypothesis based on observations is used to generate the **null hypothesis ($H_0$)**; the hypothesis of no difference or no effect. Hypotheses are expressed in the null form for the purposes of statistical testing. $H_0$ may be rejected in favor of accepting the alternative hypothesis, $H_A$.

*Accept or reject the hypothesis*

*Testing predictions may lead to new observations*

### Testing the Predictions

The predictions are tested out in the practical part of an investigation.

### Designing an Investigation

Investigations are planned so that the predictions about the system made in the hypothesis can be tested. Investigations may be laboratory or field based.

### Making Predictions

Based on a hypothesis, **predictions** (expected, repeatable outcomes) can be generated about the behavior of the system. Predictions may be made on any aspect of the material of interest, e.g. how different variables (factors) relate to each other.

**Related activities**: Experimental Method
**Web links**: Hypotheses

A 2

# Useful Types of Hypotheses

A hypothesis offers a tentative explanation to questions generated by observations. Some examples are described below. Hypotheses are often constructed in a form that allows them to be tested statistically. For every hypothesis, there is a corresponding **null hypothesis**; a hypothesis against the prediction. Predictions are tested with laboratory and field experiments and carefully focused observations. For a hypothesis to be accepted it should be possible for anyone to test the predictions with the same methods and get a similar result each time.

**Hypothesis involving manipulation**
Used when the effect of manipulating a variable on a biological entity is being investigated. **Example**: The composition of applied fertilizer influences the rate of growth of plant A.

**Hypothesis of choice**
Used when species preference, e.g. for a particular habitat type or microclimate, is being investigated. **Example**: Woodpeckers (species A) show a preference for tree type when nesting.

**Hypothesis involving observation**
Used when organisms are being studied in their natural environment and conditions cannot be changed. **Example**: Fern abundance is influenced by the degree to which the canopy is established.

1.  Generate a prediction for the hypothesis: *"Moisture level of the microhabitat influences woodlouse distribution"*:

    _____

2.  During the course of any investigation, new information may arise as a result of observations unrelated to the original hypothesis. This can lead to the generation of further hypotheses about the system. For each of the incidental observations described below, formulate a prediction, and an outline of an investigation to test it. *The observation described in each case was not related to the hypothesis the experiment was designed to test:*

    (a) **Bacterial cultures**

    Prediction: _____

    _____

    Outline of the investigation: _____

    _____

    _____

    _____

    _____

    _____

    ### Bacterial Cultures

    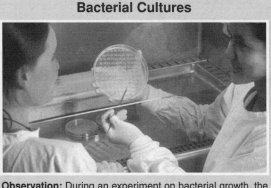

    **Observation:** During an experiment on bacterial growth, the girls noticed that the cultures grew at different rates when the dishes were left overnight in different parts of the laboratory.

    (b) **Plant cloning**

    Prediction: _____

    _____

    _____

    Outline of the investigation: _____

    _____

    _____

    _____

    _____

    _____

    ### Plant Cloning

    **Observation:** During an experiment on plant cloning, a scientist noticed that the root length of plant clones varied depending on the concentration of a hormone added to the agar.

# Planning an Investigation

Investigations involve written stages (planning and reporting), at the start and end. The middle stage is the practical work when the data are collected. Practical work may be laboratory or field based. Typical lab based studies involve investigating how a biological response is affected by manipulating a particular **variable**, e.g. temperature. Field work often involves investigating features of a population or community. These may be interrelationships, such as competition, or patterns, such as zonation. Where quantitative information must be gathered from the population or community, particular techniques (such as quadrat sampling) and protocols (e.g. random placement of sampling units) apply. These aspects of practical work are covered in the topic *Practical Ecology*. Investigations in the field are usually more complex than those in the laboratory because natural systems have many more variables that cannot easily be controlled or accounted for.

### Planning

- Formulate your hypothesis from an observation.
- Use a checklist (see the next activity) or a template (above) to construct a plan.

### Execution

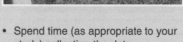

- Spend time (as appropriate to your study) collecting the data.
- Record the data in a systematic format (e.g. a table or spreadsheet).

### Analysis and Reporting

- Analyze the data using graphs, tables, or statistics to look for trends or patterns.
- Write up your report including all the necessary sections.

## Identifying Variables

A variable is any characteristic or property able to take any one of a range of values. Investigations often look at the effect of changing one variable on another. It is important to identify all variables in an investigation: independent, dependent, and controlled, although there may be nuisance factors of which you are unaware. In all fair tests, only one variable is changed by the investigator.

## Assumptions

In any experimental work, you will make certain assumptions about the biological system you are working with.

Assumptions are features of the system (and your experiment) that you assume to be true but do not (or cannot) test.

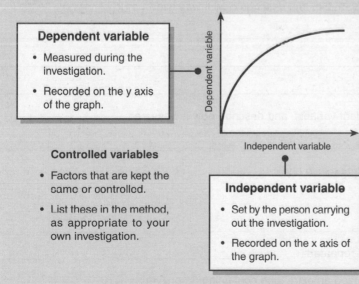

**Dependent variable**
- Measured during the investigation.
- Recorded on the y axis of the graph.

**Controlled variables**
- Factors that are kept the same or controlled.
- List these in the method, as appropriate to your own investigation.

**Independent variable**
- Set by the person carrying out the investigation.
- Recorded on the x axis of the graph.

## Examples of Investigations

| Aim | | Variables | |
|---|---|---|---|
| Investigate the effect of varying ... | on the following ... | Independent variable | Dependent variable |
| Temperature | Leaf width | Temperature | Leaf width |
| Light intensity | Activity of woodlice | Light intensity | Woodlice activity |
| Soil pH | Plant height at age 6 months | pH | Plant height |

In order to write a sound method for your investigation, you need to determine how the independent, dependent, and controlled variables will be set and measured (or monitored). A good understanding of your methodology is crucial to a successful investigation. You must be clear about how much data, and what type of data, you will collect. You should also have a good idea about how you plan to analyze the data. Use the example below to practise your skills in identifying this type of information.

### Case Study: Catalase Activity

Catalase is an enzyme that converts hydrogen peroxide ($H_2O_2$) to oxygen and water. An experiment investigated the effect of temperature on the rate of the catalase reaction. Small (10 cm$^3$) test tubes were used for the reactions, each containing 0.5 cm$^3$ of enzyme and 4 cm$^3$ of hydrogen peroxide. Reaction rates were assessed at four temperatures (10°C, 20°C, 30°C, and 60°C). For each temperature, there were two reaction tubes (e.g. tubes 1 and 2 were both kept at 10°C). The height of oxygen bubbles present after one minute of reaction was used as a measure of the reaction rate; a faster reaction rate produced more bubbles. The entire experiment, involving eight tubes, was repeated on two separate days.

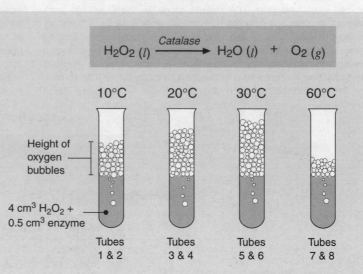

$$H_2O_2 \,(l) \xrightarrow{\text{Catalase}} H_2O \,(l) \;+\; O_2 \,(g)$$

Height of oxygen bubbles

4 cm$^3$ $H_2O_2$ + 0.5 cm$^3$ enzyme

10°C — Tubes 1 & 2
20°C — Tubes 3 & 4
30°C — Tubes 5 & 6
60°C — Tubes 7 & 8

1. Write a suitable aim for this experiment: _____

_____

2. Write a suitable hypothesis for this experiment: _____

_____

3. (a) Name the **independent variable**: _____

   (b) State the range of values for the independent variable: _____

   (c) Name the unit for the independent variable: _____

   (d) List the equipment needed to set the independent variable, and describe how it was used: _____

_____

4. (a) Name the **dependent variable**: _____

   (b) Name the unit for the dependent variable: _____

   (c) List the equipment needed to measure the dependent variable, and describe how it was used: _____

_____

5. (a) Each temperature represents a treatment/sample/trial (circle one):

   (b) State the number of tubes at each temperature: _____

   (c) State the sample size for each treatment: _____

   (d) State how many times the whole investigation was repeated: _____

6. Explain why it would have been desirable to have included an extra tube containing no enzyme: _____

_____

7. Identify three variables that might have been controlled in this experiment, and how they could have been monitored:

   (a) _____

   (b) _____

   (c) _____

8. Explain why controlled variables should be monitored carefully: _____

_____

# Experimental Method

An aim, hypothesis, and method for an experiment are described below. Explanations of the types of variables for which data are collected, and methods of recording these, are provided in the next two activities. The method described below includes numbered steps and incorporates other features identified in the previous activity. The method can be thought of as a 'statement of intent' for the practical work, and it may need slight changes during execution. The investigation described below was based on the observation that plant species 'A' was found growing in soil with a low pH (pH 4-5). The investigators wondered whether plant species 'A' was adapted to grow more vigorously under acid conditions than under alkaline or neutral conditions.

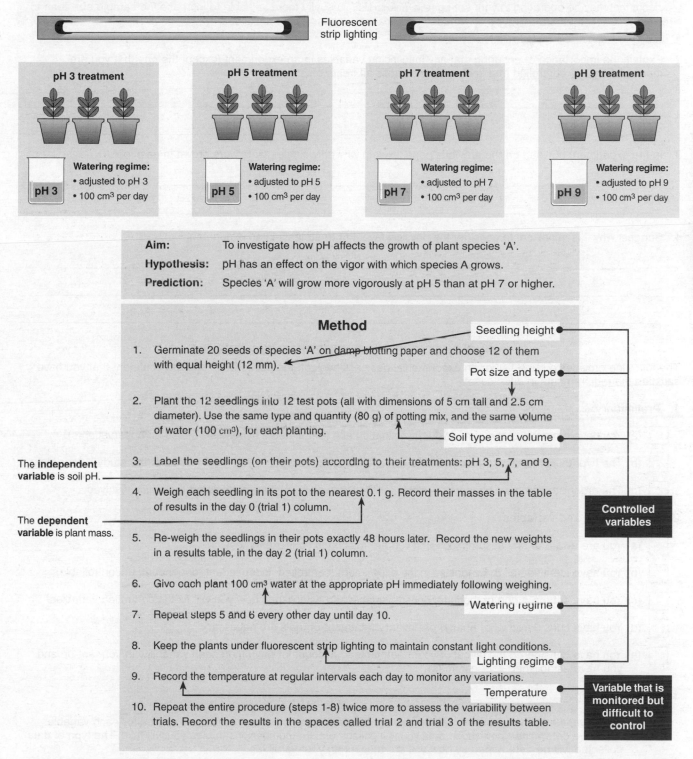

Fluorescent strip lighting

**pH 3 treatment**

Watering regime:
• adjusted to pH 3
• 100 cm³ per day
pH 3

**pH 5 treatment**

Watering regime:
• adjusted to pH 5
• 100 cm³ per day
pH 5

**pH 7 treatment**

Watering regime:
• adjusted to pH 7
• 100 cm³ per day
pH 7

**pH 9 treatment**

Watering regime:
• adjusted to pH 9
• 100 cm³ per day
pH 9

**Aim:** To investigate how pH affects the growth of plant species 'A'.

**Hypothesis:** pH has an effect on the vigor with which species A grows.

**Prediction:** Species 'A' will grow more vigorously at pH 5 than at pH 7 or higher.

## Method

Seedling height

1. Germinate 20 seeds of species 'A' on damp blotting paper and choose 12 of them with equal height (12 mm).

Pot size and type

2. Plant the 12 seedlings into 12 test pots (all with dimensions of 5 cm tall and 2.5 cm diameter). Use the same type and quantity (80 g) of potting mix, and the same volume of water (100 cm³), for each planting.

Soil type and volume

The **independent variable** is soil pH.

3. Label the seedlings (on their pots) according to their treatments: pH 3, 5, 7, and 9.

4. Weigh each seedling in its pot to the nearest 0.1 g. Record their masses in the table of results in the day 0 (trial 1) column.

**Controlled variables**

The **dependent variable** is plant mass.

5. Re-weigh the seedlings in their pots exactly 48 hours later. Record the new weights in a results table, in the day 2 (trial 1) column.

6. Give each plant 100 cm³ water at the appropriate pH immediately following weighing.

Watering regime

7. Repeat steps 5 and 6 every other day until day 10.

8. Keep the plants under fluorescent strip lighting to maintain constant light conditions.

Lighting regime

9. Record the temperature at regular intervals each day to monitor any variations.

Temperature

**Variable that is monitored but difficult to control**

10. Repeat the entire procedure (steps 1-8) twice more to assess the variability between trials. Record the results in the spaces called trial 2 and trial 3 of the results table.

1. Explain the best way to take account of natural variability between individuals when designing an experiment:

_____

_____

_____

_____

Skills in Biology

## Replication in Experiments

Replication refers to the number of times you repeat your entire experimental design (including controls). True replication is not the same as increasing the sample size (*n*) although it is often used to mean the same thing. Replication accounts for any unusual and unforeseen effects that may be operating in your set-up (e.g. field trials of plant varieties where soil type is variable). Replication is necessary when you expect that the response of treatments will vary because of factors outside your control. It is a feature of higher level experimental designs, and complex statistics are needed to separate differences between replicate treatments. For simple experiments, it is usually more valuable to increase the sample size than to worry about replicates.

2. Explain the importance of ensuring that any influencing variables in an experiment (except the one that you are manipulating) are controlled and kept constant across all treatments:

_____

_____

3. In the experiment outlined on the previous page, explain why only single plants were grown in each pot:

_____

_____

4. Suggest why it is important to consider the physical layout of treatments in an experiment: _____

_____

_____

_____

### YOUR CHECKLIST FOR EXPERIMENTAL DESIGN

The following provides a checklist for an experimental design. Check off the points when you are confident that you have satisfied the requirements in each case:

1. **Preliminary:**

   ☐ (a) You have determined the aim of your investigation and formulated a hypothesis based on observation(s).

   ☐ (b) The hypothesis (and its predictions) are testable using the resources you have available (the study is feasible).

   ☐ (c) The organism you have chosen is suitable for the study and you have considered the ethics involved.

2. **Assumptions and variables:**

   ☐ (a) You are aware of any assumptions that you are making in your experiment.

   ☐ (b) You have identified all the variables in the experiment (controlled, independent, dependent, uncontrollable).

   ☐ (c) You have set the range of the independent variable and established how you will fix the controlled variables.

   ☐ (d) You have considered what (if any) preliminary treatment or trials are necessary.

   ☐ (e) You have considered the layout of your treatments to account for any unforeseen variability in your set-up and you have established your control(s).

3. **Data collection:**

   ☐ (a) You have identified the units for all variables and determined how you will measure or monitor each variable. You have determined how much data you will collect, e.g. the number of samples you will take. The type of data collected will be determined by how you are measuring your variables.

   ☐ (b) You have considered how you will analyze the data you collect and made sure that your experimental design allows you to answer the questions you have asked.

   ☐ (c) You have designed a method for systematically recording your results and had this checked with a teacher. The format of your results table or spreadsheet accommodates all your raw results, any transformations you intend to make, and all trials and treatments.

   ☐ (d) You have recorded data from any preliminary trials and any necessary changes to your methodology.

# Recording Results

Designing a table to record your results is part of planning your investigation. Once you have collected all your data, you will need to analyze and present it. To do this, it may be necessary to transform your data first, by calculating a mean or a rate. An example of a table for recording results is presented below. This example relates to the investigation described in the previous activity, but it represents a relatively standardized layout. The labels on the columns and rows are chosen to represent the design features of the investigation. The first column contains the entire range chosen for the independent variable. There are spaces for multiple sampling units, repeats (trials), and averages. A version of this table should be presented in your final report.

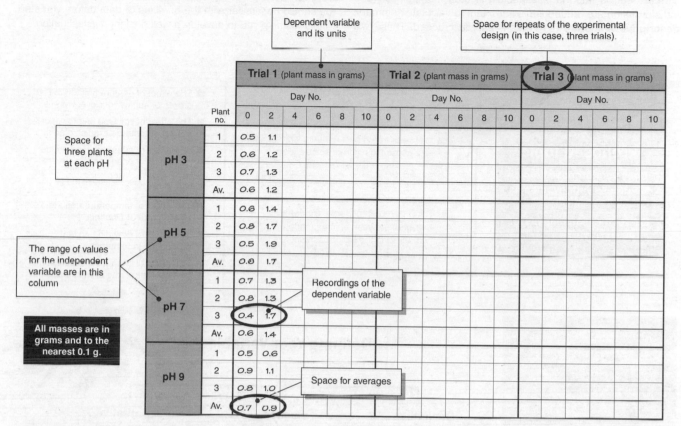

Dependent variable and its units

Space for repeats of the experimental design (in this case, three trials).

Space for three plants at each pH

The range of values for the independent variable are in this column

Recordings of the dependent variable

All masses are in grams and to the nearest 0.1 g.

Space for averages

| | Plant no. | Trial 1 (plant mass in grams) | | | | | | Trial 2 (plant mass in grams) | | | | | | Trial 3 (plant mass in grams) | | | | | |
|---|---|---|---|---|---|---|---|---|---|---|---|---|---|---|---|---|---|---|---|
| | | Day No. | | | | | | Day No. | | | | | | Day No. | | | | | |
| | | 0 | 2 | 4 | 6 | 8 | 10 | 0 | 2 | 4 | 6 | 8 | 10 | 0 | 2 | 4 | 6 | 8 | 10 |
| pH 3 | 1 | 0.5 | 1.1 | | | | | | | | | | | | | | | | |
| | 2 | 0.6 | 1.2 | | | | | | | | | | | | | | | | |
| | 3 | 0.7 | 1.3 | | | | | | | | | | | | | | | | |
| | Av. | 0.6 | 1.2 | | | | | | | | | | | | | | | | |
| pH 5 | 1 | 0.6 | 1.4 | | | | | | | | | | | | | | | | |
| | 2 | 0.8 | 1.7 | | | | | | | | | | | | | | | | |
| | 3 | 0.5 | 1.9 | | | | | | | | | | | | | | | | |
| | Av. | 0.8 | 1.7 | | | | | | | | | | | | | | | | |
| pH 7 | 1 | 0.7 | 1.3 | | | | | | | | | | | | | | | | |
| | 2 | 0.8 | 1.3 | | | | | | | | | | | | | | | | |
| | 3 | 0.4 | 1.7 | | | | | | | | | | | | | | | | |
| | Av. | 0.6 | 1.4 | | | | | | | | | | | | | | | | |
| pH 9 | 1 | 0.5 | 0.6 | | | | | | | | | | | | | | | | |
| | 2 | 0.9 | 1.1 | | | | | | | | | | | | | | | | |
| | 3 | 0.8 | 1.0 | | | | | | | | | | | | | | | | |
| | Av. | 0.7 | 0.9 | | | | | | | | | | | | | | | | |

1. In the space (below) design a table to collect data from the case study below. Include space for individual results and averages from the three set ups (use the table above as a guide).

### Case Study
### Carbon dioxide levels in a respiration chamber

A datalogger was used to monitor the concentrations of carbon dioxide ($CO_2$) in respiration chambers containing five green leaves from one plant species. The entire study was performed in conditions of full light (quantified) and involved three identical set-ups. The $CO_2$ concentrations were measured every minute, over a period of ten minutes, using a $CO_2$ sensor. A mean $CO_2$ concentration (for the three set-ups) was calculated. The study was carried out two more times, two days apart.

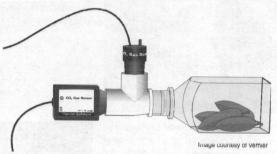

Image courtesy of vernier

2. Next, the effect of various light intensities (low light, half-light, and full light) on $CO_2$ concentration was investigated. Describe how the results table for this investigation would differ from the one you have drawn above (for full light only):

_____

_____

**Related activities**: Transforming Raw Data, Data Presentation

DA 2

Skills in Biology

# Variables and Data

When planning a biological investigation, it is important to consider the type of data that will be collected. It is best, whenever possible, to collect quantitative data, as these data lend themselves well to analysis and statistical testing. Recording data in a systematic way as you collect it, e.g. using a table or spreadsheet, is important, especially if data manipulation and transformation are required. It is important to calculate summary, **descriptive statistics** (e.g. mean) as you proceed. These will help you to recognize important trends or features in your data as they become apparent. The biggest hurdle in undertaking an experimental study will be in choosing a topic that lends itself to the aims of the investigation and is designed in such a way that analysis is straightforward and biologically meaningful. Guidelines are given below, together with a synopsis of types of variables. You should be familiar with the qualities of data before you start, as this will help you to develop a well designed investigation.

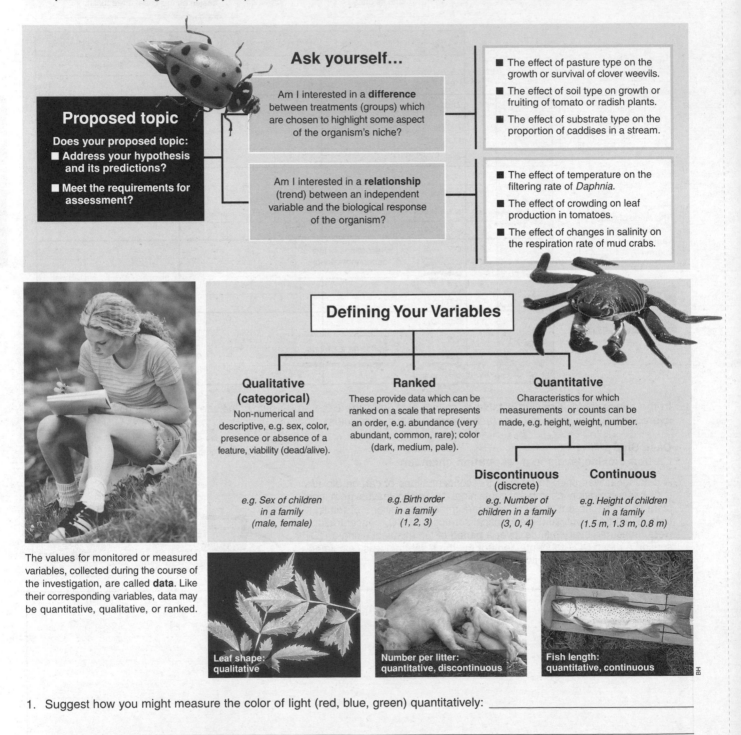

### Ask yourself...

**Proposed topic**

Does your proposed topic:
- Address your hypothesis and its predictions?
- Meet the requirements for assessment?

Am I interested in a **difference** between treatments (groups) which are chosen to highlight some aspect of the organism's niche?

- The effect of pasture type on the growth or survival of clover weevils.
- The effect of soil type on growth or fruiting of tomato or radish plants.
- The effect of substrate type on the proportion of caddises in a stream.

Am I interested in a **relationship** (trend) between an independent variable and the biological response of the organism?

- The effect of temperature on the filtering rate of *Daphnia*.
- The effect of crowding on leaf production in tomatoes.
- The effect of changes in salinity on the respiration rate of mud crabs.

### Defining Your Variables

**Qualitative (categorical)**

Non-numerical and descriptive, e.g. sex, color, presence or absence of a feature, viability (dead/alive).

*e.g. Sex of children in a family (male, female)*

**Ranked**

These provide data which can be ranked on a scale that represents an order, e.g. abundance (very abundant, common, rare); color (dark, medium, pale).

*e.g. Birth order in a family (1, 2, 3)*

**Quantitative**

Characteristics for which measurements or counts can be made, e.g. height, weight, number.

**Discontinuous (discrete)**

*e.g. Number of children in a family (3, 0, 4)*

**Continuous**

*e.g. Height of children in a family (1.5 m, 1.3 m, 0.8 m)*

The values for monitored or measured variables, collected during the course of the investigation, are called **data**. Like their corresponding variables, data may be quantitative, qualitative, or ranked.

**Leaf shape: qualitative**

**Number per litter: quantitative, discontinuous**

**Fish length: quantitative, continuous**

1. Suggest how you might measure the color of light (red, blue, green) quantitatively: _____

_____

_____

2. Sometimes, ranked data are given numerical values, e.g. rare = 1, occasional = 2, frequent = 3, common = 4, abundant = 5. Suggest why these data are sometimes called semi-quantitative:

_____

_____

**Related activities**: Descriptive Statistics

# Transforming Raw Data

Data often have to be transformed as a first step in the initial analysis of results. Transforming data can make them more useful by helping to highlight trends and making important features more obvious. Data transformations may be quite simple (e.g. percentages, totals, and rates) or they may be more complex transformations used before statistical procedures (e.g. log transformations). Some of the simple transformations are outlined below.

| Transformation | Rationale for Transformation |
|---|---|
| **Frequency table** | A tally chart of the number of times a value occurs in a data set. It is a useful first step in data analysis as a neatly constructed tally chart can double as a simple histogram. |
| **Total** | The sum of all data values for a variable. Useful as an initial stage in data handling, especially in comparing replicates. Used in making other data transformations. |
| **Percentages** | Provide a clear expression of what proportion of data fall into any particular category. This relationship may not be obvious from the raw data values. |
| **Rates** | Expressed as a measure per unit time. Rates show how a variable changes over a standard time period (e.g. one second, one minute or one hour). Rates allow meaningful comparison of data that may have been recorded over different time periods. |
| **Reciprocals** | Reciprocals of time (1/data value) can provide a crude measure of rate in situations where the variable measured is the total time taken to complete a task e.g. time taken for a color change to occur in an enzyme reaction. |
| **Relative values** | These involve expression of data values relative to a standard value e.g. number of road deaths per 1000 cars or calorie consumption per gram of body weight. They allow data from different sample sizes or different organisms to be meaningfully compared. Sometimes they are expressed as a percentage (e.g. 35%) or as a proportion (e.g. 0.35). |

Skills in Biology

1. (a) Explain what it means to **transform data**: _____

_____

(b) Briefly explain the general purpose of transforming data: _____

_____

_____

2. For each of the following examples, state a suitable transformation, together with a reason for your choice:

(a) Determining relative abundance from counts of four plant species in two different habitat areas:

Suitable transformation: _____

Reason: _____

(b) Making a meaningful comparison between animals of different size in the volume of oxygen each consumed:

Suitable transformation: _____

Reason: _____

(c) Making a meaningful comparison of the time taken for chemical precipitation to occur in a flask at different pH values:

Suitable transformation: _____

Reason: _____

(d) Determining the effect of temperature on the production of carbon dioxide by respiring seeds:

Suitable transformation: _____

Reason: _____

3. Complete the transformations for each of the tables on the right. The first value is provided in each case.

(a) TABLE: *Incidence of cyanogenic clover in different areas*

Working:  124 ÷ 159 = 0.78 = 78%

This is the number of cyanogenic clover out of the total.

### Incidence of cyanogenic clover in different areas

| Clover plant type | Frost free area | | Frost prone area | | Totals |
|---|---|---|---|---|---|
| | Number | % | Number | % | |
| Cyanogenic | 124 | 78 | 26 | | |
| Acyanogenic | 35 | | 115 | | |
| Total | 159 | | | | |

(b) TABLE: *Plant transpiration loss using a bubble potometer*

Working:  (9.0 − 8.0) ÷ 5 min = 0.2

This is the distance the bubble moved over the first 5 minutes. Note that there is no data entry possible for the first reading (0 min) because no difference can be calculated.

### Plant transpiration loss using a bubble potometer

| Time (min) | Pipette arm reading (cm$^3$) | Plant water loss (cm$^3$ min$^{-1}$) |
|---|---|---|
| 0 | 9.0 | – |
| 5 | 8.0 | 0.2 |
| 10 | 7.2 | |
| 15 | 6.2 | |
| 20 | 4.9 | |

(c) TABLE: *Photosynthetic rate at different light intensities*

Working:  1 ÷ 15 = 0.067

This is time taken for the leaf to float. A reciprocal gives a per minute rate (the variable measured is the time taken for an event to occur).

NOTE: In this experiment, the flotation time is used as a crude measure of photosynthetic rate. As oxygen bubbles are produced as a product of photosynthesis, they stick to the leaf disc and increase its buoyancy. The faster the rate, the sooner they come to the surface. The rates of photosynthesis should be measured over similar time intervals, so the rate is transformed to a 'per minute' basis (the reciprocal of time).

### Photosynthetic rate at different light intensities

| Light intensity % | Average time for leaf disc to float (min) | Reciprocal of time (min$^{-1}$) |
|---|---|---|
| 100 | 15 | 0.067 |
| 50 | 25 | |
| 25 | 50 | |
| 11 | 93 | |
| 6 | 187 | |

(d) TABLE: *Frequency of size classes in a sample of eels*

Working:  (7 ÷ 270) x 100 = 2.6 %

This is the number of individuals out of the total that appear in the size class 0-50 mm. The relative frequency is rounded to one decimal place.

### Frequency of size classes in a sample of eels

| Size class (mm) | Frequency | Relative frequency (%) |
|---|---|---|
| 0-50 | 7 | 2.6 |
| 50-99 | 23 | |
| 100-149 | 59 | |
| 150-199 | 98 | |
| 200-249 | 50 | |
| 250-299 | 30 | |
| 300-349 | 3 | |
| Total | 270 | |

# Data Presentation

Data can be presented in a number of ways. Tables provide an accurate record of numerical values and allow you to organize your data in a way that allows you to clarify the relationships and trends that are apparent. Graphical presentation provides a visual image of trends in the data in a minimum of space. The choice between graphing or tabulation depends on the type and complexity of the data and the information that you are wanting to convey. Outlined below are some of the basic rules for constructing tables and graphs. Values for standard errors are included in this example, although it is not a requirement to calculate these. In your report, always allow enough space for a graph e.g. one third to one half of a page. The examples in this workbook are usually reduced for reasons of space.

## Presenting Data in Tables

Tables should have an accurate, descriptive title. Number tables consecutively through the report.

Independent variable in left column.

Control values (if present) should be placed at the beginning of the table.

Each row should show a different experimental treatment, organism, sampling site etc.

Table 1: Length and growth of the third internode of bean plants receiving three different hormone treatments (data are given ± standard deviation).

| Treatment | Sample size | Mean rate of internode growth (mm day $^{-1}$) | Mean internode length (mm) | Mean mass of tissue added (g day $^{-1}$) |
|---|---|---|---|---|
| Control | 50 | $0.60 \pm 0.025$ | $32.3 \pm 2.3$ | $0.36 \pm 0.025$ |
| Hormone 1 | 46 | $1.52 \pm 0.030$ | $41.6 \pm 3.4$ | $0.51 \pm 0.030$ |
| Hormone 2 | 98 | $0.82 \pm 0.018$ | $38.4 \pm 0.9$ | $0.56 \pm 0.028$ |
| Hormone 3 | 85 | $2.06 \pm 0.019$ | $50.2 \pm 1.4$ | $0.68 \pm 0.020$ |

Heading and subheadings identify each set of data and show units of measurement.

Tables can be used to show a calculated measure of spread of the values about the mean (e.g. standard deviation or 95% confidence interval).

Show values only to the level of significance allowable by your measuring technique.

Columns that need to be compared should be placed alongside each other.

Organize the columns so that each category of like numbers or attributes is listed vertically.

## Presenting Data in Graph Format

Plot points accurately. Different responses can be distinguished using different symbols, lines or bar colors.

Label both axes (provide SI units of measurement if necessary).

Place the dependent variable, e.g. biological response, on the vertical (y) axis (if you are drawing a scatter graph it does not matter).

A break in an axis allows economical use of space if there are no data in the "broken" area. A floating axis (where zero points do not meet) allows data points to be plotted away from the vertical axis.

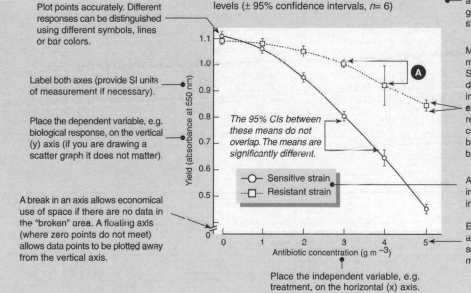

Fig. 1: Yield of two bacterial strains at different antibiotic levels (± 95% confidence intervals, $n = 6$)

*The 95% CIs between these means do not overlap. The means are significantly different.*

Graphs (called figures) should have a concise, explanatory title. If several graphs appear in your report they should be numbered consecutively.

Measures of spread about the plotted mean value can be shown on the graph. Such measures include standard deviation and the 95% confidence intervals (CI). The values are plotted as **error bars** and give an indication of the reliability of the mean value. If the 95% confidence intervals do not overlap between points, then these means will be significantly different.

A key identifies symbols. This information sometimes appears in the title or the legend.

Each axis should have an appropriate scale. Decide on the scale by finding the maximum and minimum values for each variable.

Place the independent variable, e.g. treatment, on the horizontal (x) axis.

---

1. What can you conclude about the difference (labeled A) between the two means plotted above? Explain your answer:

_____

2. Discuss the reasons for including both graphs and tables in a final report: _____

_____

_____

_____

_____

# Drawing Bar Graphs

## Guidelines for Bar Graphs

Bar graphs are appropriate for data that are non-numerical and **discrete** for at least one variable, i.e. they are grouped into separate categories. There are no dependent or independent variables. Important features of this type of graph include:

- Data are collected for discontinuous, non-numerical categories (e.g. place, color, and species), so the bars do not touch.

- Data values may be entered on or above the bars if you wish.

- Multiple sets of data can be displayed side by side for direct comparison (e.g. males and females in the same age group).

- Axes may be reversed so that the categories are on the x axis, i.e. the bars can be vertical or horizontal. When they are vertical, these graphs are sometimes called column graphs.

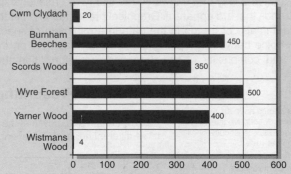

**Size of various woodlands in Britain**

Cwm Clydach 20
Burnham Beeches 450
Scords Wood 350
Wyre Forest 500
Yarner Wood 400
Wistmans Wood 4

Area of woodland (Hectares)

1. Counts of eight mollusc species were made from a series of quadrat samples at two sites on a rocky shore. The summary data are presented here.

   (a) Tabulate the mean (**average**) numbers per square meter at each site in Table 1 (below left).

   (b) Plot a **bar graph** of the tabulated data on the grid below. For each species, plot the data from both sites side by side using different colors to distinguish the sites.

Average abundance of 8 molluscan species from two sites along a rocky shore.

| Species | Mean (no. m$^{-2}$) | |
|---|---|---|
| | Site 1 | Site 2 |
| | | |
| | | |
| | | |
| | | |
| | | |
| | | |
| | | |
| | | |

### Field data notebook

Total counts at site 1 (11 quadrats) and site 2 (10 quadrats). Quadrats 1 sq. m.

| Species | Site 1 | | Site 2 | |
|---|---|---|---|---|
| | No m$^{-2}$ | | No m$^{-2}$ | |
| | Total | Mean | Total | Mean |
| Ornate limpet | 232 | 21 | 299 | 30 |
| Radiate limpet | 68 | 6 | 344 | 34 |
| Limpet sp. A | 420 | 38 | 0 | 0 |
| Cats-eye | 68 | 6 | 16 | 2 |
| Top shell | 16 | 2 | 43 | 4 |
| Limpet sp. B | 628 | 57 | 389 | 39 |
| Limpet sp. C | 0 | 0 | 22 | 2 |
| Chiton | 12 | 1 | 30 | 3 |

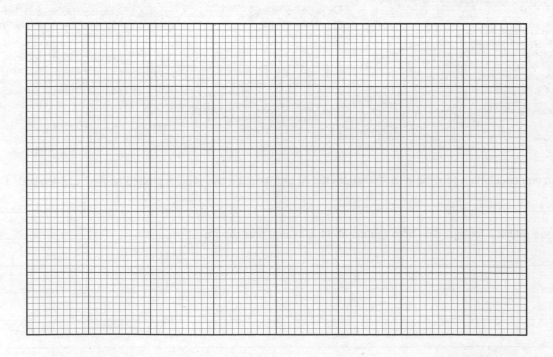

# Drawing Histograms

## Guidelines for Histograms

Histograms are plots of **continuous** data and are often used to represent frequency distributions, where the y-axis shows the number of times a particular measurement or value was obtained. For this reason, they are often called frequency histograms. Important features of this type of graph include:

- The data are numerical and continuous (e.g. height or weight), so the bars touch.

- The x-axis usually records the class interval. The y-axis usually records the number of individuals in each class interval (frequency).

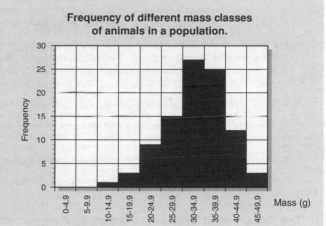

**Frequency of different mass classes of animals in a population.**

1. The weight data provided below were recorded from 95 individuals (male and female), older than 17 years.

   (a) Create a tally chart (frequency table) in the frame provided, organizing the weight data into a form suitable for plotting. An example of the tally for the weight grouping 55-59.9 kg has been completed for you as an example. Note that the raw data values, once they are recorded as counts on the tally chart, are crossed off the data set in the notebook. It is important to do this in order to prevent data entry errors.

   (b) Plot a **frequency histogram** of the tallied data on the grid provided below.

| Weight (kg) | Tally | Total |
|---|---|---|
| 45-49.9 | | |
| 50-54.9 | | |
| 55-59.9 | ̵L̵H̵t̵ // | 7 |
| 60-64.9 | | |
| 65-69.9 | | |
| 70-74.9 | | |
| 75-79.9 | | |
| 80-84.9 | | |
| 85-89.9 | | |
| 90-94.9 | | |
| 95-99.9 | | |
| 100-104.9 | | |
| 105-109.9 | | |

### Lab notebook

**Weight (in kg) of 95 individuals**

| | | |
|---|---|---|
| 63.4 | 81.2 | 65 |
| 56.5 | 83.3 | 75.8 |
| 84 | 95 | 76.8 |
| 81.5 | 105.5 | 67.8 |
| 73.4 | 82 | 68.3 |
| 56 | 73.5 | 63.5 |
| 60.4 | 75.2 | 58 |
| 83.5 | 63 | 58.5 |
| 82 | 70.4 | 50 |
| 61 | 82.2 | 92 |
| 55.2 | 87.8 | 91.5 |
| 48 | 86.5 | 88.3 |
| 53.5 | 85.5 | 81 |
| 63.8 | 87 | 72 |
| 69 | 98 | 66.5 |
| 82.8 | 71 | 61.5 |
| 68.5 | 76 | 66 |
| 67.2 | 72.5 | 65.5 |
| 82.5 | 61 | 67.4 |
| 83 | 60.5 | 73 |
| 78.4 | 67 | 67 |
| 76.5 | 86 | 71 |
| 83.4 | 85 | 70.5 |
| 77.5 | 93.5 | 65.5 |
| 71 | 62 | 68 |
| 87 | 62.5 | 90 |
| 89 | 63 | 83.5 |
| 93.4 | 60 | 73 |
| 83 | 71.5 | 66 |
| 80 | 73.8 | 57.5 |
| 76 | 77.5 | 76 |
| 56 | 74 | |

Skills in Biology

# Drawing Pie Graphs

### Guidelines for Pie Graphs

Pie graphs can be used instead of bar graphs, generally in cases where there are six or fewer categories involved. A pie graph provides strong visual impact of the relative proportions in each category, particularly where one of the categories is very dominant. Features of pie graphs include:

- The data for one variable are discontinuous (non-numerical or categories).

- The data for the dependent variable are usually in the form of counts, proportions, or percentages.

- Pie graphs are good for visual impact and showing relative proportions.

- They are not suitable for data sets with a large number of categories.

**Average residential water use**

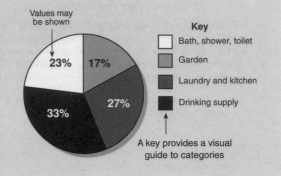

Values may be shown

23%  17%  27%  33%

**Key**
- Bath, shower, toilet
- Garden
- Laundry and kitchen
- Drinking supply

A key provides a visual guide to categories

1. The data provided below are from a study of the diets of three vertebrates.

(a) Tabulate the data from the notebook in the frame provided. Calculate the angle for each percentage, given that each percentage point is equal to 3.6° (the first example is provided: 23.6 x 3.6 = 85).

(b) Plot a pie graph for each animal in the circles provided. The circles have been marked at 5° intervals to enable you to do this exercise without a protractor. For the purposes of this exercise, begin your pie graphs at the 0° (= 360°) mark and work in a clockwise direction from the largest to the smallest percentage. Use one key for all three pie graphs.

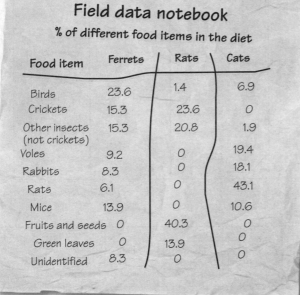

### Field data notebook

#### % of different food items in the diet

| Food item | Ferrets | Rats | Cats |
|---|---|---|---|
| Birds | 23.6 | 1.4 | 6.9 |
| Crickets | 15.3 | 23.6 | 0 |
| Other insects (not crickets) | 15.3 | 20.8 | 1.9 |
| Voles | 9.2 | 0 | 19.4 |
| Rabbits | 8.3 | 0 | 18.1 |
| Rats | 6.1 | 0 | 43.1 |
| Mice | 13.9 | 0 | 10.6 |
| Fruits and seeds | 0 | 40.3 | 0 |
| Green leaves | 0 | 13.9 | 0 |
| Unidentified | 8.3 | 0 | 0 |

Percentage occurrence of different foods in the diet of ferrets, rats, and cats. Graph angle representing the % is shown to assist plotting.

| Food item in diet | Ferrets | | Rats | | Cats | |
|---|---|---|---|---|---|---|
| | % in diet | Angle (°) | % in diet | Angle (°) | % in diet | Angle (°) |
| Birds | 23.6 | 85 | | | | |
| | | | | | | |
| | | | | | | |
| | | | | | | |
| | | | | | | |
| | | | | | | |
| | | | | | | |
| | | | | | | |
| | | | | | | |
| | | | | | | |

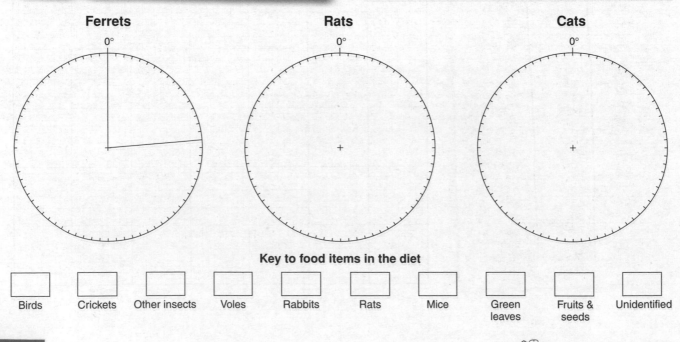

**Ferrets**    **Rats**    **Cats**

0°    0°    0°

### Key to food items in the diet

| Birds | Crickets | Other insects | Voles | Rabbits | Rats | Mice | Green leaves | Fruits & seeds | Unidentified |

# Drawing Kite Graphs

## Guidelines for Kite Graphs

Kite graphs are ideal for representing distributional data, e.g. abundance along an environmental gradient. They are elongated figures drawn along a baseline. Important features of kite graphs include:

- Each kite represents changes in species abundance across a landscape. The abundance can be calculated from the kite width.

- They often involve plots for more than one species; this makes them good for highlighting probable differences in habitat preferences between species.

- A thin line on a kite graph represents species absence.

- The axes can be reversed depending on preference.

- Kite graphs may also be used to show changes in distribution with time, for example, with daily or seasonal cycles of movement.

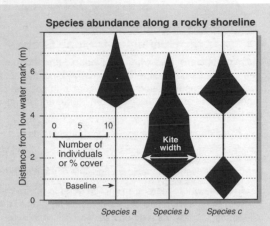

Species abundance along a rocky shoreline

1. The following data were collected from three streams of different lengths and flow rates. Invertebrates were collected at 0.5 km intervals from the headwaters (0 km) to the stream mouth. Their wet weight was measured and recorded (per m$^2$).

   (a) Tabulate the data below for plotting.

   (b) Plot a **kite graph** of the data from all three streams on the grid provided below. Do not forget to include a scale so that the weight at each point on the kite can be calculated.

Wet mass of invertebrates along three different streams

| Distance from mouth (km) | Wet weight (g m$^{-2}$) | | |
|---|---|---|---|
| | Stream A | Stream B | Stream C |
| | | | |
| | | | |
| | | | |
| | | | |
| | | | |
| | | | |
| | | | |

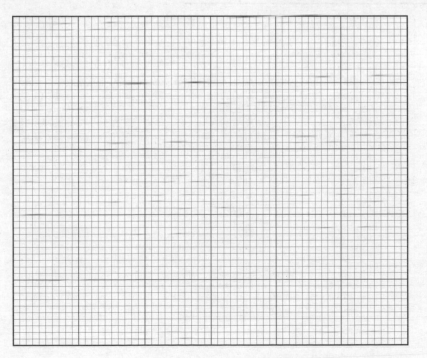

### Field data notebook

Mass per m$^2$ of invertebrates from 3 streams.

**Stream A: Slow flowing**

| Km from mouth | g m$^{-2}$ |
|---|---|
| 5.0 | 0.3 |
| 4.5 | 2.5 |
| 4.0 | 0.2 |
| 3.5 | 0.7 |
| 3.0 | 0.1 |
| 2.5 | 0.6 |
| 2.0 | 0.3 |
| 1.5 | 0.3 |
| 1.0 | 0.4 |
| 0.5 | 0.5 |
| 0 | 0.4 |

**Stream B: Fast, steep**

| Km from mouth | g m$^{-2}$ |
|---|---|
| 2.5 | 0.3 |
| 2.0 | 0.4 |
| 1.5 | 0.5 |
| 1.0 | 0.1 |
| 0.5 | 0.6 |
| 0 | 0.4 |

**Stream C: Steep torrent**

| Km from mouth | g m$^{-2}$ |
|---|---|
| 1.5 | 0.2 |
| 1.0 | 0 |
| 0.5 | 0.5 |
| 0 | 0 |

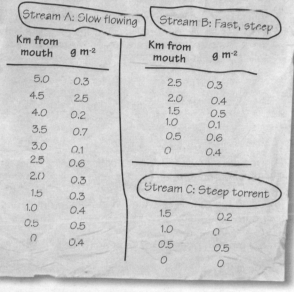

# Drawing Line Graphs

## Guidelines for Line Graphs

Line graphs are used when one variable (the independent variable) affects another, the dependent variable. Line graphs can be drawn without a measure of spread (top figure, right) or with some calculated measure of data variability (bottom figure, right). Important features of line graphs include:

- The data must be continuous for both variables.

- The dependent variable is usually the biological response.

- The independent variable is often time or the experimental treatment.

- In cases where there is an implied trend (e.g. one variable increases with the other), a line of best fit is usually plotted through the data points to show the relationship.

- If fluctuations in the data are likely to be important (e.g. with climate and other environmental data) the data points are usually connected directly (point to point).

- Line graphs may be drawn with measure of error. The data are presented as points (the calculated means), with bars above and below, indicating a measure of variability or spread in the data (e.g. standard error, standard deviation, or 95% confidence intervals).

- Where no error value has been calculated, the scatter can be shown by plotting the individual data points vertically above and below the mean. By convention, bars are not used to indicate the range of raw values in a data set.

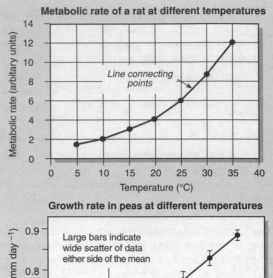

**Metabolic rate of a rat at different temperatures**

Line connecting points

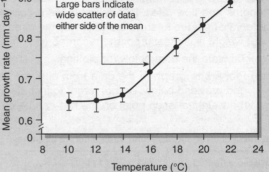

**Growth rate in peas at different temperatures**

Large bars indicate wide scatter of data either side of the mean

1. The results (shown right) were collected in a study investigating the effect of temperature on the activity of an enzyme.

   (a) Using the results provided in the table (right), plot a line graph on the grid below:

   (b) Estimate the rate of reaction at 15°C: _____

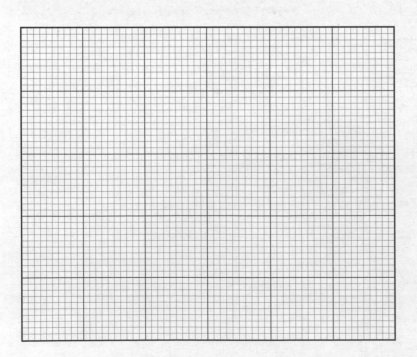

### Lab Notebook

**An enzyme's activity at different temperatures**

| Temperature (°C) | Rate of reaction (mg of product formed per minute) |
|---|---|
| 10 | 1.0 |
| 20 | 2.1 |
| 30 | 3.2 |
| 35 | 3.7 |
| 40 | 4.1 |
| 45 | 3.7 |
| 50 | 2.7 |
| 60 | 0 |

**Related activities**: The Reliability of the Mean, Interpreting Line Graphs

## Plotting Multiple Data Sets

A single figure can be used to show two or more data sets, i.e. more than one curve can be plotted per set of axes. This type of presentation is useful when you want to visually compare the trends for two or more treatments, or the response of one species against the response of another. Important points regarding this format are:

- If the two data sets use the same measurement units and a similar range of values for the independent variable, one scale on the y axis is used.

- If the two data sets use different units and/or have a very different range of values for the independent variable, two scales for the y axis are used (see example provided). The scales can be adjusted if necessary to avoid overlapping plots.

- The two curves must be distinguished with a key.

**Transpiration and root uptake rates in peas at different relative humidity**

2. A census of a deer population on an island indicated a population of 2000 animals in 1960. In 1961, ten wolves (natural predators of deer) were brought to the island in an attempt to control deer numbers. Over the next nine years, the numbers of deer and wolves were monitored. The results of these population surveys are presented in the table, right.

(a) Plot a line graph (joining the data points) for the tabulated results. Use one scale (on the left) for numbers of deer and another scale (on the right) for the number of wolves. Use different symbols or colors to distinguish the lines and include a key.

### Field data notebook
#### Results of a population survey on an island

| Time (yr) | Wolf numbers | Deer numbers |
|-----------|--------------|--------------|
| 1961 | 10 | 2000 |
| 1962 | 12 | 2300 |
| 1963 | 16 | 2500 |
| 1964 | 22 | 2360 |
| 1965 | 28 | 2244 |
| 1966 | 24 | 2094 |
| 1967 | 21 | 1968 |
| 1968 | 18 | 1916 |
| 1969 | 19 | 1952 |

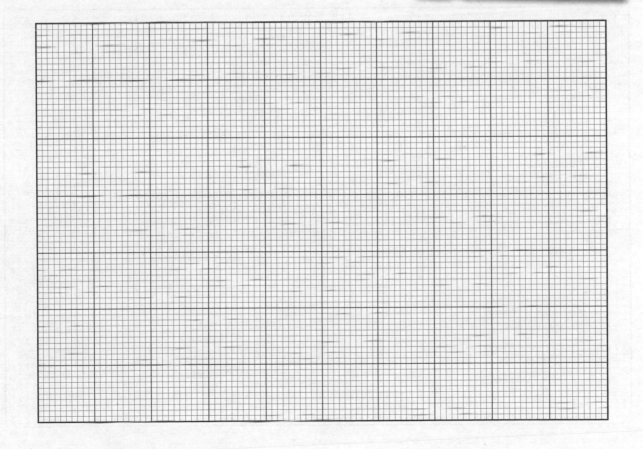

Skills in Biology

(b) Study the line graph that you plotted for the wolf and deer census on the previous page. Provide a plausible explanation for the pattern in the data, stating the evidence available to support your reasoning:

_____

_____

_____

_____

3. In a sampling program, the number of perch and trout in a hydro-electric reservoir were monitored over a period of time. A colony of black shag was also present. Shags take large numbers of perch and (to a lesser extent) trout. In 1960-61, 424 shags were removed from the lake during the nesting season and nest counts were made every spring in subsequent years. In 1971, 60 shags were removed from the lake, and all existing nests dismantled. The results of the population survey are tabulated below (for reasons of space, the entire table format has been repeated to the right for 1970-1978).

(a) Plot a line graph (joining the data points) for the survey results. Use one scale (on the left) for numbers of perch and trout and another scale for the number of shag nests. Use different symbols to distinguish the lines and include a key.

(b) Use a vertical arrow to indicate the point at which shags and their nests were removed.

### Results of population survey at a reservoir

| Time (yr) | Fish number (average per haul) | | Shag nest numbers | Time (yr) continued | Fish number (average per haul) | | Shag nest numbers |
|---|---|---|---|---|---|---|---|
| | Trout | Perch | | | Trout | Perch | |
| 1960 | – | – | 16 | 1970 | 1.5 | 6 | 35 |
| 1961 | – | – | 4 | 1971 | 0.5 | 0.7 | 42 |
| 1962 | 1.5 | 11 | 5 | 1972 | 1 | 0.8 | 0 |
| 1963 | 0.8 | 9 | 10 | 1973 | 0.2 | 4 | 0 |
| 1964 | 0 | 5 | 22 | 1974 | 0.5 | 6.5 | 0 |
| 1965 | 1 | 1 | 25 | 1975 | 0.6 | 7.6 | 2 |
| 1966 | 1 | 2.9 | 35 | 1976 | 1 | 1.2 | 10 |
| 1967 | 2 | 5 | 40 | 1977 | 1.2 | 1.5 | 32 |
| 1968 | 1.5 | 4.6 | 26 | 1978 | 0.7 | 2 | 28 |
| 1969 | 1.5 | 6 | 32 | | | | |

Source: Data adapted from 1987 Bursary Examination

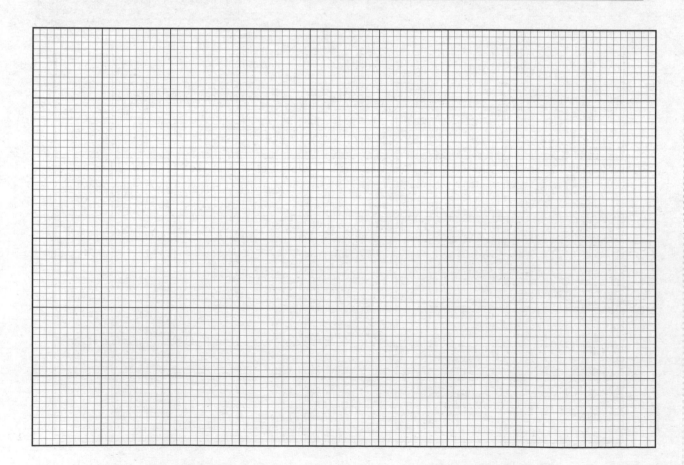

# Interpreting Line Graphs

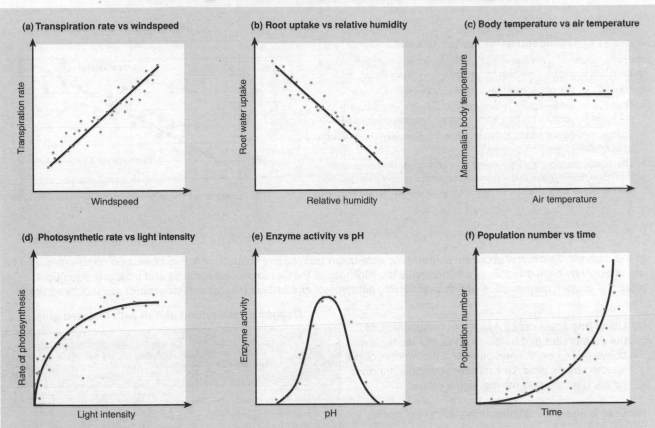

**(a) Transpiration rate vs windspeed**

Transpiration rate / Windspeed

**(b) Root uptake vs relative humidity**

Root water uptake / Relative humidity

**(c) Body temperature vs air temperature**

Mammalian body temperature / Air temperature

**(d) Photosynthetic rate vs light intensity**

Rate of photosynthesis / Light intensity

**(e) Enzyme activity vs pH**

Enzyme activity / pH

**(f) Population number vs time**

Population number / Time

1. For each of the graphs (b-f) above, give a description of the slope and an interpretation of how one variable changes with respect to the other. For the purposes of your description, call the independent variable (horizontal or x-axis) in each example "variable X" and the dependent variable (vertical or y-axis) "variable Y". Be aware that the existence of a relationship between two variables does not necessarily mean that the relationship is causative (although it may be).

   (a) Slope: _Positive linear relationship, with constantly rising slope_

   Interpretation: _Variable Y (transpiration) increases regularly with increase in variable X (windspeed)_

   (b) Slope: _____

   Interpretation: _____

   (c) Slope: _____

   Interpretation: _____

   (d) Slope: _____

   Interpretation: _____

   (e) Slope: _____

   Interpretation: _____

   (f) Slope: _____

   Interpretation: _____

2. Study the line graph of trout, perch and shag numbers that you plotted on the previous page:

   (a) Describe the evidence suggesting that the shag population is exercising some control over perch numbers:

   _____

   (b) Describe evidence that the fluctuations in shag numbers are related to fluctuations in trout numbers: _____

   _____

   _____

**Related activities**: Drawing Line Graphs

**RDA 2**

# Drawing Scatter Plots

## Guidelines for Scatter Graphs

A scatter graph is a common way to display continuous data where there is a relationship between two interdependent variables.

- The data for this graph must be continuous for both variables.
- There is no independent (manipulated) variable, but the variables are often correlated, i.e. they vary together in some predictable way.
- Scatter graphs are useful for determining the relationship between two variables.
- The points on the graph need not be connected, but a line of best fit is often drawn through the points to show the relationship between the variables (this may be drawn be eye or computer generated).

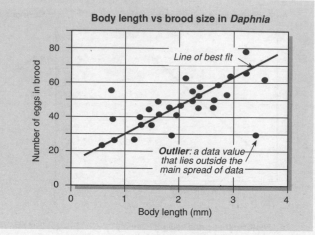

**Body length vs brood size in *Daphnia***

1. In the example below, metabolic measurements were taken from seven Antarctic fish *Pagothenia borchgrevinski*. The fish are affected by a gill disease, which increases the thickness of the gas exchange surfaces and affects oxygen uptake. The results of oxygen consumption of fish with varying amounts of affected gill (at rest and swimming) are tabulated below.

   (a) Using **one** scale only for oxygen consumption, plot the data on the grid below to show the relationship between oxygen consumption and the amount of gill affected by disease. Use different symbols or colors for each set of data (at rest and swimming).

   (b) Draw a line of best fit through each set of points.

2. Describe the relationship between the amount of gill affected and oxygen consumption in the fish:

   (a) For the **at rest** data set:

   _____

   _____

   _____

   _____

   _____

   _____

   _____

   (b) For the **swimming** data set:

   _____

   _____

   _____

   _____

   _____

   _____

   _____

### Oxygen consumption of fish with affected gills

| Fish number | Percentage of gill affected | Oxygen consumption $(cm^3\ g^{-1}\ h^{-1})$ | |
| --- | --- | --- | --- |
| | | At rest | Swimming |
| 1 | 0 | 0.05 | 0.29 |
| 2 | 95 | 0.04 | 0.11 |
| 3 | 60 | 0.04 | 0.14 |
| 4 | 30 | 0.05 | 0.22 |
| 5 | 90 | 0.05 | 0.08 |
| 6 | 65 | 0.04 | 0.18 |
| 7 | 45 | 0.04 | 0.20 |

3. Describe how the gill disease affects oxygen uptake in resting fish:

_____

_____

**Related activities:** Interpreting Line Graphs

# Biological Drawings

Microscopes are a powerful tool for examining cells and cell structures. In order to make a permanent record of what is seen when examining a specimen, it is useful to make a drawing. It is important to draw **what is actually seen**. This will depend on the **resolution** of the microscope being used. Resolution refers to the ability of a microscope to separate small objects that are very close together. Making drawings from mounted specimens is a skill. Drawing forces you to observe closely and accurately. While photographs are limited to representing appearance at a single moment in time, drawings can be composites of the observer's cumulative experience, with many different specimens of the same material. The total picture of an object thus represented can often communicate information much more effectively than a photograph. Your attention to the outline of suggestions below will help you to make more effective drawings. If you are careful to follow the suggestions at the beginning, the techniques will soon become habitual.

1. **Drawing materials**: All drawings should be done with a clear pencil line on good quality paper. A sharp HB pencil is recommended. A soft eraser of good quality is essential. Diagrams in ballpoint or fountain pen are unacceptable because they cannot be corrected.

2. **Positioning**: Center your diagram on the page. Do not draw it in a corner. This will leave plenty of room for the addition of labels once the diagram is completed.

3. **Size**: A drawing should be large enough to easily represent all the details you see without crowding. Rarely, if ever, are drawings too large, but they are often too small. Show only as much as is necessary for an understanding of the structure; a small section shown in detail will often suffice. It is time consuming and unnecessary, for example, to reproduce accurately the entire contents of a microscope field.

4. **Accuracy**: Your drawing should be a complete, accurate representation of the material you have observed, and should communicate your understanding of the material to anyone who looks at it. Avoid making "idealized" drawings; your drawing should be a picture of what you actually see, not what you imagine should be there. Proportions should be accurate. If necessary, measure the lengths of various parts with a ruler. If viewing through a microscope, estimate them as a proportion of the field of view, then translate these proportions onto the page. When drawing shapes that indicate an outline, make sure the line is complete. Where two ends of a line do not meet (as in drawing a cell outline) then this would indicate that it has a hole in it.

5. **Technique**: Use only simple, narrow lines. Represent depth by stippling (dots close together). Indicate depth only when it is essential to your drawing (usually it is not). Do not use shading. Look at the specimen while you are drawing it.

6. **Labels**: Leave a good margin for labels. All parts of your diagram must be labeled accurately. Labeling lines should be drawn with a ruler and should not cross. Where possible, keep label lines vertical or horizontal. Label the drawing with:
   - A title, which should identify the material (organism, tissues or cells).
   - Magnification under which it was observed, or a scale to indicate the size of the object.
   - Names of structures.
   - In living materials, any movements you have seen.

Remember that drawings are intended as records for you, and as a means of encouraging close observation; artistic ability is not necessary. Before you turn in a drawing, ask yourself if you know what every line represents. If you do not, look more closely at the material. *Take into account the rules for biological drawings and draw what you see, not what you think you see!*

**Examples of acceptable biological drawings**: The diagrams below show two examples of biological drawings that are acceptable. The example on the left is of a whole organism and its size is indicated by a scale. The example on the right is of plant tissue: a group of cells that are essentially identical in the structure. It is not necessary to show many cells even though your view through the microscope may show them. As few as 2-4 will suffice to show their structure and how they are arranged. Scale is indicated by stating how many times larger it has been drawn. Do not confuse this with what magnification it was viewed at under the microscope. The abbreviation **T.S.** indicates that the specimen was a *cross* or *transverse section*.

Skills in Biology

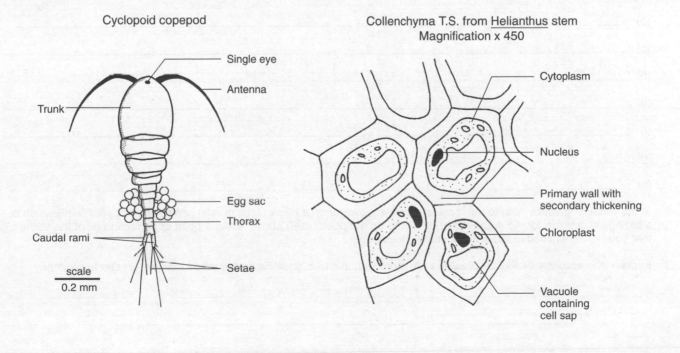

Cyclopoid copepod

- Single eye
- Antenna
- Trunk
- Egg sac
- Thorax
- Caudal rami
- Setae

scale
0.2 mm

Collenchyma T.S. from Helianthus stem
Magnification x 450

- Cytoplasm
- Nucleus
- Primary wall with secondary thickening
- Chloroplast
- Vacuole containing cell sap

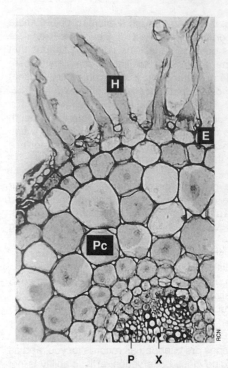

P        X

**Specimen used for drawing**

The photograph above is a light microscope view of a stained transverse section (cross section) of a root from a *Ranunculus* (buttercup) plant. It shows the arrangement of the different tissues in the root. The vascular bundle is at the center of the root, with the larger, central xylem vessels (**X**) and smaller phloem vessels (**P**) grouped around them. The root hair cells (**H**) are arranged on the external surface and form part of the epidermal layer (**E**). Parenchyma cells (**Pc**) make up the bulk of the root's mass. The distance from point **X** to point **E** on the photograph (above) is about 0.15 mm (150 μm).

# An Unacceptable Biological Drawing

The diagram below is an example of how *not* to produce a biological drawing; it is based on the photograph to the left. There are many aspects of the drawing that are unacceptable. The exercise below asks you to identify the errors in this student's attempt.

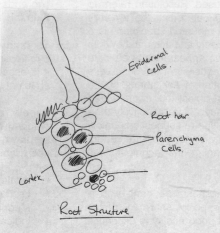

1. Identify and describe eight unacceptable features of the student's biological diagram above:

   (a) _____

   (b) _____

   (c) _____

   (d) _____

   (e) _____

   (f) _____

   (g) _____

   (h) _____

2. In the remaining space next to the 'poor example' (above) or on a blank piece of refill paper, attempt your own version of a biological drawing for the same material, based on the photograph above. Make a point of correcting all of the errors that you have identified in the sample student's attempt.

3. Explain why accurate biological drawings are more valuable to a scientific investigation than an 'artistic' approach:

   _____

   _____

   _____

# Descriptive Statistics

For most investigations, measures of the biological response are made from more than one sampling unit. The sample size (the number of sampling units) will vary depending on the resources available. In lab based investigations, the sample size may be as small as two or three (e.g. two test-tubes in each treatment). In field studies, each individual may be a sampling unit, and the sample size can be very large (e.g. 100 individuals). It is useful to summarize the data collected using **descriptive statistics**.

Descriptive statistics, such as mean, median, and mode, can help to highlight trends or patterns in the data. Each of these statistics is appropriate to certain types of data or distributions, e.g. a mean is not appropriate for data with a skewed distribution (see below). Frequency graphs are useful for indicating the distribution of data. Standard deviation and standard error are statistics used to quantify the amount of spread in the data and evaluate the reliability of estimates of the true (population) mean.

## Variation in Data

Whether they are obtained from observation or experiments, most biological data show variability. In a set of data values, it is useful to know the value about which most of the data are grouped; the center value. This value can be the mean, median, or mode depending on the type of variable involved (see schematic below). The main purpose of these statistics is to summarize important trends in your data and to provide the basis for statistical analyses.

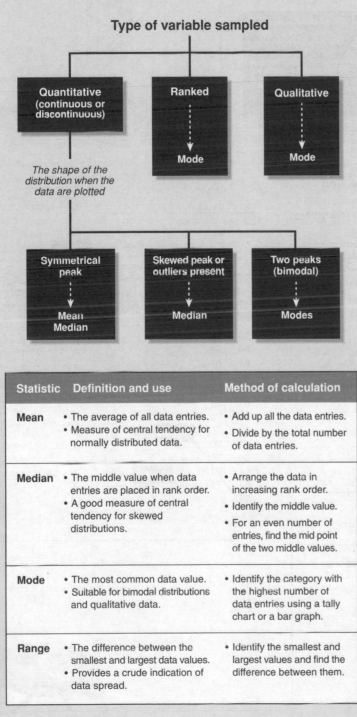

## Distribution of Data

Variability in continuous data is often displayed as a **frequency distribution**. A frequency plot will indicate whether the data have a normal distribution (A), with a symmetrical spread of data about the mean, or whether the distribution is skewed (B), or bimodal (C). The shape of the distribution will determine which statistic (mean, median, or mode) best describes the central tendency of the sample data.

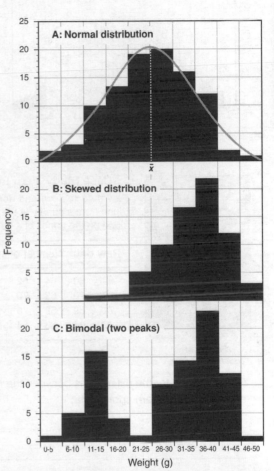

| Statistic | Definition and use | Method of calculation |
|---|---|---|
| **Mean** | • The average of all data entries.<br>• Measure of central tendency for normally distributed data. | • Add up all the data entries.<br>• Divide by the total number of data entries. |
| **Median** | • The middle value when data entries are placed in rank order.<br>• A good measure of central tendency for skewed distributions. | • Arrange the data in increasing rank order.<br>• Identify the middle value.<br>• For an even number of entries, find the mid point of the two middle values. |
| **Mode** | • The most common data value.<br>• Suitable for bimodal distributions and qualitative data. | • Identify the category with the highest number of data entries using a tally chart or a bar graph. |
| **Range** | • The difference between the smallest and largest data values.<br>• Provides a crude indication of data spread. | • Identify the smallest and largest values and find the difference between them. |

### When NOT to calculate a mean:

In certain situations, calculation of a simple arithmetic mean is inappropriate.

**Remember**:

• *DO NOT* calculate a mean from values that are already means (averages) themselves.

• *DO NOT* calculate a mean of ratios (e.g. percentages) for several groups of different sizes; go back to the raw values and recalculate.

• *DO NOT* calculate a mean when the measurement scale is not linear, e.g. pH units are not measured on a linear scale.

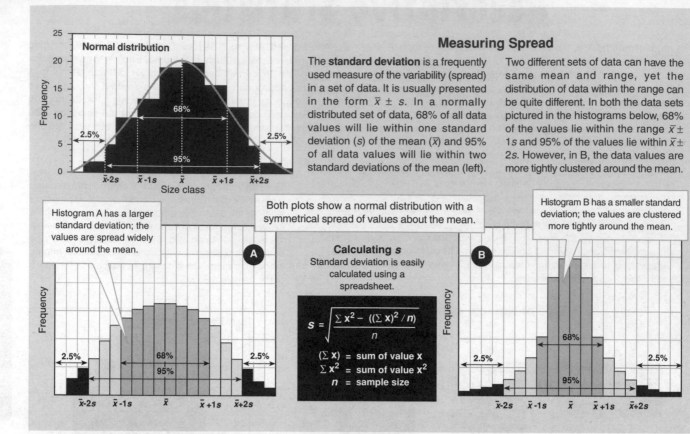

## Measuring Spread

The **standard deviation** is a frequently used measure of the variability (spread) in a set of data. It is usually presented in the form $\bar{x} \pm s$. In a normally distributed set of data, 68% of all data values will lie within one standard deviation (s) of the mean ($\bar{x}$) and 95% of all data values will lie within two standard deviations of the mean (left).

Two different sets of data can have the same mean and range, yet the distribution of data within the range can be quite different. In both the data sets pictured in the histograms below, 68% of the values lie within the range $\bar{x} \pm 1s$ and 95% of the values lie within $\bar{x} \pm 2s$. However, in B, the data values are more tightly clustered around the mean.

**Normal distribution**

Histogram A has a larger standard deviation; the values are spread widely around the mean.

Both plots show a normal distribution with a symmetrical spread of values about the mean.

Histogram B has a smaller standard deviation; the values are clustered more tightly around the mean.

### Calculating s
Standard deviation is easily calculated using a spreadsheet.

$$s = \sqrt{\frac{\sum x^2 - ((\sum x)^2 / n)}{n}}$$

$(\sum x)$ = sum of value x
$\sum x^2$ = sum of value $x^2$
$n$ = sample size

## Case Study: Fern Reproduction

**Fern spores**

Raw data (below) and descriptive statistics (right) from a survey of the number of spores found on the fronds of a fern plant.

**Raw data:** Number of spores per frond

| | | | | | | |
|---|---|---|---|---|---|---|
| 64 | 60 | 64 | 62 | 68 | 66 | 63 |
| 69 | 70 | 63 | 70 | 70 | 63 | 62 |
| 71 | 69 | 59 | 70 | 66 | 61 | 70 |
| 67 | 64 | 63 | 64 | | | |

$$\frac{\text{Total of data entries}}{\text{Number of entries}} = \frac{1641}{25} = 66 \text{ spores}$$

**Mean**

| Number of spores per frond (in rank order) | |
|---|---|
| 59 | 66 |
| 60 | 66 |
| 61 | 67 |
| 62 | 68 |
| 62 | 69 |
| 63 | 69 |
| 63 | 70 |
| 63 | 70 — **Median** |
| 63 | 70 |
| 63 | 70 |
| 64 | 70 |
| 64 | 70 |
| 64 | 71 |
| **64** | |

| Spores per frond | Tally | Total |
|---|---|---|
| 59 | ✔ | 1 |
| 60 | ✔ | 1 |
| 61 | ✔ | 1 |
| 62 | ✔✔ | 2 |
| 63 | ✔✔✔✔ | 4 |
| 64 | ✔✔✔✔ | 4 |
| 65 | | 0 |
| 66 | ✔✔ | 2 |
| 67 | ✔ | 1 |
| 68 | ✔ | 1 |
| 69 | ✔✔ | 2 |
| 70 | ✔✔✔✔✔ — **Mode** | 5 |
| 71 | ✔ | 1 |

1. Give a reason for the differences between the mean, median, and mode of the fern spore data:

_____

_____

_____

_____

2. Calculate the mean, median, and mode of the data on beetle masses below. Draw up a tally chart and show all calculations:

| Beetle masses (g) | | |
|---|---|---|
| 2.2 | 2.1 | 2.6 |
| 2.5 | 2.4 | 2.8 |
| 2.5 | 2.7 | 2.5 |
| 2.6 | 2.6 | 2.5 |
| 2.2 | 2.8 | 2.4 |

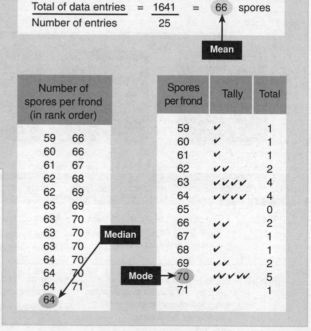

# Taking the Next Step

By this stage, you will have completed many of the early stages of your investigation. Now is a good time to review what you have done and reflect on the biological significance of what you are investigating. Review the first page of this flow chart in light of your findings so far. You are now ready to begin a more in-depth analysis of your results. Never under-estimate the value of plotting your data, even at a very early stage. This will help you decide on the best type of data analysis (see next page).

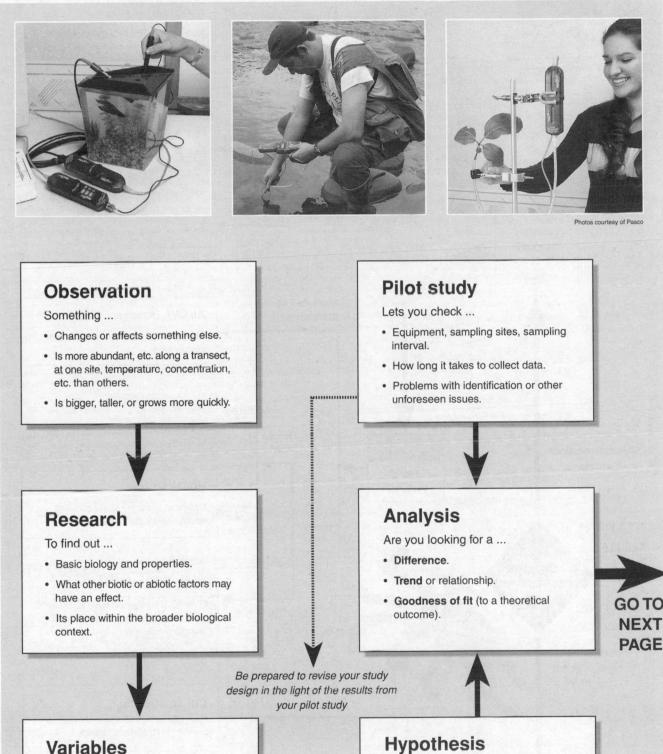

Photos courtesy of Pasco

Skills in Biology

## Observation

Something ...

- Changes or affects something else.
- Is more abundant, etc. along a transect, at one site, temperature, concentration, etc. than others.
- Is bigger, taller, or grows more quickly.

## Pilot study

Lets you check ...

- Equipment, sampling sites, sampling interval.
- How long it takes to collect data.
- Problems with identification or other unforeseen issues.

## Research

To find out ...

- Basic biology and properties.
- What other biotic or abiotic factors may have an effect.
- Its place within the broader biological context.

## Analysis

Are you looking for a ...

- **Difference**.
- **Trend** or relationship.
- **Goodness of fit** (to a theoretical outcome).

GO TO NEXT PAGE

*Be prepared to revise your study design in the light of the results from your pilot study*

## Variables

Next you need to ...

- Identify the key variables likely to cause the effect.
- Identify variables to be controlled in order to give the best chance of showing the effect that you want to study.

## Hypothesis

Must be ...

- Testable
- Able to generate predictions

so that in the end you can say whether your data supports or allows you to reject your hypothesis.

**Related activities**: The Reliability of the Mean, The Student's *t*-Test
**Web links**: Statistical Tests, Using the Chi-squared Test in Genetics

44

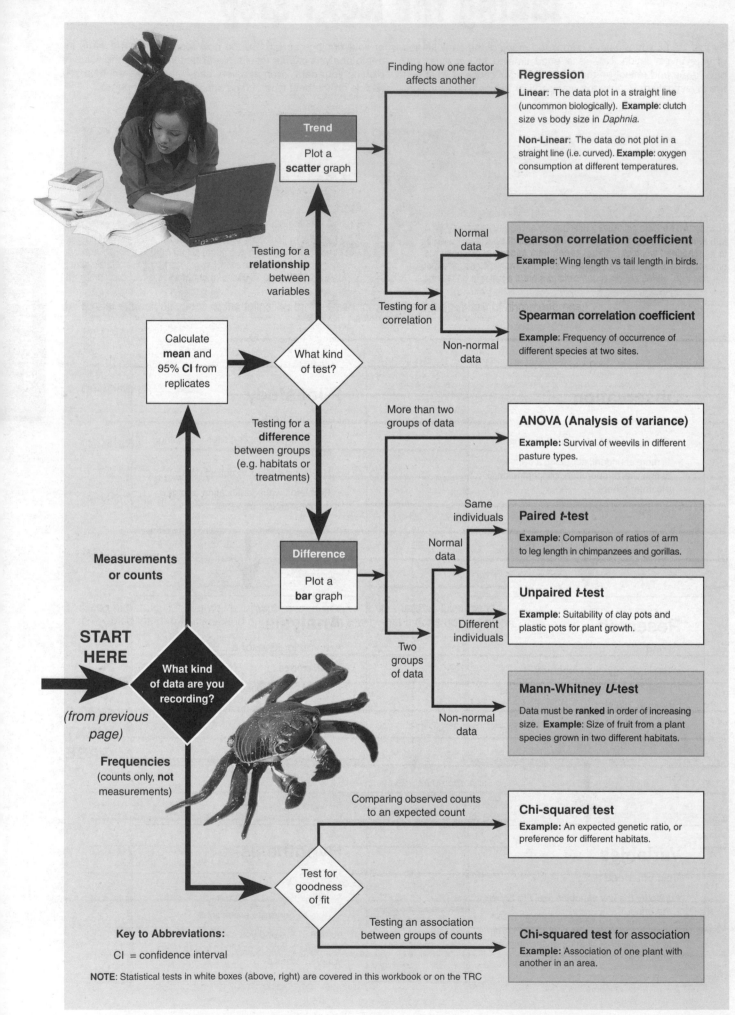

**Trend**

Plot a **scatter** graph

Finding how one factor affects another

**Regression**

**Linear**: The data plot in a straight line (uncommon biologically). **Example**: clutch size vs body size in *Daphnia*.

**Non-Linear**: The data do not plot in a straight line (i.e. curved). **Example**: oxygen consumption at different temperatures.

Testing for a **relationship** between variables

Normal data

**Pearson correlation coefficient**

**Example**: Wing length vs tail length in birds.

Testing for a correlation

Non-normal data

**Spearman correlation coefficient**

**Example**: Frequency of occurrence of different species at two sites.

Calculate **mean** and 95% **CI** from replicates

What kind of test?

Testing for a **difference** between groups (e.g. habitats or treatments)

More than two groups of data

**ANOVA (Analysis of variance)**

**Example**: Survival of weevils in different pasture types.

**Measurements or counts**

**Difference**

Plot a **bar** graph

Same individuals

Normal data

**Paired *t*-test**

**Example**: Comparison of ratios of arm to leg length in chimpanzees and gorillas.

Different individuals

**Unpaired *t*-test**

**Example**: Suitability of clay pots and plastic pots for plant growth.

**START HERE**

*(from previous page)*

What kind of data are you recording?

Two groups of data

Non-normal data

**Mann-Whitney *U*-test**

Data must be **ranked** in order of increasing size. **Example**: Size of fruit from a plant species grown in two different habitats.

**Frequencies**
(counts only, **not** measurements)

Comparing observed counts to an expected count

**Chi-squared test**

**Example**: An expected genetic ratio, or preference for different habitats.

Test for goodness of fit

Testing an association between groups of counts

**Chi-squared test** for association

**Example**: Association of one plant with another in an area.

**Key to Abbreviations:**

CI = confidence interval

**NOTE**: Statistical tests in white boxes (above, right) are covered in this workbook or on the TRC

# The Reliability of the Mean

You have already seen how to use the **standard deviation** (*s*) to quantify the spread or **dispersion** in your data. The **variance** ($s^2$) is another such measure of dispersion, but the standard deviation is usually the preferred of these two measures because it is expressed in the original units. Usually, you will also want to know how good your sample mean ($\bar{x}$) is as an estimate of the true population mean ($\mu$). This can be indicated by the standard error of the mean (or just **standard error** or SE). **SE** is often used as an error measurement simply because it is small, rather than for any good statistical reason. However, it is does allow you calculate the **95% confidence interval (95% CI)**. The calculation and use of 95% CIs is outlined below and opposite. By the end of this activity you should be able to:

- Enter data and calculate descriptive statistics using a spreadsheet program such as *Microsoft Excel*. You can follow this procedure for any set of data.
- Calculate standard error and 95% confidence intervals for sample data and plot these data appropriately with error bars.
- Interpret the graphically presented data and reach tentative conclusions about the findings of the experiment.

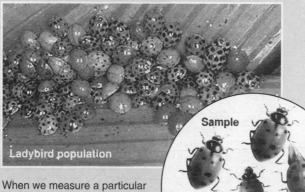

Ladybird population

When we measure a particular attribute from a sample of a larger population and calculate a mean for that attribute, we can calculate how closely our sample mean (the statistic) is to the true population mean for that attribute (the parameter). **Example:** If we calculated the mean number of carapace spots from a sample of six ladybird beetles, how reliable is this statistic as an indicator of the mean number of carapace spots in the whole population? We can find out by calculating the **95% confidence interval**.

Sample

## Reliability of the Sample Mean

When we take measurements from samples of a larger population, we are using those samples as indicators of the trends in the whole population. Therefore, when we calculate a sample mean, it is useful to know how close that value is to the true population mean ($\mu$). This is not merely an academic exercise; it will enable you to make **inferences** about the aspect of the population in which you are interested. For this reason, statistics based on samples and used to estimate population parameters are called **inferential statistics**.

## The Standard Error (SE)

The standard error (SE) is simple to calculate and is usually a small value. Standard error is given by:

$$SE = \frac{s}{\sqrt{n}}$$

where *s* = the standard deviation, and *n* = sample size.

Standard errors are sometimes plotted as error bars on graphs, but it is more meaningful to plot the **95% confidence intervals** (see box below). All calculations are easily made using a spreadsheet (see opposite).

## The 95% Confidence Interval

SE is required to calculate the 95% confidence interval (CI) of the mean. This is given by:

$$95\% \ CI = SE \times t_{P(n-1)}$$

Do not be alarmed by this calculation; once you have calculated the value of the SE, it is a simple matter to multiply this value by the value of *t* at *P* = 0.05 (from the *t* table) for the appropriate degrees of freedom (df) for your sample (*n* – 1).

For example: where the SE = 0.6 and the sample size is 10, the calculation of the 95% CI is:

$$95\% \ CI = 0.6 \times 2.262 = \boxed{1.36}$$

Part of the *t* table is given to the right for *P* = 0.05. Note that, as the sample becomes very large, the value of *t* becomes smaller. For very large samples, *t* is fixed at 1.96, so the 95% CI is slightly less than twice the SE.

All these statistics, including a plot of the data with Y error bars, can be calculated using a program such as *Microsoft Excel* (opposite).

Critical values of Student's *t* distribution at *P* = 0.05.

| df | P 0.05 |
|---|---|
| 1 | 12.71 |
| 2 | 4.303 |
| 3 | 3.182 |
| 4 | 2.776 |
| 5 | 2.571 |
| 6 | 2.447 |
| 7 | 2.365 |
| 8 | 2.306 |
| 9 | 2.262 |
| 10 | 2.228 |
| 20 | 2.086 |
| 30 | 2.042 |
| 40 | 2.021 |
| 60 | 2.000 |
| 120 | 1.980 |
| >120 | 1.960 |

Value of *t* at *n*–1 = 9

Maximum value of *t* at this level of *P*

Relationship of Y against X (± 95% confidence intervals, *n* = 10)

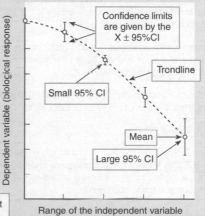

Confidence limits are given by the X ± 95%CI

Trendline

Small 95% CI

Mean

Large 95% CI

Dependent variable (biological response)

Range of the independent variable

### Plotting your confidence intervals

Once you have calculated the 95% CI for the means in your data set, you can plot them as error bars on your graph. Note that the **95% confidence limits** are given by the value of the **mean ± 95%CI**. A 95% confidence limit (i.e. *P* = 0.05) tells you that, on average, 95 times out of 100, the limits will contain the true population mean.

## Comparing Treatments Using Descriptive Statistics

In an experiment, the growth of newborn rats on four different feeds was compared by weighing young rats after 28 days on each of four feeding regimes. The suitability of each food type for maximizing growth in the first month of life was evaluated by comparing the means of the four experimental groups. Each group comprised 10 individual rats. All 40 newborns were born to sibling mothers with the same feeding history. For this activity, follow the steps outlined below and reproduce them yourself.

### Calculating Descriptive Statistics

Entering your data and calculating descriptive statistics.

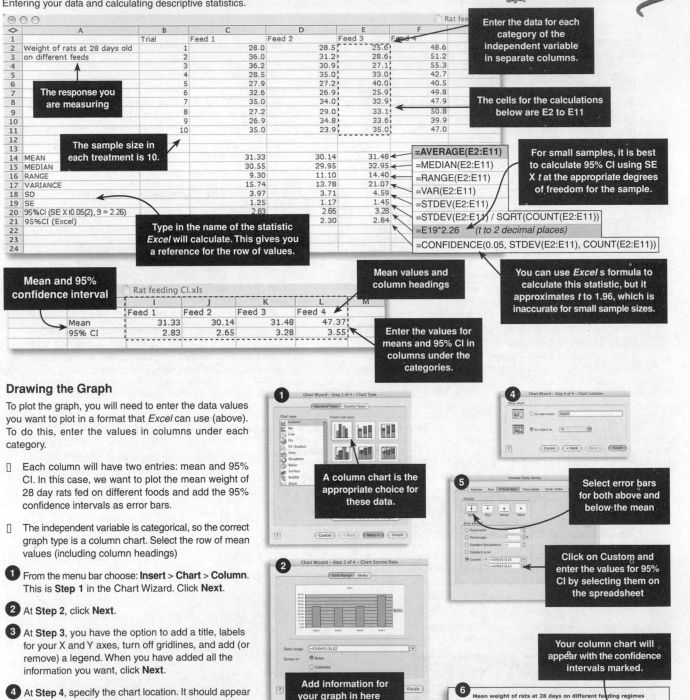

### Drawing the Graph

To plot the graph, you will need to enter the data values you want to plot in a format that *Excel* can use (above). To do this, enter the values in columns under each category.

☐ Each column will have two entries: mean and 95% CI. In this case, we want to plot the mean weight of 28 day rats fed on different foods and add the 95% confidence intervals as error bars.

☐ The independent variable is categorical, so the correct graph type is a column chart. Select the row of mean values (including column headings)

**1** From the menu bar choose: **Insert > Chart > Column**. This is **Step 1** in the Chart Wizard. Click **Next**.

**2** At **Step 2**, click **Next**.

**3** At **Step 3**, you have the option to add a title, labels for your X and Y axes, turn off gridlines, and add (or remove) a legend. When you have added all the information you want, click **Next**.

**4** At **Step 4**, specify the chart location. It should appear "as object in" Sheet 1 by default. Click on the chart and move it to reveal the data.

**5** A chart will appear on the screen. **Right click** (Ctrl-click on Mac) on any part of any column and choose **Format data series**. To add error bars, select the **Y error bars** tab, and click on the symbol that shows Display both. Click on Custom, and use the data selection window to select the row of 95% CI data for "+" and "–" fields.

**6** Click on OK and your chart will plot with error bars.

# The Student's t Test

The Student's t test is a commonly used test when comparing two sample means, e.g. means for a treatment and a control in an experiment, or the means of some measured characteristic between two animal or plant populations. The test is a powerful one, i.e. it is a good test for distinguishing real but marginal differences between samples. The t test is a simple test to apply, but it is only valid for certain situations. It is a two-group test and is not appropriate for multiple use i.e. sample 1 vs 2, then sample 1 vs 3. *You must have only two sample means to compare.* You are also assuming that the data have a normal (not skewed) distribution, and the scatter (standard deviations) of the data points is similar for both samples. You may wish to exclude obvious outliers from your data set for this reason. Below is a simple example outlining the general steps involved in the Student's t test. The following is a simple example using a set of data from a fictitious experiment involving a treatment and a control (the units are not relevant in this case, only the values). A portion of the Student's t table is provided, sufficient to carry out the test. Follow the example through, making sure that you understand what is being done at each step.

<table>
<tr><th colspan="2">Steps in performing a Student's t test</th><th>Explanatory notes</th></tr>
<tr>
<td colspan="2">Step 1   *Calculate basic summary statistics for your two data sets*<br><br>Control (A): 6.6, 5.5, 6.8, 5.8, 6.1, 5.9   $n_A = 6$,   $\bar{x}_A = 6.12$,   $s_A = 0.496$<br>Treatment (B): 6.3, 7.2, 6.5, 7.1, 7.5, 7.3   $n_B = 6$,   $\bar{x}_B = 6.98$,   $s_B = 0.475$</td>
<td>$n_A$ and $n_B$ are the number of values in the first and second data sets respectively (these need not be the same). $\bar{x}$ is the mean. $s$ is the standard deviation (a measure of scatter in the data).</td>
</tr>
<tr>
<td colspan="2">Step 2   *Set up and state your null hypothesis ($H_0$)*<br><br>$H_0$: there is no treatment effect. The differences in the data sets are the result of chance variation only and they are not really different</td>
<td>The alternative hypothesis is that there is a treatment effect and the two sets of data are truly different.</td>
</tr>
<tr>
<td colspan="2">Step 3   *Decide if your test is one or two tailed*<br><br>This tells you what section of the t table to consult. Most biological tests are two-tailed. Very few are one-tailed.</td>
<td>A one-tailed test looks for a difference only in one particular direction. A two-tailed test looks for any difference (+ or –).</td>
</tr>
<tr>
<td colspan="2">Step 4   *Calculate the t statistic*<br><br>For our sample data above the calculated value of t is –3.09. The degrees of freedom (df) are $n_1 + n_2 - 2 = 10$.<br><br>Calculation of the t value uses the variance which is simply the square of the standard deviation ($s^2$). You may compute the t value by entering your data onto a computer and using a simple statistical program.</td>
<td>It does not matter if your calculated t value is a positive or negative (the sign is irrelevant). If you do not have access to a statistical program, computation of t is not difficult. Step 4 (calculating t) is described in the t test exercise in the topic "*Practical Ecology*".</td>
</tr>
<tr>
<td colspan="2">Step 5   *Consult the t table of critical values*<br><br>Selected critical values for Student's t statistic (two-tailed test)<br><br>

| Degrees of freedom | P = 0.05 | P = 0.01 | P = 0.001 |
|---|---|---|---|
| 5 | 2.57 | 4.03 | 6.87 |
| 10 | 2.23 | 3.17 | 4.59 |
| 15 | 2.13 | 2.95 | 4.07 |
| 20 | 2.09 | 2.85 | 3.85 |

Critical value of t for 10 degrees of freedom. The calculated t value must exceed this</td>
<td>The absolute value of the t statistic (3.09) well exceeds the critical value for $P = 0.05$ at 10 degrees of freedom.<br><br>*We can reject $H_0$ and conclude that the means are different at the 5% level of significance.*<br><br>If the calculated absolute value of t had been less than 2.23, we could not have rejected $H_0$.</td>
</tr>
</table>

Skills in Biology

1. (a) In an experiment, data values were obtained from four plants in experimental conditions and three plants in control conditions. The mean values for each data set (control and experimental conditions) were calculated. The t value was calculated to be 2.16. The null hypothesis was: "The plants in the control and experimental conditions are not different". State whether the calculated t value supports the null hypothesis or its alternative (consult t table above):

   _____

   (b) The experiment was repeated, but this time using 6 control and 6 "experimental" plants. The new t value was 2.54. State whether the calculated t value supports the null hypothesis or its alternative now:

   _____

2. Explain why, in terms of applying Student's t test, extreme data values (outliers) are often excluded from the data set(s):

   _____

   _____

3. Explain what you understand by statistical significance (for any statistical test): _____

   _____

   _____

# The Structure of a Report

Once you have collected and analyzed your data, you can write your report. You may wish to present your findings as a written report, a poster presentation, or an oral presentation. The structure of a scientific report is described below using a poster presentation (which is necessarily very concise) as an example. When writing your report, it is useful to write the methods or the results first, followed by the discussion and conclusion. Although you should do some reading in preparation, the introduction should be one of the last sections that you write. Writing the other sections first gives you a better understanding of your investigation within the context of other work in the same area.

To view this and other examples of posters, see the excellent NC State University web site listed below

**1. Title (and author)**
Provides a clear and concise description of the project.

**2. Introduction**
Includes the aim, hypothesis, and background to the study

### ...n Flounder Exhibit Temperature-Dependent Sex Determination

J. Adam Luckenbach*, John Godwin and Russell Borski
Department of Zoology, Box 7617, North Carolina State University, Raleigh, NC 27695

#### Introduction

Southern flounder (*Paralichthys lethostigma*) support valuable fisheries and show great promise for aquaculture. Female flounder are known to grow faster and reach larger adult ... Therefore, information on sex det... might increase the ratio of female... important for aquaculture.

**Temperature Affects Sex Determination**

**Growth Does Not Differ by Sex**

**4. Results**
An account of results including tables and graphs. This section should not discuss the result, just present them.

**3. Materials and Methods**
A description of the materials and procedures used.

#### Objective

This study was conducted to determine whether southern flounder exhibit temperature-dependent sex determination (TSD), and if growth is affected by rearing temperature.

Temperature (°C)

18    23    28

#### Methods

- Southern flounder broodstock were strip spawned to collect eggs and sperm for *in vitro* fertilization.
- Hatched larvae were weaned from a natural diet (rotifers/*Artemia*) to high protein pelleted feed and fed until satiation at least twice daily.
- Upon reaching a mean total length of 40 mm, the juvenile flounder were stocked at equal densities into one of three temperatures 18, 23, or 28°C for 245 days.
- Gonads were preserved and later sectioned at 2-6 microns.
- Sex-distinguishing markers were used to distinguish males (spermatogenesis) from females (oogenesis).

**5. Discussion**
An discussion of the findings in light of the biological concepts involved. It should include comments on any limitations of the study.

**6. Conclusion**
A clear statement of whether tor not the findings support the hypothesis. In abbreviated poster presentations, these sections may be combined.

#### Results

- Sex was discernible in most fish greater than 120 mm long.
- High (28°C) temperature produced 4% females.
- Low (18°C) temperature produced 22% females.
- Mid-range (23°C) temperature produced 44% females.
- Fish raised at high or low temperatures showed reduced growth compared to those at the mid-range temperature.
- Up to 245 days, no differences in growth existed between sexes.

#### Conclusions

- These findings indicate that sex determination in southern flounder is temperature-sensitive and temperature has a profound effect on growth.
- A mid-range rearing temperature (23°C) appears to maximize the number of females and promote better growth in young southern flounder.
- Although adult females are known to grow larger than males, no difference in growth between sexes occurred in age-0 (< 1 year) southern flounder.

#### Histological Analysis

Male Differentiation    Female Differen...

**7. References & acknowledgements**
An organised list of all sources of information. Entries should be consistent within your report. Your teacher will advise you as to the preferred format.

#### Acknowledgements

The authors acknowledge the Salstonstall-Kennedy Program of the National Marine Fisheries Service and the University of North Carolina Sea Grant College Program for funding this research. Special thanks to Lea Ware and Beth Shimps for help with the work.

Image courtesy: Adam Luckenbach, NC State University

1. Explain the purpose of each of the following sections of a report. The first has one been completed for you:

(a) Introduction: _Provides the reader with the background to the topic and the rationale for the study_

(b) Methods: _____

_____

(c) Results: _____

(d) Discussion: _____

_____

(e) References and acknowledgements: _____

_____

2. Posters are a highly visual method of presenting the findings of a study. Describe the positive features of this format:

_____

_____

**Related activities**: Hypotheses and Predictions, Report Checklist
**Web links**: NC State University: Creating Effective Poster Presentations

© Biozone International 2001-2008
**Photocopying Prohibited**

# Writing the Methods

The materials and methods section of your report should be brief but informative. All essential details should be included but those not necessary for the repetition of the study should be omitted. The following diagram illustrates some of the important details that should be included in a methods section. Obviously, a complete list of all possible equipment and procedures is not possible because each experiment or study is different. However, the sort of information that is required for both lab and field based studies is provided.

## Field Studies

### Study site & organisms
- Site location and features
- Why that site was chosen
- Species involved

### Specialized equipment
- pH and oxygen meters
- Thermometers
- Nets and traps

### Data collection
- Number and timing of observations/collections
- Time of day or year
- Sample sizes and size of the sampling unit
- Methods of preservation
- Temperature at time of sampling
- Weather conditions on the day(s) of sampling
- Methods of measurement/sampling
- Methods of recording

## Laboratory Based Studies

### Data collection
- Pre-treatment of material before experiments
- Details of treatments and controls
- Duration and timing of experimental observations
- Temperature
- Sample sizes and details of replication
- Methods of measurement or sampling
- Methods of recording

### Experimental organisms
- Species or strain
- Age and sex
- Number of individuals used

### Specialized equipment
- pH meters
- Water baths & incubators
- Spectrophotometers
- Centrifuges
- Aquaria & choice chambers
- Microscopes and videos

### Special preparations
- Techniques for the preparation of material (staining, grinding)
- Indicators, salt solutions, buffers, special dilutions

## General guidelines for writing a methods section

- Choose a suitable level of detail. *Too little detail and the study could not be repeated. Too much detail obscures important features.*
- Do NOT include the details of standard procedures (e.g. how to use a balance) or standard equipment (e.g. beakers and flasks).
- Include details of any statistical analyses and data transformations.

- Outline the reasons why procedures were done in a certain way or in a certain order, if this is not self-evident.
- If your methodology involves complicated preparations (e.g. culture media) then it is acceptable to refer just to the original information source (e.g. lab manual) or include the information as an appendix.

1. The following text is part of the methods section from a report. Using the information above and on the checklist on page 52, describe eight errors (there are ten) in the methods. The errors are concerned with a lack of explanation or detail that would be necessary to repeat the experiment (they are not typographical, nor are they associated with the use of the active voice, which is now considered preferable to the passive):

*"We collected the worms for this study from a pond outside the school. We carried out the experiment at room temperature on April 16, 2004. First we added full strength seawater to each of three 200 cm³ glass jars; these were the controls. We filled another three jars with diluted seawater. We blotted the worms dry and weighed them to the nearest 0.1 g, then we added one worm to each jar. We reweighed the worms (after blotting) at various intervals over the next two hours."*

(a) _____

(b) _____

(c) _____

(d) _____

(e) _____

(f) _____

(g) _____

(h) _____

**Related activities:** Report Checklist

**RA 3**

# Writing Your Results

The results section is arguably the most important part of any research report; it is the place where you can bring together and present your findings. When properly constructed, this section will present your results clearly and in a way that shows you have organized your data and carefully considered the appropriate analysis. A portion of the results section from a scientific paper on the habitat preference of black mudfish is presented below (Hicks, B. and Barrier, R. (1996), NZJMFR. 30, 135-151). It highlights some important features of the results section and shows you how you can present information concisely, even if your results are relatively lengthy. Use it as a guide for content when you write up this section.

## Results

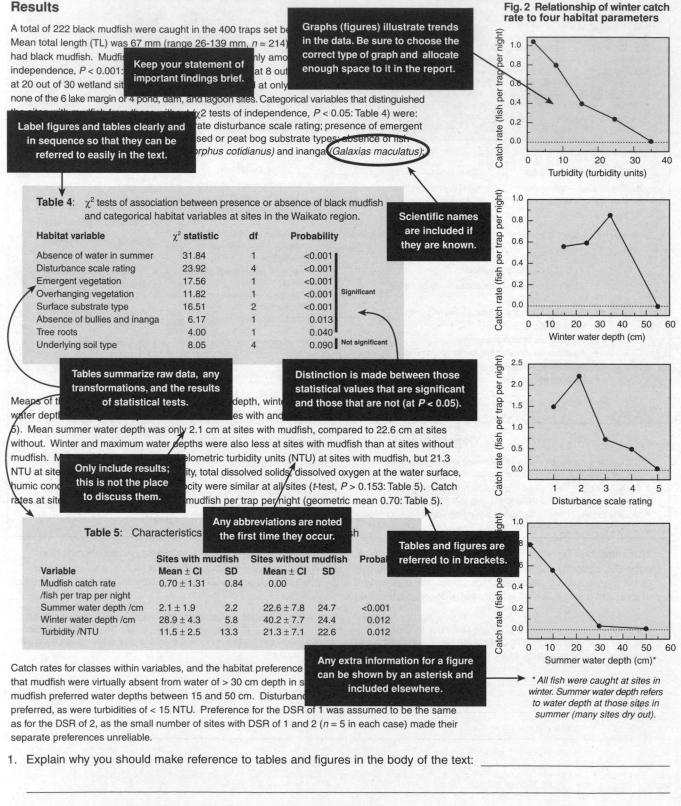

A total of 222 black mudfish were caught in the 400 traps set be... Mean total length (TL) was 67 mm (range 26-139 mm, n = 214) had black mudfish. Mudfish ... nly amo... independence, P < 0.001: ... at 8 out ... at 20 out of 30 wetland sit... d at only ... none of the 6 lake margin or 4 pond, dam, and lagoon sites. Categorical variables that distinguished the sites with mudfish from those without (χ2 tests of independence, P < 0.05: Table 4) were: ... ate disturbance scale rating; presence of emergent ... sed or peat bog substrate types; absence of fish ... orphus cotidianus) and inanga (Galaxias maculatus);

**Keep your statement of important findings brief.**

**Graphs (figures) illustrate trends in the data. Be sure to choose the correct type of graph and allocate enough space to it in the report.**

**Label figures and tables clearly and in sequence so that they can be referred to easily in the text.**

**Scientific names are included if they are known.**

**Fig. 2 Relationship of winter catch rate to four habitat parameters**

**Table 4:** χ² tests of association between presence or absence of black mudfish and categorical habitat variables at sites in the Waikato region.

| Habitat variable | χ² statistic | df | Probability | |
|---|---|---|---|---|
| Absence of water in summer | 31.84 | 1 | <0.001 | Significant |
| Disturbance scale rating | 23.92 | 4 | <0.001 | |
| Emergent vegetation | 17.56 | 1 | <0.001 | |
| Overhanging vegetation | 11.82 | 1 | <0.001 | |
| Surface substrate type | 16.51 | 2 | <0.001 | |
| Absence of bullies and inanga | 6.17 | 1 | 0.013 | |
| Tree roots | 4.00 | 1 | 0.040 | |
| Underlying soil type | 8.05 | 4 | 0.090 | Not significant |

**Tables summarize raw data, any transformations, and the results of statistical tests.**

**Distinction is made between those statistical values that are significant and those that are not (at P < 0.05).**

Means of t... depth, wint... water depth ... es with and ... 5). Mean summer water depth was only 2.1 cm at sites with mudfish, compared to 22.6 cm at sites without. Winter and maximum water depths were also less at sites with mudfish than at sites without mudfish. M... elometric turbidity units (NTU) at sites with mudfish, but 21.3 NTU at site... ity, total dissolved solids, dissolved oxygen at the water surface, humic conc... ocity were similar at all sites (t-test, P > 0.153: Table 5). Catch rates at site... mudfish per trap per night (geometric mean 0.70: Table 5).

**Only include results; this is not the place to discuss them.**

**Any abbreviations are noted the first time they occur.**

**Tables and figures are referred to in brackets.**

**Table 5:** Characteristics ... sh

| Variable | Sites with mudfish Mean ± CI | SD | Sites without mudfish Mean ± CI | SD | Proba... |
|---|---|---|---|---|---|
| Mudfish catch rate /fish per trap per night | 0.70 ± 1.31 | 0.84 | 0.00 | | |
| Summer water depth /cm | 2.1 ± 1.9 | 2.2 | 22.6 ± 7.8 | 24.7 | <0.001 |
| Winter water depth /cm | 28.9 ± 4.3 | 5.8 | 40.2 ± 7.7 | 24.4 | 0.012 |
| Turbidity /NTU | 11.5 ± 2.5 | 13.3 | 21.3 ± 7.1 | 22.6 | 0.012 |

**Any extra information for a figure can be shown by an asterisk and included elsewhere.**

* All fish were caught at sites in winter. Summer water depth refers to water depth at those sites in summer (many sites dry out).

Catch rates for classes within variables, and the habitat preference ... that mudfish were virtually absent from water of > 30 cm depth in s... mudfish preferred water depths between 15 and 50 cm. Disturbanc... preferred, as were turbidities of < 15 NTU. Preference for the DSR of 1 was assumed to be the same as for the DSR of 2, as the small number of sites with DSR of 1 and 2 (n = 5 in each case) made their separate preferences unreliable.

1. Explain why you should make reference to tables and figures in the body of the text: _____

_____

2. Explain why you might present the same data in a table and as a figure: _____

_____

_____

**Related activities:** Report Checklist

# Writing Your Discussion

In the discussion section of your report, you must interpret your results in the context of the specific questions you set out to answer in the investigation. You should also place your findings in the context of any broader relevant issues. If your results coincide exactly with what you expected, then your discussion will be relatively brief. However, be prepared to discuss any unexpected or conflicting results and critically evaluate any problems with your study design. The Discussion section may (and should) refer to the findings in the Results section, but it is not the place to introduce new results. Try to work towards a point in your discussion where the reader is lead naturally to the conclusion. The conclusion may be presented within the discussion or it may be included separately after the discussion as a separate section.

Skills in Biology

## Discussion:

Black mudfish habitat in the Waikato region can be ad[...]ses by four variables that are easy to measure: summer water depth, winter wa[...]cated by vegetation), and turbidity. Catch rates of black mudfish can be extreme[...]es ranged from 0.2 to 8.4 mudfish per trap per night (mean 0.70) between May and October 1992, and were similar to those of Dean (1995) in September 1993 and October 1994 in the Whangamarino Wetland complex (0.0-2.0 mudfish per trap per night). The highest mean catch rate in our study, 8.4 mudfish per trap per night, was at Site 24 (Table 1, Figure 1). The second highest (6.4 mudfish per trap per night) was at Site 32, in a drain about 4 km east of Hamilton. Black mudfish in the Waikato region were most commonly found at sites in wetlands with absence of water in summer, moderate depth of water in winter, limited modification of the vegetation (low DSR), and low turbidity (Fig. 2). There are similarities between the habitat requirements of black mudfish and those of brown mudfish and the common river galaxias *(Galaxias vulgaris)*. Brown mudfish inhabited shallow water, sometimes at the edges of deeper water bodies, but were usually absent from water deeper than about 30-50 cm (Eldon 1978). The common river galaxias also has a preference for shallow water, occupying river margins < 20 cm deep (Jowett and Richardson 1995).

> **Support your statements with reference to Tables and Figures from the Results section.**

> **The discussion describes the relevance of the results of the investigation.**

Sites where black mudfish were found were not just shallow or dry in sum[...]al variation in water depth. A weakness of this study is the fact that sites were trap[...]ere spread relatively widely at each site to maximise the chance of catching any fish[...]nt for black mudfish in the form of [...]ment or overhanging vegetation, or tree roots. The significance of cover in determining the pres[...]s predictable, considering the shallow nature of their habitats. Mudfish, though noc[...] require cover during the to protect them from avian predators, such as bitterns (Bo[...]fishers *(Halcyon sancta vagans)*. Predation of black mudfish by a swamp bittern has [...]1). Cover is also important for brown mudfish (Eldon 1978). Black mudfish were found at sites with the predatory mosquitofish and juvenile eels, and the seasonal drying of their habitats may be a key to the successful coexistence of mudfish with their predators. Mosquitofish are known predators of mudfish fry (Barrier & Hicks 1994), and eels would presumably also prey on black mudfish, as t[...]h (Eldon 1979b). If, however, black mudfish are relatively uncompetitive and vulnerable to p[...]s as to how they manage to coexist with juvenile eels and mosquitofish. The habitat varia[...] can be used to classify the suitability of sites for black mudfish in future. The adaptability of black mudfish allows them to survive in some altered habitats, such as farm or roadside drains. From this study, we can conclude that the continued existence of suitable habitats appears to be more important to black mudfish than the presence of predators and competitors. This study has also improved methods of identifying suitable mudfish habitats in the Waikato region.

> **State any limitations of your approach in carrying out the investigation and what further studies might be appropriate.**

> **Reference is made to the work of others.**

> **Further research is suggested**

> **A clear conclusion is made towards the end of the discussion.**

1. Explain why it is important to discuss any weaknesses in your study design: _____

_____

_____

2. Explain why you should **critically evaluate** your results in the discussion: _____

_____

_____

_____

3. Describe the purpose of the conclusion: _____

_____

# Report Checklist

A report of your findings at the completion of your investigation may take one of the following forms: a written document, seminar, poster, web page, or multimedia presentation. The following checklist identifies points to consider when writing each section of your report. Review the list before you write your report and then, on satisfactory completion of each section of your write-up, use the check boxes to tick off the points:

**Title**:

☐ (a) Gives a clear indication of what the study is about.

☐ (b) Includes the species name and a common name of all organisms used.

**Introduction**:

☐ (a) Includes a clear aim.

☐ (b) Includes a well written hypothesis.

☐ (c) Includes a synopsis of the current state of knowledge about the topic.

**Materials and methods**:

☐ (a) Written clearly. Numbered points are appropriate at this level.

☐ (b) Describes the final methods that were used.

☐ (c) Includes details of the how data for the dependent variable were collected.

☐ (d) Includes details of how all other variables were manipulated, controlled, measured, or monitored.

☐ (e) If appropriate, it includes an explanatory diagram of the design of the experimental set-up.

☐ (f) Written in the past tense, and in the active voice (We investigated …) rather than the passive voice (An investigation was done …).

**Results**:

☐ (a) Includes the raw data (e.g. in a table).

☐ (b) Where necessary, the raw data have been averaged or transformed.

☐ (c) Includes graphs (where appropriate).

☐ (d) Each figure (table, graph, drawing, or photo) has a title and is numbered in a way that makes it possible to refer to it in the text (Fig. 1 etc.).

☐ (e) Written in the past tense and, where appropriate, in the active voice.

**Discussion**:

☐ (a) Includes an analysis of the data in which the findings, including trends and patterns, are discussed in relation to the biological concepts involved.

☐ (b) Includes an evaluation of sources of error, assumptions, and possible improvements to design.

**Conclusion**:

☐ (a) Written as a clear statement, which relates directly to the hypothesis.

**Bibliography or References**:

☐ (a) Lists all sources of information and assistance.

☐ (b) Does not include references that were not used.

---

**A 3**

**Related activities**: The Structure of a Report, Writing the Methods, Writing Your Results, Writing Your Discussion, Citing and Listing References

# Citing and Listing References

Proper referencing of sources of information is an important aspect of report writing. It shows that you have explored the topic and recognize and respect the work of others. There are two aspects to consider: **citing sources** within the text (making reference to other work to support a statement or compare results) and **compiling a reference list** at the end of the report. A **bibliography** lists all sources of information, but these may not necessarily appear as citations in the report. In contrast, a reference list should contain only those texts cited in the report.

Citations in the main body of the report should include only the authors' surnames, publication date, and page numbers (or internet site), and the citation should be relevant to the statement it claims to support. Accepted methods for referencing vary, but your reference list should provide all the information necessary to locate the source material, it should be consistently presented, and it should contain only the references that you have read yourself (not those cited by others). A suggested format is described below.

## Preparing a Reference List

When teachers ask students to write in "APA style", they are referring to the editorial style established by the **American Psychological Association** (APA). These guidelines for citing **electronic (online) resources** differ only slightly from the **print sources**.

### For the Internet

Where you use information from the internet, you must provide the following:
• The website address (URL), the person or organization who is in charge of the web site and the date you accessed the web page.
This is written in the form: URL (person or organization's name, day, month, and year retrieved)
   This goes together as follows:
      http://www.scientificamerican.com (Scientific American, 17.12.03)

### For Periodicals (or Journals)

This is written in the form: author(s), date of publication, article title, periodical title, and publication information.
**Example**: Author's family name, A. A. (author's initials only), Author, B. B., & Author, C. C. (xxxx = year of publication in brackets). Title of article. Title of Periodical, volume number, page numbers (Note, only use "pp." before the page numbers in newspapers and magazines).
   This goes together as follows:
      Bamshad M. J., & Olson S. E. (2003). Does Race Exist? Scientific American, 289(6), 50-57.

### For Online Periodicals based on a Print Source

At present, the majority of periodicals retrieved from online publications are exact duplicates of those in their print versions and although they are unlikely to have additional analyses and data attached to them, this is likely to change in the future.

• If the article that is to be referenced has been viewed only in electronic form and not in print form, then you must add in brackets, "Electronic version", after the title.
   This goes together as follows:
      Bamshad M. J., & Olson S. E. (2003). Does Race Exist? (Electronic version). Scientific American, 289(6), 50-57.
• If you have reason to believe the article has changed in its electronic form, then you will need to add the date you retrieved the document and the URL.
   This goes together as follows:
      Bamshad M. J., & Olson S. E. (2003). Does Race Exist? (Electronic version). Scientific American, 289(6), 50-57. Retrieved December 17, 2003, from http://www.scientificamerican.com

### For Books

This is written in the form: author(s), date of publication, title, and publication information.
**Example**: Author, A. A., Author, B. B., & Author, C. C. (xxxx). Title (any additional information to enable identification is given in brackets). City of publication: publishers name.
This goes together as follows:
      Martin, R.A. (2004). Missing Links Evolutionary Concepts & Transitions Through Time. Sudbury, MA: Jones and Bartlett

### For Citation in the Text of References

This is written in the form: authors' surname(s), date of publication, page number(s) (abbreviated p.), chapter (abbreviated chap.), figure, table, equation, or internet site, in brackets at the appropriate point in text.
This goes together as follows:
      (Bamshad & Olson, 2003, p. 51) or (Bamshad & Olson, 2003, http://www.scientificamerican.com)

This can also be done in the form of footnotes. This involves the use of a superscripted number in the text next to your quoted material and the relevant information listed at the bottom of the page.
This goes together as follows:
      ....... Bamshad & Olson reported that .........[1]

[1]Bamshad & Olson, 2003, p. 51

## Example of a Reference List

Lab notes can be listed according to title if the author is unknown.

→ Advanced biology laboratory manual (2000). Cell membranes. pp. 16-18. Sunhigh College.

References are listed alphabetically according to the author's surname.

Cooper, G.M. (1997). *The cell: A molecular approach* (2nd ed.). Washington D.C.: ASM Press

Book title in italics (or underlined)     Place of publication: Publisher

Davis, P. (1996) Cellular factories. *New Scientist* 2057: Inside science supplement.

Publication date     Journal title in italics     A supplement may not need page references

If a single author appears more than once, then list the publications from oldest to most recent.

Indge, B. (2001). Diarrhea, digestion and dehydration. *Biological Sciences Review,* 14(1), 7-9.

Indge, B. (2002). Experiments. *Biological Sciences Review,* 14(3), 11-13.

Article title follows date

Kingsland, J. (2000). Border control. *New Scientist* 2247: Inside science supplement.

Spell out only the last name of authors. Use initials for first and middle names.

Laver, H. (1995). Osmosis and water retention in plants. *Biological Sciences Review* 7(3), 14-18

Volume (Issue number), Pages

Steward, M. (1996). Water channels in the cell membrane. *Biological Sciences Review,* 9(2), 18-22.

Internet sites change often so the date accessed is included. The person or organization in charge of the site is also included.

→ http://www.cbc.umn.edu/~mwd/cell_intro.html (Dalton, M. "Introduction to cell biology" 12.02.03)

1. Distinguish between a **reference list** and a **bibliography**: _____

_____

_____

_____

2. Explain why internet articles based on a print source are likely to have additional analyses and data attached in the future, and why this point should be noted in a reference list:

_____

_____

3. Following are the details of references and source material used by a student in preparing a report on enzymes and their uses in biotechnology. He provided his reference list in prose. From it, compile a correctly formatted reference list:

Pages 18-23 in the sixth edition of the textbook "Biology" by Neil Campbell. Published by Benjamin/Cummings in California (2002). New Scientist article by Peter Moore called "Fuelled for life" (January 1996, volume 2012, supplement). "Food biotechnology" published in the journal Biological Sciences Review, page 25, volume 8 (number 3) 1996, by Liam and Katherine O'Hare. An article called "Living factories" by Philip Ball in New Scientist, volume 2015 1996, pages 28-31. Pages 75-85 in the book "The cell: a molecular approach" by Geoffrey Cooper, published in 1997 by ASM Press, Washington D.C. An article called "Development of a procedure for purification of a recombinant therapeutic protein" in the journal "Australasian Biotechnology", by I Roberts and S. Taylor, pages 93-99 in volume 6, number 2, 1996.

### REFERENCE LIST

_____

_____

_____

_____

_____

_____

# The Chemistry of Life

**IB SL**
Complete:
1-4, 6-10, 12-19, 22, 27, 32-33, 39-40
Extension: 5, 11, 21, 30-31, 41-42

**IB HL**
Complete:
1-4, 6-10, 12-20, 22-29, 32-40
Extension: 5, 11, 21, 30-31, 41-42

**IB Options**
Complete:
Option C:
SL: 20, 22-26, 28-29, 34-38

**AP Biology**
Complete:
1-29, 32-40
Extension 30-31, 41-42 or as appropriate

## Learning Objectives

*The learning objectives relating to the structure and function of **nucleic acids** are provided in the topic "Molecular Genetics".*

☐ 1. Compile your own glossary from the **KEY WORDS** displayed in **bold type** in the learning objectives below.

## Understanding Organic Chemistry *(pages 57-58)*

☐ 2. List the four most common elements found in living things. Provide examples of where these elements occur in cells. Distinguish between an atom and an ion. Explain what is meant by **organic chemistry** and explain its importance in biology.

☐ 3. Distinguish between ionic bonds and covalent bonds and understand the importance of **covalent bonds** in carbon-based compounds.

☐ 4. Distinguish between **monomers** and **polymers** and provide examples of each type. Explain clearly what is meant by a **macromolecule** and give examples.

☐ 5. Explain how the laws of thermodynamics relate to the biochemical processes occurring in living systems. Explain how the concept of **free energy** helps to determine whether or not a process will occur spontaneously. Explain the terms **endergonic** and **exergonic** in relation to their free energy changes.

## Water and Inorganic Ions *(pages 57, 59)*

☐ 6. Describe the structure of water, including reference to the polar nature of the water molecule, the nature of the bonding within the molecule, and the importance of **hydrogen bonding** *between* water molecules.

☐ 7. Identify the physical properties of water that are important in biological systems. Explain why water is termed the **universal solvent** and describe its various biological roles: *e.g. metabolic role, as a solvent, as a lubricant, as a coolant, as a transport medium, and as a fluid in hydrostatic skeletons and cell turgor.*

☐ 8. Provide a definition of an **inorganic** (mineral) **ion**. With reference to specific examples, describe the role of inorganic ions in biological systems. Examples could include: $Na^+$, $K^+$, $Mg^{2+}$, $Cl^-$, $NO_3^-$, and $PO_4^{3-}$.

## Carbohydrates *(pages 61-62)*

☐ 9. Describe the basic composition and general formula of carbohydrates. Explain the main roles of carbohydrates in both plants and animals.

☐ 10. Describe what is meant by a **monosaccharide** and give its general formula. Provide examples of **triose**, **pentose**, and **hexose sugars** (including fructose and galactose). For each, identify its biological role.

☐ 11. Appreciate that monosaccharides show **isomerism**. Recognize structural isomers of glucose ($\alpha$ **and** $\beta$ **glucose**) and understand their biological significance.

☐ 12. Describe what is meant by a **disaccharide**. Explain how disaccharides are formed by a **condensation** reaction and broken apart by **hydrolysis**. Identify the **glycosidic bond** formed and broken in each case. Give examples of disaccharides and their functions, and name the monosaccharides involved in each case.

☐ 13. Explain what is meant by a **polysaccharide** and describe how polysaccharides are formed. Describe the molecular structure of the following examples of polysaccharides: *starch, glycogen, cellulose* and relate their structure to their function in biological systems.

## Lipids *(pages 63-64)*

☐ 14. Describe the general properties of lipids. Recognize the diversity of lipids in biological systems and describe their functional roles. Consider: *phospholipids, waxes, sterols,* and *fats and oils.*

☐ 15. Recognize that most lipids are **triglycerides** (triacylglycerols). Describe how triglycerides are classified as *fats* or *oils* and explain the basis of the classification.

☐ 16. Using a diagram, describe the basic structure of a triglyceride. Explain their formation by **condensation** reactions between glycerol and three fatty acids. Identify the **ester bonds** that result from this. Distinguish between **saturated** and **unsaturated fatty acids** and relate this difference to the properties of the fat or oil that results.

☐ 17. Using a diagram, describe the basic structure of a **phospholipid** and explain how it differs from the structure of a triglyceride. Explain how the structure of phospholipids is important to their role in membranes.

## Amino Acids and Proteins *(pages 65-68)*

☐ 18. Draw or describe the general structure and formula of an **amino acid**. Explain the basis for the different properties of amino acids.

☐ 19. Recognize that, of over 170 amino acids, only 20 are commonly found in proteins. Distinguish between **essential** and **non-essential amino acids**.

☐ 20. Distinguish between **polar** and **non-polar amino acids** and explain their biological significance.

☐ 21. Appreciate the basis of **optical isomerism** in amino acids. Distinguish L- and D- forms and identify which form is active in biological systems.

☐ 22. Using a diagram, describe how amino acids are joined together in a **condensation reaction** to form **dipeptides** and **polypeptides**. Describe the nature of **peptide bonds** that result. Describe how polypeptides are broken down by **hydrolysis**.

☐ 23. Identify where (in the cell) proteins are made and recognize the ways in which they can be modified after production. Distinguish between the **primary structure** of a protein and its **secondary structure**. Recognize the two main types of secondary structure found in proteins: *alpha-helix* and *ß-pleated sheet*.

☐ 24. Explain what is meant by the **tertiary structure** of a protein and explain how it arises. Describe the relationship between the tertiary structure of a **globular protein** and its biological function.

☐ 25. With reference to examples, distinguish between **globular** and **fibrous proteins**. Consider the structure, properties, and biological functions of the protein.

☐ 26. With reference to specific examples (e.g. collagen, insulin, hemoglobin), describe the role of different types of bonds in proteins: *hydrogen bonds, ionic bonds, disulfide bonds, hydrophobic interactions.*

☐ 27. Explain what is meant by protein **denaturation** and explain why it destroys the activity of proteins. Describe how different agents denature proteins.

☐ 28. Explain what is meant by the **quaternary structure** of a protein. In a named example (e.g. *hemoglobin, a globular protein*) describe how the quaternary structure arises and relate it to the protein's function.

☐ 29. Recognize the ways in which proteins can be classified:
- By their structure (e.g. *globular* or *fibrous*)
- By their functional role (e.g. *structural* or *regulatory*)

## Tests for Organic Compounds *(page 60)*

☐ 30. Explain the basis of **chromatography** as a technique for separating and identifying biological molecules. Describe the calculation and use **R$_f$ values**.

☐ 31. Demonstrate an understanding of some basic tests for organic compounds. For each of the following simple "food tests", explain the basis of the test and its result:
- the **I$_2$/KI** (*iodine in potassium iodide*) **test** for starch
- the **Benedict's test** for **reducing** sugars
- the **emulsion test** for lipids
- the **biuret test** for proteins.

## Enzymes *(pages 69-76, also see 159-160)*

☐ 32. Define: **enzyme**, **catalyst**, **active site**, and **substrate**. Describe the general properties of enzymes and explain their role in regulating cell metabolism.

☐ 33. With reference to **enzyme-substrate complex** and **activation energy**, explain how enzymes work as catalysts to bring about reactions in cells. Describe the **lock and key** model of enzyme function.

☐ 34. Explain the **induced fit** model of enzyme function, contrasting it with the older lock and key model.

☐ 35. Describe ways in which the time course of an enzyme-catalyzed reaction can be followed: by measuring the rate of product formation (*e.g. catalase*) or by measuring the rate of substrate use (*e.g. amylase*).

☐ 36. Distinguish between **coenzymes** and **cofactors**. Explain how cofactors enable an enzyme to work.

☐ 37. Distinguish **reversible** from **irreversible** inhibition. Describe the effects of **competitive** and **non-competitive inhibitors** on enzyme activity.

☐ 38. Appreciate the role of **allostery** in the control of metabolic pathways by end-product inhibition.

☐ 39. Describe the effect of the following factors on enzyme activity: *substrate concentration, enzyme concentration, pH, temperature*. Identify the **optimum conditions** for some named enzymes. Recognize that enzymes (being proteins) can be **denatured**.

☐ 40. Appreciate some of the commercial applications of microbial enzymes, e.g. *pectinases* and *rennin* in the food industry and *proteases* in biological detergents.

☐ 41. Distinguish between **intracellular** and **extracellular** enzymes and outline the basic procedure for producing enzymes from microorganisms (including growth in culture and **downstream processing**).

☐ 42. Explain the advantages of enzyme isolation and immobilization in industry. Identify properties of enzymes used in industry (e.g. thermostability).

---

See the 'Textbook Reference Grid' on pages 8-9 for textbook page references relating to material in this topic.

### Supplementary Texts

See pages 5-6 for additional details of these texts:
- **Adds, J.** *et al.,* 2003. **Molecules and Cells**, (NelsonThornes), chpt. 1 & 3.
- **Helms, D.R.** *et al.,* 1998. **Biology in the Laboratory** (W.H. Freeman), #3, #4, #10.
- Tobin, A.J. and Morel, R.E., 1997. **Asking About Cells**, (Thomson Brooks/Cole), part I.

See page 6 for details of publishers of periodicals:

### STUDENT'S REFERENCE

- **Biochemistry** Biol. Sci. Rev., 20(2) Nov. 2007, pp. 21-24. *An outline of what constitutes biochemistry and its role as a essential discipline within science.*
- **Stuck with Structures?** Biol. Sci. Rev., 19(1) Sept. 2006, pp. 10-11. *A guide to interpreting the structural formulae of common organic compounds.*
- **Designer Starches** Biol. Sci. Rev., 19(3) Feb. 2007, pp. 18-20. *The composition of starch, and an excellent account of its properties and functions.*

- **Glucose & Glucose-Containing Carbohydrates** Biol. Sci. Rev., 19(1) Sept. 2006, pp. 12-15. *The structure of glucose and its polymers.*
- **Exploring Proteins** Biol. Sci. Rev., 16(4) April 2004, pp. 32-36. *Understanding how proteins function as complexes within the cell. Chromatographic techniques are also described.*
- **Smart Proteins** New Scientist, 17 March 2001 (Inside Science). *An excellent account of the structure of proteins and their roles in metabolism.*
- **Making Proteins Work (I)** Biol. Sci. Rev., 15(1) Sept. 2002, pp. 22-25. *A synopsis of how globular and fibrous proteins become functional.*
- **Making Proteins Work (II)** Biol. Sci. Rev., 15(2) Nov. 2002, pp. 24-27. *How carbohydrates are added to proteins to make them functional.*
- **Enzymes: Fast and Flexible** Biol. Sci. Rev., 19(1) Sept. 2006, pp. 2-5. *The structure of enzymes and how they work so efficiently at relatively low temperatures.*
- **Enzyme Technology** Biol. Sci. Rev., 12 (5) May 2000, pp. 26-27. *The range and importance of industrial enzymes in modern biotechnology.*

### TEACHER'S REFERENCE

- **Using Gel Electrophoresis to Illustrate Protein Diversity and Isoelectric Point** The Am. Biology Teacher 64(7) Sept. 2002, pp. 535-537. *Techniques for examining the structure and diversity of proteins.*
- **Modeling Protein Folding** The Am. Biology Teacher 66(4) Apr. 2004, pp. 287-289. *How protein folding produces physical structures.*
- **An Introduction to Lipid Analysis** The Am. Biology Teacher 64(2) Feb. 2002, pp. 122-129. *Thin-layer chromatography to examine lipid mixes.*
- **Using Trypsin & Soybean Trypsin Inhibitor to Teach the Principles of Enzyme Kinetics** The

Am. Biology Teacher 68(2) Feb. 2006, pp. 99-104. *Demonstrating the usefulness of enzyme kinetics.*
- **Using Peroxidases to Demonstrate Enzyme Kinetics** The Am. Biology Teacher 65(2) Feb. 2003, pp. 116-121. *Examining the effect of two competitive inhibitors on peroxidase.*
- **Making the Rate** The Am. Biology Teacher 66(9) Nov. 2004, pp. 621-626. *Demonstrating enzyme dynamics using 'pop' beads.*

See pages 10-11 for details of how to access **Bio Links** from our web site: **www.thebiozone.com** From Bio Links, access sites under the topics:

**BIOTECHNOLOGY > Applications in Biotechnology > Industrial Biotechnology:** • About industrial enzymes • Chapter 19: industrial microbiology • Discover enzymes ... *and others*

**CELL BIOLOGY AND BIOCHEMISTRY:** • Cell & molecular biology online • Molecular biology web book ... *and others* > **Biochemistry and Metabolic Pathways:** • Enzymes • Energy and enzymes • Energy, enzymes and catalysis problem set • Reactions and enzymes • The Biology project: Biochemistry

**Presentation MEDIA** to support this topic:

**CELL BIOLOGY AND BIOCHEMISTRY**

# The Biochemical Nature of the Cell

The molecules that make up living things can be grouped into five classes: water, carbohydrates, lipids, proteins, and nucleic acids. Water is the main component of organisms and provides an environment in which metabolic reactions can occur. Water molecules attract each other, forming large numbers of hydrogen bonds. It is this feature that gives water many of its unique properties, including its low viscosity and its chemical behavior as a **universal solvent**. Apart from water, most other substances in cells are compounds of carbon, hydrogen, oxygen, and nitrogen. The combination of carbon atoms with the atoms of other elements provides a huge variety of molecular structures. These are described on the following pages.

## Important Properties of Water

Water is a liquid at room temperature and many substances dissolve in it. It is a medium inside cells and for aquatic life.

A lot of energy is required before water will change state so aquatic environments are thermally stable and sweating and transpiration cause rapid cooling.

**Carbohydrates** form the structural components of cells, they are important in energy storage, and they are involved in cellular recognition.

**Proteins** may be structural (e.g. collagen), catalytic (enzymes), or they may be involved in movement, message signaling, internal defense and transport, or storage.

**Nucleotides and nucleic acids** Nucleic acids encode information for the construction and functioning of an organism. The nucleotide, ATP, is the energy currency of the cell.

**Lipids** provide insulation and a concentrated source of energy. Phospholipids are a major component of cellular membranes.

**Water** is a major component of cells: many substances dissolve in it, metabolic reactions occur in it, and it provides support and turgor.

Ice is less dense than water. Consequently ice floats, insulating the underlying water and providing valuable habitat.

Water has a high surface tension and low viscosity. It forms droplets on surfaces and can flow freely through narrow vessels.

Water is colorless, with a high transmission of visible light, so light penetrates tissue and aquatic environments.

1. Explain the biological significance of each of the following physical properties of water:

   (a) Low viscosity: _____

   (b) Colorless and transparent: _____

   (c) Universal solvent: _____

   (d) Ice is less dense than water: _____

2. Identify the biologically important role of each of the following molecules:

   (a) Lipids: _____

   (b) Carbohydrates: _____

   (c) Proteins: _____

   (d) Nucleic acids: _____

# Organic Molecules

Organic molecules are those chemical compounds containing carbon, and all biology are carbon-based. Specific groups of atoms, called **functional groups**, attach to a carbon-hydrogen core and confer specific chemical properties on the molecule. Some organic molecules in organisms are small and simple, containing only one or a few **functional groups**, while others are large complex assemblies called **macromolecules**. The macromolecules that make up living things can be grouped into four classes: carbohydrates, lipids, proteins, and nucleic acids. An understanding of the structure and function of these

molecules is necessary to many branches of biology, especially biochemistry, physiology, and molecular genetics. The diagram below illustrates some of the common ways in which biological molecules are portrayed. Note that the **molecular formula** expresses the number of atoms in a molecule, but does not convey its structure; this is indicated by the **structural formula**. Molecules can also be represented as **models**. A ball and stick model shows the arrangement and type of bonds while a space filling model gives a more realistic appearance of a molecule, showing how close the atoms really are.

## Portraying Organic Molecules

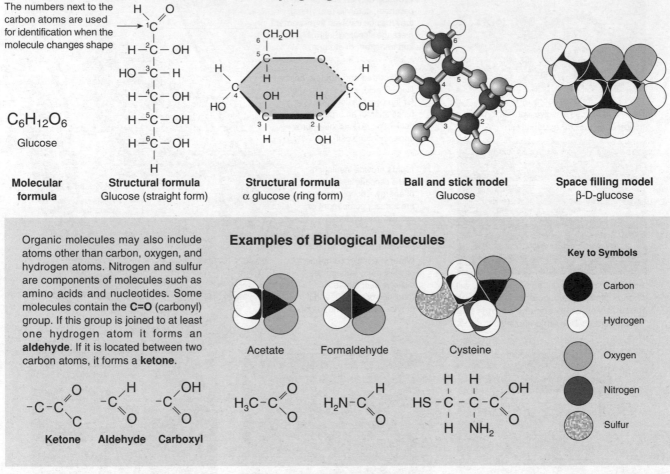

The numbers next to the carbon atoms are used for identification when the molecule changes shape

$C_6H_{12}O_6$
Glucose

| **Molecular formula** | **Structural formula** Glucose (straight form) | **Structural formula** α glucose (ring form) | **Ball and stick model** Glucose | **Space filling model** β-D-glucose |

## Examples of Biological Molecules

Organic molecules may also include atoms other than carbon, oxygen, and hydrogen atoms. Nitrogen and sulfur are components of molecules such as amino acids and nucleotides. Some molecules contain the **C=O** (carbonyl) group. If this group is joined to at least one hydrogen atom it forms an **aldehyde**. If it is located between two carbon atoms, it forms a **ketone**.

**Ketone**    **Aldehyde**    **Carboxyl**

Acetate    Formaldehyde    Cysteine

**Key to Symbols**

- Carbon
- Hydrogen
- Oxygen
- Nitrogen
- Sulfur

1. Identify the three main elements comprising the structure of organic molecules: _____

2. Name two other elements that are also frequently part of organic molecules: _____

3. State how many covalent bonds a carbon atom can form with neighboring atoms: _____

4. Distinguish between molecular and structural formulae for a given molecule: _____
_____
_____

5. Describe what is meant by a functional group: _____
_____

6. Classify formaldehyde according to the position of the C=O group: _____

7. Identify a functional group always present in amino acids: _____

8. Identify the significance of cysteine in its formation of disulfide bonds: _____
_____

**Related activities**: The Biochemical Nature of the Cell, Amino Acids, Proteins

**RA 2**

# Water and Inorganic Ions

The Earth's crust contains approximately 100 elements but only 16 are essential for life (see the table of inorganic ions below). Of the smaller molecules making up living things water is the most abundant typically making up about two-thirds of any organism's body. Water has a simple molecular structure and the molecule is very polar, with ends that exhibit partial positive and negative charges. Water molecules have a weak attraction for each other and inorganic ions, forming weak hydrogen bonds.

## Water and Inorganic Ions

**Water** provides an environment in which metabolic reactions can happen. Water takes part in, and is a common product of, many reactions. The most important feature of the chemical behavior of water is its **dipole** nature. It has a small positive charge on each of the two hydrogens and a small negative charge on the oxygen.

**Inorganic ions** are important for the structure and metabolism of all living organisms. An ion is simply an atom (or group of atoms) that has gained or lost one or more electrons. Many of these ions are soluble in water. Some of the inorganic ions required by organisms are listed in the table (right).

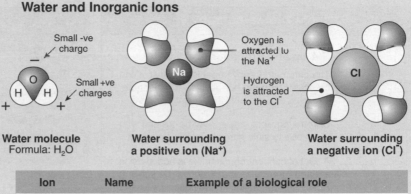

Water molecule
Formula: $H_2O$

Small -ve charge

Small +ve charges

Water surrounding a positive ion ($Na^+$)

Oxygen is attracted to the $Na^+$

Hydrogen is attracted to the $Cl^-$

Water surrounding a negative ion ($Cl^-$)

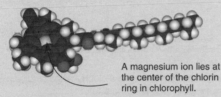

A magnesium ion lies at the center of the chlorin ring in chlorophyll.

| Ion | Name | Example of a biological role |
|---|---|---|
| $Ca^{2+}$ | Calcium | Component of bones and teeth |
| $Mg^{2+}$ | Magnesium | Component of chlorophyll |
| $Fe^{2+}$ | Iron (II) | Component of hemoglobin |
| $NO_3^-$ | Nitrate | Component of amino acids |
| $PO_4^{3-}$ | Phosphate | Component of nucleotides |
| $Na^+$ | Sodium | Involved in the transmission of nerve impulses |
| $K^+$ | Potassium | Involved in controlling plant water balance |
| $Cl^-$ | Chloride | Involved in the removal of water from urine |

1. On the diagram above, showing a positive and a negative ion surrounded by water molecules, draw the positive and negative charges on the water molecules (as shown in the example provided in the same panel).

2. Explain the importance of the **dipole nature** of water molecules to the chemistry of life: _____

_____

_____

3. Distinguish between inorganic and organic compounds: _____

_____

4. Describe a role of the following elements in living organisms (plants, animals and prokaryotes) and a consequence of the element being deficient in an organism:

(a) Calcium: _____

_____

(b) Iron: _____

_____

(c) Phosphorus: _____

_____

(d) Sodium: _____

_____

(e) Sulfur: _____

_____

(f) Nitrogen: _____

_____

**Related activities**: The Biochemical Nature of the Cell, Organic Molecules

RA 2

The Chemistry of Life

# Biochemical Tests

**Biochemical** tests are used to detect the presence of nutrients such as lipids, proteins, and carbohydrates (sugar and starch) in various foods. These simple tests are useful for detecting nutrients when large quantities are present. A more accurate technique by which to separate a mixture of compounds involves **chromatography**. Chromatography is used when only a small sample is available or when you wish to distinguish between nutrients. Simple biochemical food tests will show whether sugar is present, whereas chromatography will distinguish between the different types of sugars (e.g. fructose or glucose).

## Paper Chromatography

### Set Up and Procedure

The chromatography paper is folded so it can be secured by the bung inside the test tube. The bung also prevents the solvent evaporating.

Chromatography paper may be treated with chemicals to stain normally invisible pigments.

A spot of concentrated sample is added using a pipette and suspended above the solvent. As the solvent travels up the paper it will carry the sample with it. The distance the sample travels depends on its solubility.

A pencil line is used to show the starting point.

Solvent

### Determining Rf Values

To identify the substances in a mixture an Rf value is calculated using the equation:

$$R_f = \frac{\text{Distance traveled by the spot (x)}}{\text{Distance traveled by the solvent (y)}}$$

These Rf values can then be compared with Rf values from known samples or standards, for example: Glycine's Rf value = 0.50

Alanine's Rf value = 0.70

Arginine's Rf value = 0.72

Leucine's Rf value = 0.91

## Simple Food Tests

### Proteins: The Biuret Test

Reagent:        Biuret solution.
Procedure:      A sample is added to biuret solution and gently heated.
Positive result:  Solution turns from blue to lilac.

### Starch: The Iodine Test

Reagent:        Iodine.
Procedure:      Iodine solution is added to the sample.
Positive result:  Blue-black staining occurs.

### Lipids: The Emulsion Test

Reagent:        Ethanol.
Procedure:      The sample is shaken with ethanol. After settling, the liquid portion is distilled and mixed with water.
Positive result:  The solution turns into a cloudy-white emulsion of suspended lipid molecules.

### Sugars: The Benedict's Test

Reagent:        Benedict's solution.
Procedure:      *Non reducing sugars*: The sample is boiled with dilute hydrochloric acid, then cooled and neutralized. A test for reducing sugars is then performed.

*Reducing sugar*: Benedict's solution is added, and the sample is placed in a water bath.
Positive result:  Solution turns from blue to orange.

1. Calculate the Rf value for the example given above (show your working): _____

_____

2. Explain why the Rf value of a substance is always less than 1: _____

_____

3. Discuss when it is appropriate to use chromatography instead of a simple food test: _____

_____

_____

4. Predict what would happen if a sample was immersed in the chromatography solvent, instead of suspended above it:

_____

_____

5. With reference to their Rf values, rank the four amino acids (listed above) in terms of their solubility: _____

_____

6. Outline why lipids must be mixed in ethanol before they will form an emulsion in water: _____

_____

# Carbohydrates

Carbohydrates are a family of organic molecules made up of carbon, hydrogen, and oxygen atoms with the general formula $(CH_2O)_x$. The most common arrangements found in sugars are hexose (6 sided) or pentose (5 sided) rings. Simple sugars, or monosaccharides, may join together to form compound sugars (disaccharides and polysaccharides), releasing water in the process (**condensation**). Compound sugars can be broken down into their constituent monosaccharides by the opposite reaction (**hydrolysis**). Sugars play a central role in cells, providing energy and, in some cells, contributing to support. They are the major component of most plants (60-90% of the dry weight) and are used by humans as a cheap food source, and a source of fuel, housing, and clothing. In all carbohydrates, the structure is closely related to their functional properties (below).

## Monosaccharides

Monosaccharides are used as a primary energy source for fueling cell metabolism. They are **single-sugar** molecules and include glucose (grape sugar and blood sugar) and fructose (honey and fruit juices). The commonly occurring monosaccharides contain between three and seven carbon atoms in their carbon chains and, of these, the 6C hexose sugars occur most frequently. All monosaccharides are classified as **reducing** sugars (i.e. they can participate in reduction reactions).

### Single sugars (monosaccharides)

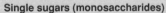
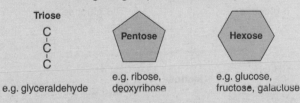

Triose

e.g. glyceraldehyde

Pentose
e.g. ribose, deoxyribose

Hexose
e.g. glucose, fructose, galactose

## Disaccharides

Disaccharides are **double-sugar** molecules and are used as energy sources and as building blocks for larger molecules. The type of disaccharide formed depends on the monomers involved and whether they are in their α- or β- form. Only a few disaccharides (e.g. lactose) are classified as reducing sugars.

**Sucrose** = α-glucose + β-fructose (simple sugar found in plant sap)
**Maltose** = α-glucose + α-glucose (a product of starch hydrolysis)
**Lactose** = β-glucose + β-galactose (milk sugar)
**Cellobiose** = β-glucose + β-glucose (from cellulose hydrolysis)

### Double sugars (disaccharides)

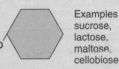

Examples
sucrose,
lactose,
maltose,
cellobiose

## Polysaccharides

**Cellulose**: Cellulose is a structural material in plants and is made up of unbranched chains of β-**glucose** molecules held together by **1, 4 glycosidic links**. As many as 10 000 glucose molecules may be linked together to form a straight chain. Parallel chains become cross-linked with hydrogen bonds and form bundles of 60-70 molecules called microfibrils. Cellulose microfibrils are very strong and are a major component of the structural components of plants, such as the cell wall (photo, right).

**Starch**: Starch is also a polymer of glucose, but it is made up of long chains of α-**glucose** molecules linked together. It contains a mixture of 25-30% **amylose** (unbranched chains linked by α-1, 4 glycosidic bonds) and 70-75% **amylopectin** (branched chains with α-1, 6 glycosidic bonds every 24-30 glucose units). Starch is an energy storage molecule in plants and is found concentrated in insoluble **starch granules** within plant cells (see photo, right). Starch can be easily hydrolyzed by enzymes to soluble sugars when required.

**Glycogen**: Glycogen, like starch, is a branched polysaccharide. It is chemically similar to amylopectin, being composed of α-**glucose** molecules, but there are more α-1,6 glycosidic links mixed with α-1,4 links. This makes it more highly branched and water-soluble than starch. Glycogen is a storage compound in animal tissues and is found mainly in **liver** and **muscle** cells (photo, right). It is readily hydrolyzed by enzymes to form glucose.

**Chitin**: Chitin is a tough modified polysaccharide made up of chains of β-**glucose** molecules. It is chemically similar to cellulose but each glucose has an amine group (–$NH_2$) attached. After cellulose, chitin is the second most abundant carbohydrate. It is found in the cell walls of fungi and is the main component of the **exoskeleton** of insects (right) and other arthropods.

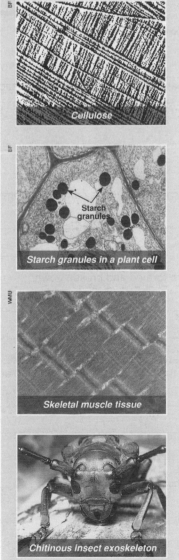

Cellulose

Starch granules in a plant cell

Skeletal muscle tissue

Chitinous insect exoskeleton

Symbolic form of cellulose

1, 4 glycosidic bonds create unbranched chains

1, 6 glycosidic bonds create branched chains

Symbolic form of amylopectin

Many 1, 6 glycosidic bonds create a highly branched molecule

Symbolic form of glycogen

Symbolic form of chitin

The Chemistry of Life

**Related activities**: Organic Molecules

A 2

## Isomerism

Compounds with the same chemical formula (same types and numbers of atoms) may differ in the arrangement of their atoms. Such variations in the arrangement of atoms in molecules are called **isomers**. In **structural isomers** (such as fructose and glucose, and the α and β glucose, right), the atoms are linked in different sequences. **Optical isomers** are identical in every way but are mirror images of each other.

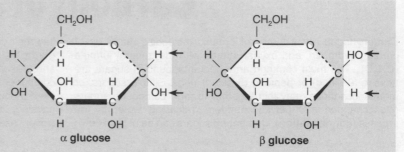

α glucose          β glucose

## Condensation and Hydrolysis Reactions

Monosaccharides can combine to form compound sugars in what is called a **condensation** reaction. Compound sugars can be broken down by **hydrolysis** to simple monosaccharides.

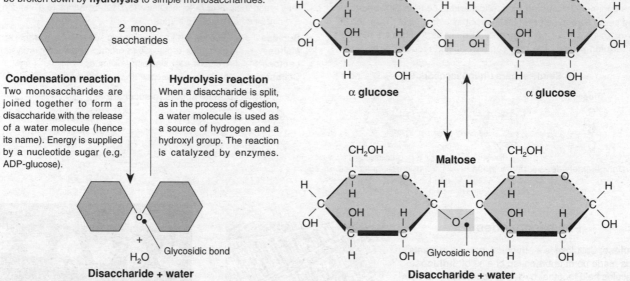

2 mono-saccharides

**Condensation reaction**
Two monosaccharides are joined together to form a disaccharide with the release of a water molecule (hence its name). Energy is supplied by a nucleotide sugar (e.g. ADP-glucose).

**Hydrolysis reaction**
When a disaccharide is split, as in the process of digestion, a water molecule is used as a source of hydrogen and a hydroxyl group. The reaction is catalyzed by enzymes.

$+$
$H_2O$
Glycosidic bond

**Disaccharide + water**

α glucose          α glucose

**Maltose**

Glycosidic bond

**Disaccharide + water**

1. Distinguish between structural and optical isomers in carbohydrates, describing examples of each:

_____

_____

_____

2. Explain how the isomeric structure of a carbohydrate may affect its chemical behavior: _____

_____

_____

3. Explain briefly how compound sugars are formed and broken down: _____

_____

_____

4. Discuss the structural differences between the polysaccharides cellulose, starch, and glycogen, explaining how the differences in structure contribute to the functional properties of the molecule:

_____

_____

_____

_____

_____

_____

_____

# Lipids

Lipids are a group of organic compounds with an oily, greasy, or waxy consistency. They are relatively insoluble in water and tend to be water-repelling (e.g. cuticle on leaf surfaces). Lipids are important biological fuels, some are hormones, and some serve as structural components in plasma membranes. Proteins and carbohydrates may be converted into fats by enzymes and stored within cells of adipose tissue. During times of plenty, this store is increased, to be used during times of food shortage.

## Neutral Fats and Oils

The most abundant lipids in living things are **neutral fats**. They make up the fats and oils found in plants and animals. Fats are an economical way to store fuel reserves, since they yield more than twice as much energy as the same quantity of carbohydrate. Neutral fats are composed of a glycerol molecule attached to one (monoglyceride), two (diglyceride) or three (triglyceride) fatty acids. The fatty acid chains may be saturated or unsaturated (see below). **Waxes** are similar in structure to fats and oils, but they are formed with a complex alcohol instead of glycerol.

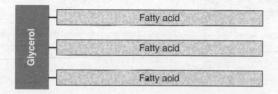

Triglyceride: an example of a neutral fat

## Condensation

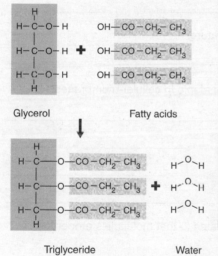

Glycerol          Fatty acids

Triglyceride      Water

Triglycerides form when glycerol bonds with three fatty acids. Glycerol is an alcohol containing three carbons. Each of these carbons is bonded to a hydroxyl (-OH) group.

When glycerol bonds with the fatty acid, an **ester bond** is formed and water is released. Three separate condensation reactions are involved in producing a triglyceride.

## Saturated and Unsaturated Fatty Acids

**Fatty acids** are a major component of neutral fats and phospholipids. About 30 different kinds are found in animal lipids. **Saturated fatty acids** contain the maximum number of hydrogen atoms. **Unsaturated fatty acids** contain some carbon atoms that are double-bonded with each other and are not fully saturated with hydrogens. Lipids containing a high proportion of saturated fatty acids tend to be solids at room temperature (e.g. butter). Lipids with a high proportion of unsaturated fatty acids are oils and tend to be liquid at room temperature. This is because the unsaturation causes kinks in the straight chains so that the fatty acids do not pack closely together. Regardless of their degree of saturation, fatty acids yield a large amount of energy when oxidized.

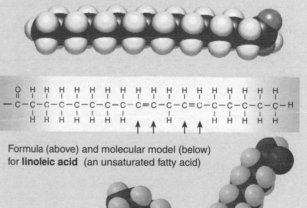

Formula (above) and molecular model (below) for **palmitic acid** (a saturated fatty acid)

Formula (above) and molecular model (below) for **linoleic acid** (an unsaturated fatty acid)

## Phospholipids

Phospholipids are the main component of cellular membranes. They consist of a glycerol attached to two fatty acid chains and a phosphate ($PO_4^{3-}$) group. The phosphate end of the molecule is attracted to water (it is hydrophilic) while the fatty acid end is repelled (hydrophobic). The hydrophobic ends turn inwards in the membrane to form a **phospholipid bilayer**.

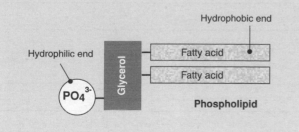

## Steroids

Although steroids are classified as lipids, their structure is quite different from that of other lipids. Steroids have a basic structure of three rings made of 6 carbon atoms each and a fourth ring containing 5 carbon atoms. Examples of steroids include the male and female sex hormones (testosterone and estrogen), and the hormones cortisol and aldosterone. Cholesterol, while not a steroid itself, is a sterol lipid and is a precursor to several steroid hormones.

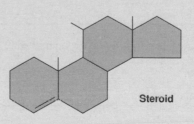

Steroid

Related activities: The Structure of Membranes

**A 2**

The Chemistry of Life

## Important Biological Functions of Lipids

Lipids are concentrated sources of energy and provide fuel for aerobic respiration.

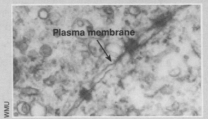

Phospholipids form the structural framework of cellular membranes.

Waxes and oils secreted on to surfaces provide waterproofing in plants and animals.

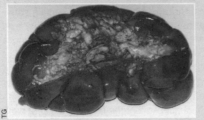

Fat absorbs shocks. Organs that are prone to bumps and shocks (e.g. kidneys) are cushioned with a relatively thick layer of fat.

Lipids are a source of metabolic water. During respiration stored lipids are metabolized for energy, producing water and carbon dioxide.

Stored lipids provide insulation. Increased body fat levels in winter reduce heat losses to the environment.

1. Outline the key **chemical** difference between a phospholipid and a triglyceride: _____
   _____
   _____

2. Name the type of fatty acids found in lipids that form the following at room temperature:

   (a) Solid fats: _____  (b) Oils: _____

3. Relate the structure of phospholipids to their chemical properties and their functional role in cellular membranes:
   _____
   _____

4. (a) Distinguish between saturated and unsaturated fatty acids: _____
   _____

   (b) Explain how the type of fatty acid present in a neutral fat or phospholipid is related to that molecule's properties:
   _____
   _____

   (c) Suggest how the cell membrane structure of an Arctic fish might differ from that of tropical fish species:
   _____
   _____

5. Describe two examples of steroids. For each example, describe its physiological function:

   (a) _____

   (b) _____

6. Explain how fats can provide an animal with:

   (a) Energy: _____

   (b) Water: _____

   (c) Insulation: _____

# Amino Acids

Amino acids are the basic units from which proteins are made. Plants can manufacture all the amino acids they require from simpler molecules, but animals must obtain a certain number of ready-made amino acids (called **essential amino acids**) from their diet. Which amino acids are essential varies from species to species, as different metabolisms are able to synthesize different substances. The distinction between essential and non-essential amino acids is somewhat unclear though, as some amino acids can be produced from others and some are interconvertible by the urea cycle.

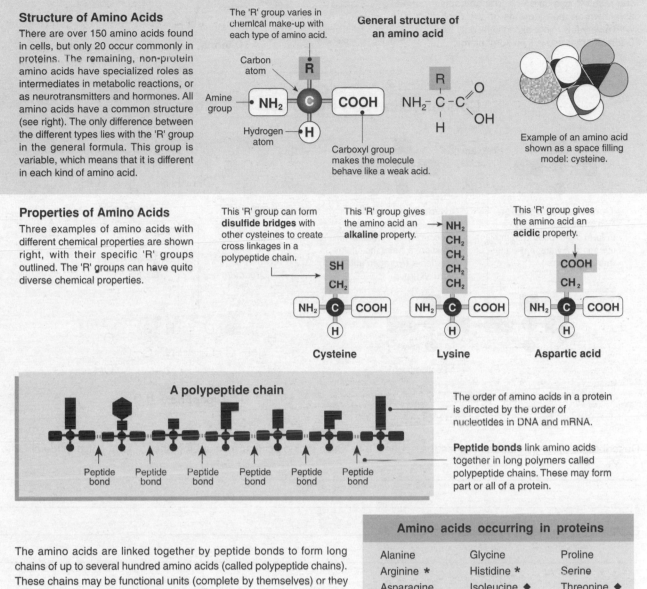

### Structure of Amino Acids

There are over 150 amino acids found in cells, but only 20 occur commonly in proteins. The remaining, non-protein amino acids have specialized roles as intermediates in metabolic reactions, or as neurotransmitters and hormones. All amino acids have a common structure (see right). The only difference between the different types lies with the 'R' group in the general formula. This group is variable, which means that it is different in each kind of amino acid.

The 'R' group varies in chemical make-up with each type of amino acid.

**General structure of an amino acid**

Carbon atom

R

Amine group • NH₂  C  COOH

Hydrogen atom  H

Carboxyl group makes the molecule behave like a weak acid.

Example of an amino acid shown as a space filling model: cysteine.

### Properties of Amino Acids

Three examples of amino acids with different chemical properties are shown right, with their specific 'R' groups outlined. The 'R' groups can have quite diverse chemical properties.

This 'R' group can form **disulfide bridges** with other cysteines to create cross linkages in a polypeptide chain.

SH
CH₂

NH₂  C  COOH
H

**Cysteine**

This 'R' group gives the amino acid an **alkaline** property.

NH₂
CH₂
CH₂
CH₂
CH₂

NH₂  C  COOH
H

**Lysine**

This 'R' group gives the amino acid an **acidic** property.

COOH
CH₂

NH₂  C  COOH
H

**Aspartic acid**

**A polypeptide chain**

Peptide bond   Peptide bond   Peptide bond   Peptide bond   Peptide bond   Peptide bond

The order of amino acids in a protein is directed by the order of nucleotides in DNA and mRNA.

**Peptide bonds** link amino acids together in long polymers called polypeptide chains. These may form part or all of a protein.

The amino acids are linked together by peptide bonds to form long chains of up to several hundred amino acids (called polypeptide chains). These chains may be functional units (complete by themselves) or they may need to be joined to other polypeptide chains before they can carry out their function. In humans, not all amino acids can be manufactured by our body: ten must be taken in with our diet (eight in adults). These are the 'essential amino acids'. They are indicated by the symbol ◆ on the right. Those indicated with as asterisk are also required by infants.

### Amino acids occurring in proteins

| | | |
|---|---|---|
| Alanine | Glycine | Proline |
| Arginine * | Histidine * | Serine |
| Asparagine | Isoleucine ◆ | Threonine ◆ |
| Aspartic acid | Leucine ◆ | Tryptophan ◆ |
| Cysteine | Lysine ◆ | Tyrosine |
| Glutamine | Methionine ◆ | Valine ◆ |
| Glutamic acid | Phenylalanine ◆ | |

1. Describe the biological functions of amino acids: _____

_____

_____

_____

2. Describe what makes each of the 20 amino acids found in proteins unique: _____

_____

_____

_____

**The Chemistry of Life**

**Related activities**: Translation

A 2

### Optical Isomers of Amino Acids

All amino acids, apart from the simplest one (glycine) show optical isomerism. The two forms that these optical isomers can take relate to the arrangement of the four bonding sites on the carbon atom. This can result in two different arrangements as shown on the diagrams on the right. With a very few minor exceptions, only the **L-forms** are found in living organisms.

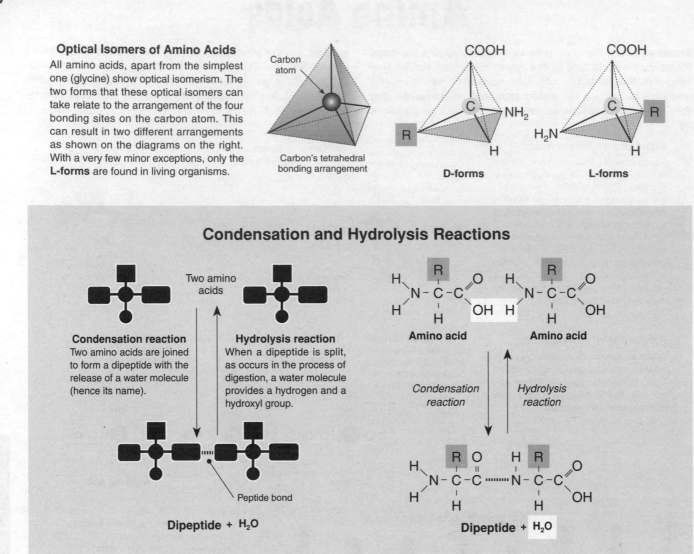

## Condensation and Hydrolysis Reactions

**Condensation reaction**
Two amino acids are joined to form a dipeptide with the release of a water molecule (hence its name).

**Hydrolysis reaction**
When a dipeptide is split, as occurs in the process of digestion, a water molecule provides a hydrogen and a hydroxyl group.

Two amino acids

Peptide bond

**Dipeptide + H₂O**

3. Describe the process that determines the sequence in which amino acids are linked together to form polypeptide chains:

_____

_____

4. Explain what is meant by **essential amino acids**: _____

_____

_____

5. Describe briefly the process of the **condensation** reaction for amino acids: _____

_____

_____

_____

_____

6. Describe briefly the process of the **hydrolysis** reaction for amino acids: _____

_____

_____

_____

7. Name the optical isomeric form that occurs in nearly all amino acids in living things: _____

# Proteins

The precise folding up of a protein into its **tertiary structure** creates a three dimensional arrangement of the active 'R' groups. The way each 'R' group faces with respect to the others gives the protein its unique chemical properties. If a protein loses this precise structure (denaturation), it is usually unable to carry out its biological function. Proteins are often classified on the basis of structure (globular vs fibrous). Some of the properties used for the basis of structural classification are outlined over the page.

### Primary Structure - 1° (amino acid sequence)
Strings of hundreds of amino acids link together with peptide bonds to form molecules called polypeptide chains. There are 20 different kinds of amino acids that can be linked together in a vast number of different combinations. This sequence is called the **primary structure**. It is the arrangement of attraction and repulsion points in the amino acid chain that determines the higher levels of organization in the protein and its biological function.

### Secondary Structure - 2° (α-helix or ß-pleated sheet)
Polypeptides become folded in various ways, referred to as the secondary (2°) structure. The most common types of 2° structures are a coiled α-**helix** and a β-**pleated sheet**. Secondary structures are maintained with hydrogen bonds between neighboring CO and NH groups. H-bonds, although individually weak, provide considerable strength when there are a large number of them. The example, right, shows the two main types of secondary structure. In both, the **'R' side groups** (not shown) project out from the structure. Most globular proteins contain regions of α-helices together with β sheets. Keratin (a fibrous protein) is composed almost entirely of α-helices. Fibroin (silk protein), is another fibrous protein, almost entirely in β-sheet form.

### Tertiary Structure - 3° (folding)
Every protein has a precise structure formed by the folding of the secondary structure into a complex shape called the **tertiary structure**. The protein folds up because various points on the secondary structure are attracted to one another. The strongest links are caused by bonding between neighboring *cysteine* amino acids which form disulfide bridges. Other interactions that are involved in folding include weak ionic and hydrogen bonds as well as hydrophobic interactions.

### Quaternary Structure - 4°
Some proteins (such as enzymes) are complete and functional with a tertiary structure only. However, many complex proteins exist as aggregations of polypeptide chains. The arrangement of the polypeptide chains into a functional protein is termed the **quaternary structure**. The example (right) shows a molecule of hemoglobin, a globular protein composed of 4 polypeptide subunits joined together; two identical *beta chains* and two identical *alpha chains*. Each has a heme (iron containing) group at the centre of the chain, which binds oxygen. Proteins containing non-protein material are **conjugated proteins**. The non-protein part is the **prosthetic group**.

### Denaturation of Proteins
Denaturation refers to the loss of the three-dimensional structure (and usually also the biological function) of a protein. Denaturation is often, although not always, permanent. It results from an alteration of the bonds that maintain the secondary and tertiary structure of the protein, even though the sequence of amino acids remains unchanged. Agents that cause denaturation are:
- **Strong acids and alkalis**: Disrupt ionic bonds and result in coagulation of the protein. Long exposure also breaks down the primary structure of the protein.
- **Heavy metals**: May disrupt ionic bonds, form strong bonds with the carboxyl groups of the R groups, and reduce protein charge. The general effect is to cause the precipitation of the protein.
- **Heat and radiation** (e.g. UV): Cause disruption of the bonds in the protein through increased energy provided to the atoms.
- **Detergents and solvents**: Form bonds with the non-polar groups in the protein, thereby disrupting hydrogen bonding.

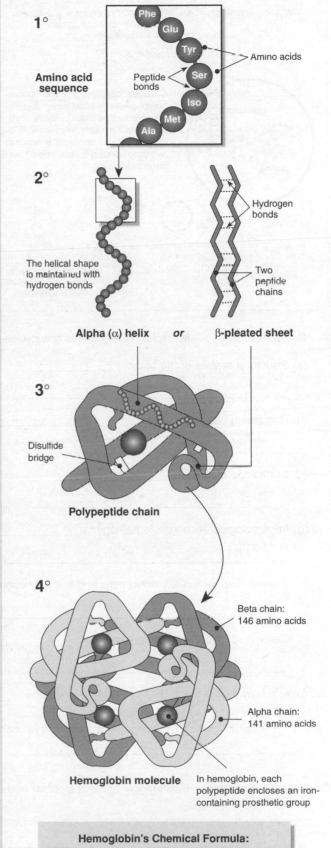

1° Amino acid sequence — Phe, Glu, Tyr, Ser, Iso, Met, Ala — Amino acids, Peptide bonds

2° The helical shape is maintained with hydrogen bonds — Hydrogen bonds, Two peptide chains

**Alpha (α) helix** *or* **β-pleated sheet**

3° Disulfide bridge

**Polypeptide chain**

4° Beta chain: 146 amino acids — Alpha chain: 141 amino acids

**Hemoglobin molecule** — In hemoglobin, each polypeptide encloses an iron-containing prosthetic group

**Hemoglobin's Chemical Formula:**

$$C_{3032} H_{4816} O_{872} N_{780} S_8 Fe_4$$

The Chemistry of Life

**Related activities**: Enzymes

RA 2

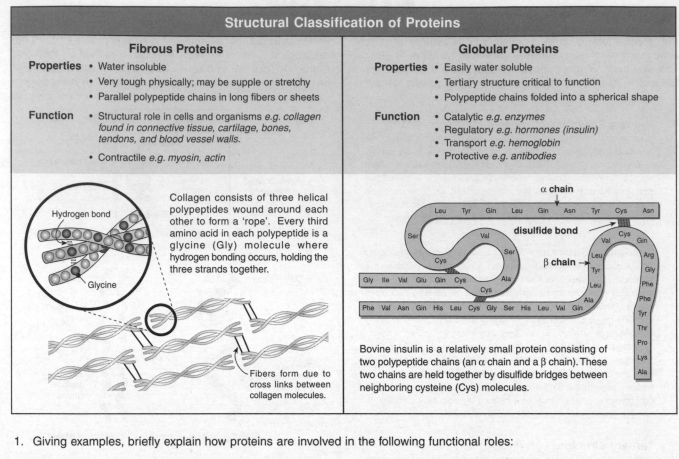

## Structural Classification of Proteins

### Fibrous Proteins

**Properties**
- Water insoluble
- Very tough physically; may be supple or stretchy
- Parallel polypeptide chains in long fibers or sheets

**Function**
- Structural role in cells and organisms *e.g. collagen found in connective tissue, cartilage, bones, tendons, and blood vessel walls.*
- Contractile *e.g. myosin, actin*

Hydrogen bond

Glycine

Collagen consists of three helical polypeptides wound around each other to form a 'rope'. Every third amino acid in each polypeptide is a glycine (Gly) molecule where hydrogen bonding occurs, holding the three strands together.

Fibers form due to cross links between collagen molecules.

### Globular Proteins

**Properties**
- Easily water soluble
- Tertiary structure critical to function
- Polypeptide chains folded into a spherical shape

**Function**
- Catalytic *e.g. enzymes*
- Regulatory *e.g. hormones (insulin)*
- Transport *e.g. hemoglobin*
- Protective *e.g. antibodies*

α chain

disulfide bond

β chain

Bovine insulin is a relatively small protein consisting of two polypeptide chains (an α chain and a β chain). These two chains are held together by disulfide bridges between neighboring cysteine (Cys) molecules.

1. Giving examples, briefly explain how proteins are involved in the following functional roles:

(a) Structural tissues of the body: _____

_____

(b) Regulating body processes: _____

_____

(c) Contractile elements: _____

_____

(d) Immunological response to pathogens: _____

_____

(e) Transporting molecules within cells and in the bloodstream: _____

_____

(f) Catalyzing metabolic reactions in cells: _____

_____

2. Explain how denaturation destroys protein function: _____

_____

_____

3. Describe one structural difference between globular and fibrous proteins: _____

_____

_____

4. Determine the total number of amino acids in the α and β chains of the insulin molecule illustrated above:

(a) α chain: _____ (b) β chain: _____

# Enzymes

Most enzymes are proteins. They are capable of catalyzing (speeding up) biochemical reactions and are therefore called biological **catalysts**. Enzymes act on one or more compounds (called the **substrate**). They may break a single substrate molecule down into simpler substances, or join two or more substrate molecules chemically together. The enzyme itself is unchanged in the reaction; its presence merely allows the reaction to take place more rapidly. When the substrate attains the required **activation energy** to enable it to change into the product, there is a 50% chance that it will proceed forward to form the product, otherwise it reverts back to a stable form of the reactant again. The part of the enzyme's surface into which the substrate is bound and undergoes reaction is known as the **active site**. This is made of different parts of polypeptide chain folded in a specific shape so they are closer together. For some enzymes, the complexity of the binding sites can be very precise, allowing only a single kind of substrate to bind to it. Some other enzymes have lower **specificity** and will accept a wide range of substrates of the same general type (e.g. lipases break up any fatty acid chain length of lipid). This is because the enzyme is specific for the type of chemical bond involved and not an exact substrate.

## Enzyme Structure

The model on the right is of an enzyme called *Ribonuclease S*, which breaks up RNA molecules. It is a typical enzyme, being a globular protein and composed of up to several hundred atoms. The darkly shaded areas are called **active sites** and make up the **cleft**; the region into which the substrate molecule(s) are drawn. The correct positioning of these sites is critical for the catalytic reaction to occur. The substrate (RNA in this case) is drawn into the cleft by the active sites. By doing so, it puts the substrate molecule under stress, causing the reaction to proceed more readily.

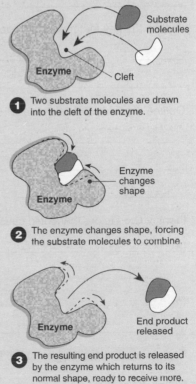

**Substrate molecule**: Substrate molecules are the chemicals that an enzyme acts on. They are drawn into the cleft of the enzyme.

**Active sites**: These attraction points draw the substrate to the enzyme's surface. Substrate molecule(s) are positioned in a way to promote a reaction: either joining two molecules together or splitting up a larger one (as in this case).

**Enzyme molecule**: The complexity of the active site is what makes each enzyme so specific (i.e. precise in terms of the substrate it acts on).

Source: *Biochemistry*, (1081) by Lubert Stryer

## How Enzymes Work

The **lock and key** model proposed earlier this century suggested that the substrate was simply drawn into a closely matching cleft on the enzyme molecule. More recent studies have revealed that the process more likely involves an **induced fit** (see diagram on the right), where the enzyme or the reactants change their shape slightly. The reactants become bound to enzymes by weak chemical bonds. This binding can weaken bonds within the reactants themselves, allowing the reaction to proceed more readily.

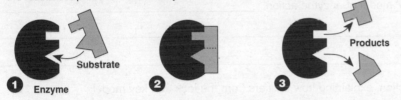

The presence of an enzyme simply makes it easier for a reaction to take place. All **catalysts** speed up reactions by influencing the stability of bonds in the reactants. They may also provide an alternative reaction pathway, thus lowering the activation energy needed for a reaction to take place (see the graph below).

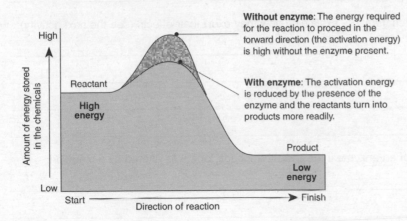

**Without enzyme**: The energy required for the reaction to proceed in the forward direction (the activation energy) is high without the enzyme present.

**With enzyme**: The activation energy is reduced by the presence of the enzyme and the reactants turn into products more readily.

### Induced Fit Model

An enzyme fits to its substrate somewhat like a lock and key. The shape of the enzyme changes when the substrate fits into the cleft (called the **induced fit**):

**1** Two substrate molecules are drawn into the cleft of the enzyme.

**2** The enzyme changes shape, forcing the substrate molecules to combine.

**3** The resulting end product is released by the enzyme which returns to its normal shape, ready to receive more.

**Related activities**: Enzyme Reaction Rates, Gene Mutations
**Web links**: How Enzymes Work

RA 2

The Chemistry of Life

The **substrate** is attracted to the enzyme by the 'active sites'.

**Substrate**

The substrate is cleaved (broken in two) and the two **products** are released to allow the enzyme to work again.

The substrate is subjected to stress which will facilitate the breaking of bonds.

**Enzyme**

**Products**

The two substrate molecules are attracted to the enzyme by the 'active sites'.

**Substrates**

The two substrate molecules form a single product and are released to allow the enzyme to work again.

The substrate molecules are subjected to stress which will aid the formation of bonds.

**Enzyme**

**Product**

## Catabolic reactions

Some enzymes can cause a single substrate molecule to be drawn into the active site. Chemical bonds are broken, causing the substrate molecule to break apart to become two separate molecules. **Examples**: *digestion, cellular respiration*.

## Anabolic reactions

Some enzymes can cause two substrate molecules to be drawn into the active site. Chemical bonds are formed, causing the two substrate molecules to form bonds and become a single molecule. **Examples**: *protein synthesis, photosynthesis*.

1. Give a brief account of enzymes as **biological catalysts**, including reference to the role of the **active site**:

_____

_____

_____

_____

_____

_____

2. Distinguish between **catabolism** and **anabolism**, giving an example of each and identifying each reaction as **endergonic** or **exergonic**:

_____

_____

3. Outline the key features of the '**lock and key**' model of enzyme action: _____

_____

_____

4. Outline the '**induced fit**' model of enzyme action, explaining how it differs from the lock and key model:

_____

_____

_____

5. Identify two factors that could cause enzyme denaturation, explaining how they exert their effects (see the next activity):

(a) _____

_____

(b) _____

_____

6. Explain what might happen to the functioning of an enzyme if the gene that codes for it was altered by a mutation:

_____

_____

# Enzyme Reaction Rates

Enzymes are sensitive molecules. They often have a narrow range of conditions under which they operate properly. For most of the enzymes associated with plant and animal metabolism, there is little activity at low temperatures. As the temperature increases, so too does the enzyme activity, until the point is reached where the temperature is high enough to damage the enzyme's structure. At this point, the enzyme ceases to function; a phenomenon called enzyme or protein **denaturation**.

Extremes in acidity (pH) can also cause the protein structure of enzymes to denature. Poisons often work by denaturing enzymes or occupying the enzyme's active site so that it does not function. In some cases, enzymes will not function without cofactors, such as vitamins or trace elements. In the four graphs below, the rate of reaction or degree of enzyme activity is plotted against each of four factors that affect enzyme performance. Answer the questions relating to each graph:

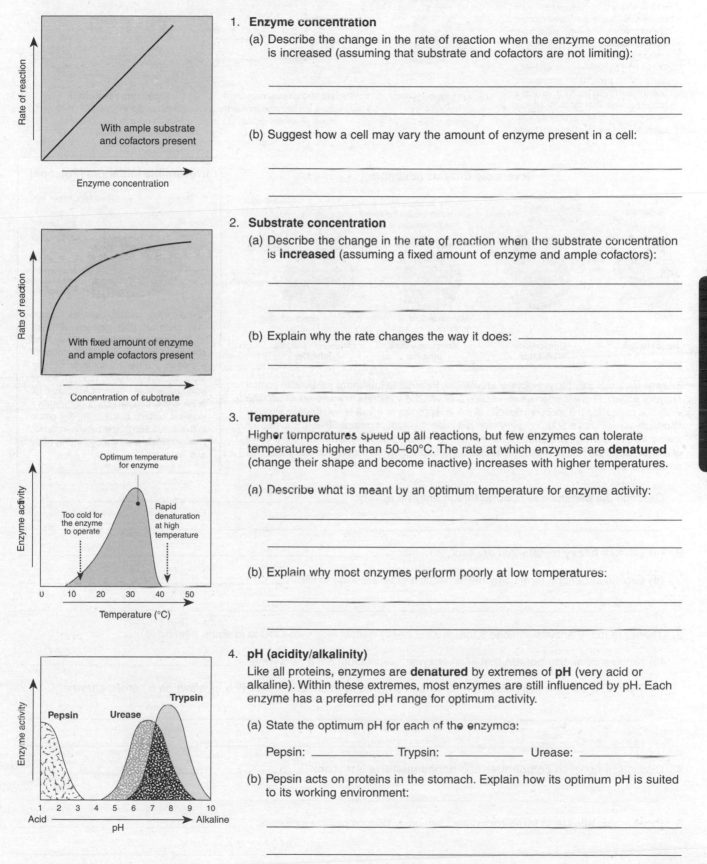

1. **Enzyme concentration**

   (a) Describe the change in the rate of reaction when the enzyme concentration is increased (assuming that substrate and cofactors are not limiting):

   _____

   _____

   (b) Suggest how a cell may vary the amount of enzyme present in a cell:

   _____

   _____

2. **Substrate concentration**

   (a) Describe the change in the rate of reaction when the substrate concentration is **increased** (assuming a fixed amount of enzyme and ample cofactors):

   _____

   _____

   (b) Explain why the rate changes the way it does: _____

   _____

   _____

3. **Temperature**

   Higher temperatures speed up all reactions, but few enzymes can tolerate temperatures higher than 50–60°C. The rate at which enzymes are **denatured** (change their shape and become inactive) increases with higher temperatures.

   (a) Describe what is meant by an optimum temperature for enzyme activity:

   _____

   _____

   (b) Explain why most enzymes perform poorly at low temperatures:

   _____

   _____

4. **pH (acidity/alkalinity)**

   Like all proteins, enzymes are **denatured** by extremes of **pH** (very acid or alkaline). Within these extremes, most enzymes are still influenced by pH. Each enzyme has a preferred pH range for optimum activity.

   (a) State the optimum pH for each of the enzymes:

   Pepsin: _____ Trypsin: _____ Urease: _____

   (b) Pepsin acts on proteins in the stomach. Explain how its optimum pH is suited to its working environment:

   _____

   _____

The Chemistry of Life

**Related activities**: Enzyme Cofactors and Inhibitors

RDA 2

# Enzyme Cofactors and Inhibitors

Enzyme activity is often influenced by the presence of other chemicals. Some of these may enhance an enzyme's activity. Called **cofactors**, they are a nonprotein component of an enzyme and may be organic molecules (**coenzymes**) or inorganic ions (e.g. $Ca^{2+}$, $Zn^{2+}$). Enzymes may also be deactivated, temporarily or permanently, by chemicals called enzyme **inhibitors**.

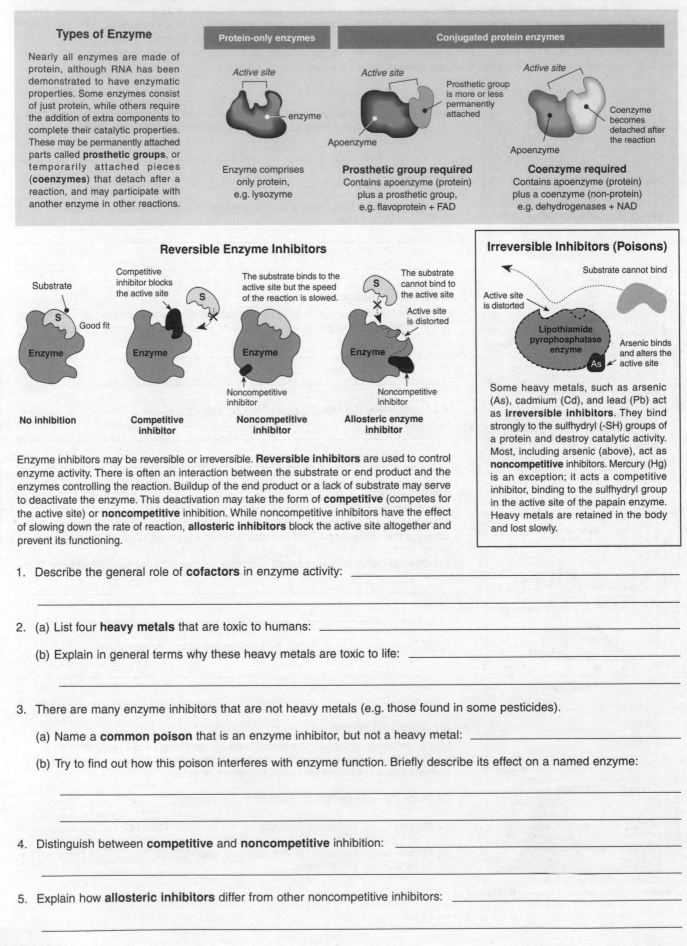

### Types of Enzyme

Nearly all enzymes are made of protein, although RNA has been demonstrated to have enzymatic properties. Some enzymes consist of just protein, while others require the addition of extra components to complete their catalytic properties. These may be permanently attached parts called **prosthetic groups**, or temporarily attached pieces (**coenzymes**) that detach after a reaction, and may participate with another enzyme in other reactions.

**Protein-only enzymes**

*Active site*

enzyme

Enzyme comprises only protein, e.g. lysozyme

**Conjugated protein enzymes**

*Active site*

Prosthetic group is more or less permanently attached

Apoenzyme

**Prosthetic group required**
Contains apoenzyme (protein) plus a prosthetic group, e.g. flavoprotein + FAD

*Active site*

Coenzyme becomes detached after the reaction

Apoenzyme

**Coenzyme required**
Contains apoenzyme (protein) plus a coenzyme (non-protein) e.g. dehydrogenases + NAD

### Reversible Enzyme Inhibitors

Substrate

S

Good fit

Enzyme

**No inhibition**

Competitive inhibitor blocks the active site

S

Enzyme

**Competitive inhibitor**

The substrate binds to the active site but the speed of the reaction is slowed.

Enzyme

Noncompetitive inhibitor

**Noncompetitive inhibitor**

The substrate cannot bind to the active site

S

X

Active site is distorted

Enzyme

Noncompetitive inhibitor

**Allosteric enzyme inhibitor**

### Irreversible Inhibitors (Poisons)

Substrate cannot bind

Active site is distorted

Lipothiamide pyrophosphatase enzyme

As

Arsenic binds and alters the active site

Some heavy metals, such as arsenic (As), cadmium (Cd), and lead (Pb) act as **irreversible inhibitors**. They bind strongly to the sulfhydryl (-SH) groups of a protein and destroy catalytic activity. Most, including arsenic (above), act as **noncompetitive** inhibitors. Mercury (Hg) is an exception; it acts a competitive inhibitor, binding to the sulfhydryl group in the active site of the papain enzyme. Heavy metals are retained in the body and lost slowly.

Enzyme inhibitors may be reversible or irreversible. **Reversible inhibitors** are used to control enzyme activity. There is often an interaction between the substrate or end product and the enzymes controlling the reaction. Buildup of the end product or a lack of substrate may serve to deactivate the enzyme. This deactivation may take the form of **competitive** (competes for the active site) or **noncompetitive** inhibition. While noncompetitive inhibitors have the effect of slowing down the rate of reaction, **allosteric inhibitors** block the active site altogether and prevent its functioning.

1. Describe the general role of **cofactors** in enzyme activity: _____

_____

2. (a) List four **heavy metals** that are toxic to humans: _____

   (b) Explain in general terms why these heavy metals are toxic to life: _____

   _____

3. There are many enzyme inhibitors that are not heavy metals (e.g. those found in some pesticides).

   (a) Name a **common poison** that is an enzyme inhibitor, but not a heavy metal: _____

   (b) Try to find out how this poison interferes with enzyme function. Briefly describe its effect on a named enzyme:

   _____

   _____

4. Distinguish between **competitive** and **noncompetitive** inhibition: _____

   _____

5. Explain how **allosteric inhibitors** differ from other noncompetitive inhibitors: _____

   _____

# Industrial Production of Enzymes

Humans have used enzymes for thousands of years in food and beverage production, but the use of enzymes in industry is a comparatively recent development. Many industries now rely on the large scale production of microbial enzymes to catalyze a range of reactions. In the absence of enzymes, these reactions sometimes require high temperatures or pressures to proceed. Industrial enzymes must be relatively robust against denaturation and capable of maintaining activity over a wide temperature and pH range. Enzyme technology involves the production, isolation, purification, and application of useful enzymes. Commercial enzymes are produced from three main

sources: plants, animals, and microorganisms (mainly bacteria and fungi). Most enzymes used in industrial processes today are microbial in origin and are produced in industrial-scale microbial fermentations using liquid or semi-solid growth media. Note that the term **fermentation**, when used in reference to industrial microbiology, applies to both aerobic and anaerobic microbial growth in **bioreactors**. Generalized plans for the industrial production of both extracellular and intracellular enzymes are illustrated below. Note that the isolation of intracellular enzymes (below, right) is more complex because the cells must first be disrupted to release the enzymes within.

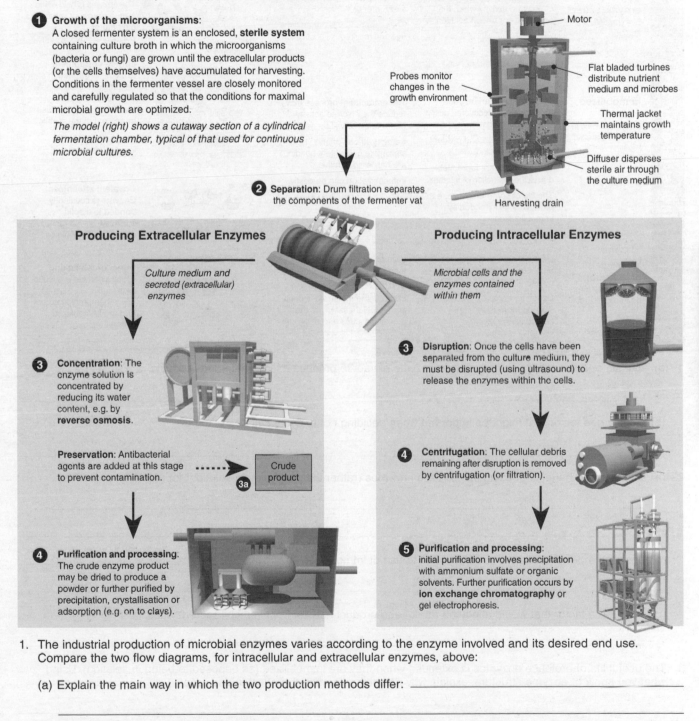

**1  Growth of the microorganisms:**
A closed fermenter system is an enclosed, **sterile system** containing culture broth in which the microorganisms (bacteria or fungi) are grown until the extracellular products (or the cells themselves) have accumulated for harvesting. Conditions in the fermenter vessel are closely monitored and carefully regulated so that the conditions for maximal microbial growth are optimized.

*The model (right) shows a cutaway section of a cylindrical fermentation chamber, typical of that used for continuous microbial cultures.*

Motor

Probes monitor changes in the growth environment

Flat bladed turbines distribute nutrient medium and microbes

Thermal jacket maintains growth temperature

Diffuser disperses sterile air through the culture medium

Harvesting drain

**2  Separation:** Drum filtration separates the components of the fermenter vat

### Producing Extracellular Enzymes

Culture medium and secreted (extracellular) enzymes

**3  Concentration:** The enzyme solution is concentrated by reducing its water content, e.g. by **reverse osmosis**.

**Preservation:** Antibacterial agents are added at this stage to prevent contamination.

**3a** · · · · ▸ Crude product

**4  Purification and processing.** The crude enzyme product may be dried to produce a powder or further purified by precipitation, crystallisation or adsorption (e.g. on to clays).

### Producing Intracellular Enzymes

Microbial cells and the enzymes contained within them

**3  Disruption:** Once the cells have been separated from the culture medium, they must be disrupted (using ultrasound) to release the enzymes within the cells.

**4  Centrifugation:** The cellular debris remaining after disruption is removed by centrifugation (or filtration).

**5  Purification and processing:** initial purification involves precipitation with ammonium sulfate or organic solvents. Further purification occurs by **ion exchange chromatography** or gel electrophoresis.

The Chemistry of Life

1.  The industrial production of microbial enzymes varies according to the enzyme involved and its desired end use. Compare the two flow diagrams, for intracellular and extracellular enzymes, above:

    (a) Explain the main way in which the two production methods differ: _____

    _____

    (b) Suggest the reason for this difference: _____

    _____

2.  Enzyme solutions can be packaged and used as crude extracts without further purification (**3a**). State one benefit of this:

    _____

Related activities: Putting Enzymes to Use, Applications of Enzymes

A 3

# Putting Enzymes to Use

Depending on the way in which the desired end-product is produced, enzymes may be used as crude whole cell preparations or as cell-free enzyme extracts. Whole cell preparations are cost effective, and appropriate when the processes involved in production of the end product are complex, as in waste treatment and the production of semi-synthetic antibiotics. Cell free enzyme extracts are more expensive to produce, but can be a more efficient option overall. To reduce costs and improve the efficiency of product production, enzymes are sometimes immobilized within a matrix of some kind and the reactants are passed over them. The various methods by which enzymes are put to work are compared in the diagram below.

## Industrial enzymes

| | Advantages | Disadvantages | Methods of Enzyme Immobilization |
|---|---|---|---|
| **Cell free enzyme extract**<br>Enzyme is used in solution | There is generally a high level of enzyme activity when the enzymes are free in solution. | The enzyme may be washed away after use.<br><br>The end-product is not enzyme free and may require purification. | **Micro-encapsulation**<br>The enzyme is held within a membrane, or within alginate or polyacrylamide capsules.<br><br>Partially permeable membrane |
| **Immobilized enzyme**<br>Enzyme is held in an inert material | The enzymes can be used repeatedly and recovered easily (this reduces costs).<br><br>The enzyme-free end-product is easily harvested.<br><br>The enzymes are more stable due to the protection of a matrix.<br><br>The life of some enzymes, e.g. proteases, is extended by immobilization. | The entrapment process may reduce the enzyme activity (more enzyme will be needed).<br><br>Some methods offering high stability (e.g. covalent bonding) are harder to achieve.<br><br>Immobilization can be costly. | **Lattice entrapment**<br>Enzyme is trapped in a gel lattice, e.g. silica gel. The substrate and reaction products diffuse in and out of the matrix.<br><br>Enzymes trapped in a gel lattice<br><br>**Covalent attachment**<br>Enzyme is covalently bonded to a solid surface e.g. collagen or a synthetic polymer.<br><br>Enzyme / Substrate, e.g. collagen |
| **Whole cell preparation**<br>Whole cells may be immobilized | Useful for enzymes that are unstable or inactivated when outside the cell.<br><br>Useful for complex processes utilizing more than one intracellular enzyme. | Less expensive and more rapid than first producing a pure enzyme extract.<br><br>Some of the substrate is used for microbial growth, so the process is less efficient overall. | **Direct cross-linking**<br>Glutaraldehyde is used to cross-link the enzymes. They then precipitate out and are immobilized without support.<br><br>Glutaraldehyde |

1. (a) Explain one benefit of using a cell free enzyme extract to produce a high-value end-product:

_____

(b) Identify one factor that might be important when deciding not to use a cell free extract:

_____

2. (a) Describe two benefits of using immobilized enzymes (rather than enzymes in solution) for industrial processes:

_____

_____

(b) Describe a disadvantage associated with the use of immobilized enzymes: _____

_____

(c) Describe a factor that would affect the rate of end-product harvest from immobilized enzymes:

_____

3. The useful life of protease enzymes is extended when they are immobilized (as opposed to being in solution). Using what you know of enzyme structure, explain why immobilization has this effect in this case:

_____

_____

4. Suggest why immobilization would reduce the activity of certain enzymes: _____

_____

_____

# Applications of Enzymes

Microbes are ideal organisms for the industrial production of enzymes because of their high productivity, ease of culture in industrial fermenters, and the ease with which they can be genetically modified to produce particular products. In addition, because there is an enormous diversity in microbial metabolism, the variety of enzymes available for exploitation is very large. Some of the microorganisms involved in industrial fermentations, and their enzymes and their applications are described below.

Enzymes are used in various stages of **cheese production**, e.g. chymosin from GE microbes now replaces the rennin previously obtained from calves.

In **beer brewing**, **proteases** (from bacteria) are added to prevent cloudiness. Amyloglucosidases are used to produce low calorie beers.

**Citric acid** is used in **jam production** and is synthesized by a mutant strain of the fungus *Aspergillus niger*, which produces the enzyme citrate synthase.

Biological detergents use **proteases**, **lipases**, and **amylases** extracted from fungi and thermophilic bacteria to break down organic material in stains.

**Fungal ligninases** are used in **pulp and paper industries** to remove lignin from wood pulp and treat wood waste.

Medical treatment of blood clots employs protease enzymes such as streptokinase from *Streptomyces* spp.

### Some of the many applications of microbial enzymes in medicine, industry, and food manufacture.

In **soft centered chocolates**, **invertase** from yeast breaks down the solid filling to produce the soft center.

Bacterial proteases are used to break down the wheat protein (gluten) in flour, to produce low gluten breads.

Cellulases and pectinases are used in the manufacture of packaged (as opposed to fresh) fruit juices to speed juice extraction and prevent cloudiness.

The silver residues from old photographs can be reclaimed for reuse when proteases are employed to digest the gelatin of old films.

The lactase from bacteria is used to convert lactose to glucose and galactose in the production of low-lactose and lactose free milk products.

Tanning industries now use proteases from *Bacillus subtilis* instead of toxic chemicals, such as sulfide pastes, to remove hairs and soften hides.

The enzyme, **glucose oxidase**, from *Aspergillus niger*, is immobilized in a semi-conducting silicon chip. It catalyzes the conversion of glucose (from the blood sample) to gluconic acid.

Hydrogen ions from the gluconic acid cause a movement of electrons in the silicon, which is detected by a transducer. The strength of the electric current is directly proportional to the blood glucose concentration.

Plastic sleeve | Membrane permeable to glucose | Biological recognition layer | Transducer | Amplifier | The signal is amplified | Results are shown on a liquid crystal display — 932

**Biosensors** are electronic monitoring devices that use biological material to detect the presence or concentration of a particular substance. Enzymes are ideally suited for use in biosensors because of their specificity and sensitivity. This example illustrates how **glucose oxidase** from the fungus *Aspergillus niger* is used in a biosensor to measure blood glucose level in diabetics.

The Chemistry of Life

RA 3

1. Identify two probable consequences of the absence of enzymes from a chemical reaction that normally uses them:

   (a) _____

   (b) _____

2. Identify three properties of microbial enzymes that make them highly suitable as industrial catalysts. For each, explain why the property is important:

   (a) _____

   _____

   (b) _____

   _____

   _____

   (c) _____

   _____

3. Choose one example from those described in the diagram on the previous page and, in more detail, identify:

   (a) The enzyme and its specific microbial source: _____

   _____

   (b) The application of the enzyme in industry and the specific reaction it catalyzes: _____

   _____

   _____

   _____

4. (a) Outline the basic principle of enzyme-based biosensors: _____

   _____

   (b) Suggest how a biosensor could be used to monitor blood alcohol level: _____

   _____

   _____

   _____

5. For each of the examples described below, suggest how the use of microbial enzymes has improved the efficiency, cost effectiveness, and/or safety of processing compared with traditional methods:

   (a) Use of microbial proteases to treat hides in the tanning industry: _____

   _____

   _____

   _____

   (b) Use of microbial chymosin in cheese production: _____

   _____

   _____

   _____

   (c) Use of fungal ligninases to treat wood waste: _____

   _____

   _____

   _____

# Cell Structure

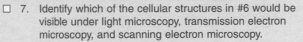

**IB SL**
Complete:
*1-9, 11-14*
*Extension: 10*

**IB HL**
Complete:
*1-9, 11-14*
*Extension: 10*

**IB Options**
Complete:
*Option F: 4-5*

**AP Biology**
Complete:
*1-14*

## Learning Objectives

☐ 1. Compile your own glossary from the **KEY WORDS** displayed in **bold type** in the learning objectives below.

### Features of Cells *(pages 78-92, 97-98)*

☐ 2. Recognize the contribution of microscopy to the development of **cell theory** and to our present knowledge of cell structure. Recognize the **cell** as the basic unit of living things.

☐ 3. Use different units of measurement (mm, μm, nm) to express cell sizes and to describe a range of cell sizes.

☐ 4. Contrast the structure of **prokaryote** and **eukaryote** cells and provide examples of each type. If required, describe the specific features of protistan and fungal cells. Explain why viruses are regarded as non-cellular.

☐ 5. Describe the structure of a **bacterial cell**, including the **bacterial cell wall** and the structures associated with it (**flagella**, pili), the **bacterial chromosome** and **plasmids**, and the plasma membrane. Identify which of these are unique to prokaryotes.

☐ 6. Describe and interpret drawings and photographs of typical **plant** and **animal cells** as seen using light and electron microscopy. Describe the role of the following:
   - **nucleus, nuclear envelope, nucleolus**
   - **mitochondria, chloroplasts** (if present),
   - rough/smooth **endoplasmic reticulum, ribosomes**,
   - **plasma membrane, cell wall** (if present)
   - **Golgi apparatus, lysosomes, vacuoles** (if present),
   - **cytoplasm, cytoskeleton** (of **microtubules**), **centrioles, cilia** (if present)

☐ 7. Identify which of the cellular structures in #6 would be visible under light microscopy, transmission electron microscopy, and scanning electron microscopy.

☐ 8. Outline the interrelationship between the organelles involved in the production and secretion of proteins.

☐ 9. Identify the differences between plant and animal cells, noting relative size and shape, and presence or absence of particular structures and organelles.

☐ 10. Describe the role of **cell fractionation** in separating cellular components. Explain how it is achieved through homogenisation of a sample followed by **ultracentrifugation**. Explain the role of speed of centrifugation in separating the cellular fractions.

### Microscopy *(pages 93-96)*

☐ 11. Describe the basic structure of **optical** and **electron microscopes**. With respect to these, explain and distinguish between **magnification** and **resolution**.

☐ 12. Distinguish between TEM (**transmission electron microscopy**) and SEM (**scanning electron microscopy**). Recognize EM as an important tool in investigating cell structure and function.

☐ 13. Distinguish between **compound** and **stereo light microscopes**. Identify the situations in which these different microscopes would be used.

☐ 14. Demonstrate an ability to correctly use a light microscope to locate material and focus images. Identify the steps required for preparing a **temporary mount** for viewing with a compound light microscope. Understand why **stains** are useful in the preparation of specimens. If required, use simple **staining techniques** to show specific features of cells.

---

**Textbooks**

See the 'Textbook Reference Grid' on page 7 for textbook page references relating to material in this topic.

**Supplementary Texts**

See pages 5-6 for additional details of these texts:

■ Adds, J., *et al.*, 2003. **Molecules and Cells**, (NelsonThornes), chpt. 4.

■ Adds, J., *et al.*, 1999. **Tools, Techniques and Assessment in Biology**, (NelsonThornes), pp. 13-26.

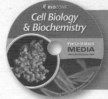

**Presentation MEDIA**
to support this topic:
**CELL BIOLOGY & BIOCHEMISTRY**

**Periodicals**

See page 7 for details of publishers of periodicals:

**STUDENT'S REFERENCE**
■ **The Beat Goes On: Cilia and Flagella** Biol. Sci. Rev., 18(4) April 2006, pp. 2-6. *The structure and function of cilia and flagella.*

■ **Border Control** New Scientist, 15 July 2000 (Inside Science). *The role of the plasma membrane in cell function: membrane structure and transport, and the role of membrane receptors.*

■ **Lysosomes: The Cell's Recycling Centres** Biol. Sci. Rev., 17(2) Nov. 2004, pp. 21-23. *The nature and role of lysosomes: small membrane-bound organelles found in all eukaryotic cells.*

■ **Lysosomes and their Versatile and Potentially Fatal Membranes** Biol. Sci. Rev., 17(3) Feb. 2005, pp. 14-16. *The critical importance of the lysosome membrane.*

■ **Light Microscopy** Biol. Sci. Rev., 13(1) Sept. 2000, pp. 36-38. *An excellent account of the basis and various techniques of light microscopy.*

■ **Transmission Electron Microscopy** Biol. Sci. Rev., 13(2) Nov. 2000, pp. 32-35. *The techniques and applications of TEM. Includes a diagram comparing features of TEM and light microscopy.*

■ **Scanning Electron Microscopy** Biol. Sci. Rev., 20(1) Sept. 2007, pp. 38-41. *An excellent account of the techniques and applications of SEM. Includes details of specimen preparation and recent advancements in the technology.*

**Internet**

See pages 10-11 for details of how to access **Bio Links** from our web site: **www.biozone.co.uk**. From Bio Links, access sites under the topics:

**CELL BIOLOGY AND BIOCHEMISTRY:** • Cell and molecular biology online • Cell structure and function web links > **Microscopy:** • A guide to microscopy and microanalysis • Biological applications of electron and light microscopy • Microscopy UK • Scanning Electron Microscope *... and others* > **Cell Structure and Transport:** • Animal cells • CELLS alive! • Cell breakage and fractionation • Nanoworld *... and others*

# The Cell Theory

The idea that all living things are composed of cells developed over many years and is strongly linked to the invention and refinement of the microscope. Early microscopes in the 1600's (such as Leeuwenhoek's below) opened up a whole new field of biology: the study of cell biology and microorganisms. The cell theory is a fundamental idea of biology.

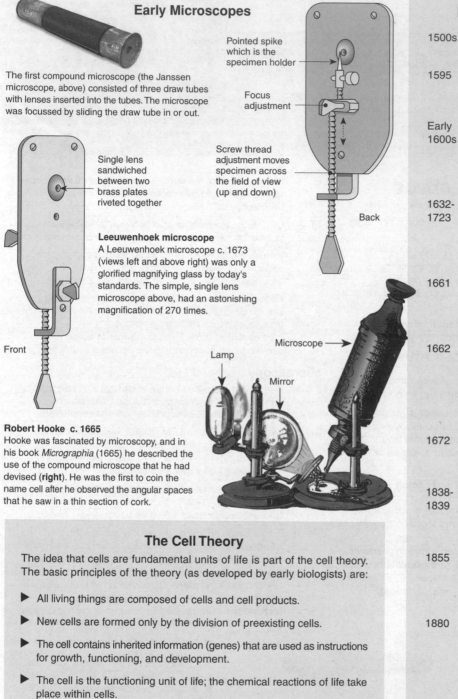

## Early Microscopes

The first compound microscope (the Janssen microscope, above) consisted of three draw tubes with lenses inserted into the tubes. The microscope was focussed by sliding the draw tube in or out.

Single lens sandwiched between two brass plates riveted together

**Leeuwenhoek microscope**
A Leeuwenhoek microscope c. 1673 (views left and above right) was only a glorified magnifying glass by today's standards. The simple, single lens microscope above, had an astonishing magnification of 270 times.

Front

Pointed spike which is the specimen holder

Focus adjustment

Screw thread adjustment moves specimen across the field of view (up and down)

Back

**Robert Hooke c. 1665**
Hooke was fascinated by microscopy, and in his book *Micrographia* (1665) he described the use of the compound microscope that he had devised (**right**). He was the first to coin the name cell after he observed the angular spaces that he saw in a thin section of cork.

Lamp

Mirror

Microscope →

## Milestones in Cell Biology

| | |
|---|---|
| 1500s | Convex lenses with a magnification greater than x5 became available. |
| 1595 | Zacharias Janssen of Holland has been credited with the first compound microscope (more than one lens). |
| Early 1600s | First compound microscopes used in Europe (used two convex lenses to make objects look larger). Suffered badly from color distortion; an effect called 'spherical aberration'. |
| 1632-1723 | **Antoni van Leeuwenhoek** of Holland produced over 500 single lens microscopes, discovering bacteria, human blood cells, spermatozoa, and protozoa. Friend of Robert Hooke. |
| 1661 | **Marcello Malpighi** used lenses to study insects. Discovered capillaries and may have described cells in writing of 'globules' and 'saccules'. |
| 1662 | **Robert Hooke** of England used the term 'cell' in describing the microscopic structure of cork. He believed that the cell walls were the important part of otherwise empty structures. Published *Micrographia* in 1665. |
| 1672 | **Nehemlah Grew** wrote the first of two well-illustrated books on the microscopic anatomy of plants. |
| 1838-1839 | Botanist **Matthias Schleiden** and zoologist **Theodor Schwann** proposed the cell theory based on their observations of plant and animal cells. |
| 1855 | **Rudolph Virchow** extended the cell theory by stating that "new cells are formed only by the division of previously existing cells". |
| 1880 | **August Weismann** added to Virchow's idea by pointing out that "all the cells living today can trace their ancestry back to ancient times", thus making the link between cell theory and evolution. |

## The Cell Theory

The idea that cells are fundamental units of life is part of the cell theory. The basic principles of the theory (as developed by early biologists) are:

▶ All living things are composed of cells and cell products.

▶ New cells are formed only by the division of preexisting cells.

▶ The cell contains inherited information (genes) that are used as instructions for growth, functioning, and development.

▶ The cell is the functioning unit of life; the chemical reactions of life take place within cells.

1. Briefly describe the impact the invention of microscopes has had on biology: _____

_____

_____

2. Before the development of the cell theory, it was commonly believed that living organisms could arise by spontaneous generation. Explain what this term means and why it has been discredited as a theory:

_____

_____

_____

# Characteristics of Life

With each step in the hierarchy of biological order, new properties emerge that were not present at simpler levels of organization. Life itself is associated with numerous **emergent properties**, including **metabolism** and growth. The cell is the site of life; it is the functioning unit structure from which living organisms are made. Viruses and cells are profoundly different. Viruses are non-cellular, lack the complex structures found in cells, and show only some of the properties we associate with living things. The traditional view of viruses is as a minimal particle, although the identification in 2004 of a new family of viruses, called mimiviruses, is forcing a rethink of this conservative view. Note the different scale to which the examples below are drawn. Refer to the scale bars for the comparative sizes (1000 nm = 1 µm – 0.001 mm).

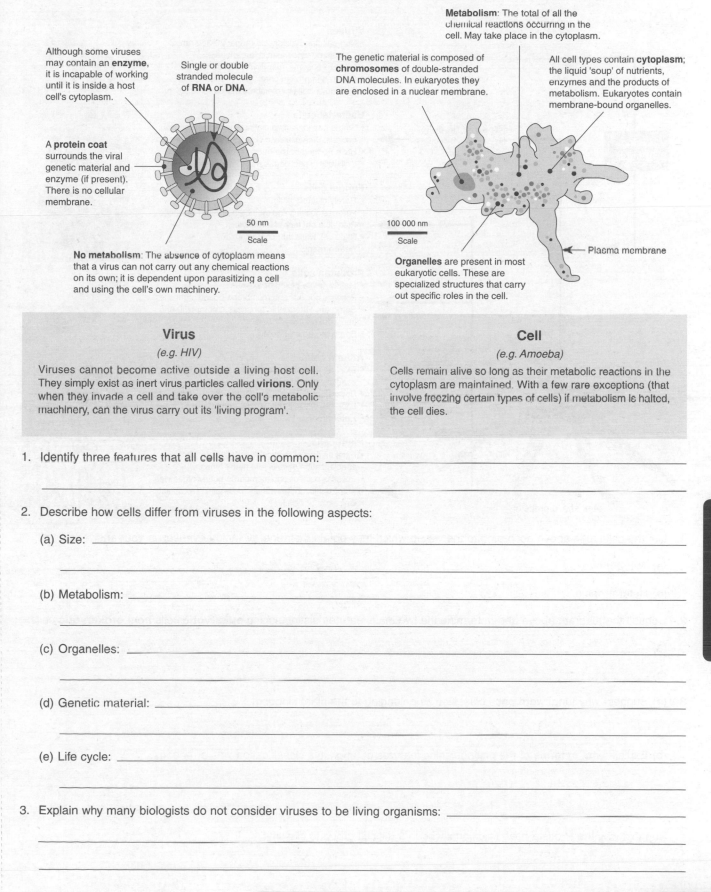

Although some viruses may contain an **enzyme**, it is incapable of working until it is inside a host cell's cytoplasm.

Single or double stranded molecule of **RNA** or **DNA**.

A **protein coat** surrounds the viral genetic material and enzyme (if present). There is no cellular membrane.

**No metabolism**: The absence of cytoplasm means that a virus can not carry out any chemical reactions on its own; it is dependent upon parasitizing a cell and using the cell's own machinery.

50 nm
Scale

**Metabolism**: The total of all the chemical reactions occurring in the cell. May take place in the cytoplasm.

The genetic material is composed of **chromosomes** of double-stranded DNA molecules. In eukaryotes they are enclosed in a nuclear membrane.

All cell types contain **cytoplasm**; the liquid 'soup' of nutrients, enzymes and the products of metabolism. Eukaryotes contain membrane-bound organelles.

100 000 nm
Scale

**Organelles** are present in most eukaryotic cells. These are specialized structures that carry out specific roles in the cell.

Plasma membrane

## Virus
*(e.g. HIV)*

Viruses cannot become active outside a living host cell. They simply exist as inert virus particles called **virions**. Only when they invade a cell and take over the cell's metabolic machinery, can the virus carry out its 'living program'.

## Cell
*(e.g. Amoeba)*

Cells remain alive so long as their metabolic reactions in the cytoplasm are maintained. With a few rare exceptions (that involve freezing certain types of cells) if metabolism is halted, the cell dies.

1.  Identify three features that all cells have in common: _____

    _____

2.  Describe how cells differ from viruses in the following aspects:

    (a) Size: _____

    _____

    (b) Metabolism: _____

    _____

    (c) Organelles: _____

    _____

    (d) Genetic material: _____

    _____

    (e) Life cycle: _____

    _____

3.  Explain why many biologists do not consider viruses to be living organisms: _____

    _____

    _____

Cell Structure

**Related activities**: Types of Living Things

A 2

# Types of Living Things

Living things are called organisms and **cells** are the functioning unit structure from which organisms are made. Under the five kingdom system, cells can be divided into two basic kinds: the **prokaryotes**, which are simple cells without a distinct, membrane-bound nucleus, and the more complex **eukaryotes**. The eukaryotes can be further organized into broad groups according to their basic cell type: the protists, fungi, plants, and animals. Viruses are non-cellular and have no cellular machinery of their own. All cells must secure a source of energy if they are to survive and carry out metabolic processes. **Autotrophs** can meet their energy requirements using light or chemical energy from the physical environment. Other types of cell, called **heterotrophs**, obtain their energy from other living organisms or their dead remains.

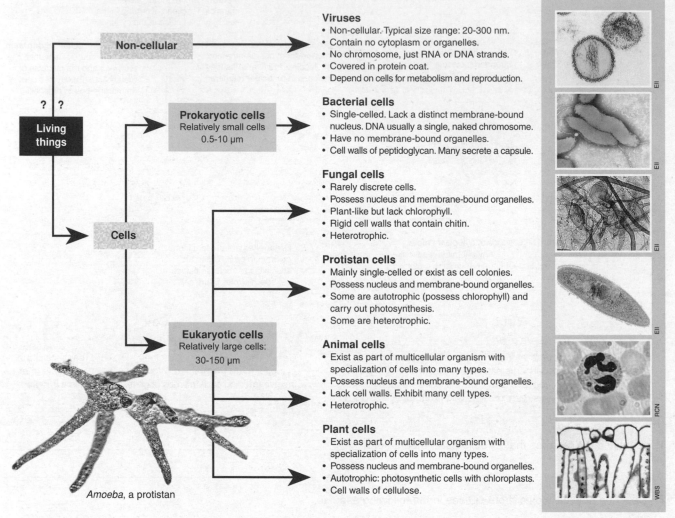

**Non-cellular**

**Viruses**
• Non-cellular. Typical size range: 20-300 nm.
• Contain no cytoplasm or organelles.
• No chromosome, just RNA or DNA strands.
• Covered in protein coat.
• Depend on cells for metabolism and reproduction.

**Living things**

**Prokaryotic cells**
Relatively small cells
0.5-10 µm

**Bacterial cells**
• Single-celled. Lack a distinct membrane-bound nucleus. DNA usually a single, naked chromosome.
• Have no membrane-bound organelles.
• Cell walls of peptidoglycan. Many secrete a capsule.

**Fungal cells**
• Rarely discrete cells.
• Possess nucleus and membrane-bound organelles.
• Plant-like but lack chlorophyll.
• Rigid cell walls that contain chitin.
• Heterotrophic.

**Cells**

**Protistan cells**
• Mainly single-celled or exist as cell colonies.
• Possess nucleus and membrane-bound organelles.
• Some are autotrophic (possess chlorophyll) and carry out photosynthesis.
• Some are heterotrophic.

**Eukaryotic cells**
Relatively large cells:
30-150 µm

**Animal cells**
• Exist as part of multicellular organism with specialization of cells into many types.
• Possess nucleus and membrane-bound organelles.
• Lack cell walls. Exhibit many cell types.
• Heterotrophic.

**Plant cells**
• Exist as part of multicellular organism with specialization of cells into many types.
• Possess nucleus and membrane-bound organelles.
• Autotrophic: photosynthetic cells with chloroplasts.
• Cell walls of cellulose.

*Amoeba*, a protistan

1. List the cell types above according to the way in which they obtain their energy. Include viruses in your answer as well:

   (a) Autotrophic: _____

   (b) Heterotrophic: _____

2. Consult the diagram above and determine the two main features distinguishing **eukaryotic** cells from **prokaryotic** cells:

   (a) _____

   (b) _____

3. (a) Suggest why fungi were once classified as belonging to the plant kingdom: _____

   _____

   (b) Explain why, in terms of the distinguishing features of fungi, this classification was erroneous: _____

   _____

   _____

4. Suggest why the Protista have traditionally been a difficult group to classify: _____

   _____

**A 2**     **Related activities:** Features of Taxonomic Groups, Unicellular Eukaryotes

# Bacterial Cells

Bacterial (prokaryotic) cells are much smaller and simpler than the cells of eukaryotes. They lack many eukaryotic features (e.g. a distinct nucleus and membrane-bound cellular organelles). The bacterial cell wall is an important feature. It is a complex, multi-layered structure and often has a role in virulence. These pages illustrate some features of bacterial structure and diversity.

## Structure of a Generalized Bacterial Cell

**Plasmids**: Small, circular DNA molecules (accessory chromosomes) which can reproduce independently of the main chromosome. They can move between cells, and even between species, by **conjugation**. This property accounts for the transmission of antibiotic resistance between bacteria. Plasmids are also used as vectors in recombinant DNA technology.

**Single, circular main chromosome**: Makes them haploid for most genes. It is possible for some genes to be found on both the plasmid and chromosome and there may be several copies of a gene on a group of plasmids.

The cell lacks a nuclear membrane, so there is no distinct nucleus and the chromosomes are in direct contact with the cytoplasm. It is possible for free ribosomes to attach to mRNA while the mRNA is still in the process of being transcribed from the DNA.

**Fimbriae**: Hairlike structures that are shorter, straighter, and thinner than flagella. They are used for attachment, not movement. Pili are similar to fimbriae, but are longer and less numerous. They are involved in bacterial conjugation (below) and as phage receptors (opposite).

1 µm

Cytoplasm

**Cell surface membrane**: Similar in composition to eukaryotic membranes, although less rigid.

**Glycocalyx**. A viscous, gelatinous layer outside the cell wall. It is composed of polysaccharide and/or polypeptide. If it is firmly attached to the wall, it is called a **capsule**. If loosely attached, it is called a **slime layer**. Capsules may contribute to virulence in pathogenic species, e.g. by protecting the bacteria from the host's immune attack. In some species, the glycocalyx allows attachment to substrates.

**Cell wall**. A complex, semi-rigid structure that gives the cell shape, prevents rupture, and serves as an anchorage point for flagella. The cell wall is composed of a macromolecule called **peptidoglycan**; repeating disaccharides attached by polypeptides to form a lattice. The wall also contains varying amounts of lipopolysaccharides and lipoproteins. The amount of peptidoglycan present in the wall forms the basis of the diagnostic **gram stain**. In many species, the cell wall contributes to their virulence (disease-causing ability).

**Flagellum** (pl. flagella). Some bacteria have long, filamentous appendages, called flagella, that are used for locomotion. There may be a single polar flagellum (monotrichous), one or more flagella at each end of the cell, or the flagella may be distributed over the entire cell (peritrichous).

---

### Bacterial cell shapes

Most bacterial cells range between 0.20-2.0 µm in diameter and 2-10 µm length. Although they are a very diverse group, much of this diversity is in their metabolism. In terms of gross morphology, there are only a few basic shapes found (illustrated below). The way in which members of each group aggregate after division is often characteristic and is helpful in identifying certain species.

**Bacilli**
Rod-shaped

**Bacilli:** Rod-shaped bacteria that divide only across their short axis. Most occur as single rods, although pairs and chains are also found. The term bacillus can refer (as here) to shape. It may also denote a genus.

**Cocci**
Ball-shaped

**Cocci:** usually round, but sometimes oval or elongated. When they divide, the cells stay attached to each other and remain in aggregates e.g. pairs (diplococci) or clusters (staphylococci), that are usually a feature of the genus.

**Spirilla**
Spiral-shaped

**Spirilla and vibrio**: Bacteria with one or more twists. Spirilla bacteria have a helical (corkscrew) shape which may be rigid or flexible (as in spirochetes). Bacteria that look like curved rods (comma shaped) are called vibrios.

### Bacterial conjugation

The two bacteria illustrated below are involved in 'pseudo sex'. This involves a one-way exchange of genetic information from a donor cell to a recipient cell. The plasmid, which must be of the 'conjugative' type, passes through a tube called a **sex pilus** to the other cell. Which is donor and which is recipient appears to be genetically determined.

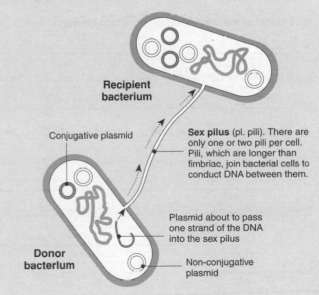

**Recipient bacterium**

Conjugative plasmid

**Sex pilus** (pl. pili). There are only one or two pili per cell. Pili, which are longer than fimbriae, join bacterial cells to conduct DNA between them.

Plasmid about to pass one strand of the DNA into the sex pilus

**Donor bacterium**

Non-conjugative plasmid

---

**Related activities**: Antibiotic Resistance, Features of Taxonomic Groups
**Web links**: Gram Stain Animation

RA 2

**Cell Structure**

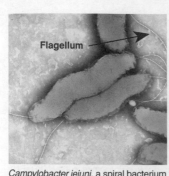

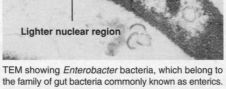

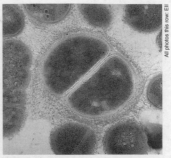

*Campylobacter jejuni*, a spiral bacterium responsible for foodborne intestinal disease. Note the single flagellum at each end (amphitrichous arrangement).

*Helicobacter pylori*, a comma-shaped vibrio bacterium that causes stomach ulcers in humans. This bacterium moves by means of multiple polar flagella.

A species of *Spirillum*, a spiral shaped bacterium with a tuft of polar flagella. Most of the species in this genus are harmless aquatic organisms.

Bacteria usually divide by binary fission. During this process, DNA is copied and the cell splits into two cells, as in these gram positive cocci.

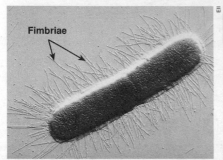

*Escherichia coli*, a common gut bacterium with **peritrichous** (around the entire cell) **fimbriae**. *E. coli* is a gram negative rod; it does not take up the gram stain but can be counter stained with safranin.

TEM showing *Enterobacter* bacteria, which belong to the family of gut bacteria commonly known as enterics. They are widely distributed in water, sewage, and soil. The family includes motile and non-motile species.

SEM showing a large rod-shaped bacterium with an approaching bacteriophage (viral particle). The bacterium has hair-like **pili** (not visible) protruding from the surface which act as phage receptors.

1. (a) Describe the function of flagella in bacteria: _____

_____

   (b) Explain how fimbriae differ structurally and functionally from flagella: _____

_____

_____

2. (a) Describe the location and general composition of the bacterial cell wall: _____

_____

_____

   (b) Describe how the glycocalyx differs from the cell wall: _____

_____

3. (a) Describe the main method by which bacteria reproduce: _____

_____

   (b) Explain how conjugation differs from this usual method: _____

_____

   (c) Comment on the evolutionary significance of conjugation: _____

_____

_____

4. Briefly describe how the artificial manipulation of plasmids has been used for technological applications:

_____

_____

_____

# Unicellular Eukaryotes

**Unicellular** (single-celled) **eukaryotes** comprise the majority of the diverse kingdom, Protista. They are found almost anywhere there is water, including within larger organisms (as parasites or symbionts). The protists are a very diverse group, exhibiting some features typical of generalized eukaryotic cells, as well as specialized features, which may be specific to one genus. Note that even within the genera below there is considerable variation in size and appearance. *Amoeba* and *Paramecium* are both **heterotrophic**, ingesting food, which accumulates inside a **vacuole**. *Euglena* and *Chlamydomonas* are autotrophic algae, although *Euglena* is heterotrophic when deprived of light. Other protists include the marine foraminiferans and radiolarians, specialized intracellular parasites such as *Plasmodium*, and zooflagellates such as the parasites *Trypanosoma* and *Giardia*.

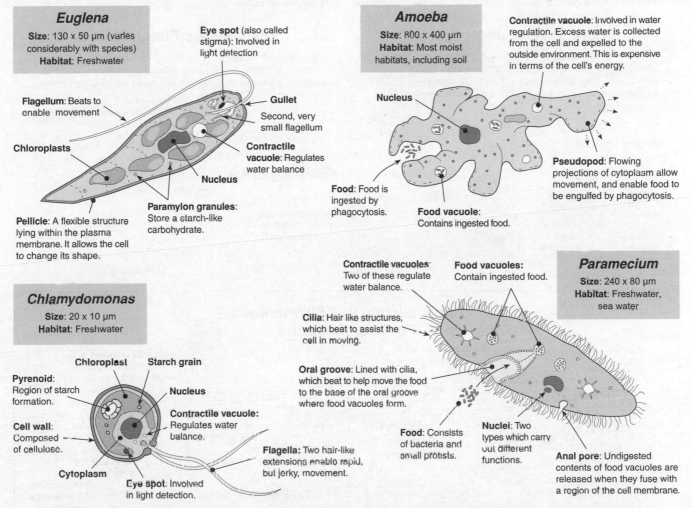

### Euglena
**Size:** 130 x 50 µm (varies considerably with species)
**Habitat:** Freshwater

**Eye spot** (also called stigma): Involved in light detection

**Flagellum:** Beats to enable movement

**Gullet**
Second, very small flagellum

**Chloroplasts**

**Contractile vacuole:** Regulates water balance

**Nucleus**

**Pellicle:** A flexible structure lying within the plasma membrane. It allows the cell to change its shape.

**Paramylon granules:** Store a starch-like carbohydrate.

### Amoeba
**Size:** 800 x 400 µm
**Habitat:** Most moist habitats, including soil

**Contractile vacuole:** Involved in water regulation. Excess water is collected from the cell and expelled to the outside environment. This is expensive in terms of the cell's energy.

**Nucleus**

**Pseudopod:** Flowing projections of cytoplasm allow movement, and enable food to be engulfed by phagocytosis.

**Food:** Food is ingested by phagocytosis.

**Food vacuole:** Contains ingested food.

### Chlamydomonas
**Size:** 20 x 10 µm
**Habitat:** Freshwater

**Pyrenoid:** Region of starch formation.

**Chloroplast**

**Starch grain**

**Nucleus**

**Cell wall:** Composed of cellulose.

**Contractile vacuole:** Regulates water balance.

**Cytoplasm**

**Eye spot:** Involved in light detection.

**Flagella:** Two hair-like extensions enable rapid, but jerky, movement.

### Paramecium
**Size:** 240 x 80 µm
**Habitat:** Freshwater, sea water

**Contractile vacuoles:** Two of these regulate water balance.

**Food vacuoles:** Contain ingested food.

**Cilia:** Hair like structures, which beat to assist the cell in moving.

**Oral groove:** Lined with cilia, which beat to help move the food to the base of the oral groove where food vacuoles form.

**Food:** Consists of bacteria and small protists.

**Nuclei:** Two types which carry out different functions.

**Anal pore:** Undigested contents of food vacuoles are released when they fuse with a region of the cell membrane.

1. Fill in the table below to summarize differences in some of the features and life functions of the protists shown above:

| Organism | Nutrition | Movement | Osmoregulation | Eye spot present / absent | Cell wall present / absent |
|---|---|---|---|---|---|
| *Amoeba* | | | | | |
| *Paramecium* | | | | | |
| *Euglena* | | | | | |
| *Chlamydomonas* | | | | | |

2. List the four organisms shown above in order of size (largest first): _____

_____

3. Suggest why an autotroph would have an eye spot: _____

_____

**Related activities:** Features of Taxonomic Groups

EA 1

Cell Structure

# Fungal Cells

The fungi are a large, successful group of eukaryotes that includes the yeasts, moulds, and fleshy fungi. The study of fungi is called **mycology**. All fungi are chemoheterotrophs: they lack chlorophyll and require organic compounds for a source of energy and carbon. Most fungi are also **saprophytic**, feeding on dead material, although some are parasitic or mutalistic. Fungal nutrition is absorptive and digestion is extracellular and takes place outside the fungal body. Of more than 100 000 fungal species, only about 100 are pathogenic to humans or other animals. However, many are plant pathogens and virtually every economically important plant species is attacked by one or more fungi. Note that the **lichens** have been reclassified into the fungal kingdom. They are dual organisms, formed by a mutalistic association between a green alga or a cyanobacterium, and a fungus (usually an ascomycete). Features of two fungal groups: yeasts and moulds are described below.

## Single Celled Fungi: Yeasts

Yeasts are nonfilamentous, unicellular fungi that are typically spherical or oval shaped. Yeasts reproduce asexually by fission or budding. They are facultative anaerobes, a property that is exploited in the brewing, wine making, and bread making industries.

## Filamentous Fungi: Molds

Moulds are multicellular, filamentous fungi often divided by septa into uni-nucleate, cell-like units. When conditions are favorable, hyphae grow to form a filamentous mass called a **mycelium.**

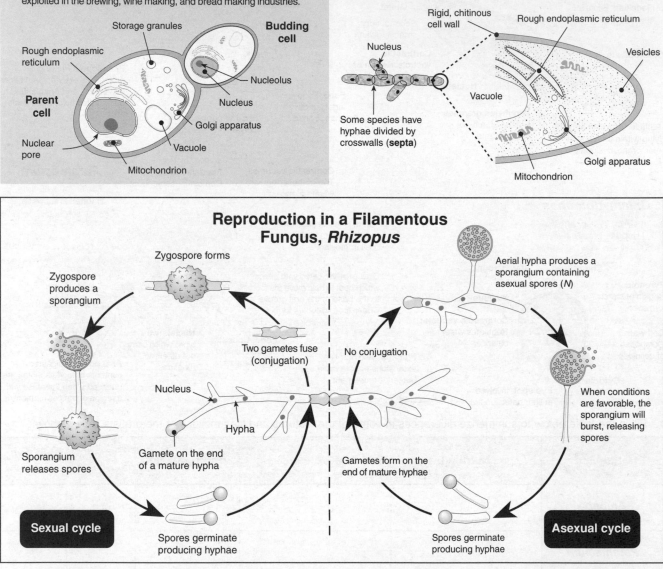

## Reproduction in a Filamentous Fungus, *Rhizopus*

1. List three distinguishing features of fungi: _____

   _____

2. Outline the key differences in the reproductive strategies of yeasts and molds: _____

   _____

   _____

3. Identify two commonly exploited fungal species and state how they are used:

   (a) _____

   (b) _____

**Related activities**: Features of Taxonomic Groups

# Plant Cells

Plant cells are enclosed in a cellulose cell wall. The cell wall protects the cell, maintains its shape, and prevents excessive water uptake. It does not interfere with the passage of materials into and out of the cell. The diagram below shows the structure and function of a typical plant cell and its organelles. Also see the following pages where further information is provided on the organelles listed here but not described.

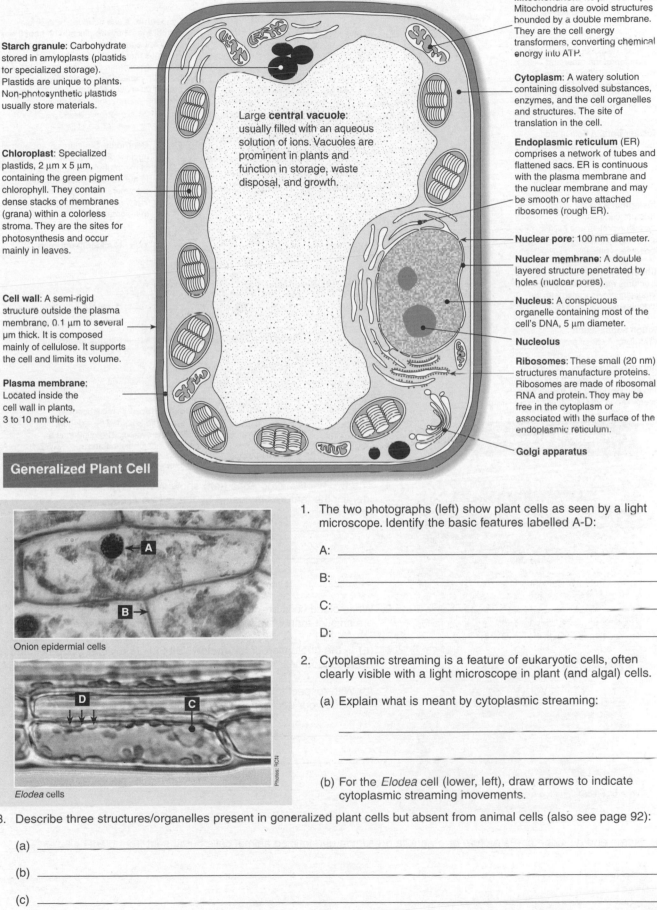

**Starch granule**: Carbohydrate stored in amyloplasts (plastids for specialized storage). Plastids are unique to plants. Non-photosynthetic plastids usually store materials.

**Chloroplast**: Specialized plastids, 2 μm x 5 μm, containing the green pigment chlorophyll. They contain dense stacks of membranes (grana) within a colorless stroma. They are the sites for photosynthesis and occur mainly in leaves.

**Cell wall**: A semi-rigid structure outside the plasma membrane, 0.1 μm to several μm thick. It is composed mainly of cellulose. It supports the cell and limits its volume.

**Plasma membrane**: Located inside the cell wall in plants, 3 to 10 nm thick.

Large **central vacuole**: usually filled with an aqueous solution of ions. Vacuoles are prominent in plants and function in storage, waste disposal, and growth.

**Mitochondrion**: 1.5 μm X 2–8 μm. Mitochondria are ovoid structures bounded by a double membrane. They are the cell energy transformers, converting chemical energy into ATP.

**Cytoplasm**: A watery solution containing dissolved substances, enzymes, and the cell organelles and structures. The site of translation in the cell.

**Endoplasmic reticulum** (ER) comprises a network of tubes and flattened sacs. ER is continuous with the plasma membrane and the nuclear membrane and may be smooth or have attached ribosomes (rough ER).

**Nuclear pore**: 100 nm diameter.

**Nuclear membrane**: A double layered structure penetrated by holes (nuclear pores).

**Nucleus**: A conspicuous organelle containing most of the cell's DNA, 5 μm diameter.

**Nucleolus**

**Ribosomes**: These small (20 nm) structures manufacture proteins. Ribosomes are made of ribosomal RNA and protein. They may be free in the cytoplasm or associated with the surface of the endoplasmic reticulum.

**Golgi apparatus**

Generalized Plant Cell

Onion epidermial cells

Elodea cells

Photos: RCN

1. The two photographs (left) show plant cells as seen by a light microscope. Identify the basic features labelled A-D:

A: _____

B: _____

C: _____

D: _____

2. Cytoplasmic streaming is a feature of eukaryotic cells, often clearly visible with a light microscope in plant (and algal) cells.

(a) Explain what is meant by cytoplasmic streaming:

_____

_____

(b) For the *Elodea* cell (lower, left), draw arrows to indicate cytoplasmic streaming movements.

3. Describe three structures/organelles present in generalized plant cells but absent from animal cells (also see page 92):

(a) _____

(b) _____

(c) _____

Cell Structure

**Related activities**: Animal Cells, Cell Structures and Organelles
**Web links**: Review of Eukaryotic Cells

RA 2

# Animal Cells

Animal cells, unlike plant cells, do not have a regular shape. In fact, some animal cells (such as phagocytes) are able to alter their shape for various purposes (e.g. engulfment of foreign material). The diagram below shows the structure and function of a typical animal cell and its organelles. Note the differences between this cell and the generalized plant cell. Also see the previous page and following two pages, where further information is provided on the organelles listed here but not described.

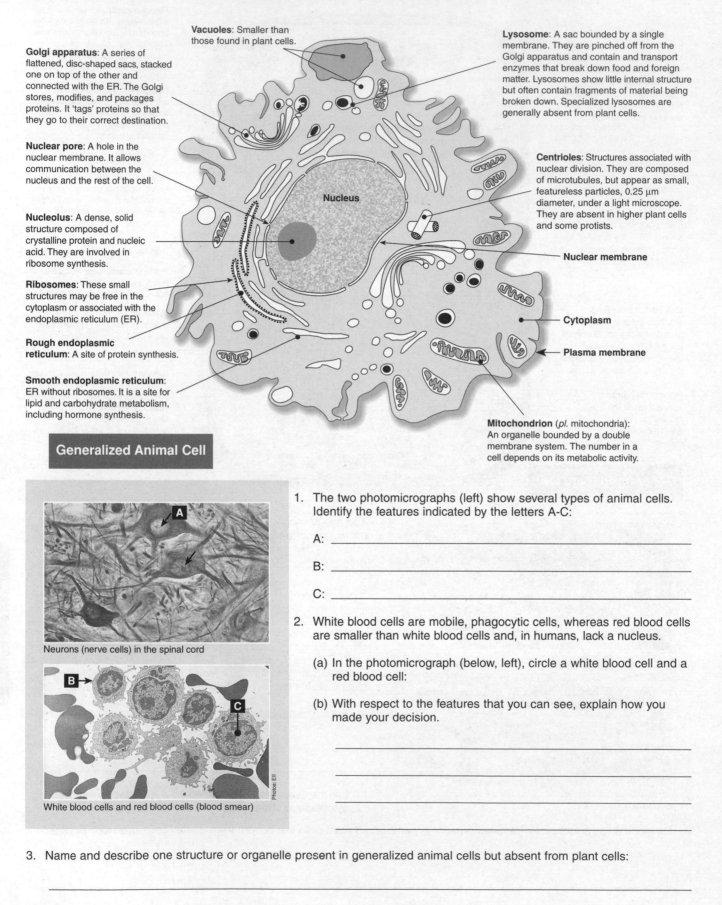

**Vacuoles**: Smaller than those found in plant cells.

**Golgi apparatus**: A series of flattened, disc-shaped sacs, stacked one on top of the other and connected with the ER. The Golgi stores, modifies, and packages proteins. It 'tags' proteins so that they go to their correct destination.

**Nuclear pore**: A hole in the nuclear membrane. It allows communication between the nucleus and the rest of the cell.

**Nucleolus**: A dense, solid structure composed of crystalline protein and nucleic acid. They are involved in ribosome synthesis.

**Ribosomes**: These small structures may be free in the cytoplasm or associated with the endoplasmic reticulum (ER).

**Rough endoplasmic reticulum**: A site of protein synthesis.

**Smooth endoplasmic reticulum**: ER without ribosomes. It is a site for lipid and carbohydrate metabolism, including hormone synthesis.

**Lysosome**: A sac bounded by a single membrane. They are pinched off from the Golgi apparatus and contain and transport enzymes that break down food and foreign matter. Lysosomes show little internal structure but often contain fragments of material being broken down. Specialized lysosomes are generally absent from plant cells.

**Centrioles**: Structures associated with nuclear division. They are composed of microtubules, but appear as small, featureless particles, 0.25 µm diameter, under a light microscope. They are absent in higher plant cells and some protists.

**Nuclear membrane**

**Cytoplasm**

**Plasma membrane**

**Mitochondrion** (*pl.* mitochondria): An organelle bounded by a double membrane system. The number in a cell depends on its metabolic activity.

Nucleus

**Generalized Animal Cell**

Neurons (nerve cells) in the spinal cord

White blood cells and red blood cells (blood smear)

Photos: EII

1. The two photomicrographs (left) show several types of animal cells. Identify the features indicated by the letters A-C:

   A: _____

   B: _____

   C: _____

2. White blood cells are mobile, phagocytic cells, whereas red blood cells are smaller than white blood cells and, in humans, lack a nucleus.

   (a) In the photomicrograph (below, left), circle a white blood cell and a red blood cell:

   (b) With respect to the features that you can see, explain how you made your decision.

   _____

   _____

   _____

   _____

3. Name and describe one structure or organelle present in generalized animal cells but absent from plant cells:

   _____

   _____

**Related activities**: Plant Cells, Cell Structures and Organelles
**Web links**: Review of Eukaryotic Cells

# Cell Sizes

Cells are extremely small and they can only be seen properly when viewed through the magnifying lenses of a microscope. The diagrams and photographs below show a variety of cell types, together with a virus and a microscopic animal for comparison. For each of these images, note the scale and relate this to the type of microscopy used.

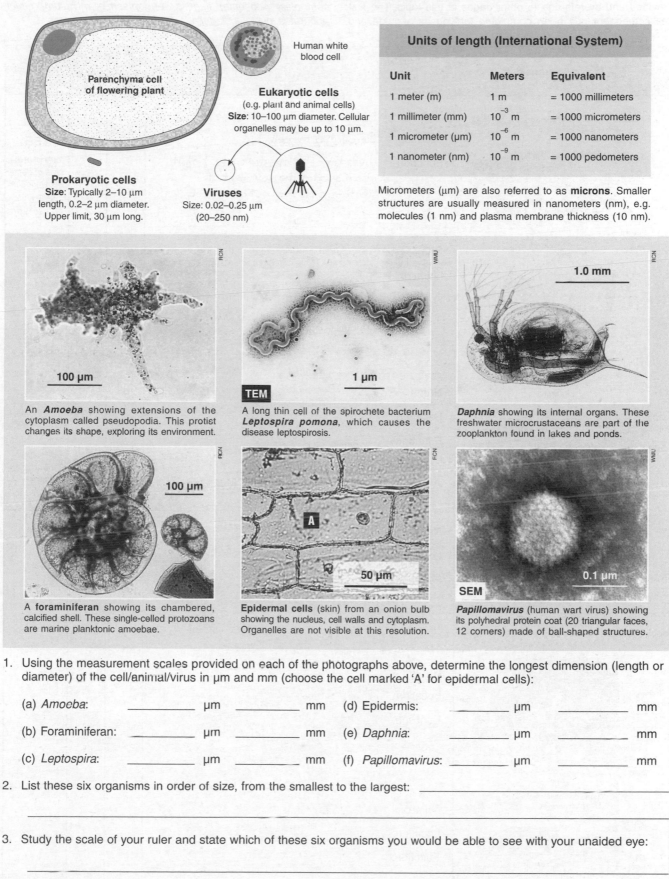

**Parenchyma cell of flowering plant**

**Human white blood cell**

**Eukaryotic cells**
(e.g. plant and animal cells)
**Size**: 10–100 μm diameter. Cellular organelles may be up to 10 μm.

**Prokaryotic cells**
**Size**: Typically 2–10 μm length, 0.2–2 μm diameter. Upper limit, 30 μm long.

**Viruses**
Size: 0.02–0.25 μm
(20–250 nm)

### Units of length (International System)

| Unit | Meters | Equivalent |
|---|---|---|
| 1 meter (m) | 1 m | = 1000 millimeters |
| 1 millimeter (mm) | $10^{-3}$ m | = 1000 micrometers |
| 1 micrometer (μm) | $10^{-6}$ m | = 1000 nanometers |
| 1 nanometer (nm) | $10^{-9}$ m | = 1000 pedometers |

Micrometers (μm) are also referred to as **microns**. Smaller structures are usually measured in nanometers (nm), e.g. molecules (1 nm) and plasma membrane thickness (10 nm).

**100 μm**

An **Amoeba** showing extensions of the cytoplasm called pseudopodia. This protist changes its shape, exploring its environment.

**TEM** **1 μm**

A long thin cell of the spirochete bacterium **Leptospira pomona**, which causes the disease leptospirosis.

**1.0 mm**

**Daphnia** showing its internal organs. These freshwater microcrustaceans are part of the zooplankton found in lakes and ponds.

**100 μm**

A **foraminiferan** showing its chambered, calcified shell. These single-celled protozoans are marine planktonic amoebae.

**A** **50 μm**

**Epidermal cells** (skin) from an onion bulb showing the nucleus, cell walls and cytoplasm. Organelles are not visible at this resolution.

**SEM** **0.1 μm**

**Papillomavirus** (human wart virus) showing its polyhedral protein coat (20 triangular faces, 12 corners) made of ball-shaped structures.

**Cell Structure**

1. Using the measurement scales provided on each of the photographs above, determine the longest dimension (length or diameter) of the cell/animal/virus in μm and mm (choose the cell marked 'A' for epidermal cells):

   (a) *Amoeba*: _____ μm _____ mm   (d) Epidermis: _____ μm _____ mm

   (b) Foraminiferan: _____ μm _____ mm   (e) *Daphnia*: _____ μm _____ mm

   (c) *Leptospira*: _____ μm _____ mm   (f) *Papillomavirus*: _____ μm _____ mm

2. List these six organisms in order of size, from the smallest to the largest: _____

   _____

3. Study the scale of your ruler and state which of these six organisms you would be able to see with your unaided eye:

   _____

4. Calculate the equivalent length in millimeters (mm) of the following measurements:

   (a) 0.25 μm: _____   (b) 450 μm: _____   (c) 200 nm: _____

**Related activities**: Electron Microscopes

**DA 2**

# Cell Structures and Organelles

The table below, and the following page, provides a format to summarize information about the structures and organelles of typical eukaryotic cells. Complete the table using the list provided and by referring to other pages in this topic. The first cell component has been completed for you as a guide and

the log scale of measurements (top of next page) illustrates the relative sizes of some cellular structures. **List of structures and organelles**: *cell wall, mitochondrion, chloroplast, cell junctions, centrioles, ribosome, flagella, endoplasmic reticulum, Golgi apparatus, nucleus, flagella, cytoskeleton and vacuoles.*

| Cell Component | Details | Present in Plant cells | Present in Animal cells | Visible under light microscope |
|---|---|---|---|---|
| (a) Double layer of phospholipids (called the lipid bilayer) / Proteins | **Name:** Plasma (cell surface) membrane  **Location:** Surrounding the cell  **Function:** Gives the cell shape and protection. It also regulates the movement of substances into and out of the cell. | YES | YES | YES (but not at the level of detail shown in the diagram) |
| (b) | **Name:**  **Location:**  **Function:** | | | |
| (c) Outer membrane / Inner membrane / Matrix / Cristae | **Name:**  **Location:**  **Function:** | | | |
| (d) Secretory vesicles budding off / Cisternae / Transfer vesicles from the smooth endoplasmic reticulum | **Name:**  **Location:**  **Function:** | | | |
| (e) Ribosomes / Transport pathway / Rough / Smooth / Vesicles budding off / Flattened membrane sacs | **Name:**  **Location:**  **Function:** | | | |
| (f) Grana comprise stacks of thylakoids / Stroma / Lamellae | **Name:**  **Location:**  **Function:** | | | |

**Related activities**: Plant Cells, Animal Cells
**Web links**: Eukaryotic Cells Interactive Animation

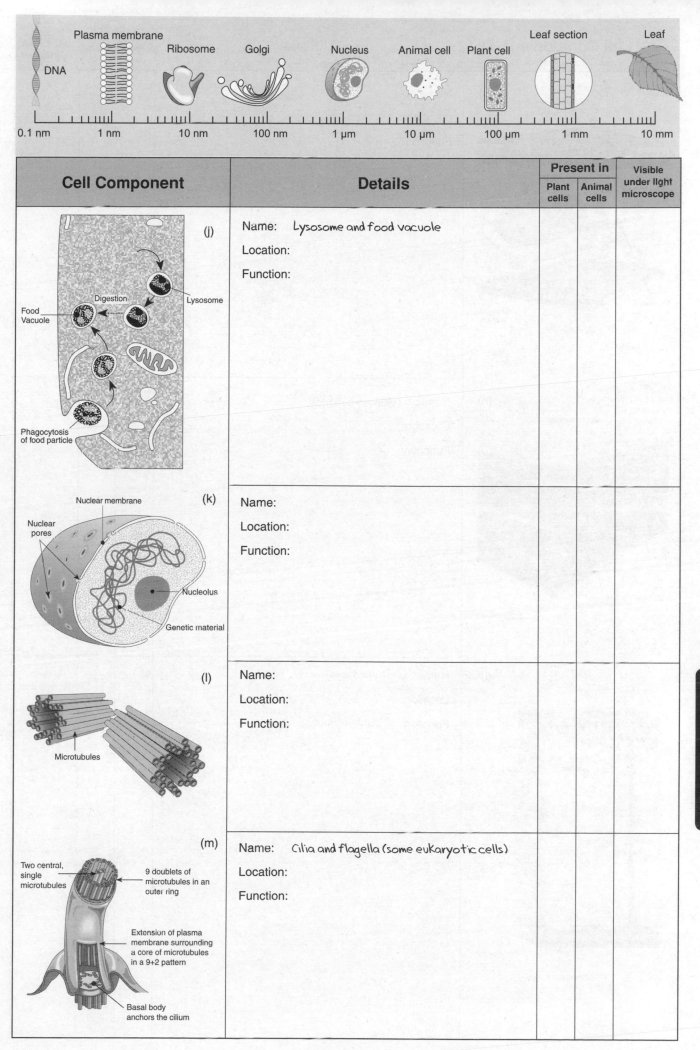

| Cell Component | Details | Present in | | Visible under light microscope |
| --- | --- | --- | --- | --- |
| | | Plant cells | Animal cells | |

**(j)** Name: Lysosome and food vacuole
Location:
Function:

**(k)** Name:
Location:
Function:

**(l)** Name:
Location:
Function:

**(m)** Name: Cilia and flagella (some eukaryotic cells)
Location:
Function:

Cell Structure

| Cell Component | Details | Present in | | Visible under light microscope |
|---|---|---|---|---|
| | | Plant cells | Animal cells | |

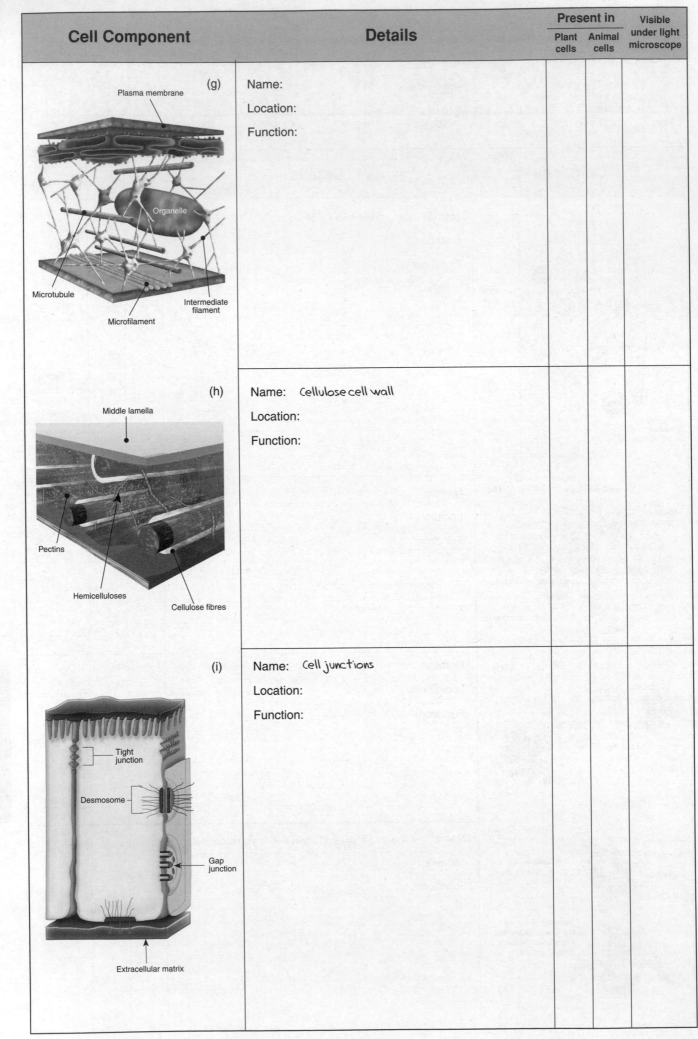

**(g)**

Plasma membrane

Organelle

Microtubule

Microfilament

Intermediate filament

Name:

Location:

Function:

**(h)**

Middle lamella

Pectins

Hemicelluloses

Cellulose fibres

Name:   Cellulose cell wall

Location:

Function:

**(i)**

Tight junction

Desmosome

Gap junction

Extracellular matrix

Name:   Cell junctions

Location:

Function:

# Differential Centrifugation

**Differential centrifugation** (also called cell fractionation) is a technique used to extract organelles from cells so that they can be studied. The aim is to extract undamaged intact organelles. Samples must be kept very cool so that metabolism is slowed and self digestion of the organelles is prevented. The samples must also be kept in a buffered, isotonic solution so that the organelles do not change volume and the enzymes are not denatured by changes in pH.

## Differential Centrifugation

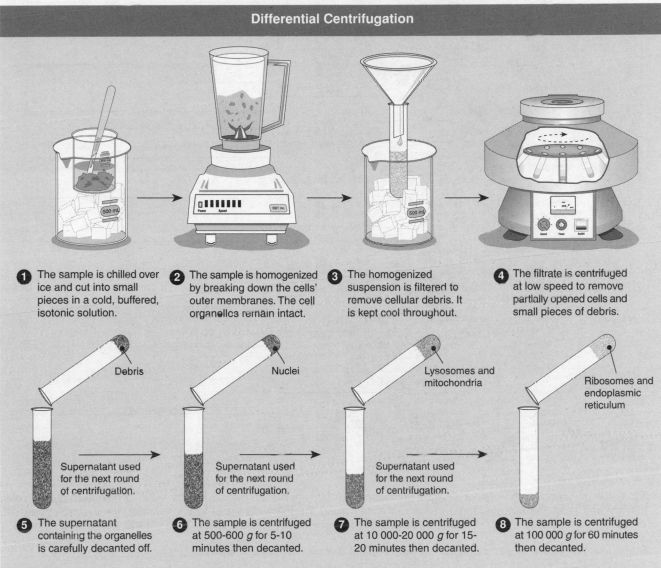

**1** The sample is chilled over ice and cut into small pieces in a cold, buffered, isotonic solution.

**2** The sample is homogenized by breaking down the cells' outer membranes. The cell organelles remain intact.

**3** The homogenized suspension is filtered to remove cellular debris. It is kept cool throughout.

**4** The filtrate is centrifuged at low speed to remove partially opened cells and small pieces of debris.

Debris — Supernatant used for the next round of centrifugation.

Nuclei — Supernatant used for the next round of centrifugation.

Lysosomes and mitochondria — Supernatant used for the next round of centrifugation.

Ribosomes and endoplasmic reticulum

**5** The supernatant containing the organelles is carefully decanted off.

**6** The sample is centrifuged at 500-600 *g* for 5-10 minutes then decanted.

**7** The sample is centrifuged at 10 000-20 000 *g* for 15-20 minutes then decanted.

**8** The sample is centrifuged at 100 000 *g* for 60 minutes then decanted.

*NOTE: In centrifugation, the relative centrifugal force (RCF) is expressed as  g , where g represents the gravitational field strength.*

1. Explain why it is possible to separate cell organelles using centrifugation: _____

_____

_____

2. Suggest why the sample is homogenized before centrifugation: _____

_____

3. Explain why the sample must be kept in a solution that is:

   (a) Isotonic: _____

   (b) Cool: _____

   (c) Buffered: _____

4. **Density gradient centrifugation** is another method of cell fractionation. Sucrose is added to the sample, which is then centrifuged at high speed. The organelles will form layers according to their specific densities. Using the information above, label the centrifuge tube on the right with the organelles you would find in each layer.

**Density gradient centrifugation**

(a)

(b)

(c)

(d) *Cellular debris*

**Cell Structure**

**Related activities**: Enzyme Reaction Rates

**A 1**

# Identifying Cell Structures

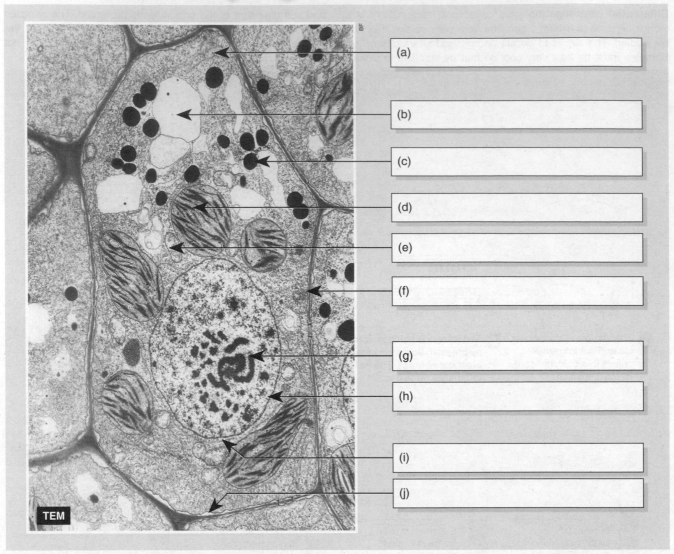

(a)

(b)

(c)

(d)

(e)

(f)

(g)

(h)

(i)

(j)

TEM

1. Study the diagrams on the previous pages to become familiar with the various structures found in plant and animal cells. Identify and label the ten structures in the cell above using the following list of terms: *nuclear membrane, cytoplasm, endoplasmic reticulum, mitochondrion, starch granules, chromosome, vacuole, plasma membrane, cell wall, chloroplast*

2. State how many cells, or parts of cells, are visible in the electron micrograph above: _____

3. Identify the **type** of cell illustrated above (bacterial cell, plant cell, or animal cell). Explain your answer:

_____

_____

4. (a) Explain where cytoplasm is found in the cell: _____

(b) Describe what cytoplasm is made up of: _____

_____

(c) Explain why nucleoplasm is only found in eukaryotic cells: _____

_____

5. Describe two structures, pictured in the cell above, that are associated with storage:

(a) _____

_____

(b) _____

_____

**Related activities**: Bacterial Cells, Plant Cells, Animal Cells

# Optical Microscopes

The light microscope is one of the most important instruments used in biology practicals, and its correct use is a basic and essential skill of biology. High power light microscopes use a combination of lenses to magnify objects up to several hundred times. They are called **compound microscopes** because there are two or more separate lenses involved. A typical compound light microscope (bright field) is shown below (top photograph). The specimens viewed with these microscopes must be thin and mostly transparent. Light is focused up through the condenser and specimen; if the specimen is thick or opaque, little or no detail will be visible. The microscope below has two eyepieces (**binocular**), although monocular microscopes, with a mirror rather than an internal light source, may still be encountered. Dissecting microscopes (lower photograph) are a type of binocular microscope used for observations at low total magnification (x4 to x50), where a large working distance between objectives and stage is required. A dissecting microscope has two separate lens systems, one for each eye. Such microscopes produce a 3-D view of the specimen and are sometimes called stereo microscopes for this reason.

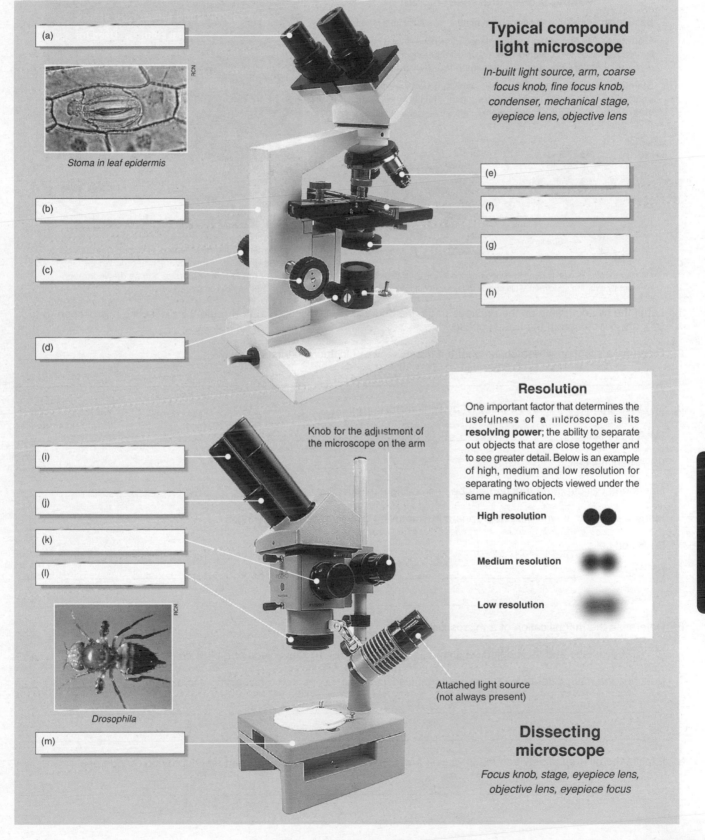

(a)

*Stoma in leaf epidermis*

(b)

(c)

(d)

## Typical compound light microscope

*In-built light source, arm, coarse focus knob, fine focus knob, condenser, mechanical stage, eyepiece lens, objective lens*

(e)

(f)

(g)

(h)

(i)

(j)

(k)

(l)

Knob for the adjustment of the microscope on the arm

*Drosophila*

(m)

### Resolution

One important factor that determines the usefulness of a microscope is its **resolving power**; the ability to separate out objects that are close together and to see greater detail. Below is an example of high, medium and low resolution for separating two objects viewed under the same magnification.

**High resolution**

**Medium resolution**

**Low resolution**

Attached light source (not always present)

## Dissecting microscope

*Focus knob, stage, eyepiece lens, objective lens, eyepiece focus*

Cell Structure

**Related activities**: Plant Cells, Animal Cells

RDA 2

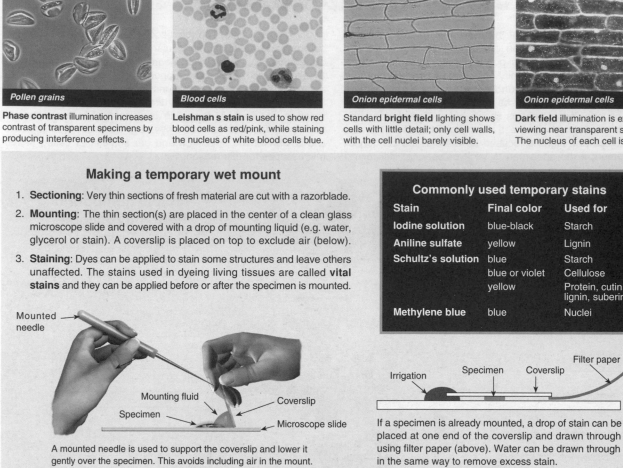

**Pollen grains**

**Phase contrast** illumination increases contrast of transparent specimens by producing interference effects.

**Blood cells**

**Leishman s stain** is used to show red blood cells as red/pink, while staining the nucleus of white blood cells blue.

**Onion epidermal cells**

Standard **bright field** lighting shows cells with little detail; only cell walls, with the cell nuclei barely visible.

**Onion epidermal cells**

**Dark field** illumination is excellent for viewing near transparent specimens. The nucleus of each cell is visible.

## Making a temporary wet mount

1. **Sectioning**: Very thin sections of fresh material are cut with a razorblade.

2. **Mounting**: The thin section(s) are placed in the center of a clean glass microscope slide and covered with a drop of mounting liquid (e.g. water, glycerol or stain). A coverslip is placed on top to exclude air (below).

3. **Staining**: Dyes can be applied to stain some structures and leave others unaffected. The stains used in dyeing living tissues are called **vital stains** and they can be applied before or after the specimen is mounted.

### Commonly used temporary stains

| Stain | Final color | Used for |
| --- | --- | --- |
| **Iodine solution** | blue-black | Starch |
| **Aniline sulfate** | yellow | Lignin |
| **Schultz's solution** | blue | Starch |
| | blue or violet | Cellulose |
| | yellow | Protein, cutin, lignin, suberin |
| **Methylene blue** | blue | Nuclei |

Mounted needle

Mounting fluid

Specimen

Coverslip

Microscope slide

A mounted needle is used to support the coverslip and lower it gently over the specimen. This avoids including air in the mount.

Irrigation   Specimen   Coverslip   Filter paper

If a specimen is already mounted, a drop of stain can be placed at one end of the coverslip and drawn through using filter paper (above). Water can be drawn through in the same way to remove excess stain.

1. Label the two diagrams on the previous page, the bright field microscope (a) to (h) and the dissecting microscope (i) to (m), using words from the lists supplied.

2. Describe a situation where phase contrast microscopy would improve image quality: _____

_____

3. List two structures that could be seen by light microscopy in:

   (a) A plant cell: _____

   (b) An animal cell: _____

4. Name one cell structure that can not be seen by light microscopy: _____

5. Identify a stain that would be appropriate for improving definition of the following:

   (a) Blood cells: _____     (d) Lignin: _____

   (b) Starch: _____     (e) Nuclei and DNA: _____

   (c) Protein: _____     (f) Cellulose: _____

6. Determine the magnification of a microscope using:

   (a) 15 X eyepiece and 40 X objective lens: _____     (b) 10 X eyepiece and 60 X objective lens: _____

7. Describe the main difference between a bright field light microscope and a dissecting microscope. _____

_____

_____

8. Explain the difference between magnification and resolution (resolving power) with respect to microscope use:

_____

_____

# Electron Microscopes

Electron microscopes (EMs) use a beam of electrons, instead of light, to produce an image. The higher resolution of EMs is due to the shorter wavelengths of electrons. There are two basic types of electron microscope: **scanning electron microscopes** (SEM) and **transmission electron microscopes** (TEM). In SEMs, the electrons are bounced off the surface of an object to produce detailed images of the external appearance. TEMs produce very clear images of specially prepared thin sections.

## Transmission Electron Microscope (TEM)

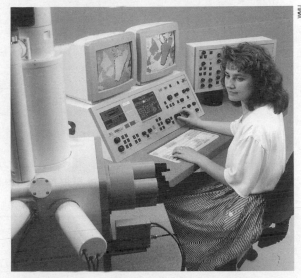

The transmission electron microscope is used to view extremely thin sections of material. Electrons pass through the specimen and are scattered. Magnetic lenses focus the image onto a fluorescent screen or photographic plate. The sections are so thin that they have to be prepared with a special machine, called an **ultramicrotome**, that can cut wafers to just 30 thousandths of a millimeter thick. It can magnify several hundred thousand times.

## Scanning Electron Microscope (SEM)

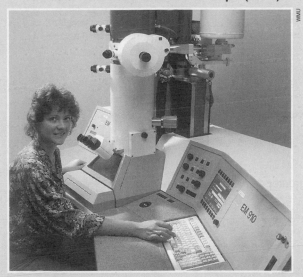

The scanning electron microscope scans a sample with a beam of primary electrons that knock electrons from its surface. These secondary electrons are picked up by a collector, amplified, and transmitted onto a viewing screen or photographic plate, producing a superb 3-D image. A microscope of this power can easily obtain clear pictures of organisms as small as bacteria and viruses. The image produced is of the outside surface only.

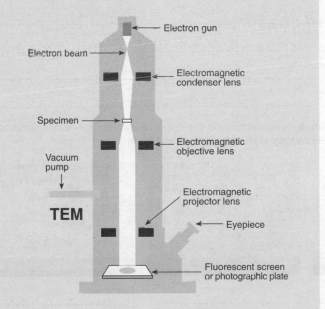

**TEM**

- Electron gun
- Electron beam
- Electromagnetic condenser lens
- Specimen
- Electromagnetic objective lens
- Vacuum pump
- Electromagnetic projector lens
- Eyepiece
- Fluorescent screen or photographic plate

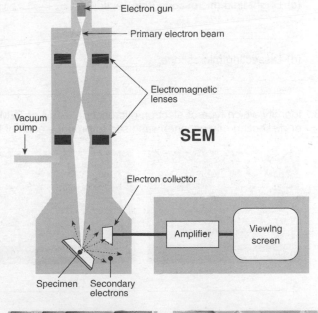

**SEM**

- Electron gun
- Primary electron beam
- Electromagnetic lenses
- Vacuum pump
- Electron collector
- Amplifier
- Viewing screen
- Specimen
- Secondary electrons

**Cell Structure**

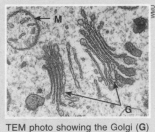

TEM photo showing the Golgi (**G**) and a mitochondrion (**M**).

Three HIV viruses budding out of a human lymphocyte (TEM).

SEM photo of stoma and epidermal cells on the upper surface of a leaf.

Image of hair louse clinging to two hairs on a Hooker's sealion (SEM).

**Related activities**: Optical Microscopes

**RA 2**

| | Light Microscope | Transmission Electron Microscope (TEM) | Scanning Electron Microscope (SEM) |
|---|---|---|---|
| Radiation source: | light | electrons | electrons |
| Wavelength: | 400-700 nm | 0.005 nm | 0.005 nm |
| Lenses: | glass | electromagnetic | electromagnetic |
| Specimen: | living or non-living supported on glass slide | non-living supported on a small copper grid in a vacuum | non-living supported on a metal disc in a vacuum |
| Maximum resolution: | 200 nm | 1 nm | 10 nm |
| Maximum magnification: | 1500 x | 250 000 x | 100 000 x |
| Stains: | colored dyes | impregnated with heavy metals | coated with carbon or gold |
| Type of image: | colored | monochrome (black & white) | monochrome (black & white) |

1. Explain why electron microscopes are able to resolve much greater detail than a light microscope:

   _____

   _____

   _____

2. Describe two typical applications for each of the following types of microscope:

   (a) Transmission electron microscope (TEM): _____

   _____

   (b) Scanning electron microscope (SEM): _____

   _____

   (c) Bright field microscope (thin section): _____

   _____

   (d) Dissecting microscope: _____

   _____

3. Identify which type of electron microscope (SEM or TEM) or optical microscope (compound light (bright field) microscope or dissecting microscope) was used to produce each of the images in the photos below (A-H):

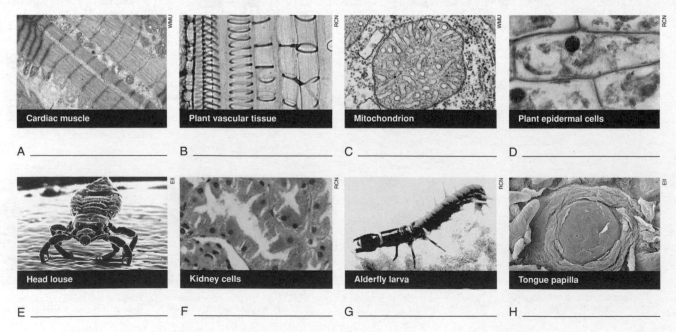

Cardiac muscle

Plant vascular tissue

Mitochondrion

Plant epidermal cells

A _____   B _____   C _____   D _____

Head louse

Kidney cells

Alderfly larva

Tongue papilla

E _____   F _____   G _____   H _____

# Interpreting Electron Micrographs

The photographs below were taken using a transmission electron microscope (TEM). They show some of the cell organelles in great detail. Remember that these photos are showing only **parts of cells, not whole cells**. Some of the photographs show more than one type of organelle. The questions refer to the main organelle in the center of the photo.

1.  (a) Name this organelle (arrowed): _____

    (b) State which kind of cell(s) this organelle would be found in:

    _____

    (c) Describe the function of this organelle: _____

    _____

    _____

    (d) Label two structures that can be seen inside this organelle.

2.  (a) Name this organelle (arrowed): _____

    (b) State which kind of cell(s) this organelle would be found in:

    _____

    (c) Describe the function of this organelle: _____

    _____

    _____

    _____

    _____

3.  (a) Name the large, circular organelle: _____

    (b) State which kind of cell(s) this organelle would be found in:

    _____

    (c) Describe the function of this organelle: _____

    _____

    _____

    (d) Label two regions that can be seen inside this organelle.

4.  (a) Name and label the ribbon-like organelle in this photograph (arrowed):

    _____

    (b) State which kind of cell(s) this organelle is found in:

    _____

    (c) Describe the function of these organelles: _____

    _____

    _____

    (d) Name the dark 'blobs' attached to the organelle you have labeled:

    _____

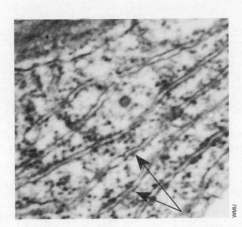

**Cell Structure**

**Related activities**: Electron Microscopes, Plant Cells, Animal Cells, Cell Structures and Organelles

**RA 2**

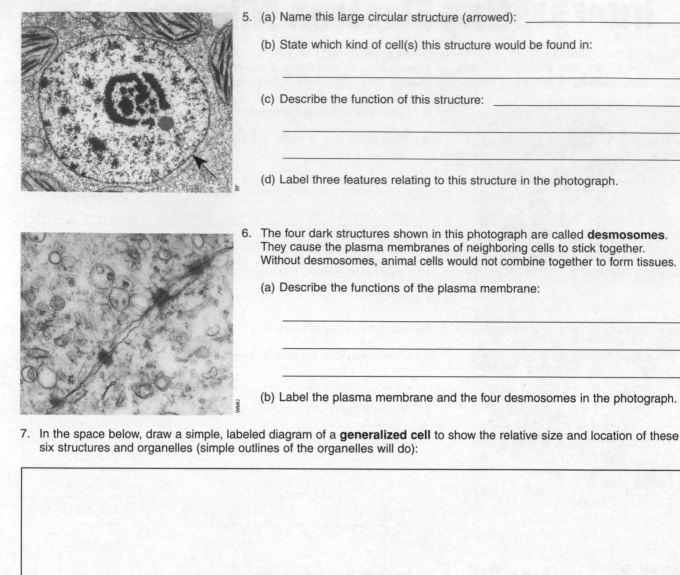

5. (a) Name this large circular structure (arrowed): _____

(b) State which kind of cell(s) this structure would be found in:

_____

(c) Describe the function of this structure: _____

_____

_____

(d) Label three features relating to this structure in the photograph.

6. The four dark structures shown in this photograph are called **desmosomes**. They cause the plasma membranes of neighboring cells to stick together. Without desmosomes, animal cells would not combine together to form tissues.

(a) Describe the functions of the plasma membrane:

_____

_____

_____

(b) Label the plasma membrane and the four desmosomes in the photograph.

7. In the space below, draw a simple, labeled diagram of a **generalized cell** to show the relative size and location of these six structures and organelles (simple outlines of the organelles will do):

# Cell Membranes

**IB SL**
Complete:
*1-3, 5-7, 9, 11-13*
*Extension: 4, 8, 14*

**IB HL**
Complete:
*1-3, 5-7, 9, 11-13*
*Extension: 4, 8, 14*

**IB Options**
Not applicable to options

**AP Biology**
Complete:
*1-14*

## Learning Objectives

☐ 1. Compile your own glossary from the **KEY WORDS** displayed in **bold type** in the learning objectives below.

### Cell Membranes *(pages 100-106, 126-127)*

☐ 2. Draw a simple labeled diagram of the structure of the **plasma membrane** (cell surface membrane), clearly identifying the arrangement of the lipids and proteins.

☐ 3. Describe and explain the current **fluid mosaic model** of membrane structure, including the terms **lipid bilayer** and **partially permeable membrane**. Explain the roles of **phospholipids**, **cholesterol**, **glycolipids**, **proteins**, and **glycoproteins** in membrane structure. Explain how the **hydrophobic** and **hydrophilic** properties of phospholipids help to maintain membrane structure. Appreciate that the plasma membrane is essentially no different to the membranes of organelles.

☐ 4. Outline the evidence from **freeze-fracture studies** in support of the current model of membrane structure. Contrast this currently accepted model with the earlier Davson-Danielli model.

☐ 5. Describe the functions of membranes (including the **plasma membrane**) in cells, identifying their role in the structure of organelles and in regulating the transport of materials within cells, and into and out of cells.

### Cellular Transport *(pages 107-114)*

☐ 6. Summarize the types of movements that occur across membranes. Outline the role of proteins in membranes as receptors and carriers in membrane transport. Define: **passive transport**, **concentration gradient**.

☐ 7. Describe **diffusion** and **osmosis**, identifying the types of substances moving in each case. Describe **facilitated diffusion** (facilitated transport). Identify when and where this process might occur in a cell.

☐ 8. Identify factors determining the rate of diffusion. Explain how **Fick's law** provides a framework for determining maximum diffusion rates across cell surfaces.

☐ 9. Suggest why cell size is limited by the rate of diffusion. Discuss the significance of **surface area to volume ratio** to cells. Explain why organisms without efficient transport mechanisms remain small.

☐ 10. Define the term **water potential** ($\psi$) and identify its significance to the net movement of water in cells. Define the components of water potential: **solute potential** and **pressure potential**. Determine the net direction of water movement between solutions of different water potential.

☐ 11. With reference to plant cells, explain **turgor** and **plasmolysis**. With respect to solutions of differing solute concentration, distinguish between **hypotonic**, **isotonic**, **hypertonic**.

☐ 12. Distinguish between passive and **active transport** mechanisms. Understand the principles involved in active transport, clearly identifying the involvement of protein molecules and energy.

☐ 13. Describe the following active transport mechanisms: **ion-exchange pumps**, **exocytosis**, **endocytosis**, **phagocytosis**, and **pinocytosis**. Give examples of when and where each transport mechanism occurs.

☐ 14. Identify the mechanisms involved in the transport of: water, fatty acids, glucose, amino acids, $O_2$, $CO_2$, ions (e.g. mineral and metal ions), and sucrose (in plants).

---

See the 'Textbook Reference Grid' on pages 8-9 for textbook page references relating to material in this topic.

**Supplementary Texts**

See pages 5-6 for additional details of these texts:
■ Adds, J., *et al.*, 2003. **Molecules and Cells**, (NelsonThornes), chpt. 4 as reqd.
■ Helms, D.R. *et al.*, 1998. **Biology in the Laboratory** (W.H. Freeman), #8.
■ Tobin, A.J. and Morel, R.E., 1997. **Asking About Cells**, (Thomson Brooks/Cole), part II.

See page 6 for details of publishers of periodicals:

**STUDENT'S REFERENCE**
■ **Getting in and Out** Biol. Sci. Rev., 20(3), Feb. 2008, pp. 14-16. *An excellent account of diffusion: common misunderstandings and some adaptations.*

■ **Cellular Factories** New Scientist, 23 Nov. 1996 (Inside Science). *Ccellular processes and the role of organelles in plant and animal cells.*

■ **Border Control** New Scientist, 15 July 2000 (Inside Science). *The structure and role of the plasma membrane (includes membrane receptors).*

■ **High Tension** Biol. Sci. Rev., 13(1), Sept. 2000, pp. 14-18. *An excellent account of water and solute transport mechanisms in vascular plants.*

■ **Budding Vesicles in Living Cells** Scientific American, March 1996, pp. 50-55. *Vesicles and the role of the Golgi apparatus in cell transport.*

**TEACHER'S REFERENCE**
■ **Phosphate Uptake in Carrot and Yeast** The Am. Biology Teacher, 63(7) Sept. 2001, pp. 498-502. *Investigating active transport mechanisms in isolated cells.*

See pages 10-11 for details of how to access **Bio Links** from our web site: **www.thebiozone.com** From Bio Links, access sites under the topics:

**GENERAL BIOLOGY ONLINE RESOURCES > Online Textbooks and Lecture Notes:** • Biology online org • Kimball's biology pages • Learn.co.uk • Mr Biology's biology web site … *and others*

**CELL BIOLOGY AND BIOCHEMISTRY:** • Cell and molecular biology online • Cell structure and function web links > **Cell Structure and Transport:** • Aquaporins • Animal cells • CELLS alive! • The virtual cell • Transport in and out of cells

**Presentation MEDIA** to support this topic: **CELL BIOLOGY AND BIOCHEMISTRY**

# Cell Processes

All of the organelles and other structures in the cell have functions. The cell can be compared to a factory with an assembly line. Organelles in the cell provide the equivalent of the power supply, assembly line, packaging department, repair and maintenance, transport system, and the control center. The sum total of all the processes occurring in a cell is known as **metabolism**. Some of these processes store energy in molecules (anabolism) while others release that stored energy (catabolism). Below is a summary of the major processes that take place in a cell.

**Autolysis**
Lysosomes contain powerful digestive enzymes that destroy unwanted cell organelles and foreign objects brought into the cell.

**Transport in and out of the cell**
Simple diffusion and active transport move substances into and out of the cell across the plasma (cell surface) membrane.

**Protein synthesis**
Chromosomes in the nucleus store genetic instructions for the production of specific proteins. These proteins are put together by ribosomes on the endoplasmic reticulum.

**Cell division**
Centrioles control the movement of chromosomes during cell division.

**Secretion**
The Golgi apparatus is the packaging department of the cell. It produces secretory vesicles (small membrane-bound sacs) that are used to store useful chemicals, prepare substances for movement out of the cell (e.g. hormones), or to package digestive enzymes.

**Phagocytosis**
The plasma membrane can engulf objects (such as food particles or bacteria). The membrane pinches off to become a vesicle, and the particles are then digested by powerful enzymes.

**Pinocytosis**
The plasma membrane can pinch off to trap some of the surrounding watery fluid in a vesicle.

**Cellular respiration**
Respiration is a complex chemical process which starts in the cell cytoplasm but is completed in the mitochondria. This process supplies the cell with energy to carry out the many other chemical reactions of metabolism.

Chloroplasts are found only in plant cells. The diagram above is of an animal cell.

**Photosynthesis**
Chloroplasts (found only in plant cells) carry out the chemical process of photosynthesis. This captures light energy and transfers it into useful chemical energy.

1. State which organelles or structures are associated with each of the processes listed below:

   (a) Secretion: _____

   (b) Respiration: _____

   (c) Pinocytosis: _____

   (d) Phagocytosis: _____

   (e) Protein synthesis: _____

   (f) Photosynthesis: _____

   (g) Cell division: _____

   (h) Autolysis: _____

   (i) Transport in/out of cell: _____

2. Explain what is meant by **metabolism** and describe an example of a metabolic process: _____
   _____
   _____

Related activities: Cell Structures and Organelles

# The Structure of Membranes

All cells have a plasma membrane that forms the outer limit of the cell. Bacteria, fungi, and plant cells have a cell wall outside this, but it is quite distinct and outside the plasma membrane. Membranes are also found inside eukaryotic cells as part of membranous **organelles**. Present day knowledge of membrane structure has been built up as a result of many observations and experiments.

The original model of membrane structure, proposed by Davson and Danielli, was the unit membrane (a lipid bilayer coated with protein). This model was later modified after the discovery that the protein molecules were embedded *within* the bilayer rather than coating the outside. The now-accepted model of membrane structure is the **fluid mosaic model** described below.

The **nuclear membrane** that surrounds the nucleus helps to control the passage of genetic information to the cytoplasm. It may also serve to protect the DNA.

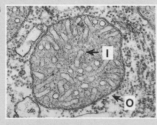

**Mitochondria** have an outer membrane (**O**) which controls the entry and exit of materials involved in aerobic respiration. Inner membranes (**I**) provide attachment sites for enzyme activity.

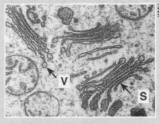

The **Golgi apparatus** comprises stacks of membrane-bound sacs (**S**). It is involved in packaging materials for transport or export from the cell as secretory vesicles (**V**).

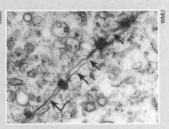

The cell is surrounded by a **plasma membrane** which controls the movement of most substances into and out of the cell. This photo shows two neighboring cells (arrows).

## The Fluid Mosaic Model

The currently accepted model for the structure of membranes is called the **fluid mosaic model**. In this model there is a double layer of lipids (fats) which are arranged with their tails facing inwards. The double layer of lipids is thought to be quite fluid, with proteins floating in this layer. The mobile proteins are thought to have a number of functions, including a role in active transport.

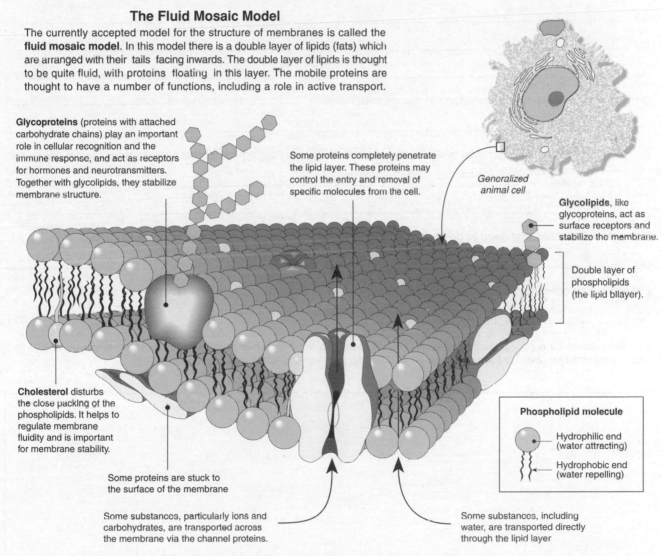

**Glycoproteins** (proteins with attached carbohydrate chains) play an important role in cellular recognition and the immune response, and act as receptors for hormones and neurotransmitters. Together with glycolipids, they stabilize membrane structure.

Some proteins completely penetrate the lipid layer. These proteins may control the entry and removal of specific molecules from the cell.

*Generalized animal cell*

**Glycolipids**, like glycoproteins, act as surface receptors and stabilize the membrane.

Double layer of phospholipids (the lipid bilayer).

**Cholesterol** disturbs the close packing of the phospholipids. It helps to regulate membrane fluidity and is important for membrane stability.

Some proteins are stuck to the surface of the membrane

Some substances, particularly ions and carbohydrates, are transported across the membrane via the channel proteins.

Some substances, including water, are transported directly through the lipid layer

**Phospholipid molecule**

Hydrophilic end (water attracting)

Hydrophobic end (water repelling)

1. (a) Describe the modern fluid mosaic model of membrane structure: _____

_____

_____

_____

**Related activities**: Cell Structure and Organelles, The Role of Membranes in Cells, Modification of Proteins   **Web links**: Membrane Structure Tutorial

RA 2

**Cell Membranes**

(b) Explain how the modern fluid mosaic model of membrane structure differs from the earlier Davson-Danielli model:

_____

_____

_____

2. Discuss the various functional roles of membranes in cells: _____

_____

_____

_____

3. (a) Name a cellular organelle that possesses a membrane: _____

(b) Describe the membrane's purpose in this organelle: _____

_____

4. Identify three other cell organelles that are made up of membrane systems:

(a) _____

(b) _____

(c) _____

5. (a) Describe the purpose of cholesterol in plasma membranes: _____

_____

(b) Suggest why marine organisms living in polar regions have a very high proportion of cholesterol in their membranes:

_____

_____

6. List three substances that need to be transported **into** all kinds of animal cells, in order for them to survive:

(a) _____ (b) _____ (c) _____

7. List two substances that need to be transported **out** of all kinds of animal cells, in order for them to survive:

(a) _____ (b) _____

8. Use the symbol for a phospholipid molecule (below) to draw a **simple labeled diagram** to show the structure of a plasma membrane (include features such as lipid bilayer and various kinds of proteins):

Symbol for phospholipid

# The Role of Membranes in Cells

Many of the important structures and organelles in cells are composed of, or are enclosed by, membranes. These include: the endoplasmic reticulum, mitochondria, nucleus, Golgi body, chloroplasts, lysosomes, vesicles and the cell plasma membrane itself. All membranes within eukaryotic cells share the same basic structure as the plasma membrane that encloses the entire cell. They perform a number of critical functions in the cell: serving to compartmentalise regions of different function within the cell, controlling the entry and exit of substances, and fulfilling a role in recognition and communication between cells. Some of these roles are described below and electron micrographs of the organelles involved are on the following page.

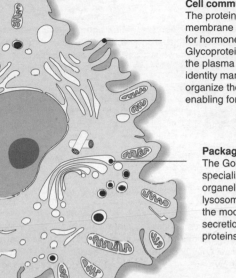

**Isolation of enzymes** Membrane-bound lysosomes contain enzymes for the destruction of wastes and foreign material. Peroxisomes are the site for destruction of the toxic and reactive molecule, hydrogen peroxide (formed as a result of some cellular reactions).

**Role in lipid synthesis**
The smooth ER is the site of lipid and steroid synthesis.

**Containment of DNA**
The nucleus is surrounded by a nuclear envelope of two membranes, forming a separate compartment for the cell's genetic material.

**Role in protein and membrane synthesis**
Some protein synthesis occurs on free ribosomes, but much occurs on membrane-bound ribosomes on the rough endoplasmic reticulum. Here, the protein is synthesized directly into the space within the ER membranes. The rough ER is also involved in membrane synthesis, growing in place by adding proteins and phospholipids.

**Entry and export of substances** The plasma membrane may take up fluid or solid material and form membrane-bound vesicles (or larger vacuoles) within the cell. Membrane-bound transport vesicles move substances to the inner surface of the cell where they can be exported from the cell by exocytosis.

**Cell communication and recognition**
The proteins embedded in the membrane act as receptor molecules for hormones and neurotransmitters. Glycoproteins and glycolipids stabilize the plasma membrane and act as cell identity markers, helping cells to organize themselves into tissues, and enabling foreign cells to be recognized.

**Packaging and secretion**
The Golgi apparatus is a specialized membrane-bound organelle which produces lysosomes and compartmentalizes the modification, packaging and secretion of substances such as proteins and hormones.

**Transport processes**
Channel and carrier proteins are involved in selective transport across the plasma membrane. Cholesterol in the membrane can help to prevent ions or polar molecules from passing through the membrane (acting as a plug).

**Energy transfer** The reactions of cellular respiration (and photosynthesis in plants) take place in the membrane-bound energy transfer systems occurring in mitochondria and chloroplasts respectively. See the example explained below.

## Compartmentation within Membranes

Membranes play an important role in separating regions within the cell (and within organelles) where particular reactions occur. Specific enzymes are therefore often located in particular organelles. The reaction rate is controlled by controlling the rate at which substrates enter the organelle and therefore the availability of the raw materials required for the reactions.

**Example:** *The enzymes involved in cellular respiration are arranged in different parts of the mitochondria. The various reactions are localized and separated by membrane systems.*

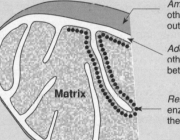

*Amine oxidases* and other enzymes on the outer membrane surface

*Adenylate kinase* and other *phosphorylases* between the membranes

*Respiratory assembly* enzymes embedded in the membrane (ATPase)

Many soluble enzymes of the *Krebs cycle* floating in the matrix, as well as enzymes for fatty acid degradation.

Matrix

*Cross-section of a mitochondrion*

1. Discuss the importance of membrane systems and organelles in providing compartments within the cell:

_____

_____

_____

_____

**Related activities**: Cell Structures and Organelles, Packaging Macromolecules
**Web links**: Cell Membranes

A 2

Cell Membranes

# Functional Roles of Membranes in Cells

The **nuclear membrane**, which surrounds the nucleus, regulates the passage of genetic information to the cytoplasm and may also protect the DNA from damage.

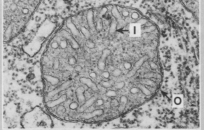

**Mitochondria** have an outer membrane (**O**) which controls the entry and exit of materials involved in aerobic respiration. Inner membranes (**I**) provide attachment sites for enzyme activity.

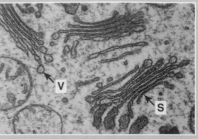

The **Golgi apparatus** comprises stacks of membrane-bound sacs (**S**). It is involved in packaging materials for transport or export from the cell as secretory vesicles (**V**).

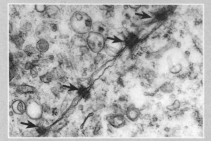

The **plasma membrane** surrounds the cell. In this photo, intercellular junctions called **desmosomes**, which connect neighbouring cells, are indicated with arrows.

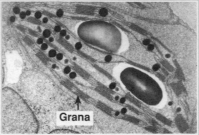

**Chloroplasts** are large organelles found in plant cells. The stacked membrane systems of chloroplasts (grana) trap light energy which is then used to fix carbon into 6-C sugars.

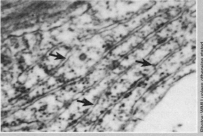

This EM shows stacks of rough endoplasmic reticulum (arrows). The membranes are studded with ribosomes, which synthesize proteins into the intermembrane space.

2. Match each of the following organelles with the correct description of its functional role in the cell:

*chloroplast, rough endoplasmic reticulum, lysosome, smooth endoplasmic reticulum, mitochondrion, Golgi apparatus*

(a) Active in synthesis, sorting, and secretion of cell products: _____

(b) Digestive organelle where macromolecules are hydrolyzed: _____

(c) Organelle where most cellular respiration occurs and most ATP is generated: _____

(d) Active in membrane synthesis and synthesis of secretory proteins: _____

(e) Active in lipid and hormone synthesis and secretion: _____

(f) Photosynthetic organelle converts light energy to chemical energy stored in sugar molecules: _____

3. Explain how the membrane surface area is increased within cells and organelles: _____

_____

4. Discuss the importance of each of the following to cellular function:

(a) High membrane surface area: _____

_____

(b) Channel proteins and carrier proteins in the plasma membrane: _____

_____

5. Non-polar (lipid-soluble) molecules diffuse more rapidly through membranes than polar (lipid-insoluble) molecules:

(a) Explain the reason for this: _____

_____

(b) Discuss the implications of this to the transport of substances into the cell through the plasma membrane:

_____

_____

© Biozone International 2001-2008
**Photocopying Prohibited**

# Modification of Proteins

Proteins may be modified after they have been produced by ribosomes. After they pass into the interior of rough endoplasmic reticulum, some proteins may have carbohydrates added to them to form **glycoproteins**. Proteins may be further altered in the Golgi apparatus. The **Golgi apparatus** functions principally as a system for processing, sorting, and modifying proteins. Proteins that are to be secreted from the cell are synthesized by

ribosomes on the rough endoplasmic reticulum and transported to the Golgi apparatus. At this stage, carbohydrates may be removed or added in a step-wise process. Some of the possible functions of glycoproteins are illustrated below. Other proteins may have fatty acids added to them to form **lipoproteins**. These modified proteins transport lipids in the plasma between various organs in the body (e.g. gut, liver, and adipose tissue).

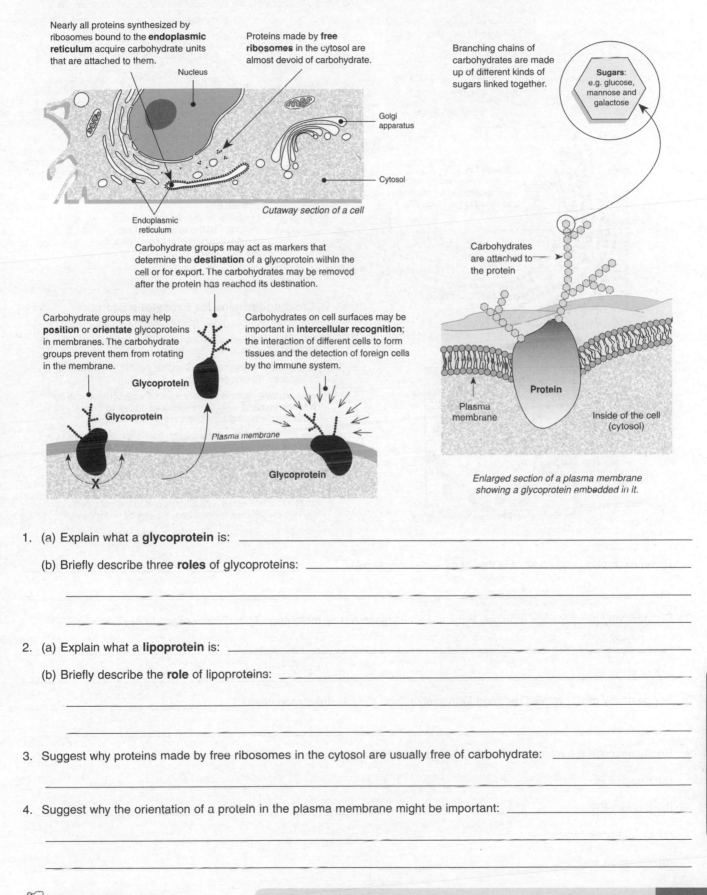

Nearly all proteins synthesized by ribosomes bound to the **endoplasmic reticulum** acquire carbohydrate units that are attached to them.

Proteins made by **free ribosomes** in the cytosol are almost devoid of carbohydrate.

Branching chains of carbohydrates are made up of different kinds of sugars linked together.

**Sugars:** e.g. glucose, mannose and galactose

Nucleus

Golgi apparatus

Cytosol

Endoplasmic reticulum

*Cutaway section of a cell*

Carbohydrate groups may act as markers that determine the **destination** of a glycoprotein within the cell or for export. The carbohydrates may be removed after the protein has reached its destination.

Carbohydrate groups may help **position** or **orientate** glycoproteins in membranes. The carbohydrate groups prevent them from rotating in the membrane.

Carbohydrates on cell surfaces may be important in **intercellular recognition**; the interaction of different cells to form tissues and the detection of foreign cells by the immune system.

Carbohydrates are attached to the protein

**Glycoprotein**

**Glycoprotein**

*Plasma membrane*

**Glycoprotein**

Plasma membrane

Protein

Inside of the cell (cytosol)

*Enlarged section of a plasma membrane showing a glycoprotein embedded in it.*

1. (a) Explain what a **glycoprotein** is: _____

   (b) Briefly describe three **roles** of glycoproteins: _____

   _____

   _____

2. (a) Explain what a **lipoprotein** is: _____

   (b) Briefly describe the **role** of lipoproteins: _____

   _____

   _____

3. Suggest why proteins made by free ribosomes in the cytosol are usually free of carbohydrate: _____

   _____

4. Suggest why the orientation of a protein in the plasma membrane might be important: _____

   _____

   _____

**Related activities**: The Structure of Membranes, Packaging Macromolecules

A 2

Cell Membranes

# Packaging Macromolecules

Cells produce a range of organic polymers made up of repeating units of smaller molecules. The synthesis, packaging and movement of these **macromolecules** inside the cell involves a number of membrane bound organelles, as indicated below. These organelles provide compartments where the enzyme systems involved can be isolated.

**Golgi apparatus**
The Golgi apparatus comprises stacks of flattened membranes in the shape of curved sacs. This organelle receives transport vesicles and the products they contain from smooth ER. They are modified, stored and eventually shipped to the surface of the cell or other destinations.

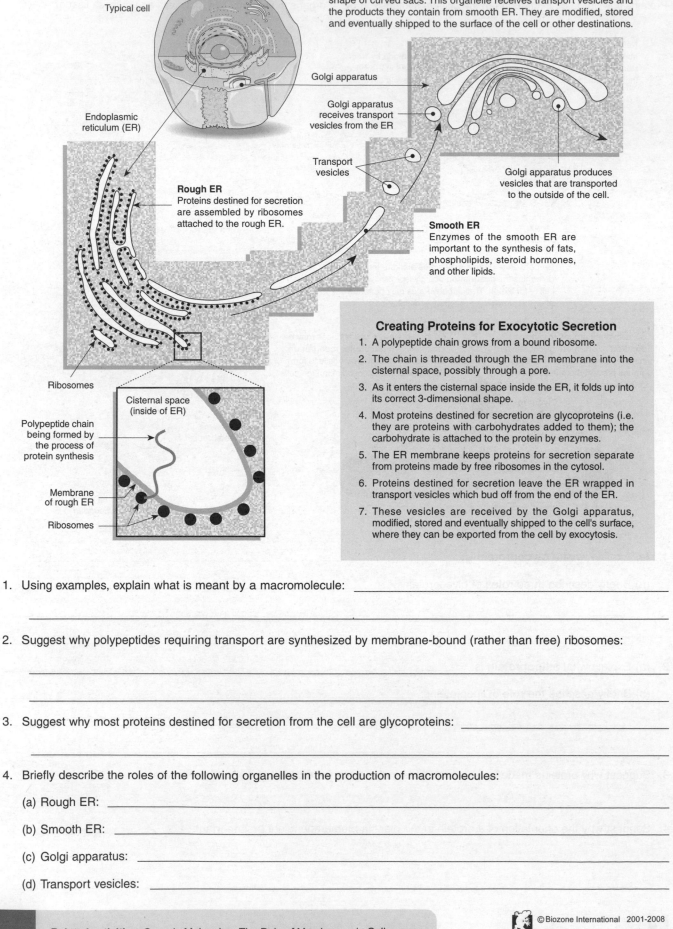

Typical cell

Endoplasmic reticulum (ER)

Golgi apparatus

Golgi apparatus receives transport vesicles from the ER

Golgi apparatus produces vesicles that are transported to the outside of the cell.

Transport vesicles

**Rough ER**
Proteins destined for secretion are assembled by ribosomes attached to the rough ER.

**Smooth ER**
Enzymes of the smooth ER are important to the synthesis of fats, phospholipids, steroid hormones, and other lipids.

Ribosomes

Cisternal space (inside of ER)

Polypeptide chain being formed by the process of protein synthesis

Membrane of rough ER

Ribosomes

## Creating Proteins for Exocytotic Secretion

1. A polypeptide chain grows from a bound ribosome.

2. The chain is threaded through the ER membrane into the cisternal space, possibly through a pore.

3. As it enters the cisternal space inside the ER, it folds up into its correct 3-dimensional shape.

4. Most proteins destined for secretion are glycoproteins (i.e. they are proteins with carbohydrates added to them); the carbohydrate is attached to the protein by enzymes.

5. The ER membrane keeps proteins for secretion separate from proteins made by free ribosomes in the cytosol.

6. Proteins destined for secretion leave the ER wrapped in transport vesicles which bud off from the end of the ER.

7. These vesicles are received by the Golgi apparatus, modified, stored and eventually shipped to the cell's surface, where they can be exported from the cell by exocytosis.

1. Using examples, explain what is meant by a macromolecule: _____

_____

2. Suggest why polypeptides requiring transport are synthesized by membrane-bound (rather than free) ribosomes:

_____

_____

3. Suggest why most proteins destined for secretion from the cell are glycoproteins: _____

_____

4. Briefly describe the roles of the following organelles in the production of macromolecules:

(a) Rough ER: _____

(b) Smooth ER: _____

(c) Golgi apparatus: _____

(d) Transport vesicles: _____

**Related activities**: Organic Molecules, The Role of Membranes in Cells, Modification of Proteins

# Active and Passive Transport

Cells have a need to move materials both into and out of the cell. Raw materials and other molecules necessary for metabolism must be accumulated from outside the cell. Some of these substances are scarce outside of the cell and some effort is required to accumulate them. Waste products and molecules for use in other parts of the body must be 'exported' out of the cell.

Some materials (e.g. gases and water) move into and out of the cell by **passive transport** processes, without the expenditure of energy on the part of the cell. Other molecules (e.g. sucrose) are moved into and out of the cell using **active transport**. Active transport processes involve the expenditure of energy in the form of ATP, and therefore use oxygen.

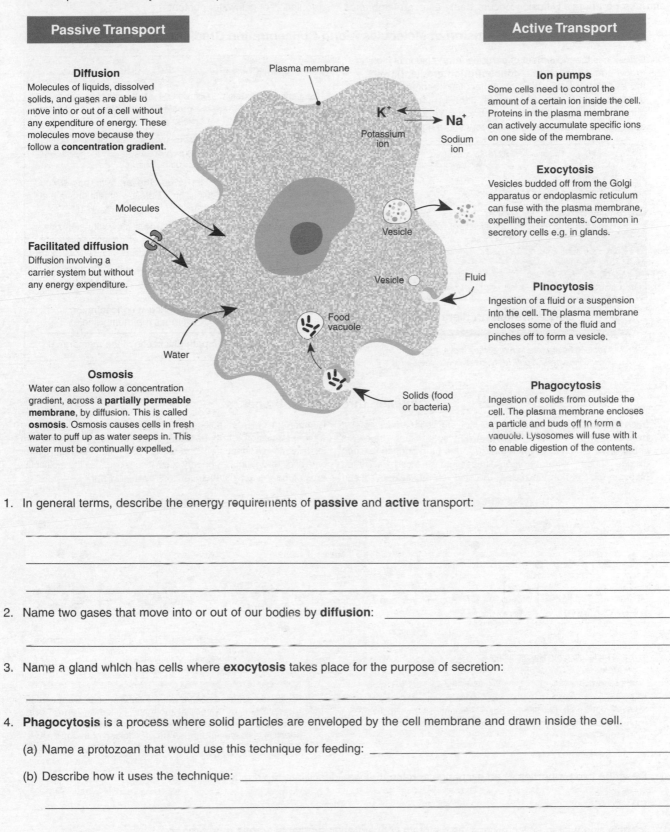

## Passive Transport

### Diffusion
Molecules of liquids, dissolved solids, and gases are able to move into or out of a cell without any expenditure of energy. These molecules move because they follow a **concentration gradient**.

Molecules

### Facilitated diffusion
Diffusion involving a carrier system but without any energy expenditure.

Water

### Osmosis
Water can also follow a concentration gradient, across a **partially permeable membrane**, by diffusion. This is called **osmosis**. Osmosis causes cells in fresh water to puff up as water seeps in. This water must be continually expelled.

Plasma membrane

K⁺ Potassium ion
Na⁺ Sodium ion

Vesicle

Vesicle    Fluid

Food vacuole

Solids (food or bacteria)

## Active Transport

### Ion pumps
Some cells need to control the amount of a certain ion inside the cell. Proteins in the plasma membrane can actively accumulate specific ions on one side of the membrane.

### Exocytosis
Vesicles budded off from the Golgi apparatus or endoplasmic reticulum can fuse with the plasma membrane, expelling their contents. Common in secretory cells e.g. in glands.

### Pinocytosis
Ingestion of a fluid or a suspension into the cell. The plasma membrane encloses some of the fluid and pinches off to form a vesicle.

### Phagocytosis
Ingestion of solids from outside the cell. The plasma membrane encloses a particle and buds off to form a vacuole. Lysosomes will fuse with it to enable digestion of the contents.

1. In general terms, describe the energy requirements of **passive** and **active** transport: _____

_____

_____

_____

2. Name two gases that move into or out of our bodies by **diffusion**: _____

_____

3. Name a gland which has cells where **exocytosis** takes place for the purpose of secretion:

_____

4. **Phagocytosis** is a process where solid particles are enveloped by the cell membrane and drawn inside the cell.

(a) Name a protozoan that would use this technique for feeding: _____

(b) Describe how it uses the technique: _____

_____

_____

(c) Name a type of cell found in human blood that uses this technique for capturing and destroying bacteria:

_____

**Cell Membranes**

**Related activities**: Unicellular Eukaryotes, Human Cell Specialization
**Web links**: Cellular Transport

RA 1

# Diffusion

The molecules that make up substances are constantly moving about in a random way. This random motion causes molecules to disperse from areas of high to low concentration; a process called **diffusion**. The molecules move along a **concentration gradient**. Diffusion and osmosis (diffusion of water molecules across a partially permeable membrane) are **passive** processes, and use no energy. Diffusion occurs freely across membranes, as long as the membrane is permeable to that molecule (partially permeable membranes allow the passage of some molecules but not others). Each type of molecule diffuses along its own concentration gradient. Diffusion of molecules in one direction does not hinder the movement of other molecules. Diffusion is important in allowing exchanges with the environment and in the regulation of cell water content.

## Diffusion of Molecules Along Concentration Gradients

Diffusion is the movement of particles from regions of high to low concentration (the **concentration gradient**), with the end result being that the molecules become evenly distributed. In biological systems, diffusion often occurs across partially permeable membranes. Various factors determine the rate at which this occurs (see right).

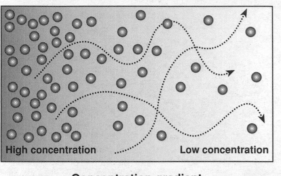

**High concentration**                **Low concentration**

### Concentration gradient

*If molecules are free to move, they move from high to low concentration until they are evenly dispersed.*

| Factors affecting rates of diffusion | |
|---|---|
| Concentration gradient: | Diffusion rates will be higher when there is a greater difference in concentration between two regions. |
| The distance involved: | Diffusion over shorter distances occurs at a greater rate than diffusion over larger distances. |
| The area involved: | The larger the area across which diffusion occurs, the greater the rate of diffusion. |
| Barriers to diffusion: | Thicker barriers slow diffusion rate. Pores in a barrier enhance diffusion. |

These factors are expressed in **Fick's law**, which governs the rate of diffusion of substances within a system. It is described by:

$$\frac{\text{Surface area of membrane} \quad \times \quad \text{Difference in concentration across the membrane}}{\text{Length of the diffusion path (thickness of the membrane)}}$$

## Diffusion through Membranes

Each type of diffusing molecule (gas, solvent, solute) moves **along its own concentration gradient**. Two-way diffusion (below) is common in biological systems, e.g. at the lung surface, carbon dioxide diffuses out and oxygen diffuses into the blood. Facilitated diffusion (below, right) increases the diffusion rate selectively and is important for larger molecules (e.g. glucose, amino acids) where a higher diffusion rate is desirable (e.g. transport of glucose into skeletal muscle fibers, transport of ADP into mitochondria). Neither type of diffusion requires energy expenditure because the molecules are not moving against their concentration gradient.

### Unaided diffusion

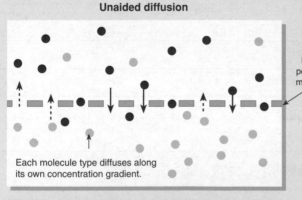

Each molecule type diffuses along its own concentration gradient.

Partially permeable membrane

Diffusion rates depend on the concentration gradient. Diffusion can occur in either direction but **net** movement is in the direction of the concentration gradient. An equilibrium is reached when concentrations are equal.

### Facilitated diffusion

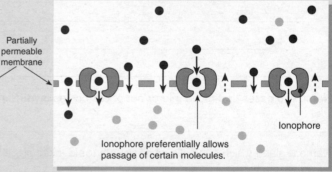

Ionophore

Ionophore preferentially allows passage of certain molecules.

Facilitated diffusion occurs when a substance is aided across a membrane by a special molecule called an **ionophore**. Ionophores allow some molecules to diffuse but not others, effectively speeding up the rate of diffusion of that molecule.

1. Describe two properties of an exchange surface that would facilitate rapid diffusion rates:

(a) _____ (b) _____

2. Identify one way in which organisms maintain concentration gradients across membranes: _____

_____

3. State how facilitated diffusion is achieved: _____

**Related activities**: Osmosis and Water Potential
**Web links**: Osmosis and Diffusion

# Osmosis and Water Potential

Osmosis is the term describing the diffusion of water along its concentration gradient across a partially permeable membrane. It is the principal mechanism by which water enters and leaves cells in living organisms. As it is a type of diffusion, the rate at which osmosis occurs is affected by the same factors that affect all diffusion rates (see earlier). The tendency for water to move in any particular direction can be calculated on the basis of the **water potential** ($\psi$) of the cell sap relative to its surrounding environment. The use of water potential to express the water relations of cells has replaced the terms osmotic potential and osmotic pressure although these are still frequently used in areas of animal physiology and medicine. An alternative version which does not use this terminology is available on the *TRC: Osmosis and Diffusion* (or see web links below).

## Osmosis and the Water Potential of Cells

**Osmosis** is simply the diffusion of water molecules from high concentration to lower concentration, across a partially permeable membrane. The direction of this movement can be predicted on the basis of the water potential of the solutions involved. The **water potential** of a solution (denoted with the symbol $\psi$) is the term given to the tendency for water molecules to enter or leave a solution by osmosis. Pure water has the highest water potential, set at zero. Dissolving any solute into pure water lowers the water potential (makes it more negative). *Water always diffuses from regions of less negative to more negative water potential.* Water potential is determined by two components: the **solute potential**, $\psi s$ (of the cell sap) and the **pressure potential**, $\psi p$. This is expressed as a simple equation:

$$\psi cell \ = \ \psi s \ + \ \psi p$$

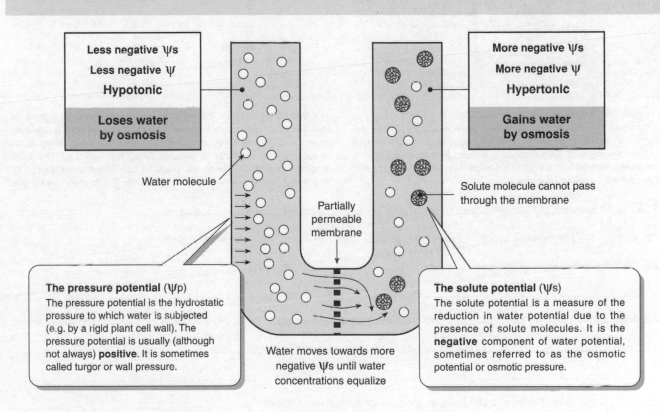

**Less negative $\psi s$**
**Less negative $\psi$**
**Hypotonic**

**Loses water by osmosis**

Water molecule

**More negative $\psi s$**
**More negative $\psi$**
**Hypertonic**

**Gains water by osmosis**

Solute molecule cannot pass through the membrane

Partially permeable membrane

**The pressure potential ($\psi p$)**
The pressure potential is the hydrostatic pressure to which water is subjected (e.g. by a rigid plant cell wall). The pressure potential is usually (although not always) **positive**. It is sometimes called turgor or wall pressure.

Water moves towards more negative $\psi s$ until water concentrations equalize

**The solute potential ($\psi s$)**
The solute potential is a measure of the reduction in water potential due to the presence of solute molecules. It is the **negative** component of water potential, sometimes referred to as the osmotic potential or osmotic pressure.

1. State the water potential of pure water at standard temperature and pressure: _____

2. The three diagrams below show the solute and pressure potential values for three hypothetical situations where two solutions are separated by a selectively permeable membrane. For each example (a) - (c) calculate $\psi$ for the solutions on each side of the membrane, as indicated:

3. Draw arrows on each diagram to indicate the direction of net flow of water:

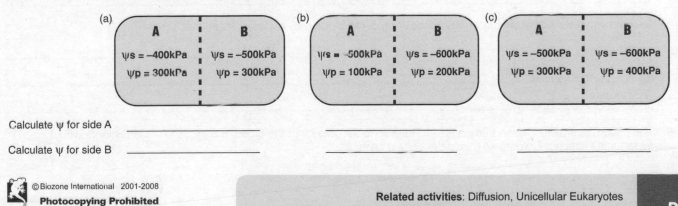

(a)

| A | B |
|---|---|
| $\psi s = -400kPa$ | $\psi s = -500kPa$ |
| $\psi p = 300kPa$ | $\psi p = 300kPa$ |

(b)

| A | B |
|---|---|
| $\psi s = -500kPa$ | $\psi s = -600kPa$ |
| $\psi p = 100kPa$ | $\psi p = 200kPa$ |

(c)

| A | B |
|---|---|
| $\psi s = -500kPa$ | $\psi s = -600kPa$ |
| $\psi p = 300kPa$ | $\psi p = 400kPa$ |

Calculate $\psi$ for side A _____    _____    _____

Calculate $\psi$ for side B _____    _____    _____

**Cell Membranes**

**Related activities**: Diffusion, Unicellular Eukaryotes
**Web links**: Osmosis and Diffusion

**DA 2**

# Water Relations in Plant Cells

The plasma membrane of cells is a partially permeable membrane and osmosis is the principal mechanism by which water enters and leaves the cell. When the external water potential is the same as that of the cell there is no net movement of water. Two systems (cell and environment) with the same water potential are termed **isotonic**. The diagram below illustrates two different situations: when the external water potential is less negative than the cell (**hypotonic**) and when it is more negative than the cell (**hypertonic**).

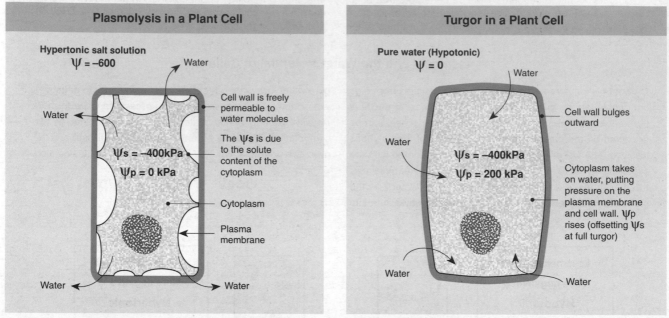

In a **hypertonic** solution, the external water potential is more negative than the water potential of the cell ($\psi$cell = $\psi$s + $\psi$p). Water leaves the cell and, because the cell wall is rigid, the plasma membrane shrinks away from the cell wall. This process is termed **plasmolysis** and the cell becomes **flaccid** ($\psi$p = 0). Full plasmolysis is irreversible; the cell cannot recover by taking up water.

In a **hypotonic** solution, the external water potential is less negative than the $\psi$cell. Water enters the cell causing it to swell tight. A pressure potential is generated when sufficient water has been taken up to cause the cell contents to press against the cell wall. $\psi$p rises progressively until it offsets $\psi$s. Water uptake stops when $\psi$cell = 0. The rigid cell wall prevents cell rupture. Cells in this state are **turgid**.

4. Fluid replacements are usually provided for heavily perspiring athletes after endurance events.

    (a) Identify the preferable tonicity of these replacement drinks (isotonic, hypertonic, or hypotonic): _____

    (b) Give a reason for your answer: _____
    _____

5. *Paramecium* is a freshwater protozoan. Describe the problem it has in controlling the amount of water inside the cell:
    _____
    _____

6. (a) Explain the role of pressure potential in generating cell turgor in plants: _____
    _____

    (b) Explain the purpose of cell turgor to plants: _____
    _____

7. Explain how animal cells differ from plant cells with respect to the effects of net water movements: _____
    _____

8. Describe what would happen to an animal cell (e.g. a red blood cell) if it was placed into:

    (a) Pure water: _____

    (b) A hypertonic solution: _____

    (c) A hypotonic solution: _____

9. The malarial parasite lives in human blood. Relative to the tonicity of the blood, the parasite's cell contents would be hypertonic / isotonic / hypotonic (circle the correct answer).

# Surface Area and Volume

When an object (e.g. a cell) is small it has a large surface area in comparison to its volume. In this case diffusion will be an effective way to transport materials (e.g. gases) into the cell. As an object becomes larger, its surface area compared to its volume is smaller. Diffusion is no longer an effective way to transport materials to the inside. For this reason, there is a physical limit for the size of a cell, with the effectiveness of diffusion being the controlling factor.

## Diffusion in Organisms of Different Sizes

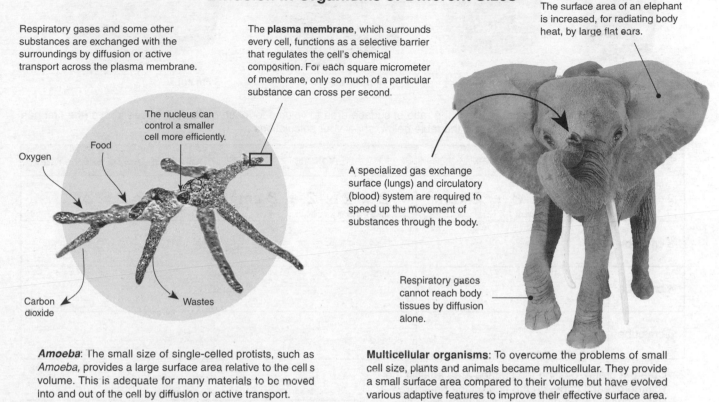

Respiratory gases and some other substances are exchanged with the surroundings by diffusion or active transport across the plasma membrane.

The **plasma membrane**, which surrounds every cell, functions as a selective barrier that regulates the cell's chemical composition. For each square micrometer of membrane, only so much of a particular substance can cross per second.

The nucleus can control a smaller cell more efficiently.

Oxygen

Food

Carbon dioxide

Wastes

The surface area of an elephant is increased, for radiating body heat, by large flat ears.

A specialized gas exchange surface (lungs) and circulatory (blood) system are required to speed up the movement of substances through the body.

Respiratory gases cannot reach body tissues by diffusion alone.

**Amoeba**: The small size of single-celled protists, such as *Amoeba*, provides a large surface area relative to the cell's volume. This is adequate for many materials to be moved into and out of the cell by diffusion or active transport.

**Multicellular organisms**: To overcome the problems of small cell size, plants and animals became multicellular. They provide a small surface area compared to their volume but have evolved various adaptive features to improve their effective surface area.

## Smaller is Better for Diffusion

### One large cube

2 cm

2 cm

2 cm

**Volume:** = 8 $cm^3$

**Surface area:** = 24 $cm^2$

### Eight small cubes

1 cm

1 cm

1 cm

**Volume:** = 8 $cm^3$ for 8 cubes

**Surface area:** = 6 $cm^2$ for 1 cube

= 48 $cm^2$ for 8 cubes

The eight small cells and the single large cell have the same total volume, but their surface areas are different. The small cells together have twice the total surface area of the large cell, because there are more exposed (inner) surfaces. Real organisms have complex shapes, but the same principles apply.

The surface-area volume relationship has important implications for processes involving transport into and out of cells across membranes. For activities such as gas exchange, the surface area available for diffusion is a major factor limiting the rate at which oxygen can be supplied to tissues.

The diagram below shows four hypothetical cells of different sizes (cells do not actually grow to this size, their large size is for the sake of the exercise). They range from a small 2 cm cube to a larger 5 cm cube. This exercise investigates the effect of cell size on the efficiency of diffusion.

**2 cm cube**      **3 cm cube**      **4 cm cube**      **5 cm cube**

1. Calculate the volume, surface area and the ratio of surface area to volume for each of the four cubes above (the first has been done for you). When completing the table below, show your calculations.

| Cube size | Surface area | Volume | Surface area to volume ratio |
|---|---|---|---|
| 2 cm cube | $2 \times 2 \times 6 = 24 \text{ cm}^2$ <br> (2 cm x 2 cm x 6 sides) | $2 \times 2 \times 2 = 8 \text{ cm}^3$ <br> (height x width x depth) | 24 to 8 = 3:1 |
| 3 cm cube | | | |
| 4 cm cube | | | |
| 5 cm cube | | | |

2. Create a graph, plotting the surface area against the volume of each cube, on the grid on the right. Draw a line connecting the points and label axes and units.

3. State which increases the fastest with increasing size: the **volume** or **surface area**.

_____

4. Explain what happens to the ratio of surface area to volume with increasing size:

_____

_____

_____

_____

5. Diffusion of substances into and out of a cell occurs across the cell surface. Describe how increasing the size of a cell will affect the ability of diffusion to transport materials into and out of a cell:

_____

_____

_____

_____

_____

_____

# Ion Pumps

Diffusion alone cannot supply the cell's entire requirements for molecules (and ions). Some molecules (e.g. glucose) are required by the cell in higher concentrations than occur outside the cell. Others (e.g. sodium) must be removed from the cell in order to maintain cell fluid balance. These molecules must be moved across the plasma membrane by active transport mechanisms. **Active transport** requires the expenditure of energy because the molecules (or ions) must be moved **against** their concentration gradient. The work of active transport is performed by specific carrier proteins in the membrane. These transport proteins harness the energy of ATP to pump molecules from a low to a high concentration. When ATP transfers a phosphate group to the carrier protein, the protein changes its shape in such a way as to move the bound molecule across the membrane. Three types of membrane pump are illustrated below. The sodium-potassium pump (below, left) is almost universal in animal cells and is common in plant cells also. The concentration gradient created by ion pumps such as this and the proton pump (center) is frequently coupled to the transport of other molecules such as glucose and sucrose (below, right).

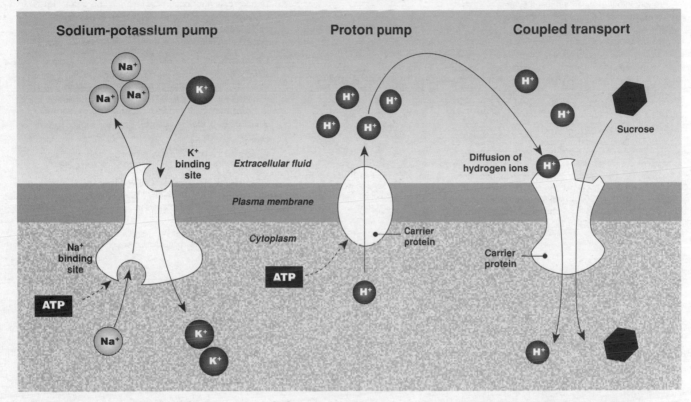

### Sodium-potassium pump
The sodium-potassium pump is a specific protein in the membrane that uses energy in the form of ATP to exchange sodium ions ($Na^+$) for potassium ions ($K^+$) across the membrane. The unequal balance of $Na^+$ and $K^+$ across the membrane creates large concentration gradients that can be used to drive other active transport mechanisms.

### Proton pumps
ATP driven proton pumps use energy to remove hydrogen ions ($H^+$) from inside the cell to the outside. This creates a large difference in the proton concentration either side of the membrane, with the inside of the plasma membrane being negatively charged. This potential difference can be coupled to the transport of other molecules.

### Coupled transport (cotransport)
Plant cells use the gradient in hydrogen ions created by proton pumps to drive the active transport of nutrients into the cell. The specific transport protein couples the return of $H^+$ to the transport of sucrose into the phloem cells. The sucrose rides with the $H^+$ as it diffuses down the concentration gradient maintained by the proton pump.

1. The sodium-potassium pump plays an important role in the water balance of cells. In terms of osmosis, explain the consequences of the sodium-potassium pumps not working:

_____

_____

2. Explain how the transport of molecules such as sucrose can be coupled to the activity of an ion exchange pump:

_____

_____

_____

3. Explain why the ATP is required for membrane pump systems to operate: _____

_____

_____

4. Name a type of cell that relies on coupled transport to perform its function: _____

Cell Membranes

**Related activities**: Active and Passive Transport

A 2

# Exocytosis and Endocytosis

Most cells carry out **cytosis**: a form of **active transport** involving the in- or outfolding of the plasma membrane. The ability of cells to do this is a function of the flexibility of the plasma membrane. Cytosis results in the bulk transport into or out of the cell and is achieved through the localized activity of microfilaments and microtubules in the cell cytoskeleton. Engulfment of material is termed **endocytosis**. Endocytosis typically occurs in protozoans and certain white blood cells of the mammalian defense system (e.g. neutrophils, macrophages). **Exocytosis** is the reverse of endocytosis and involves the release of material from vesicles or vacuoles that have fused with the plasma membrane. Exocytosis is typical of cells that export material (secretory cells).

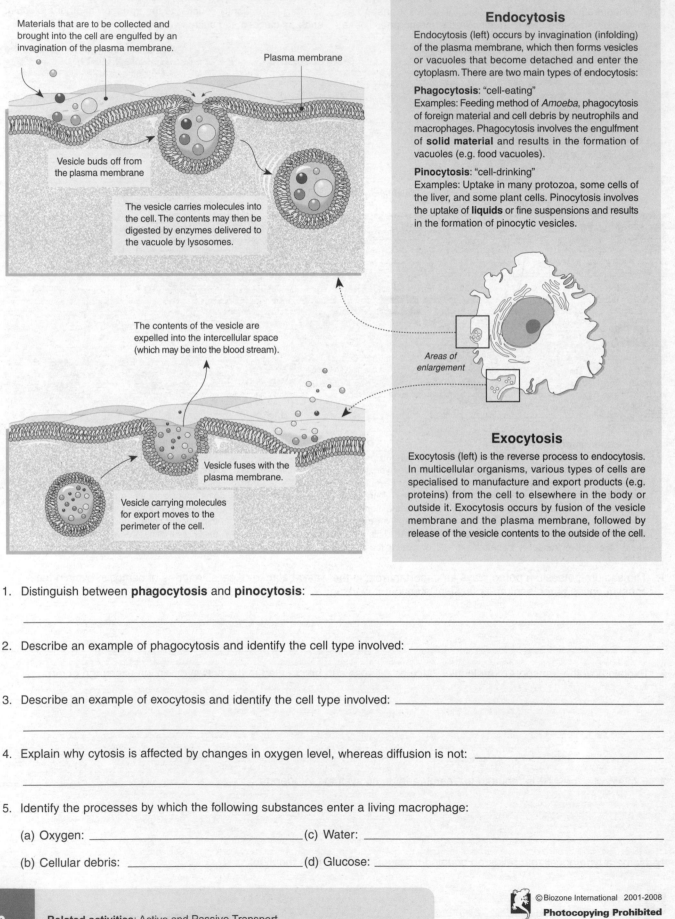

Materials that are to be collected and brought into the cell are engulfed by an invagination of the plasma membrane.

Plasma membrane

Vesicle buds off from the plasma membrane

The vesicle carries molecules into the cell. The contents may then be digested by enzymes delivered to the vacuole by lysosomes.

The contents of the vesicle are expelled into the intercellular space (which may be into the blood stream).

Vesicle fuses with the plasma membrane.

Vesicle carrying molecules for export moves to the perimeter of the cell.

Areas of enlargement

### Endocytosis

Endocytosis (left) occurs by invagination (infolding) of the plasma membrane, which then forms vesicles or vacuoles that become detached and enter the cytoplasm. There are two main types of endocytosis:

**Phagocytosis**: "cell-eating"
Examples: Feeding method of *Amoeba*, phagocytosis of foreign material and cell debris by neutrophils and macrophages. Phagocytosis involves the engulfment of **solid material** and results in the formation of vacuoles (e.g. food vacuoles).

**Pinocytosis**: "cell-drinking"
Examples: Uptake in many protozoa, some cells of the liver, and some plant cells. Pinocytosis involves the uptake of **liquids** or fine suspensions and results in the formation of pinocytic vesicles.

### Exocytosis

Exocytosis (left) is the reverse process to endocytosis. In multicellular organisms, various types of cells are specialised to manufacture and export products (e.g. proteins) from the cell to elsewhere in the body or outside it. Exocytosis occurs by fusion of the vesicle membrane and the plasma membrane, followed by release of the vesicle contents to the outside of the cell.

1. Distinguish between **phagocytosis** and **pinocytosis**: _____

_____

2. Describe an example of phagocytosis and identify the cell type involved: _____

_____

3. Describe an example of exocytosis and identify the cell type involved: _____

_____

4. Explain why cytosis is affected by changes in oxygen level, whereas diffusion is not: _____

_____

5. Identify the processes by which the following substances enter a living macrophage:

(a) Oxygen: _____ (c) Water: _____

(b) Cellular debris: _____ (d) Glucose: _____

# Cell Division and Organization

| IB SL | IB HL | IB Options | AP Biology |
|---|---|---|---|
| Complete: 1-5, 7-13 Extension: 6 | Complete: 1-16, 19-26, 29-32 Extension: 17-18, 27-28, 33-34 | Does not apply to options | Complete: 1-13 |

## Learning Objectives

☐ 1. Compile your own glossary from the **KEY WORDS** displayed in **bold type** in the learning objectives below.

### Mitosis and the Cell Cycle  *(pages 116-120)*

☐ 2. Using diagrams, describe the behaviour of **chromosomes** during a mitotic **cell cycle** in eukaryotes. Include reference to: **mitosis**, **growth** ($G_1$ and $G_2$), and DNA replication (S).

☐ 3. Recognize and describe the following events in mitosis: **prophase**, **metaphase**, **anaphase**, and **telophase**. With respect to both plant and animal cells, understand the term **cytokinesis**, and distinguish between nuclear division and division of the cytoplasm.

☐ 4. Describe the role of mitosis in growth and repair, and asexual reproduction (e.g. in yeast). Recognize the importance of **daughter nuclei** with chromosomes identical in number and type. Recognize cell division as a prelude to **cellular differentiation**.

☐ 5. Explain how **carcinogens** can upset the normal controls regulating cell division. Define the terms: **cancer**, **tumour suppressor genes**, **oncogenes**. List factors that increase the chances of cancerous growth.

☐ 6. Describe the process of programmed cell death (**apoptosis** or PCD) and describe the situations in which apoptosis plays a crucial role, e.g. during development or when DNA is damaged beyond repair.

### Stem Cells  *(pages 123-124)*

☐ 7. Explain what is meant by a **stem cell** and distinguish between embryonic and adult stem cells. Describe the role of stem cells in multicellular organisms.

☐ 8. Describe the two important properties of stem cells: **self-renewal** and **potency**. Explain the terms: **totipotent** and **pluripotent**.

☐ 9. Describe the potentially valuable roles of stem cells in medical therapies and explain why stem cell technology offers such therapeutic promise.

### Tissues and Organs  *(pages 121-122, 126-130)*

☐ 10. Describe how a **zygote** undergoes cell division and differentiation to produce an adult. With reference to specific examples, explain what is meant by **differentiation** and **specialized cell**.

☐ 11. Recognize the hierarchy of organisation in multicellular organisms. Explain the terms: tissue, organ, and organ system. With reference to specific examples (e.g. epithelial tissues, blood, xylem, and/or phloem), explain how cells are organized into **tissues**.

☐ 12. Discuss the importance of cooperation between cells, tissues, organs, and organ systems in the structure and function of multicellular organisms.

☐ 13. Appreciate that each step in the hierarchy of biological order is associated with the emergence of properties not present at simpler levels of organisation. Explain how these **emergent properties** (e.g. metabolism) result from the interactions of component parts.

See the 'Textbook Reference Grid' on page 7 for textbook page references relating to material in this topic.

### Supplementary Texts

See pages 5-6 for additional details of these texts:
■ Adds, J. *et al.*, 2003. **Molecules and Cells**, (NelsonThornes), pp. 48-49 and chpt. 5.
■ Jones, N., *et al.*, 2001. **The Essentials of Genetics**, (John Murray), pp. 9-16.

See page 7 for details of publishers of periodicals:

### STUDENT'S REFERENCE

■ **To Divide or Not to Divide**  Biol. Sci. Rev., 11(4) March 1999, pp. 2-5. *The cell cycle: cell growth and stages of cell division and their control.*

■ **The Cell Cycle and Mitosis**  Biol. Sci. Rev., 14(4) April 2002, pp. 37-41. *Cell growth and division, key stages in the cell cycle, and the complex control over different stages of mitosis.*

■ **Rebels without a Cause**  New Scientist, 13 July 2002, (Inside Science). *The causes of cancer: the uncontrolled division of cells that results in tumour formation. Breast cancer is a case example.*

■ **What is a Stem Cell?**  Biol. Sci. Rev., 16(2) Nov. 2003, pp. 22-23. *The nature of stem cells and their therapeutic applications.*

■ **What is Cell Suicide?**  Biol. Sci. Rev., 20(1) Sept. 2007, pp. 17-20. *An account of the mechanisms behind cell suicide and its role in normal growth and development.*

■ **Fast Tissue Culture**  Biol. Sci. Rev., 10(3) Jan. 1998, pp. 2-6. *Techniques for plant propagation (includes design for a tissue culture project).*

■ **Human Cloning**  Biol. Sci. Rev. 11(3) Jan. 1999, pp. 7-9. *Nuclear transfer and the ethics of the issues surrounding human and livestock cloning.*

■ **The Power to Divide**  National Geographic, July 2005, pp. 2-27. *A series of case studies on different illnesses treated with therapeutic cloning.*

■ **Out of Control - Unlocking the Genetic Secrets of Cancer**  Biol. Sci. Rev., 11(3) Jan. 1999, pp. 36-39. *The control of cell division: oncogenes and their role in the development of cancer.*

See pages 10-11 for details of how to access **Bio Links** from our web site: **www.biozone.co.uk**. From Bio Links, access sites under the topics:

**GENERAL BIOLOGY ONLINE RESOURCES**
• AP interactive animation • Ken's bio-web resources • Biology I interactive animations

**CELL BIOLOGY AND BIOCHEMISTRY:** • Mollecular biology web book > **Cell Division**: • Cell division: Binary fission and mitosis • Cell cycle and mitosis tutorial

**BIOTECHNOLOGY > Applications > Cloning and Tissue Culture:** • Contact the Stem Cell Research Foundation • Stem cells: gateway to 21st Century medicine... *and others*

**Presentation MEDIA** to support this topic:

**CELL BIOLOGY AND BIOCHEMISTRY**

# Cell Division

The life cycle of **diploid sexually reproducing organisms** (such as humans) is illustrated in the diagram below. **Gametogenesis** is the process responsible for the production of male and female gametes for the purpose of sexual reproduction. The difference between meiosis in males and in females should be noted (see spermatogenesis and oogenesis in the box below).

Human embryos have cells which are rapidly dividing by **mitosis**. The term **somatic** means 'body', so the cell divisions are creating new body cells (as opposed to gametes or sex cells). The **2N** number refers to how many whole sets of chromosomes are present in each body cell. For a normal human embryo, all cells will have a 2N number of 46.

Adults still continue to produce somatic cells by mitosis for cell replacement and growth. Blood cells are replaced by the body at the astonishing rate of two million per second, and a layer of skin cells is constantly lost and replaced about every 28 days.

Gamete production begins at puberty, and lasts until menopause for women, and indefinitely for men. Gametes are produced by the special type of cell division, called **meiosis**, which reduces the chromosome number to half. Human males produce about 200 million sperm per day (whether they are used or not), while females usually release a single egg only once a month.

Fertilization involves fusion of the sperm and the egg to produce a single cell called the **zygote**. This cell has all the genetic information to build a human body as well as maintain it (metabolism).

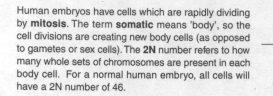
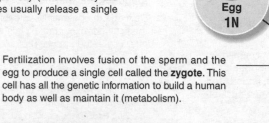
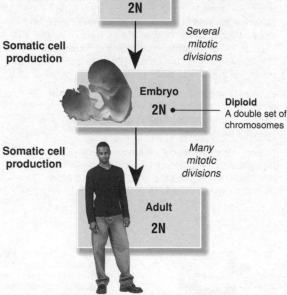

**Female embryo 2N**

*Many mitotic divisions*

**Somatic cell production**

**Female adult 2N**

*Meiosis*

**Gamete production**

**Egg 1N**

**Fertilisation**

**Male embryo 2N**

*Many mitotic divisions*

**Male adult 2N**

*Meiosis*

**Sperm 1N**

**Haploid**
A single set of chromosomes

**Zygote 2N**

**Somatic cell production**

*Several mitotic divisions*

**Embryo 2N**

**Diploid**
A double set of chromosomes

**Somatic cell production**

*Many mitotic divisions*

**Adult 2N**

### Spermatogenesis

**Sperm production**: Meiotic division of spermatogonia produces the male gametes. This process is called spermatogenesis. The nucleus of the **germ cell** in the male divides twice to produce four similar-sized sperm cells. Many organisms produce vast quantities of male gametes in this way (e.g. pollen and sperm).

### Oogenesis

**Egg production**: In females, meiosis in the oogonium produces the egg cell or ovum. Unlike gamete production in males, the divison of the cytoplasm during oogenesis is unequal. Most of the cytoplasm and one of the four nuclei form the egg cell or **ovum**. The remainder of the cytoplasm, plus the other three nuclei, form much smaller **polar bodies** and are abortive (i.e. do not take part in fertilization and formation of the zygote).

1. Describe the purpose of the following types of cell division:

   (a) Mitosis: _____

   _____

   (b) Meiosis: _____

   _____

2. Explain the significance of the **zygote**: _____

3. Describe the basic difference between the cell divisions involved in spermatogenesis and oogenesis:

   _____

   _____

Related activities: Mitosis and the Cell Cycle

# Mitosis and the Cell Cycle

**Mitosis** is part of the 'cell cycle' in which an existing cell (the parent cell) divides into two (the daughter cells). Mitosis does not result in a change of chromosome numbers (unlike meiosis) and the daughter cells are identical to the parent cell. Although mitosis is part of a continuous cell cycle, it is divided into stages (below). The example below illustrates the cell cycle in a plant cell. Note that in animal cells, **cytokinesis** involves the formation of a constriction that divides the cell in two. It is usually well underway by the end of telophase and does not involve the formation of a cell plate.

## The Cell Cycle and Stages of Mitosis

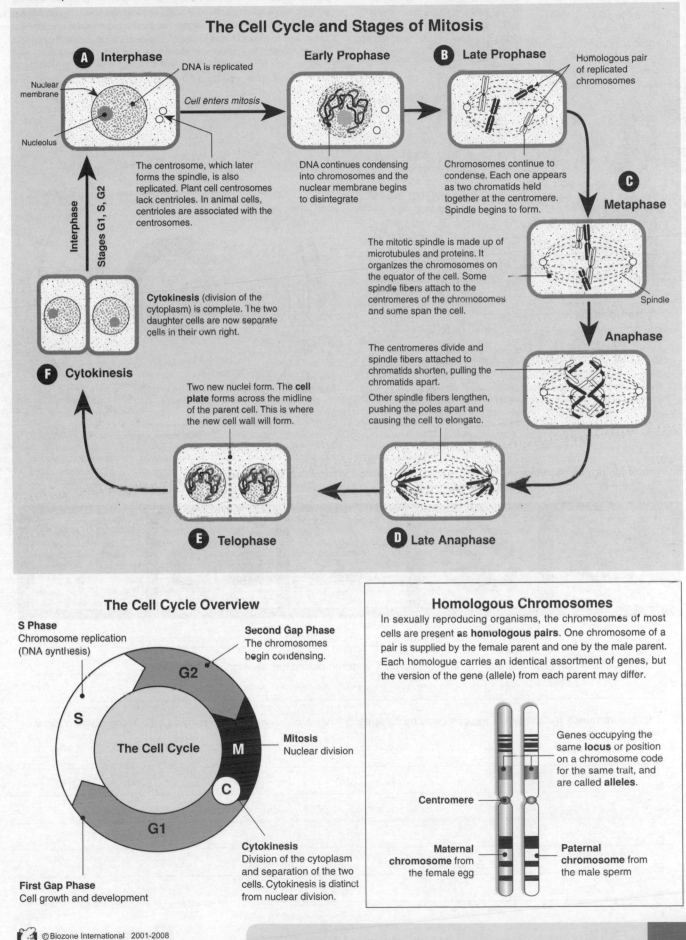

**A  Interphase**

Nuclear membrane

Nucleolus

DNA is replicated

Cell enters mitosis

The centrosome, which later forms the spindle, is also replicated. Plant cell centrosomes lack centrioles. In animal cells, centrioles are associated with the centrosomes.

Interphase
Stages G1, S, G2

**Early Prophase**

DNA continues condensing into chromosomes and the nuclear membrane begins to disintegrate

**B  Late Prophase**

Homologous pair of replicated chromosomes

Chromosomes continue to condense. Each one appears as two chromatids held together at the centromere. Spindle begins to form.

**C  Metaphase**

The mitotic spindle is made up of microtubules and proteins. It organizes the chromosomes on the equator of the cell. Some spindle fibers attach to the centromeres of the chromosomes and some span the cell.

Spindle

**Anaphase**

The centromeres divide and spindle fibers attached to chromatids shorten, pulling the chromatids apart.

Other spindle fibers lengthen, pushing the poles apart and causing the cell to elongate.

**Cytokinesis** (division of the cytoplasm) is complete. The two daughter cells are now separate cells in their own right.

**F  Cytokinesis**

Two new nuclei form. The **cell plate** forms across the midline of the parent cell. This is where the new cell wall will form.

**E  Telophase**

**D  Late Anaphase**

## The Cell Cycle Overview

**S Phase**
Chromosome replication (DNA synthesis)

**Second Gap Phase**
The chromosomes begin condensing.

G2

S

**The Cell Cycle**

M

C

G1

**Mitosis**
Nuclear division

**Cytokinesis**
Division of the cytoplasm and separation of the two cells. Cytokinesis is distinct from nuclear division.

**First Gap Phase**
Cell growth and development

## Homologous Chromosomes

In sexually reproducing organisms, the chromosomes of most cells are present as **homologous pairs**. One chromosome of a pair is supplied by the female parent and one by the male parent. Each homologue carries an identical assortment of genes, but the version of the gene (allele) from each parent may differ.

Genes occupying the same **locus** or position on a chromosome code for the same trait, and are called **alleles**.

**Centromere**

**Maternal chromosome** from the female egg

**Paternal chromosome** from the male sperm

**Related activities:** The Genetic Origins of Cancer, Root Cell Development

A 1

Mitotic cell division has several purposes (below left). In multicellular organisms, mitosis repairs damaged cells and tissues, and produces the growth in an organism that allows it to reach its adult size. In unicellular organisms, and some small multicellular organisms, cell division allows organisms to reproduce asexually (as in the budding yeast cell cycle below).

## The Functions of Mitosis

### ❶ Growth

In plants, cell division occurs in regions of **meristematic tissue**. In the plant root tip (right), the cells in the root apical meristem are dividing by mitosis to produce new cells. This elongates the root, resulting in **plant growth**.

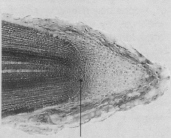

Root apical meristem

### ❷ Repair

Photo: AB Sheldon

Some animals, such as this skink (left), detach their limbs as a defence mechanism in a process called **autotomy**. The limbs can be **regenerated** via the mitotic process, although the tissue composition of the new limb differs slightly from that of the original.

### ❸ Reproduction

Mitotic division enables some animals to reproduce **asexually**. The cells of this Hydra (left) undergo mitosis, forming a 'bud' on the side of the parent organism. Eventually the bud, which is genetically identical to its parent, detaches to continue the life cycle.

Parent

## The Budding Yeast Cell Cycle

Yeasts can reproduce asexually through **budding**. In *Saccharomyces cerevisiae* (baker's yeast), budding involves mitotic division in the parent cell, with the formation of a daughter cell (or bud). As budding begins, a ring of chitin stabilises the area where the bud will appear and enzymatic activity and turgor pressure act to weaken and extrude the cell wall. New cell wall material is incorporated during this phase. The nucleus of the parent cell also divides in two, to form a daughter nucleus, which migrates into the bud. The daughter cell is genetically identical to its parent cell and continues to grow, eventually separating from the parent cell.

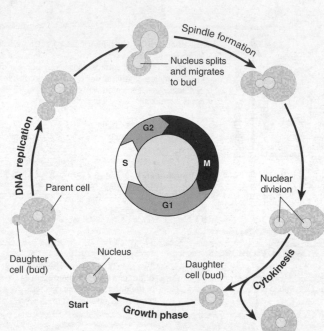

1. The photographs below were taken at various stages through mitosis in a plant cell. They are not in any particular order. Study the diagram on the previous page and determine the stage represented in each photograph (e.g. anaphase).

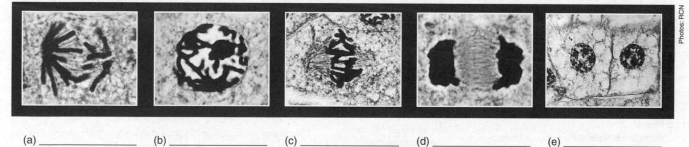

Photos: RCN

(a) _____   (b) _____   (c) _____   (d) _____   (e) _____

2. State two important changes that chromosomes must undergo before cell division can take place: _____

_____

3. Briefly summarise the stages of the cell cycle by describing what is happening at the points (**A-F**) in the diagram on the previous page:

A. _____

B. _____

C. _____

D. _____

E. _____

F. _____

# Apoptosis: Programmed Cell Death

**Apoptosis** or programmed cell death (PCD) is a normal and necessary mechanism in multicellular organisms to trigger the death of a cell. Apoptosis has a number of crucial roles in the body, including the maintenance of adult cell numbers, and defence against damaged or dangerous cells, such as virus-infected cells and cells with DNA damage. Apoptosis also has a role in "sculpting" embryonic tissue during its development, e.g. in the formation of fingers and toes in a developing human embryo. Programmed cell death involves an orderly series of biochemical events that result in set changes in cell morphology

and end in cell death. The process is carried out in such a way as to safely dispose of cell remains and fragments. This is in contrast to another type of cell death, called **necrosis**, in which traumatic damage to the cell results in spillage of cell contents. Apoptosis is tightly regulated by a balance between the factors that promote cell survival and those that trigger cell death. An imbalance between these regulating factors leads to defective apoptotic processes and is implicated in an extensive variety of diseases. For example, low rates of apoptosis result in uncontrolled proliferation of cells and cancers.

## Stages in Apoptosis

Apoptosis is a normal cell suicide process in response to particular cell signals. It characterized by an overall compaction (shrinking) of the cell and its nucleus, and the orderly dissection of chromatin by endonucleases. Death is finalized by a rapid engulfment of the dying cell by phagocytosis. The cell contents remain membrane-bound and there is no inflammation.

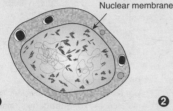

Nuclear membrane

Chromatin

**1** The cell shrinks and loses contact with neighboring cells. The chromatin condenses and begins to degrade.

**2** The nuclear membrane degrades. The cell loses volume. The chromatin clumps into **chromatin bodies**.

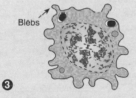

Blebs

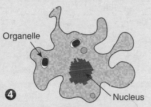

Organelle

Nucleus

**3** **Zeiosis**: The plasma membrane forms bubble like **blebs** on its surface.

**4** The nucleus collapses, but many membrane-bound organelles are unaffected.

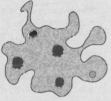

Apoptotic body

**5** The nucleus breaks up into spheres and the DNA breaks up into small fragments.

**6** The cell breaks into numerous **apoptotic bodies**, which are quickly resorbed by phagocytosis.

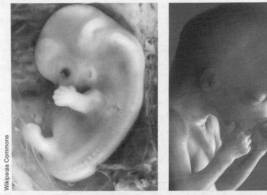

Wikipedia Commons

In humans, the mesoderm initially formed between the fingers and toes is removed by apoptosis. 41 days after fertilization (top left), the digits of the hands and feet are webbed, making them look like small paddles. Apoptosis selectively destroys this superfluous webbing and, later in development, each of the digits can be individually seen (right).

## Regulating Apoptosis

Apoptosis is a complicated and tightly controlled process, distinct from cell necrosis (uncontrolled cell death), when the cell contents are spilled. Apoptosis is regulated through both:

Positive signals, which prevent apoptosis and allow a cell to function normally. They include:
▶ Interleukin-2
▶ bcl-2 protein and growth factors

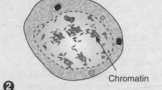

*Interleukin-2 is a positive signal for cell survival. Like other signalling molecules, it binds to surface receptors on the cell to regulate metabolism.*

Negative signals (death activators), which trigger the changes leading to cell death. They include:
▶ inducer signals generated from within the cell itself in response to stress, e.g. DNA damage or cell starvation.
▶ signalling proteins and peptides such as lymphotoxin.

1. The photograph (right) depicts a condition called syndactyly. Explain what might have happened during development to result in this condition.

   _____

   _____

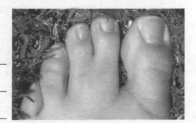

2. Describe one difference between apoptosis and necrosis: _____

   _____

3. Describe two situations, other than digit formation in development, in which apoptosis plays a crucial role:

   (a) _____

   _____

   (b) _____

   _____

**Related activities**: Cancer: Cells Out of Control
**Web links**: Apoptosis: Dance of Death

**A 2**

# Cancer: Cells out of Control

Normal cells do not live forever. Under certain circumstances, cells are programed to die, particularly during development. Cells that become damaged beyond repair will normally undergo this programed cell death (called **apoptosis** or **cell suicide**). Cancer cells evade this control and become immortal, continuing to divide regardless of any damage incurred. **Carcinogens** are agents capable of causing cancer. Roughly 90% of carcinogens are also mutagens, i.e. they damage DNA. Chronic exposure to carcinogens accelerates the rate at which dividing cells make errors. Susceptibility to cancer is also influenced by genetic make-up. Any one or a number of cancer-causing factors (including defective genes) may interact to induce cancer.

## Cancer: Cells out of Control

Cancerous transformation results from changes in the genes controlling normal cell growth and division. The resulting cells become immortal and no longer carry out their functional role. Two types of gene are normally involved in controlling the cell cycle: proto-oncogenes, which start the cell division process and are essential for normal cell development, and **tumor-suppressor** genes, which switch off cell division. In their normal form, both kinds of genes work as a team, enabling the body to perform vital tasks such as repairing defective cells and replacing dead ones. But mutations in these genes can disrupt these finely tuned checks and balances. Proto-oncogenes, through mutation, can give rise to **oncogenes**; genes that lead to uncontrollable cell division. Mutations to tumor-suppressor genes initiate most human cancers. The best studied tumor-suppressor gene is **p53**, which encodes a protein that halts the cell cycle so that DNA can be repaired before division.

The panel, right, shows the mutagenic action of some selected carcinogens on four of five codons of the **p53 gene**.

### Features of Cancer Cells

The diagram right shows a single **lung cell** that has become cancerous. It no longer carries out the role of a lung cell, and instead takes on a parasitic lifestyle, taking from the body what it needs in the way of nutrients and contributing nothing in return. The rate of cell division is greater than in normal cells in the same tissue because there is no *resting phase* between divisions.

A mutation in one or two of the controlling genes causes a **benign** (nonmalignant) **tumor**. As the number of controlling genes with mutations increases, so too does the loss of control until the cell becomes cancerous.

Normal cell

Damaged DNA

If the damage is too serious to repair, p53 activates other genes that cause the cell to self-destruct.

If repairs are made, then p53 allows the cell cycle to continue.

**Tumor-suppressor genes**
When damage occurs, the tumor-suppressor gene p53 commands other genes to bring cell division to a halt.

DNA molecule

**Proto-oncogenes**
Genes that turn on cell division. The mutated form or **oncogene** somehow leads to unregulated cell multiplication.

Benzo(a)pyrene from tobacco smoke changes G to T

Aflatoxin from moldy grain changes G to T

| --GGC------ | ATG------ | AAG------ | CGG------ | AGG |
|---|---|---|---|---|
| 245 | 246 | 247 | 248 | 249 |
| --CCG------ | TAC------ | TTC------ | GCC------ | TCC |

UV exposure changes CC to TT

Deamination changes C to T

Given a continual supply of nutrients, cancer cells can go on dividing indefinitely and are said to be immortal.

Cancer cells may have unusual numbers of chromosomes.

The bloated, lumpy shape is readily distinguishable from a healthy cell, which has a flat, scaly appearance.

Metabolism is disrupted and the cell ceases to function constructively.

Cancerous cells lose their attachments to neighboring cells.

1. Explain how cancerous cells differ from normal cells: _____

_____

2. Explain how the cell cycle is normally controlled, including reference to the role of **tumor-suppressor genes**:

_____

_____

_____

_____

3. With reference to the role of **oncogenes**, explain how the normal controls over the cell cycle can be lost:

_____

_____

_____

**Related activities**: Mutagens

# Differentiation of Human Cells

A zygote commences development by dividing into a small ball of a few dozen identical cells called **embryonic stem cells**. These cells start to take different developmental paths to become specialised cells such as nerve stem cells which means they can no longer produce any other type of cell. **Differentiation** is cell specialization that occurs at the end of a developmental pathway.

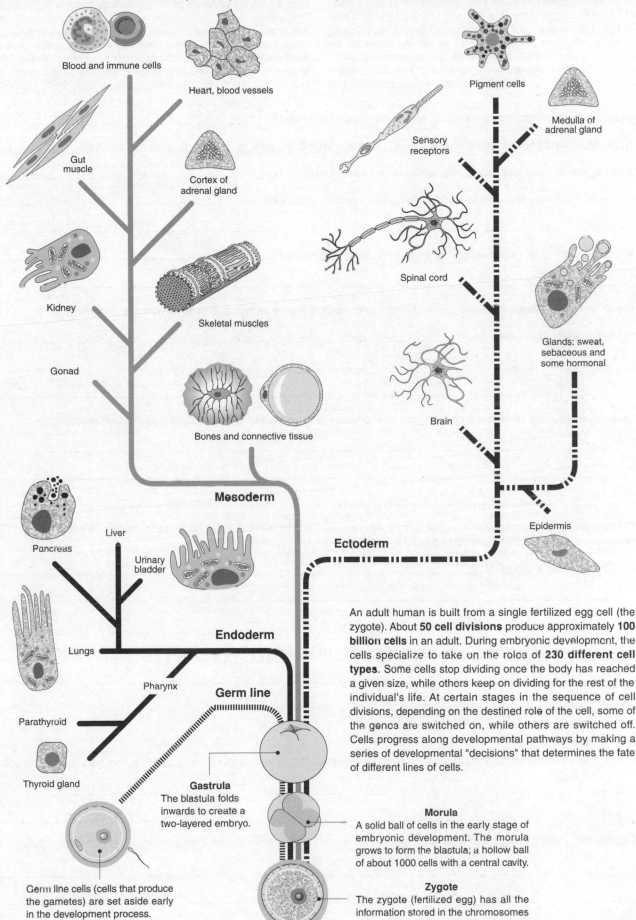

Blood and immune cells

Heart, blood vessels

Gut muscle

Cortex of adrenal gland

Kidney

Skeletal muscles

Gonad

Bones and connective tissue

**Mesoderm**

Pancreas

Liver

Urinary bladder

Lungs

Pharynx

**Endoderm**

Parathyroid

Thyroid gland

**Germ line**

Pigment cells

Sensory receptors

Medulla of adrenal gland

Spinal cord

Glands: sweat, sebaceous and some hormonal

Brain

**Ectoderm**

Epidermis

**Gastrula**
The blastula folds inwards to create a two-layered embryo.

Germ line cells (cells that produce the gametes) are set aside early in the development process.

An adult human is built from a single fertilized egg cell (the zygote). About **50 cell divisions** produce approximately **100 billion cells** in an adult. During embryonic development, the cells specialize to take on the roles of **230 different cell types**. Some cells stop dividing once the body has reached a given size, while others keep on dividing for the rest of the individual's life. At certain stages in the sequence of cell divisions, depending on the destined role of the cell, some of the genes are switched on, while others are switched off. Cells progress along developmental pathways by making a series of developmental "decisions" that determines the fate of different lines of cells.

**Morula**
A solid ball of cells in the early stage of embryonic development. The morula grows to form the blastula; a hollow ball of about 1000 cells with a central cavity.

**Zygote**
The zygote (fertilized egg) has all the information stored in the chromosomes to make a complete new individual

**Related activities**: Stem Cells and Tissue Engineering, Cloning by Nuclear transfer

RA 2

Development is the process of progressive change through the lifetime of an organism. Part of this process involves growth (increase in size) and cell division (to generate the multicellular body). Cellular **differentiation** (the generation of specialized cells) and **morphogenesis** (the creation of the shape and form of the body) are also part of development. Differentiation defines the specific structure and function of a cell. As development proceeds, the possibilities available to individual cells become fewer, until each cell's **fate** is determined. The tissues and organs making up the body form from the aggregation and organization of these differentiated cells. In animals, the final body form is the result of cell migration and the programed death of certain cells (**apoptosis**) during embryonic development. The diagram on the previous page shows how a single fertilized egg (zygote) gives rise to the large number of specialized cell types that make up the adult human body. The morula, blastula, and gastrula stages mentioned at the bottom of the diagram show the early development of the embryo from the zygote. The gastrula gives rise to the three layers of cells (ectoderm, mesoderm, and endoderm), from which specific cell types develop.

1. State how many different types of cell are found in the human body: _____

2. State approximately how many cell divisions take place from fertilized egg (zygote) to produce an adult: _____

3. State approximately how many cells make up an adult human body: _____

4. Name one cell type that continues to divide throughout a person's lifetime: _____

   _____

5. Name one cell type that does not continue to divide throughout a person's lifetime: _____

   _____

6. Germ line cells diverge (become isolated) from other cells at a very early stage in embryonic development.

   (a) Explain what the **germ line** is: _____

   _____

   _____

   (b) Explain why it is necessary for the germ line to become separated at such an early stage of development:

   _____

   _____

   _____

7. Cloning whole new organisms is possible by taking a nucleus from a cell during the blastula stage of embryonic development and placing it into an egg cell that has had its own nucleus removed.

   (a) Explain what a **clone** is: _____

   _____

   _____

   (b) Explain why the cell required for cloning needs to be taken at such an early stage of embryonic development:

   _____

   _____

   _____

8. Cancer cells are particularly damaging to organisms. Explain what has happened to a cell that has become cancerous:

   _____

   _____

9. Explain the genetic events that enable so many different cell types to arise from one unspecialized cell (the zygote):

   _____

   _____

   _____

# Stem Cells and Tissue Engineering

**Stem cells** are undifferentiated cells found in multicellular organisms. They are characterized by two features. The first, **self renewal**, is the ability to undergo numerous cycles of cell division while maintaining an unspecialized state. The second, **potency**, is the ability to differentiate into specialized cells. **Totipotent** cells, produced in the first few divisions of a fertilized egg, can differentiate into any cell type, embryonic or extra-embryonic. **Pluripotent cells** are descended from totipotent cells and can give rise to any of the cells derived from the three germ layers (endoderm, mesoderm, and ectoderm). Embryonic stem cells at the blastocyst stage and fetal stem cells are pluripotent. Adult (somatic) stem cells are termed **multipotent**. They are undifferentiated cells found among differentiated cells in a tissue or organ. These cells can give rise to several other cell types, but those types are limited mainly to the cells of the blood, heart, muscle and nerves. The primary roles of adult stem cells are to maintain and repair the tissue in which they are found. A potential use of stem cells is making cells and tissues for medical therapies, such as **cell replacement therapy** and **tissue engineering**. One example is described on the following page.

## Stem Cells and Blood Cell Production

New blood cells are produced in the red bone marrow, which becomes the main site of blood production after birth, taking over from the fetal liver. All types of blood cells develop from a single cell type: called a **multipotent stem cell** or hemocytoblast. These cells are capable of mitosis and of differentiation into 'committed' precursors of each of the main types of blood cell.

Each of the different cell lines is controlled by a specific **growth factor**. When a stem cell divides, one of its daughters remains a stem cell, while the other becomes a precursor cell, either a **lymphoid cell** or **myeloid cell**. These cells continue to mature into the various type of blood cells, developing their specialized features and characteristic roles as they do so.

1. Describe the two defining features of stem cells:

   (a) _____

   (b) _____

2. Distinguish between embryonic stem cells and adult stem cells with respect to their **potency** and their potential applications in medical technologies:

   _____

   _____

   _____

3. Using an example, explain the purpose of stem cells in an adult: _____

   _____

   _____

4. Describe one potential advantage of using embryonic stem cells for tissue engineering technology: _____

   _____

   _____

**Related activities**: Differentiation of Human Cells
**Web links**: Stem Cells in the Spotlight, Stem Cell Resources

RA 3

# Engineering a Living Skin

New technologies such as cell replacement therapy and tissue engineering require a disease-free and plentiful supply of cells of specific types. Tissue engineering, for example, involves inducing living cells to grow on a scaffold of natural or synthetic material to produce a three-dimensional tissue such as bone or skin.

In 1998, an artificial skin called **Apligraf** became the first product of this type to be approved for use as a biomedical device. It is now widely used in place of skin grafts to treat diabetic ulcers and burns, with the patient's own cells and tissues helping to complete the biological repair. Producing Apligraf is a three stage process (right), which results in a bilayered, living structure capable of stimulating wound repair through its own growth factors and proteins. The cells used to start the culture are usually obtained from discarded neonatal foreskins collected after circumcision. The key to future tissue engineering will be the developments in stem cell research. The best source of stem cells is from very early embryos, but some adult tissues (e.g. bone marrow) also contain stem cells.

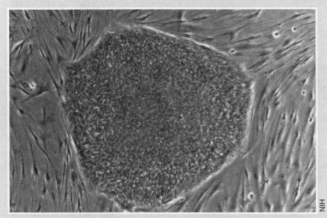

*Human embryonic stem cells (ESCs) growing on mouse embryonic fibroblasts. The mouse fibroblasts act as feeder cells for the culture, releasing nutrients and providing a surface for the ESCs to grow on.*

*Human dermal cells*

**Day 0**
Undifferentiated human dermal cells (fibroblasts) are combined with a gel containing **collagen**, the primary protein of skin. The dermal cells move through the gel, rearranging the collagen and producing a fibrous, living matrix similar to the natural dermis.

Collagen

**Step 1**
Form the lower dermal layer

*Human epidermal cells*

**Day 6**
Human epidermal cells (called **keratinocytes**) are placed on top of the dermal layer. These cells multiply to cover the dermal layer.

**Step 2**
Form the upper epidermal layer

**Day 10**
Exposing the culture to air prompts the epidermal cells to form the outer protective (keratinized) layer of skin. The final size of the Apligraf product is about 75 mm and, from this, tens of thousands of pieces can be made.

Air exposure

**Step 3**
Form the outer layer

5. Describe the benefits of using a tissue engineered skin product, such as Apligraf, to treat wounds that require grafts:

_____

_____

_____

6. Discuss the present and potential medical applications of tissue engineering: _____

_____

_____

_____

_____

_____

_____

_____

_____

_____

_____

# Human Cell Specialization

Animal cells are often specialized to perform particular functions. The eight specialized cell types shown below are representative of some 230 different cell types in humans. Each has specialized features that suit it to performing a specific role.

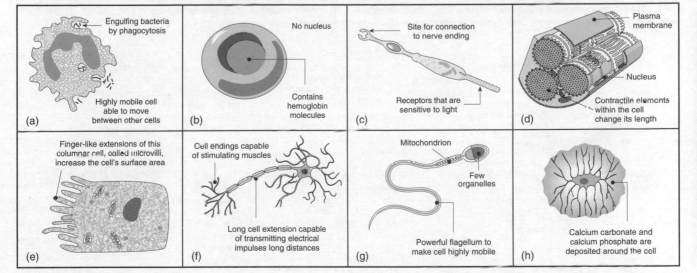

(a) Engulfing bacteria by phagocytosis. Highly mobile cell able to move between other cells

(b) No nucleus. Contains hemoglobin molecules

(c) Site for connection to nerve ending. Receptors that are sensitive to light

(d) Plasma membrane. Nucleus. Contractile elements within the cell change its length

(e) Finger-like extensions of this columnar cell, called microvilli, increase the cell's surface area

(f) Cell endings capable of stimulating muscles. Long cell extension capable of transmitting electrical impulses long distances

(g) Mitochondrion. Few organelles. Powerful flagellum to make cell highly mobile

(h) Calcium carbonate and calcium phosphate are deposited around the cell

1.  **Identify** each of the cells (b) to (h) pictured above, and describe their **specialized features** and **role** in the body:

(a) Type of cell: _Phagocytic white blood cell (neutrophil)_

Specialized features: _Engulfs bacteria and other foreign material by phagocytosis_

Role of cell within body: _Destroys pathogens and other foreign material as well as cellular debris_

(b) Type of cell: _____

Specialized features: _____

Role of cell within body: _____

(c) Type of cell: _____

Specialized features: _____

Role of cell within body: _____

(d) Type of cell: _____

Specialized features: _____

Role of cell within body: _____

(e) Type of cell: _____

Specialized features: _____

Role of cell within body: _____

(f) Type of cell: _____

Specialized features: _____

Role of cell within body: _____

(g) Type of cell: _____

Specialized features: _____

Role of cell within body: _____

(h) Type of cell: _____

Specialized features: _____

Role of cell within body: _____

**Related activities**: Differentiation of Human Cells, Stem Cells and Tissue Engineering

RA 2

# Plant Cell Specialization

Plants show a wide variety of cell types. The vegetative plant body consists of three organs: stems, leaves, and roots. Flowers, fruits, and seeds comprise additional organs that are concerned with reproduction. The eight cell types illustrated below are representatives of these plant organ systems. Each has structural or physiological features that set it apart from the other cell types. The differentiation of cells enables each specialized type to fulfill a specific role in the plant.

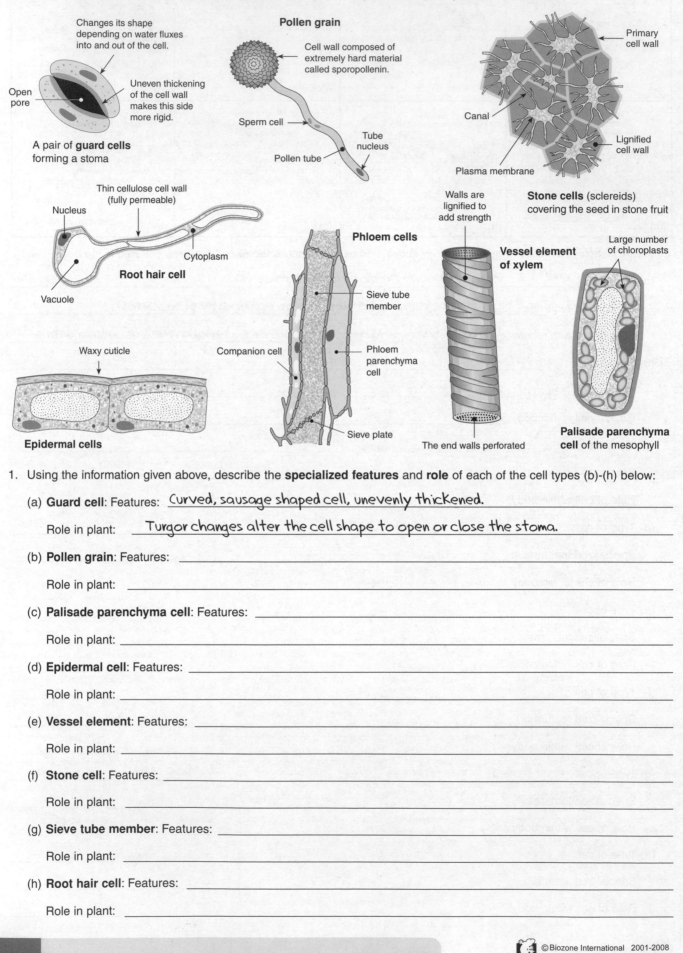

1. Using the information given above, describe the **specialized features** and **role** of each of the cell types (b)-(h) below:

(a) **Guard cell**: Features: _Curved, sausage shaped cell, unevenly thickened._

   Role in plant: _Turgor changes alter the cell shape to open or close the stoma._

(b) **Pollen grain**: Features: _____

   Role in plant: _____

(c) **Palisade parenchyma cell**: Features: _____

   Role in plant: _____

(d) **Epidermal cell**: Features: _____

   Role in plant: _____

(e) **Vessel element**: Features: _____

   Role in plant: _____

(f) **Stone cell**: Features: _____

   Role in plant: _____

(g) **Sieve tube member**: Features: _____

   Role in plant: _____

(h) **Root hair cell**: Features: _____

   Role in plant: _____

**Related activities**: Root Cell Development

# Levels of Organization

Organization and the emergence of novel properties in complex systems are two of the defining features of living organisms. Organisms are organized according to a hierarchy of structural levels (below), each level building on the one below it. At each level, novel properties emerge that were not present at the simpler level. Hierarchical organization allows specialized cells to group together into tissues and organs to perform a particular function. This improves efficiency of function in the organism.

In the spaces provided for each question below, assign each of the examples listed to one of the levels of organisation as indicated.

1. **Animals**: *adrenaline, blood, bone, brain, cardiac muscle, cartilage, collagen, DNA, heart, leukocyte, lysosome, mast cell, nervous system, neuron, phospholipid, reproductive system, ribosomes, Schwann cell, spleen, squamous epithelium.*

   (a) Organ system: _____

   _____

   (b) Organs: _____

   _____

   (c) Tissues: _____

   _____

   (d) Cells: _____

   _____

   (e) Organelles: _____

   _____

   (f) Molecular level: _____

   _____

   _____

2. **Plants**: *cellulose, chloroplasts, collenchyma, companion cells, DNA, epidermal cell, fibers, flowers, leaf, mesophyll, parenchyma, pectin, phloem, phospholipid, ribosomes, roots, sclerenchyma, tracheid.*

   (a) Organs: _____

   _____

   (b) Tissues: _____

   _____

   (c) Cells: _____

   _____

   (d) Organelles: _____

   _____

   (e) Molecular level: _____

   _____

   _____

**The Organism**

A complex, functioning whole that is the sum of all its component parts.

**Organ System Level**

In animals, organs form parts of even larger units known as organ systems. An organ system is an association of organs with a common function, e.g. digestive system, cardiovascular system, and the urinogenital system.

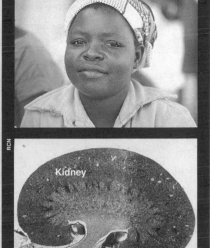

**Organ Level**

Organs are structures of definite form and structure, comprising two or more tissues.

***Animal examples*** include: heart, lungs, brain, stomach, kidney.

***Plant examples*** include: leaves, roots, storage organs, ovary.

Kidney

**Tissue Level**

Tissues are composed of groups of cells of similar structure that perform a particular, related function.

***Animal examples*** include: epithelial tissue, bone, muscle.

***Plant examples*** include: phloem, chlorenchyma, endodermis, xylem.

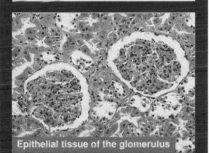

Epithelial tissue of the glomerulus

**Cellular Level**

Cells are the basic structural and functional units of an organism. Each cell type has a different structure and function (the result of cellular differentiation during development).

***Animal examples*** include: epithelial cells, osteoblasts, muscle fibers.

***Plant examples*** include: sclereids, xylem vessels, sieve tubes.

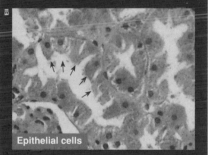

Epithelial cells

**Organelle Level**

Many diverse molecules may associate together to form complex, highly specialized structures within cells called cellular organelles, e.g. mitochondria, Golgi apparatus, endoplasmic reticulum, chloroplasts.

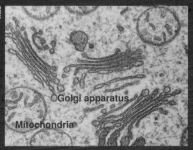

Golgi apparatus

Mitochondria

**Chemical and Molecular Level**

Atoms and molecules form the most basic, level of organization. This level includes all the chemicals essential for maintaining life, e.g. water, ions, fats, carbohydrates, amino acids, proteins, and nucleic acids.

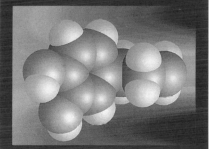

# Animal Tissues

The study of tissues (plant or animal) is called **histology**. The cells of a tissue, and their associated intracellular substances, e.g. collagen, are grouped together to perform particular functions. Tissues improve the efficiency of operation because they enable tasks to be shared amongst various specialized cells. **Animal tissues** can be divided into four broad groups: **epithelial tissues**, **connective tissues**, **muscle**, and **nervous**

**tissues**. Organs usually consist of several types of tissue. The heart mostly consists of cardiac muscle tissue, but also has epithelial tissue, which lines the heart chambers to prevent leaking, connective tissue for strength and elasticity, and nervous tissue, in the form of neurones, which direct the contractions of the cardiac muscle. The features of some of he more familiar animal tissues are described below.

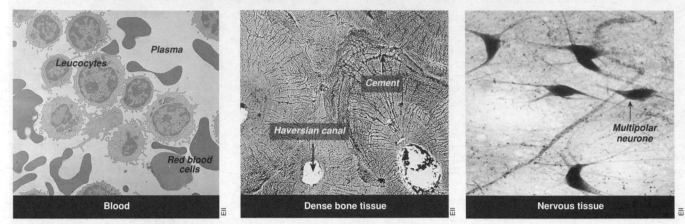

Blood | Dense bone tissue | Nervous tissue

**Connective tissue** is the major supporting tissue of the animal body. It comprises cells, widely dispersed in a semi-fluid matrix. Connective tissues bind other structures together and provide support, and protection against damage, infection, or heat loss. Connective tissues include dentine (teeth), adipose (fat) tissue, bone (above) and cartilage, and the tissues around the body's organs and blood vessels. Blood (above, left) is a special type of liquid tissue, comprising cells floating in a liquid matrix.

**Nervous tissue** contains densely packed nerve cells (neurones) which are specialized for the transmission of nerve impulses. Associated with the neurones there may also be supporting cells and connective tissue containing blood vessels.

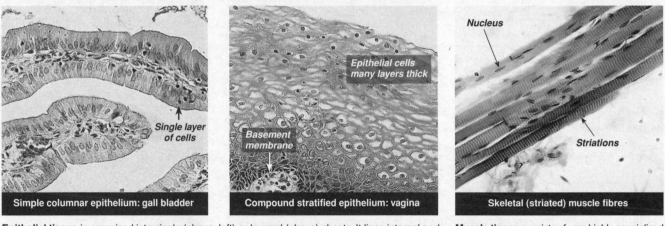

Simple columnar epithelium: gall bladder | Compound stratified epithelium: vagina | Skeletal (striated) muscle fibres

**Epithelial tissue** is organized into single (above, left) or layered (above) sheets. It lines internal and external surfaces (e.g. blood vessels, ducts, gut lining) and protects the underlying structures from wear, infection, and/or pressure. Epithelial cells rest on a basement membrane of fibres and collagen and are held together by a carbohydrate-based "glue". The cells may also be specialized for absorption, secretion, or excretion. Examples: stratified (compound) epithelium of vagina, ciliated epithelium of respiratory tract, cuboidal epithelium of kidney ducts, and the columnar epithelium of the intestine.

**Muscle tissue** consists of very highly specialized cells called fibres, held together by connective tissue. The three types of muscle in the body are cardiac muscle, skeletal muscle (above), and smooth muscle. Muscles bring about both voluntary and involuntary (unconscious) body movements.

1. Explain how the development of tissues improves functional efficiency: _____

_____

_____

2. Describe the general functional role of each of the following broad tissue types:

   (a) Epithelial tissue: _____     (c) Muscle tissue: _____

   (b) Nervous tissue: _____     (d) Connective tissue: _____

3. Identify the particular features that contribute to the particular functional role of each of the following tissue types:

   (a) Muscle tissue: _____

   _____

   (b) Nervous tissue: _____

   _____

© Biozone International 2001-2008

# Plant Tissues

Plant tissues are divided into two groups: simple and complex. **Simple tissues** contain only one cell type and form packing and support tissues. **Complex tissues** contain more than one cell type and form the conducting and support tissues of plants. Tissues are in turn grouped into tissue systems which make up the plant body. Vascular plants have three systems; the dermal, vascular, and ground tissue systems. The **dermal system** is the outer covering of the plant providing protection and reducing water loss. **Vascular tissue** provides the transport system by which water and nutrients are moved through the plant. The **ground tissue** system, which makes up the bulk of a plant, is made up mainly of simple tissues such as parenchyma, and carries out a wide variety of roles within the plant including photosynthesis, storage, and support.

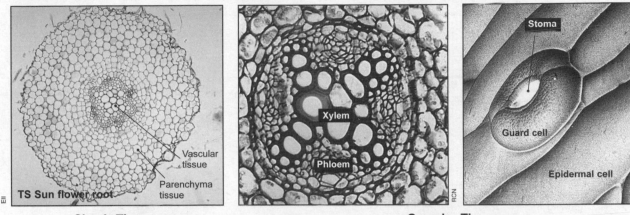

TS Sun flower root — Vascular tissue, Parenchyma tissue

Xylem, Phloem

Stoma, Guard cell, Epidermal cell

## Simple Tissues

Simple tissues consists of only one or two cell types. **Parenchyma tissue** is the most common and involved in storage, photosynthesis, and secretion. **Collenchyma tissue** comprises thick-walled collenchyma cells alternating with layers of intracellular substances (pectin and cellulose) to provide flexible support. The cells of **sclerenchyma** tissue (fibers and sclereids) have rigid cell walls which provide support.

## Complex Tissues

Xylem and phloem tissue (above left), which together make up the plant **vascular tissue** system, are complex tissues. Each comprises several tissue types including tracheids, vessel members, parenchyma and fibres in xylem, and sieve tube members, companion cells, parenchyma and sclerenchyma in phloem. **Dermal tissue** is also complex tissue and covers the outside of the plant. The composition of dermal tissue varies depending upon its location on the plant. Root epidermal tissue consist of epidermal cells which extend to root hairs (**trichomes**) for increasing surface area. In contrast, the epidermal tissue of leaves (above right) are covered by a waxy cuticle to reduce water loss, and specialised guard cells regulate water intake via the stomata (pores in the leaf through which gases enter and leave the leaf tissue).

1.  The table below lists the major types of simple and complex plant tissue. Complete the table by filling in the role each of the tissue types plays within the plant. The first example has been completed for you.

| Simple Tissue | Cell Type(s) | Role within the Plant |
|---|---|---|
| Parenchyma | Parenchyma cells | Involved in respiration, photosynthesis, storage and secretion. |
| Collenchyma | | |
| Sclerenchyma | | |
| Root endodermis | Endodermal cells | |
| Pericycle | | |
| **Complex Tissue** | | |
| Leaf mesophyll | Spongy mesophyll cells, palisade mesophyll cells | |
| Xylem | | |
| Phloem | | |
| Epidermis | | |

# Root Cell Development

In plants, cell division for growth (mitosis) is restricted to growing tips called **meristematic** tissue. These are located at the tips of every stem and root. This is unlike mitosis in a growing animal where cell divisions can occur all over the body. The diagram below illustrates the position and appearance of developing and growing cells in a plant root. Similar zones of development occur in the growing stem tips, which may give rise to specialized structures such as leaves and flowers.

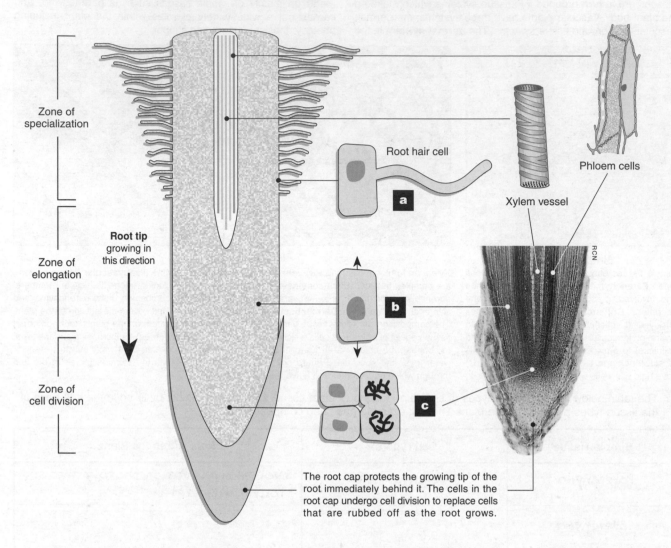

Zone of specialization

Root hair cell

**a**

Phloem cells

Xylem vessel

Root tip growing in this direction

Zone of elongation

**b**

Zone of cell division

**c**

The root cap protects the growing tip of the root immediately behind it. The cells in the root cap undergo cell division to replace cells that are rubbed off as the root grows.

1. Briefly describe what is happening to the plant cells at each of the points labelled **a** to **c** in the diagram above:

(a) _____

(b) _____

(c) _____

2. The light micrograph (below) shows a section of the cells of an onion root tip, stained to show up the chromosomes.

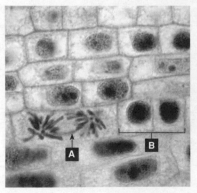

(a) State the mitotic stage of the cell labeled **A** and explain your answer:

_____

_____

(b) State the mitotic stage just completed in the cells labeled **B** and explain:

_____

_____

(c) If, in this example, 250 cells were examined and 25 were found to be in the process of mitosis, state the proportion of the cell cycle occupied by mitosis:

_____

_____

3. Identify the cells that divide and specialize when a tree increases its girth (diameter): _____

# Cellular Energetics

**IB SL**

Complete:
1-3, 6-10, 12-13, 17-18, 22-23, 25, 29
Extension:
4, 21

**IB HL**

Complete:
1-4, 6-12, 14-18, 22-30
Extension:
19-21

**IB Options**

Complete:
Option C:
SL: 14-16, 24, 26-28, 30

**AP Biology**

Complete:
1-12, 13 or 14, 15-30

## Learning Objectives

☐ 1. Compile your own glossary from the **KEY WORDS** displayed in **bold type** in the learning objectives below.

### The Role of ATP (pages 133-134)

☐ 2. Explain the need for energy in living things and the universal role of ATP in **metabolism**, as illustrated by specific examples e.g. **glycolysis**, **active transport**, **anabolic reactions**, movement, and thermoregulation.

☐ 3. Describe the structure of **ATP** as a phosphorylated nucleotide. Describe its synthesis from ADP and inorganic phosphate (P$_i$) and explain how it stores and releases its energy.

☐ 4. Recall the role of enzymes in the control of **metabolic pathways** as illustrated by specific examples (e.g. in photosynthesis and cellular respiration).

☐ 5. Recall what is meant by the terms **endergonic** and **exergonic**. Provide examples of endergonic and exergonic reactions in biological systems.

☐ 6. Outline the principles involved in **photosynthesis** and **cellular respiration**, explaining in which way the two processes can be considered opposites.

☐ 7. Appreciate that both photosynthesis and cellular respiration involve the molecule **ATP** and hydrogen carriers, and identify these for each process.

### Cellular Respiration (pages 133-139)

#### Introduction to respiration

☐ 8. Draw and label the structure of a **mitochondrion**, including the **matrix**, the outer and inner membrane and the **cristae**. Explain the relationship between the structure of the mitochondrion and its function.

☐ 9. Identify the main steps in cellular respiration: **glycolysis**, **Krebs cycle** (*tricarboxylic acid cycle*) **electron transport system** (*electron transport chain, ETS, or respiratory chain*). On a diagram of a mitochondrion, indicate where each stage occurs. Recognise glycolysis as first stage in cellular respiration and the major anaerobic pathway in cells.

☐ 10. Identify **glucose** as the main respiratory substrate. Appreciate that other substrates can, through conversion, act as substrates for cellular respiration.

☐ 11. Describe the central role of **acetyl CoA** in carbohydrate and fat metabolism.

☐ 12. Outline **glycolysis** as the phosphorylation of glucose and the subsequent splitting of a 6C sugar into two triose phosphate molecules (2 X **pyruvate**). State the net yield of ATP and NADH$_2$ from glycolysis and appreciate that the subsequent metabolism of pyruvate depends on the availability of oxygen.

### Aerobic respiration

☐ 13. Describe the complete oxidation of glucose to CO$_2$, with reference to:
- The conversion of pyruvate to **acetyl-coenzyme A**.
- The stepwise oxidation of intermediates.
- Generation of **ATP** in the electron transport chain.
- The role of oxygen as the terminal electron acceptor and the formation of water.
- The net yield of ATP from aerobic respiration compared to the yield from glycolysis.

☐ 14. Describe the complete oxidation of glucose to CO$_2$, with reference to:
- The conversion of pyruvate to **acetyl-coenzyme A**.
- The entry of acetyl CoA into the Krebs cycle by combination with **oxaloacetate**.
- The **Krebs cycle** (as a series of oxidation reactions involving release of CO$_2$, the production of NADH$_2$ or FADH$_2$, and the regeneration of oxaloacetate).
- The *role* of the coenzymes NAD and FAD.
- In simple terms, the synthesis of **ATP** by **oxidative phosphorylation** in the electron transport chain.
- The role of oxygen as the terminal electron acceptor and the formation of water.
- The net yield of ATP from aerobic respiration compared to the yield from glycolysis.

☐ 15. Explain oxidative phosphorylation in terms of **chemiosmosis** (the coupling of electron transport and the movement of hydrogen ions to the synthesis of ATP). Identify the role of the **electron carriers** and **ATP synthetase** (ATPase) in this process.

☐ 16. Understand the terms **decarboxylation** and **dehydrogenation** as they relate to the Krebs cycle.

### Fermentation

☐ 17. Understand the situations in which the pyruvate formed in glycolysis may not undergo complete oxidation. Describe the following examples of **fermentation**, identifying the H$^+$ acceptor to each case:
   (a) Formation of **lactic acid** in muscle.
   (b) Formation of **ethanol** in yeast.

   *NOTE: Although fermentation is often used synonymously with anaerobic respiration, they are not the same. Respiration always involves hydrogen ions passing down a chain of carriers to a terminal acceptor, and this does not occur in fermentation. In anaerobic respiration, the terminal H$^+$ acceptor is a molecule other than oxygen, e.g. Fe$^{2+}$ or nitrate.*

☐ 18. Compare and explain the differences in the yields of ATP from aerobic respiration and from fermentation.

### Respiratory quotients

☐ 19. Describe the relative energy values of carbohydrate, lipid, and protein as respiratory substrates. Explain the term **respiratory quotient** (RQ). Explain what RQ reveals about the substrate being respired.

☐ 20. Use a simple respirometer to measure RQ.

## Photosynthesis  (pages 140-144)

### The structure of the dicot leaf

☐ 21. Recognize the leaf as the main photosynthetic organ in plants. Appreciate structural features of the dicot leaf related to its functional role. *See SB 2: "Plant Structure and Adaptation" for coverage of this material.*

### Chloroplasts

☐ 22. Describe the structure of **chloroplasts**, identifying the **stroma**, **grana**, lamellae (**thylakoids**), and location of the chlorophylls and other pigments. Relate the chloroplast structure you have described to its function.

☐ 23. Describe the role of **chlorophyll *a* and *b*,** and **accessory pigments** (e.g. carotenoids) in light capture. Outline the differences in absorption of red, green, and blue light by chlorophyll.

☐ 24. In more detail than in #23 above, describe the absorption of light by chlorophyll a and b, and **accessory pigments**. In particular, explain what is meant by the terms **absorption spectrum** and **action spectrum** with respect to the light absorbing pigments.

### Photosynthesis in C3 plants

Describe, using diagrams, the reactions of photosynthesis in a C3 plant with reference to:

☐ 25. The *light dependent phase (LDP)* with reference to:
  • Where in the chloroplast the LDP occurs.
  • The generation of ATP and NADPH$_2$ for use in the light independent phase.

☐ 26. In more detail than in #25 above describe the light dependent phase (LDP) with reference to:

  • The location and role of the photosystems.
  • The **photoactivation** of chlorophyll.
  • The splitting of water (**photolysis**) to produce protons and electrons.
  • The production of O$_2$ as a result of photolysis.
  • The transfer of energy to ATP (photophosphorylation) and the formation of NADPH$_2$ (reduced NADP).

☐ 27. In greater detail than in #26 above, explain photophosphorylation in terms of **chemiosmosis** (the coupling of electron transport and the movement of hydrogen ions to the synthesis of ATP). Relate the accumulation of H$^+$ inside the thylakoid to the generation of ATP by **ATP synthetase** (ATPase).

☐ 28. Distinguish between cyclic and non-cyclic (photo) phosphorylation:
  • **Cyclic photophosphorylation**: electrons leaving photosystem I return to photosystem I with the generation of ATP but no NADPH$_2$.
  • **Non-cyclic photophosphorylation**: electrons leaving photosystem I are replaced by the photolysis of water by photosystem II with the generation of ATP and NADPH$_2$. This normal flow of electrons is linear from photosystem II to photosystem I.

☐ 29. The *light independent phase (LIP)* with reference to:
  • Where in the chloroplast the LIP occurs.
  • The **Calvin cycle** and the fixation of carbon dioxide using ATP and NADPH$_2$ generated in the light dependent phase.

☐ 30. In more detail than in #29 above describe the light independent phase (LIP) with reference to the **Calvin cycle** including the following:
  • The fixation of carbon dioxide into a 5C compound, **ribulose bisphosphate** (RuBP).
  • The reduction of **glycerate-3-phosphate** (PGA) to **carbohydrate** and the role of **ATP** and **NADPH$_2$** (formed in the light dependent phase) in this.
  • The regeneration of the ribulose bisphosphate.

---

 See the 'Textbook Reference Grid' on pages 8-9 for textbook page references relating to material in this topic.

### Supplementary Texts

See pages 5-6 for additional details of these texts:

■ Adds, J. *et al.*, 2003. **Respiration and Coordination** (NelsonThornes), pp. 1-8 (respiration).

■ Helms, D.R. *et al.*, 1998. **Biology in the Laboratory** (W.H. Freeman) #11, #12.

■ Tobin, A.J. and Morel, R.E., 1997. **Asking About Cells**, (Thomson Brooks/Cole), part II.

See page 6 for details of publishers of periodicals:

### STUDENT'S REFERENCE

■ **Growing Plants in the Perfect Environment** Biol. Sci. Rev., 15(2) Nov. 2002, pp. 12-16. *To manipulate the growth of plants in controlled environments, one must understand how plants grow and what influences photosynthetic rate.*

■ **Photosynthesis....Most hated Topic?** Biol. Sci. Rev., 20(1) Sept. 200, pp. 13-16. *A useful account documenting key points when learning about processes in photosynthesis.*

■ **Glucose Catabolism** Biol. Sci. Rev., 10(3) January 1998, pp. 22-24. *The biological role of glucose in cells: oxidative phosphorylation and the role of mitochondria.*

■ **Why Don't Plants Wear Sunhats?** Biol. Sci. Rev., 9(3) Jan. 1997, pp. 32-35. *Plants need light, but too much is damaging - how do they cope?*

■ **The Role of ATP in Cells** Biol. Sci. Rev., 19(2) Nov. 2006, pp. 30-33. *Synthesis and uses of ATP.*

■ **Fat Burns in the Flame of Carbohydrate** Biol. Sci. Rev., 15(3) Feb. 2003, pp. 37-41. *A thorough account of both carbohydrate metabolism and how fatty acid oxidation feeds into the Krebs cycle.*

■ **Chlorophyll** Biol. Sci. Rev., 8(3) Jan. 1996, pp. 28-30. *The chlorophyll molecule: how it absorbs light and its role in photosynthesis.*

### TEACHER'S REFERENCE

■ **The Bigger Picture** New Scientist, June 2000, pp. 54-61. *Understanding the complexity of biochemical pathways and the effects of altering genetic constitution.*

■ **Simple Inexpensive Respirometers & Demonstrations Where Plants do the Unexpected: Give off Carbon Dioxide!** The Am. Biology Teacher, 68(5) May 2006, pp. 293-295. *Students design experiments to measure plant respiration inside plastic pipettes.*

■ **The Photosynthetic Dark Reactions do not Operate in the Dark** The Am. Biology Teacher, 62(3) March 2000, pp. 166-170. *This account explores the common misconception that the 'dark' reactions occur in the dark.*

■ **Learn about Cellular Respiration** The Am. Biology Teacher, 60(9) Nov. 1998, pp. 681-683. *Some great ideas on how to explore the concepts relating to cellular respiration.*

■ **Measuring the Metabolism of Small Organisms** Scientific American, Dec. 1995, pp. 84-85. *Methods of measuring and monitoring respiration and metabolic rate in small organisms.*

See pages 10-11 for details of how to access **Bio Links** from our web site: **www.thebiozone.com** From Bio Links, access sites under the topics: **GENERAL BIOLOGY ONLINE RESOURCES >** **Online Textbooks and Lecture Notes:** • S-Cool! A level biology revision guide • Learn.co.uk • Mark Rothery's biology web site ... *and others* **CELL BIOLOGY AND BIOCHEMISTRY:** • Cell and molecular biology online • MIT biology hypertextbook ... *and others* > **Biochemistry and Metabolic Pathways:** • Calvin cycle (C3 cycle) • Cellular energy references • Cellular respiration • Cycle (Krebs cycle, citric acid cycle) • Electron transport chain • Energy, enzymes, and catalysis problem set • Glycolysis • Learning about photosynthesis • Chapter 7: Metabolism and biochemistry ... *and others*

**Presentation MEDIA** to support this topic:

**CELL BIOLOGY AND BIOCHEMISTRY**

*Cell Biology & Biochemistry*

---

# Energy in Cells

A summary of the flow of energy within a plant cell is illustrated below. Animal cells have a similar flow except the glucose is supplied by feeding rather than by photosynthesis. The energy not immediately stored in chemical bonds is lost as heat. Note the role of ATP; it is made in cellular respiration and provides the energy for metabolic reactions, including photosynthesis.

## Energy Transformations in a Photosynthetic Plant Cell

**Photosynthesis** is a chemical process that captures light energy and stores it as potential chemical energy.

**Light energy**

Oxygen

**\*Note:** Heterotrophic organisms (with the exception of photoheterotrophs) are dependent on organic molecules ('food') to provide the ultimate energy source for cellular respiration.

**Photosynthesis**

**Glucose \***

Other uses of glucose

Oxygen

Fuel

ADP

**Respiration**

Carbon dioxide + water

ATP provides energy for metabolic reactions. While some energy is stored in chemical bonds, some is lost as heat

**ATP**

Water

Heat energy

Carbon dioxide

**Cellular respiration** is a chemical process that releases energy from glucose to make the energy available (in the form of ATP) to power metabolic reactions.

**Cellular Energetics**

1. Distinguish between **heterotrophs**, **photosynthetic autotrophs**, and **chemosynthetic autotrophs** with respect to how these organisms derive their source of energy for metabolism:

_____

_____

_____

_____

_____

2. In 1977, scientists working near the Galapagos Islands in the equatorial eastern Pacific found warm water spewing from cracks in the mid-oceanic ridges 2600 meters below the surface. Clustered around these hydrothermal vents were strange and beautiful creatures new to science. The entire community depends on sulfur-oxidizing bacteria that use hydrogen sulfide dissolved in the venting water as an energy source to manufacture carbohydrates. This process is similar to photosynthesis, but does not rely on sunlight to provide the energy for generating ATP and fixing carbon:

(a) Explain why a community based on photosynthetic organisms is not found at this site: _____

_____

(b) Name the ultimate energy source for the bacteria: _____

(c) This same chemical that provides the bacteria with energy is also toxic to the process of cellular respiration; a problem that the animals living in the habitat have resolved by evolving various adaptations. Explain what would happen if these animals did not possess adaptations to reduce the toxic effect on cellular respiration:

_____

(d) Name the energy source classification for these sulfur-oxidizing bacteria: _____

**Related activities:** Photosynthesis, Cellular Respiration

**RA 2**

# The Role of ATP in Cells

The molecule ATP (adenosine triphosphate) is the universal energy carrier for the cell. ATP can release its energy quickly; only one chemical reaction (hydrolysis of the terminal phosphate) is required. This reaction is catalyzed by the enzyme ATPase. Once ATP has released its energy, it becomes ADP (adenosine diphosphate), a low energy molecule that can be recharged by adding a phosphate. This requires energy, which is supplied by the controlled breakdown of respiratory substrates in cellular respiration. The most common respiratory substrate is glucose, but other molecules (e.g. fats or proteins) may also be used.

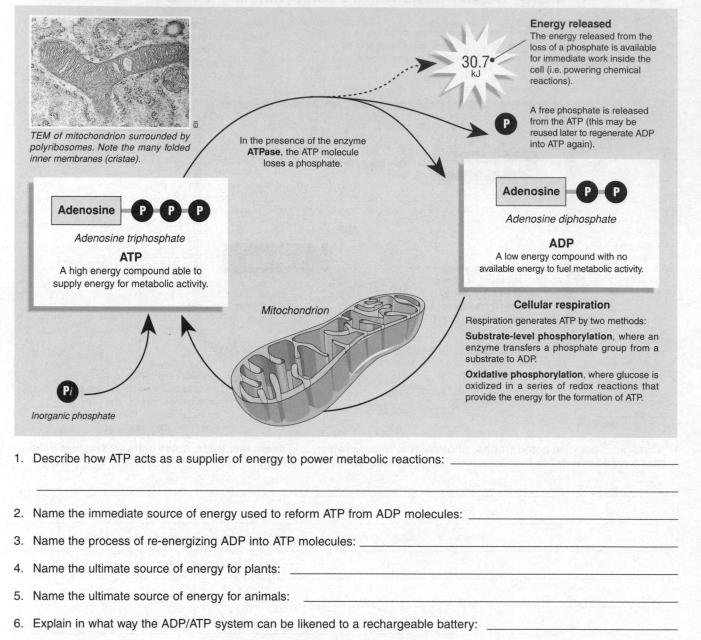

*TEM of mitochondrion surrounded by polyribosomes. Note the many folded inner membranes (cristae).*

**Energy released**
The energy released from the loss of a phosphate is available for immediate work inside the cell (i.e. powering chemical reactions).

A free phosphate is released from the ATP (this may be reused later to regenerate ADP into ATP again).

In the presence of the enzyme **ATPase**, the ATP molecule loses a phosphate.

**Adenosine** P P P
*Adenosine triphosphate*
**ATP**
A high energy compound able to supply energy for metabolic activity.

**Adenosine** P P
*Adenosine diphosphate*
**ADP**
A low energy compound with no available energy to fuel metabolic activity.

P*i*
*Inorganic phosphate*

*Mitochondrion*

**Cellular respiration**
Respiration generates ATP by two methods:

**Substrate-level phosphorylation**, where an enzyme transfers a phosphate group from a substrate to ADP.

**Oxidative phosphorylation**, where glucose is oxidized in a series of redox reactions that provide the energy for the formation of ATP.

1. Describe how ATP acts as a supplier of energy to power metabolic reactions: _____

2. Name the immediate source of energy used to reform ATP from ADP molecules: _____

3. Name the process of re-energizing ADP into ATP molecules: _____

4. Name the ultimate source of energy for plants: _____

5. Name the ultimate source of energy for animals: _____

6. Explain in what way the ADP/ATP system can be likened to a rechargeable battery: _____

7. In the following table, use brief statements to contrast photosynthesis and respiration in terms of the following:

| Feature | Photosynthesis | Cellular respiration |
|---|---|---|
| Starting materials | | |
| Waste products | | |
| Role of hydrogen carriers: NAD, NADP | | |
| Role of ATP | | |
| Overall biological role | | |

**Related activities**: Energy in Cells, Cellular Respiration, Photosynthesis

# Measuring Respiration

In small animals or germinating seeds, the rate of cellular respiration can be measured using a simple respirometer: a sealed unit where the carbon dioxide produced by the respiring tissues is absorbed by soda lime and the volume of oxygen consumed is detected by fluid displacement in a manometer. Germinating seeds are also often used to calculate the **respiratory quotient** (RQ): the ratio of the amount of carbon dioxide produced during cellular respiration to the amount of oxygen consumed. RQ provides a useful indication of the respiratory substrate being used.

## Respiratory Substrates and RQ

The respiratory quotient (RQ) can be expressed simply as:

$$RQ = \frac{CO_2 \text{ produced}}{O_2 \text{ consumed}}$$

When pure carbohydrate is oxidized in cellular respiration, the RQ is 1.0; more oxygen is required to oxidize fatty acids (RQ = 0.7). The RQ for protein is about 0.9. Organisms usually respire a mix of substrates, giving RQ values of between 0.8 and 0.9 (see table 1, below).

**Table 1**: RQ values for the respiration of various substrates

| RQ | Substrate |
|---|---|
| > 1.0 | Carbohydrate with some anaerobic respiration |
| 1.0 | Carbohydrates e.g. glucose |
| 0.9 | Protein |
| 0.7 | Fat |
| 0.5 | Fat with associated carbohydrate synthesis |
| 0.3 | Carbohydrate with associated organic acid synthesis |

## Using RQ to determine respiratory substrate

**Fig. 1**: RQ in relation to germination stage in wheat

Modified after Clegg and MacKean 1994

Mainly carbohydrates are used later in germination

Respiratory substrate is largely fat during early germination

Fig. 1, above, shows how experimental RQ values have been used to determine the respiratory substrate utilized by germinating wheat seeds (*Triticum sativum*) over the period of their germination.

**Table 2**: Rates of $O_2$ consumption and $CO_2$ production in crickets

| Time after last fed (h) | Temperature (°C) | Rate of $O_2$ consumption $(mlg^{-1}h^{-1})$ | Rate of $CO_2$ production $(mlg^{-1}h^{-1})$ |
|---|---|---|---|
| 1 | 20 | 2.82 | 2.82 |
| 48 | 20 | 2.82 | 1.97 |
| 1 | 30 | 5.12 | 5.12 |
| 48 | 30 | 5.12 | 3.57 |

Table 2 shows the rates of oxygen consumption and carbon dioxide production of crickets kept under different experimental conditions.

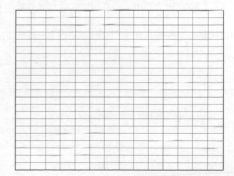

1. Table 2 above shows the results of an experiment to measure the rates of oxygen consumption and carbon dioxide production of crickets 1 hour and 48 hours after feeding at different temperatures:

   (a) Calculate the RQ of a cricket kept at 20°C, 48 hours after feeding (show working): _____

   (b) Compare this RQ to the RQ value obtained for the cricket 1 hour after being fed (20°C). Explain the difference:

   _____

   _____

2. The RQs of two species of seeds were calculated at two day intervals after germination. Results are tabulated to the right:

   (a) Plot the change in RQ of the two species during early germination:

   (b) Explain the values in terms of the possible substrates being respired:

   _____
   _____
   _____
   _____
   _____
   _____
   _____

| Days after germination | RQ | |
|---|---|---|
| | Seedling A | Seedling B |
| 2 | 0.65 | 0.70 |
| 4 | 0.35 | 0.91 |
| 6 | 0.48 | 0.98 |
| 8 | 0.68 | 1.00 |
| 10 | 0.70 | 1.00 |

Cellular Energetics

DA 2

# Cellular Respiration

Cellular respiration is the process by which organisms break down energy rich molecules (e.g. glucose) to release the energy in a usable form (ATP). All living cells respire in order to exist, although the substrates they use may vary. **Aerobic respiration** requires oxygen. Forms of cellular respiration that do not require oxygen are said to be **anaerobic**. Some plants and animals can generate ATP anaerobically for short periods of time. Other organisms use only anaerobic respiration and live in oxygen-free environments. For these organisms, there is some other final electron acceptor other than oxygen (e.g. nitrate or $Fe^{2+}$).

## An Overview of Cellular Respiration

Respiration involves three metabolic stages, summarized below. The first two stages are the catabolic pathways that decompose glucose and other organic fuels. In the third stage, the electron transport chain accepts electrons from the first two stages and passes these from one electron acceptor to another. The energy released at each stepwise transfer is used to make ATP. The final electron acceptor in this process is molecular oxygen.

1  **Glycolysis**. This occurs in the cytoplasm and involves the breakdown of glucose into two molecules of pyruvate.

2  **The Krebs cycle**. This occurs in the mitochondrial matrix, and decomposes a derivative of pyruvate to carbon dioxide.

3  **Electron transport and oxidative phosphorylation**. This occurs in the inner membranes of the mitochondrion and accounts for almost 90% of the ATP generated by respiration.

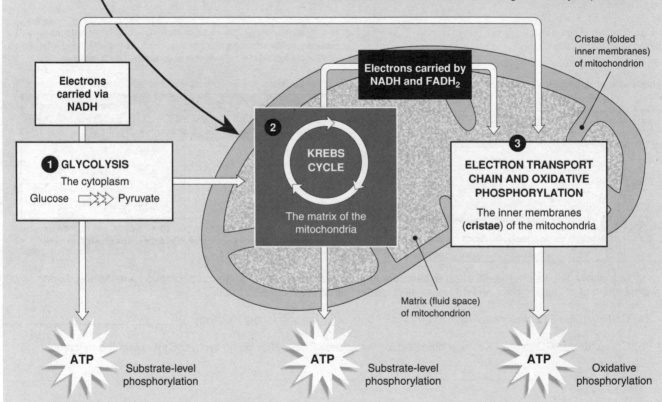

1. Describe precisely in which part of the cell the following take place:

   (a) Glycolysis: _____

   (b) Krebs cycle reactions: _____

   (c) Electron transport chain: _____

2. Provide a clear explanation of what is involved in each of the following processes:

   (a) Substrate-level phosphorylation: _____

   _____

   _____

   (b) Oxidative phosphorylation: _____

   _____

   _____

**Related activities**: The Role of ATP in Cells

# The Biochemistry of Respiration

Cellular respiration is a catabolic, energy yielding pathway. The breakdown of glucose and other organic fuels (such as fats and proteins) to simpler molecules is **exergonic** and releases energy for the synthesis of ATP. As summarized in the previous activity, respiration involves glycolysis, the Krebs cycle, and electron transport. The diagram below provides a more detailed overview of the events in each of these stages. Glycolysis and the Krebs cycle supply electrons (via NADH) to the electron transport chain, which drives **oxidative phosphorylation**. Glycolysis nets two ATP, produced by **substrate-level phosphorylation**.

The conversion of pyruvate (the end product of glycolysis) to **acetyl CoA** links glycolysis to the Krebs cycle. One "turn" of the cycle releases carbon dioxide, forms one ATP by substrate level phosphorylation, and passes electrons to three NAD+ and one FAD. Most of the ATP generated in cellular respiration is produced by oxidative phosphorylation when NADH and FADH$_2$ donate electrons to the series of electron carriers in the electron transport chain. At the end of the chain, electrons are passed to molecular oxygen, reducing it to water. Electron transport is coupled to ATP synthesis by **chemiosmosis** (following page).

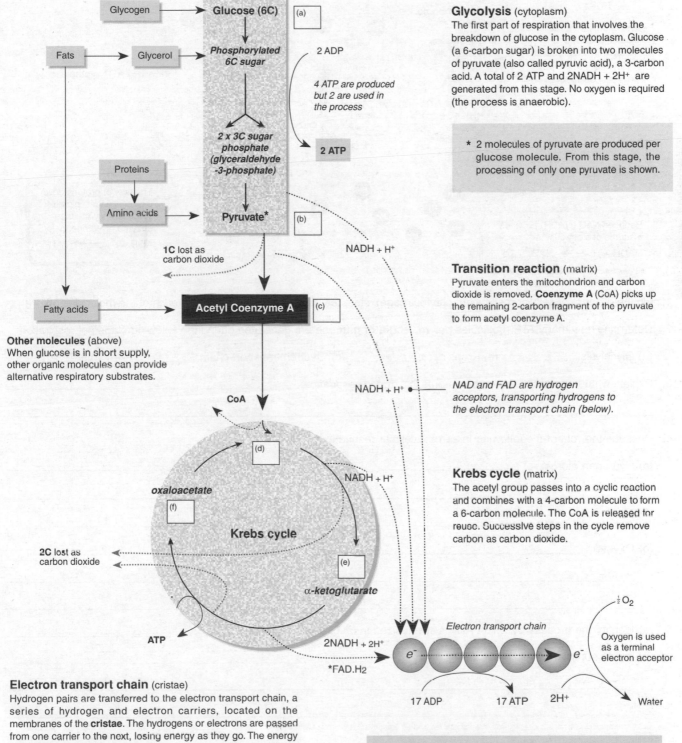

### Glycolysis (cytoplasm)
The first part of respiration that involves the breakdown of glucose in the cytoplasm. Glucose (a 6-carbon sugar) is broken into two molecules of pyruvate (also called pyruvic acid), a 3-carbon acid. A total of 2 ATP and 2NADH + 2H+ are generated from this stage. No oxygen is required (the process is anaerobic).

\* 2 molecules of pyruvate are produced per glucose molecule. From this stage, the processing of only one pyruvate is shown.

### Transition reaction (matrix)
Pyruvate enters the mitochondrion and carbon dioxide is removed. **Coenzyme A** (CoA) picks up the remaining 2-carbon fragment of the pyruvate to form acetyl coenzyme A.

**Other molecules** (above)
When glucose is in short supply, other organic molecules can provide alternative respiratory substrates.

*NAD and FAD are hydrogen acceptors, transporting hydrogens to the electron transport chain (below).*

### Krebs cycle (matrix)
The acetyl group passes into a cyclic reaction and combines with a 4-carbon molecule to form a 6-carbon molecule. The CoA is released for reuse. Successive steps in the cycle remove carbon as carbon dioxide.

**Electron transport chain** (cristae)
Hydrogen pairs are transferred to the electron transport chain, a series of hydrogen and electron carriers, located on the membranes of the **cristae**. The hydrogens or electrons are passed from one carrier to the next, losing energy as they go. The energy released in this stepwise process is used to produce ATP. Oxygen is the final electron acceptor and is reduced to water.

\*Note FAD enters the electron transport chain at a lower energy level than NAD, and only 2ATP are generated per FAD.H2.

**Total ATP yield per glucose**
*Glycolysis: 2 ATP, Krebs cycle: 2 ATP, Electron transport: 34 ATP*

© Biozone International 2001-2008
**Photocopying Prohibited**

**Related activities**: Cellular Respiration
**Web links**: Glycolysis and the Krebs Cycle

A 3

Cellular Energetics

## Chemiosmosis

Chemiosmosis is the process whereby the synthesis of ATP is coupled to electron transport and the movement of protons (H⁺ ions). **Electron transport carriers** are arranged over the inner membrane of the mitochondrion and oxidize NADH + H⁺ and FADH₂. Energy from this process forces protons to move, against their concentration gradient, from the mitochondrial matrix into the space between the two membranes. Eventually the protons flow back into the matrix via ATP synthetase molecules in the membrane. As the protons flow down their concentration gradient, energy is released and ATP is synthesized. Chemiosmotic theory also explains the generation of ATP in the light dependent phase of photosynthesis.

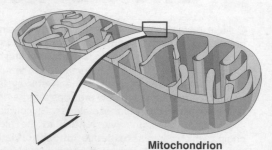

**Mitochondrion**

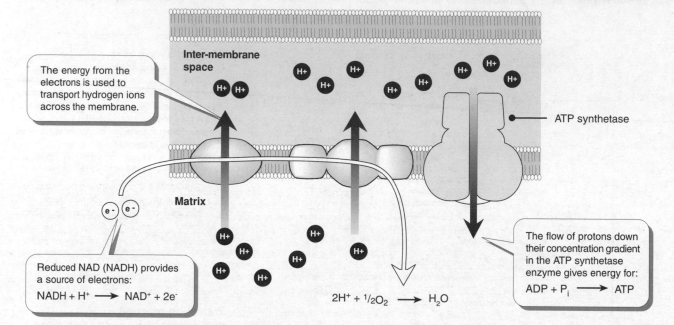

The energy from the electrons is used to transport hydrogen ions across the membrane.

**Inter-membrane space**

**Matrix**

**ATP synthetase**

The flow of protons down their concentration gradient in the ATP synthetase enzyme gives energy for:

$ADP + P_i \longrightarrow ATP$

Reduced NAD (NADH) provides a source of electrons:

$NADH + H^+ \longrightarrow NAD^+ + 2e^-$

$2H^+ + \frac{1}{2}O_2 \longrightarrow H_2O$

1. On the diagram of cellular respiration (previous page), state the number of carbon atoms in each of the molecules (a) – (f):

2. Determine how many ATP molecules **per molecule of glucose** are generated during the following stages of respiration:

   (a) Glycolysis: _____ (b) Krebs cycle: _____ (c) Electron transport chain: _____ (d) Total: _____

3. Explain what happens to the carbon atoms lost during respiration: _____

   _____

4. Describe the role of the following in aerobic cellular respiration:

   (a) Hydrogen atoms: _____

   _____

   _____

   (b) Oxygen: _____

   _____

   _____

5. (a) Identify the process by which ATP is synthesized in respiration: _____

   (b) Briefly summarize this process: _____

   _____

   _____

   _____

   _____

   _____

# Anaerobic Pathways

All organisms can metabolize glucose anaerobically (without oxygen) using glycolysis in the cytoplasm, but the energy yield from this process is low and few organisms can obtain sufficient energy for their needs this way. In the absence of oxygen, glycolysis soon stops unless there is an alternative acceptor for the electrons produced from the glycolytic pathway. In yeasts and the root cells of higher plants this acceptor is ethanal, and the pathway is called alcoholic fermentation. In the skeletal muscle of mammals, the acceptor is pyruvate itself and the end product

is lactic acid. In both cases, the duration of the fermentation is limited by the toxic effects of the organic compound produced. Although fermentation is often used synonymously with anaerobic respiration, they are not the same. Respiration always involves hydrogen ions passing down a chain of carriers to a terminal acceptor, and this does not occur in fermentation. In anaerobic respiration, the terminal $H^+$ acceptor is a molecule other than oxygen, e.g. $Fe^{2+}$ or nitrate.

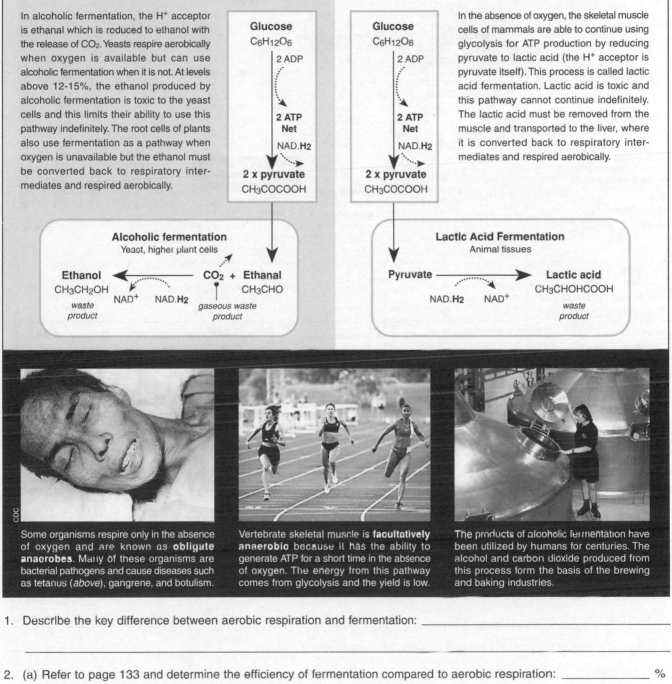

## Alcoholic Fermentation

In alcoholic fermentation, the $H^+$ acceptor is ethanal which is reduced to ethanol with the release of $CO_2$. Yeasts respire aerobically when oxygen is available but can use alcoholic fermentation when it is not. At levels above 12-15%, the ethanol produced by alcoholic fermentation is toxic to the yeast cells and this limits their ability to use this pathway indefinitely. The root cells of plants also use fermentation as a pathway when oxygen is unavailable but the ethanol must be converted back to respiratory intermediates and respired aerobically.

**Glucose**
$C_6H_{12}O_6$

2 ADP

**2 ATP Net**

$NAD.H_2$

**2 x pyruvate**
$CH_3COCOOH$

**Alcoholic fermentation**
Yeast, higher plant cells

**Ethanol**
$CH_3CH_2OH$
*waste product*

$NAD^+$    $NAD.H_2$

$CO_2$ + **Ethanal**
$CH_3CHO$
*gaseous waste product*

## Lactic Acid Fermentation

**Glucose**
$C_6H_{12}O_6$

2 ADP

**2 ATP Net**

$NAD.H_2$

**2 x pyruvate**
$CH_3COCOOH$

In the absence of oxygen, the skeletal muscle cells of mammals are able to continue using glycolysis for ATP production by reducing pyruvate to lactic acid (the $H^+$ acceptor is pyruvate itself). This process is called lactic acid fermentation. Lactic acid is toxic and this pathway cannot continue indefinitely. The lactic acid must be removed from the muscle and transported to the liver, where it is converted back to respiratory intermediates and respired aerobically.

**Lactic Acid Fermentation**
Animal tissues

**Pyruvate** ⟶ **Lactic acid**
$CH_3CHOHCOOH$
*waste product*

$NAD.H_2$    $NAD^+$

Some organisms respire only in the absence of oxygen and are known as **obligate anaerobes**. Many of these organisms are bacterial pathogens and cause diseases such as tetanus (*above*), gangrene, and botulism.

Vertebrate skeletal muscle is **facultatively anaerobic** because it has the ability to generate ATP for a short time in the absence of oxygen. The energy from this pathway comes from glycolysis and the yield is low.

The products of alcoholic fermentation have been utilized by humans for centuries. The alcohol and carbon dioxide produced from this process form the basis of the brewing and baking industries.

1. Describe the key difference between aerobic respiration and fermentation: _____

_____

2. (a) Refer to page 133 and determine the efficiency of fermentation compared to aerobic respiration: _____ %

   (b) In simple terms, explain why the efficiency of anaerobic pathways is so low: _____

   _____

3. Explain why fermentation cannot go on indefinitely: _____

_____

_____

**Cellular Energetics**

**Related activities:** The Biochemistry of Respiration

**RDA 2**

# Photosynthesis

Photosynthesis is of fundamental importance to living things because it transforms sunlight energy into chemical energy stored in molecules. This becomes part of the energy available in food chains. The molecules that trap the energy in their chemical bonds are also used as building blocks to create other molecules. Finally, photosynthesis releases free oxygen gas, essential for the survival of advanced life forms. Below is a diagram summarizing the process of photosynthesis.

## Summary of Photosynthesis in a C₃ Plant

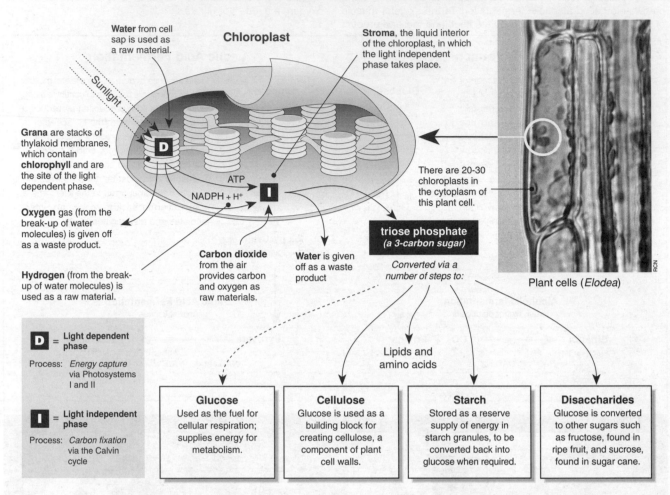

**Water** from cell sap is used as a raw material.

**Chloroplast**

**Stroma**, the liquid interior of the chloroplast, in which the light independent phase takes place.

Sunlight

**Grana** are stacks of thylakoid membranes, which contain **chlorophyll** and are the site of the light dependent phase.

**D**

ATP

NADPH + H⁺

**I**

**Oxygen** gas (from the break-up of water molecules) is given off as a waste product.

**Carbon dioxide** from the air provides carbon and oxygen as raw materials.

**Water** is given off as a waste product

**Hydrogen** (from the break-up of water molecules) is used as a raw material.

There are 20-30 chloroplasts in the cytoplasm of this plant cell.

**triose phosphate** *(a 3-carbon sugar)*

*Converted via a number of steps to:*

Plant cells (*Elodea*)

**D** = **Light dependent phase**

Process: *Energy capture via Photosystems I and II*

**I** = **Light independent phase**

Process: *Carbon fixation via the Calvin cycle*

Lipids and amino acids

| **Glucose** | **Cellulose** | **Starch** | **Disaccharides** |
|---|---|---|---|
| Used as the fuel for cellular respiration; supplies energy for metabolism. | Glucose is used as a building block for creating cellulose, a component of plant cell walls. | Stored as a reserve supply of energy in starch granules, to be converted back into glucose when required. | Glucose is converted to other sugars such as fructose, found in ripe fruit, and sucrose, found in sugar cane. |

1. Describe the three things of fundamental biological importance provided by photosynthesis:

(a) _____

(b) _____

(c) _____

2. Write the overall chemical equation for photosynthesis using:

(a) Words: _____

(b) Chemical symbols: _____

3. Discuss the potential uses for the end products of photosynthesis: _____

_____

_____

4. Distinguish between the two different regions of a chloroplast and describe the biochemical processes that occur in each:

_____

_____

_____

**Related activities**: The Biochemistry of Photosynthesis

# Pigments and Light Absorption

As light meets matter, it may be reflected, transmitted, or absorbed. Substances that absorb visible light are called **pigments**, and different pigments absorb light of different wavelengths. The ability of a pigment to absorb particular wavelengths of light can be measured with a spectrophotometer. The light absorption vs the wavelength is called the **absorption spectrum** of that pigment. The absorption spectrum of different photosynthetic pigments provides clues to their role in photosynthesis, since light can only perform work if it is absorbed. An **action spectrum** profiles the effectiveness of different wavelength light in fuelling photosynthesis. It is obtained by plotting wavelength against some measure of photosynthetic rate (e.g. $CO_2$ production). Some features of photosynthetic pigments and their light absorbing properties are outlined below.

## The Electromagnetic Spectrum

Light is a form of energy known as electromagnetic radiation. The segment of the electromagnetic spectrum most important to life is the narrow band between about 380 and 750 nanometres (nm). This radiation is known as visible light because it is detected as colors by the human eye (although some other animals, such as insects, can see in the ultraviolet range). It is the visible light that drives photosynthesis.

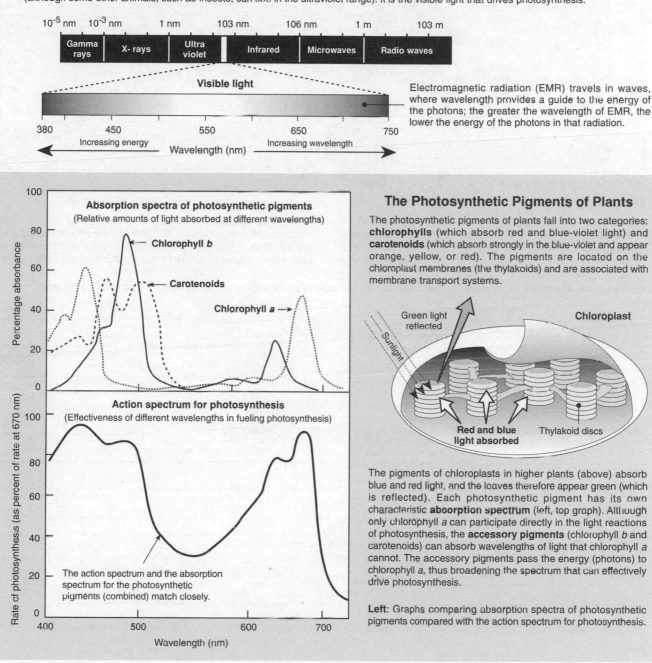

## The Photosynthetic Pigments of Plants

The photosynthetic pigments of plants fall into two categories: **chlorophylls** (which absorb red and blue-violet light) and **carotenoids** (which absorb strongly in the blue-violet and appear orange, yellow, or red). The pigments are located on the chloroplast membranes (the thylakoids) and are associated with membrane transport systems.

The pigments of chloroplasts in higher plants (above) absorb blue and red light, and the leaves therefore appear green (which is reflected). Each photosynthetic pigment has its own characteristic **absorption spectrum** (left, top graph). Although only chlorophyll *a* can participate directly in the light reactions of photosynthesis, the **accessory pigments** (chlorophyll *b* and carotenoids) can absorb wavelengths of light that chlorophyll *a* cannot. The accessory pigments pass the energy (photons) to chlorophyll *a*, thus broadening the spectrum that can effectively drive photosynthesis.

**Left:** Graphs comparing absorption spectra of photosynthetic pigments compared with the action spectrum for photosynthesis.

1. Explain what is meant by the absorption spectrum of a pigment: _____

   _____

2. Explain why the action spectrum for photosynthesis does not exactly match the absorption spectrum of chlorophyll *a*:

   _____

   _____

Cellular Energetics

# Photosynthetic Rate

The rate at which plants can make food (the photosynthetic rate) is dependent on environmental factors, particularly the amount of **light** available, the level of **carbon dioxide** ($CO_2$) and the **temperature**. The effect of these factors can be tested experimentally by altering one of the factors while holding others constant (a controlled experiment). In reality, a plant is subjected to variations in all three factors at the same time. The interaction of the different factors can also be examined in the same way, as long as only one factor at a time is altered. The results can be expressed in a graph.

## Factors Affecting Photosynthetic Rate

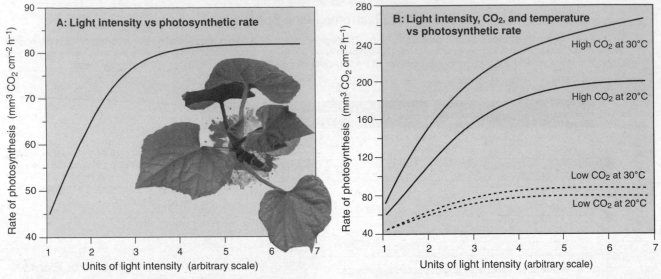

The two graphs above illustrate the effect of different variables on the rate of photosynthesis in cucumber plants. Graph A (above, left) shows the effect of different intensities of light. In this experiment, the level of carbon dioxide available and the temperature were kept constant. Graph B (above, right) shows the effect of different light intensities at two temperatures and two carbon dioxide ($CO_2$) concentrations. In each of these experiments either the carbon dioxide level or the temperature was raised at each light intensity in turn.

1.  (a) Describe the effect of increasing light intensity on the rate of photosynthesis (temperature and $CO_2$ constant):

    _____

    _____

    (b) Give a possible explanation for the shape of the curve: _____

    _____

2.  (a) Describe the effect of increasing the temperature on the rate of photosynthesis: _____

    _____

    (b) Suggest a reason for this response: _____

    _____

3.  Explain why the rate of photosynthesis declines when the $CO_2$ level is reduced: _____

    _____

    _____

4.  (a) In the graph above right, explain how the effects of $CO_2$ level were separated from the effects of temperature:

    _____

    _____

    (b) State which of the two factors, $CO_2$ level or temperature, has the greatest effect on photosynthetic rate:

    _____

    (c) Explain how you can tell this from the graph: _____

    _____

# The Biochemistry of Photosynthesis

Like cellular respiration, photosynthesis is a redox process, but the electron flow evident in respiration is reversed. In photosynthesis, water is split and electrons are transferred together with hydrogen ions from water to $CO_2$, reducing it to sugar. The electrons increase in potential energy as they move from water to sugar. The energy to do this is provided by light. Photosynthesis comprises two phases. In the **light dependent phase**, light energy is converted to chemical energy (ATP and reducing power). In the **light independent phase** (or **Calvin cycle**), the chemical energy is used for the synthesis of carbohydrate. The light dependent phase illustrated below shows **non-cyclic phosphorylation**. In **cyclic phosphorylation**, the electrons lost from photosystem II are replaced by those from photosystem I. ATP is generated, but not NADPH.

## Light Dependent Phase
### (Energy capture)

- This diagram shows **non-cyclic phosphorylation**.

- Photosystem complexes comprise hundreds of pigment molecules, including chlorophyll *a* and *b*.

- **Photosystem II** absorbs light energy to elevate electrons to a moderate energy level.

- **Photosystem I** absorbs light energy to elevate electrons to an even higher level. Its electrons are replaced by electrons from photosystem II.

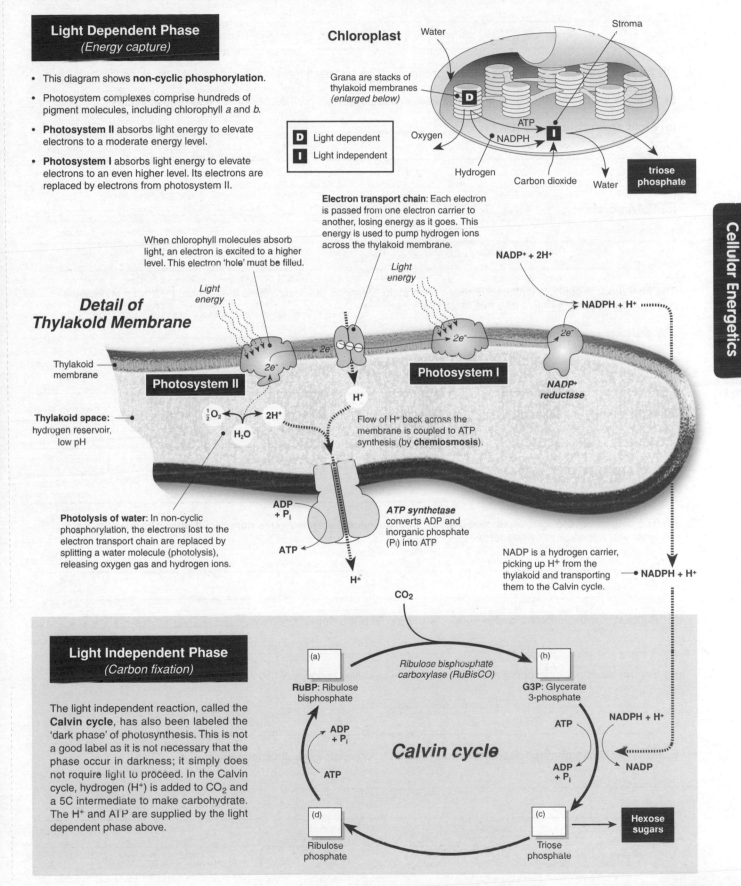

**Chloroplast**

Water

Stroma

Grana are stacks of thylakoid membranes *(enlarged below)*

**D** Light dependent
**I** Light independent

Oxygen

ATP

NADPH

Hydrogen

Carbon dioxide

Water

**triose phosphate**

**Cellular Energetics**

**Electron transport chain**: Each electron is passed from one electron carrier to another, losing energy as it goes. This energy is used to pump hydrogen ions across the thylakoid membrane.

When chlorophyll molecules absorb light, an electron is excited to a higher level. This electron 'hole' must be filled.

$NADP^+ + 2H^+$

### Detail of Thylakoid Membrane

Light energy

Light energy

$NADPH + H^+$

Thylakoid membrane

$2e^-$

$2e^-$

**Photosystem II**

$2e^-$

**Photosystem I**

*NADP+ reductase*

**Thylakoid space:** hydrogen reservoir, low pH

$\frac{1}{2}O_2$    $2H^+$

$H^+$

$H_2O$

Flow of $H^+$ back across the membrane is coupled to ATP synthesis (by **chemiosmosis**).

**Photolysis of water**: In non-cyclic phosphorylation, the electrons lost to the electron transport chain are replaced by splitting a water molecule (photolysis), releasing oxygen gas and hydrogen ions.

ADP + P_i

**ATP**

*ATP synthetase* converts ADP and inorganic phosphate (Pi) into ATP

$H^+$

NADP is a hydrogen carrier, picking up $H^+$ from the thylakoid and transporting them to the Calvin cycle.

$NADPH + H^+$

$CO_2$

## Light Independent Phase
### (Carbon fixation)

The light independent reaction, called the **Calvin cycle**, has also been labeled the 'dark phase' of photosynthesis. This is not a good label as it is not necessary that the phase occur in darkness; it simply does not require light to proceed. In the Calvin cycle, hydrogen ($H^+$) is added to $CO_2$ and a 5C intermediate to make carbohydrate. The $H^+$ and ATP are supplied by the light dependent phase above.

(a)

**RuBP**: Ribulose bisphosphate

*Ribulose bisphosphate carboxylase (RuBisCO)*

(h)

**G3P**: Glycerate 3-phosphate

ATP

$NADPH + H^+$

ADP + P_i

*Calvin cycle*

ADP + P_i

NADP

ATP

(d)

Ribulose phosphate

(c)

Triose phosphate

**Hexose sugars**

**Related activities**: Photosynthesis
**Web links**: Harvesting Light

**RA 3**

1. Describe the role of the carrier molecule **NADP** in photosynthesis: _____

_____

_____

2. Explain the role of chlorophyll molecules in the process of photosynthesis: _____

_____

_____

_____

3. On the previous diagram, write the number of carbon atoms that each molecule has at each stage of the Calvin cycle:

4. Summarize the events in each of the two phases in photosynthesis and identify where each phase occurs:

   (a) **Light dependent phase (D)**: _____

   _____

   _____

   (b) **Calvin cycle**: _____

   _____

   _____

5. The final product of photosynthesis is triose phosphate. Describe precisely where the carbon, hydrogen and oxygen molecules originate from to make this molecule:

   _____

   _____

   _____

6. Explain how ATP is produced as a result of light striking chlorophyll molecules during the light dependent phase:

   _____

   _____

   _____

7. (a) The diagram of the light dependent phase (top of previous page) describes **non-cyclic phosphorylation**. Explain what you understand by this term:

   _____

   _____

   (b) Suggest why this process is also known as non-cyclic **photo**phosphorylation: _____

   _____

   (c) Explain how photophosphorylation differs from the oxidative phosphorylation occurring in cellular respiration:

   _____

   _____

8. Explain how **cyclic photophosphorylation** differs from non-cyclic photophosphorylation: _____

_____

_____

_____

_____

# Molecular Genetics

**IB SL**
Complete:
1, 3-4, 7, 9(a), 11, 13(a)-(d),14-15, 20-22

**IB HL**
Complete:
1-27, 30-31, 33-34

**IB Options**
Not applicable to options

**AP Biology**
Complete:
1-36
*Some numbers as extension as appropriate*

## Learning Objectives

☐ 1. Compile your own glossary from the **KEY WORDS** displayed in **bold type** in the learning objectives below.

### The Genetic Blueprint

#### Nucleic acids *(pages 147-149, 151-154, 171)*

☐ 2. Name some examples of **nucleic acids** and describe their role in biological systems.

☐ 3. Describe the components of a (mono)**nucleotide**: a *5C sugar* (ribose or deoxyribose), a *nitrogenous base* (**purine** or **pyrimidine**), and a *phosphate*. Identify the bases that form nucleotides.

☐ 4. Understand the role of **condensation** reactions in joining the components of nucleotides and in the formation of di- and **polynucleotides** (nucleic acids).

☐ 5. Outline the structure of **nucleosomes**, including reference to the role of **histone proteins** in packaging of the DNA in the nucleus.

☐ 6. Understand that DNA contains **repetitive sequences** and that only a small proportion constitutes **genes**. Appreciate the role of repetitive sequences in DNA technologies such as DNA profiling.

☐ 7. Explain how the Watson-Crick **double-helix** model of DNA is formed using the **base pairing rule** and **hydrogen bonds**. Describe the importance of **complementary base pairing** to the conservation of the base sequence in DNA. Contrast the structure and function of **DNA** and **RNA**.

☐ 8. In more detail than #7 above, describe the structure of DNA including the **antiparallel strands,** the 3'–5' linkages, and the role of the hydrogen bonding between **purines** and **pyrimidines**

#### DNA replication *(pages 155-156)*

☐ 9. Describe the **semi-conservative** replication of DNA, and interpret experimental evidence for this process. Explain the role of the following in DNA replication:

  (a) **DNA polymerase, helicase, DNA ligase**.

  (b) **DNA polymerase III, RNA primase, DNA polymerase I, Okazaki fragments,** and **deoxynucleoside triphosphates**.

☐ 10. Understand that DNA replication proceeds only in the 5' → 3' direction and explain the significance of this. Explain the term: **replication fork**, and explain its significance in eukaryotic chromosomes.

☐ 11. Demonstrate an understanding of the base-pairing rule for creating a **complementary strand** from a **template strand**.

☐ 12. Appreciate the role of polymerase chain reaction (PCR) as an artificially induced form of DNA replication, used as a tool in molecular biology (see the topic *Gene Technology* for coverage of this technique).

### The genetic code *(page 150)*

☐ 13. Explain the main features of the **genetic code**, including reference to the following:

  (a) The 4-letter alphabet and the 3-letter **triplet code** (**codon**) of base sequences.

  (b) The **non-overlapping**, linear nature of the code.

  (c) The **universal nature** of the code.

  (d) The **degeneracy** of the code.

  (e) The way in which the code is always read from a start point to a finish point in a 3' → 5' direction.

  (f) Specific punctuation codons and their significance.

### Gene expression *(pages 157-163)*

☐ 14. Outline the basis by which information is transferred from DNA to protein (or functional RNA products). Explain what is meant by **gene expression**, including reference to **transcription** and **translation**. *Note: Gene expression is often used to refer only to expression of the gene as its mRNA product.*

☐ 15. Recall the structure and role of messenger RNA (**mRNA**). In simple terms, describe the process of **transcription**, identifying the role of **RNA polymerase**.

☐ 16. In more detail than in #15 above, describe the process of transcription. Demonstrate an understanding of the direction of transcription (5' → 3' direction).

☐ 17. Distinguish between the **coding (sense) strand** and **template (antisense) strand**. Relate the base sequence on each of these strands to the sequence on the mRNA molecule.

☐ 18. Distinguish between **introns** and **exons**. Explain the significance of introns with the respect to the production of a functional mRNA molecule.

☐ 19. Understand how **reverse transcriptase** catalyzes the production of DNA from RNA. Explain how this enzyme is used by retroviruses. Appreciate the use of reverse transcriptase in molecular biology.

☐ 20. Recall the structure of **proteins** as **polypeptides** with a complex (post-translational) structure.

☐ 21. Explain how the 4-letter alphabet of bases provides the code for the 20 amino acids needed to assemble proteins. Explain the relationship between one **gene** and one polypeptide.

☐ 22. In simple terms, describe the process of **translation**. Describe the role of transfer RNA (**tRNA**) molecules in translation, with reference to the significance of the **anticodons**. Understand and explain the general role of ribosomes in translation.

☐ 23. With respect to the process of **translation**, describe how the structure of transfer RNA (**tRNA**) molecules allows recognition by a tRNA-activating enzyme. Explain the role of this enzyme in binding specific amino acids to their tRNAs and identify the role of ATP in this process.

☐ 24. Outline the structure of ribosomes with reference to: small and large subunits, RNA and protein, tRNA binding sites, and mRNA binding sites. Relate the functional role of ribosomes to their specific structure.

☐ 25. Describe translation as a process involving **initiation**, **elongation**, and **termination**, occurring in a 5' → 3' direction. In more detail than in #22, explain the process of translation including more detailed reference to **ribosomes**, **polysomes** (polyribosomes), **start codons**, and **stop codons**.

☐ 26. Distinguish between protein synthesis on free ribosomes and on those bound to the endoplasmic reticulum. Explain why proteins are synthesized in these different locations in the cell.

☐ 27. Explain the process of transcription in **prokaryotes**, including the roles of the **promoter** region, RNA polymerase, nucleoside triphosphates, and the **terminator**. Identify **eukaryotic** RNA as having had the introns spliced out in forming mature mRNA.

☐ 28. Contrast **gene expression** in prokaryotic and eukaryotic cells, identifying differences in mRNA processing after transcription, movement of the mRNA to the site of translation, and the speed at which translation can take place.

☐ 29. Using an appropriate example, e.g. a bacteriophage, describe the structure and replication of **viruses**, identifying the major steps in viral reproduction and explaining how viruses transfer material between cells.
*See the TRC: Replication in Bacteriophage*

## Control of Metabolic Pathways *(pages 164-168)*

☐ 30. Recognize **enzymes** as proteins whose synthesis is controlled by DNA. Describe the role of enzymes in **metabolic pathways** and in determining phenotype.

☐ 31. Explain how enzymes control metabolic pathways as illustrated by specific examples, e.g. **oxidoreductases**, **anabolism** and **catabolism**. Explain how the amount or activity of an enzyme regulating a metabolic pathway can itself be controlled. Explain what is meant by the **end-product** and **end-product inhibition**.

☐ 32. Identify major heritable **metabolic disorders** in humans. Using an example such as the metabolism of phenylalanine, explain how the malfunction of enzymes is responsible in many cases.

☐ 33. Define the term **operon**. Discuss the extent to which the operon model is universally applicable.

☐ 34. Explain how simple metabolic pathways are regulated in prokaryotes, as illustrated by **gene induction** in the *lac* **operon** in *E. coli*. Explain how lactose activates transcription and how metabolism of the substrate is achieved. Explain the adaptive value of gene induction.

☐ 35. Using an example, e.g. control of **tryptophan** synthesis, explain how the **end-product** of a metabolic pathway can activate a **repressor** and switch genes off (**gene repression**). Describe the adaptive value of gene repression for the control of an end-product.

☐ 36. Describe the regulation of gene action (transcriptional control only) in **eukaryotes**. Identify the roles of the promoter region, RNA polymerase, **transcription factors**, **enhancers**, and the **terminator sequence**.

**Textbooks**

See the 'Textbook Reference Grid' on pages 8-9 for textbook page references relating to material in this topic.

### Supplementary Texts

See pages 5-6 for additional details of these texts:

■ Adds, J., *et al.*, 2003. **Molecules and Cells**, (NelsonThornes), chpt. 2.

■ Clegg, C.J., 1999. **Genetics & Evolution**, (John Murray), pp. 40-42, 44-47.

■ Helms, D.R. *et al.*, 1998. **Biology in the Laboratory** (W.H. Freeman), #17, #19.

■ Jones, N., *et al.*, 2001. **Essentials of Genetics**, (John Murray), pp. 123-155 as required.

■ Tobin, A.J. and Morel, R.E., 1997. **Asking About Cells**, (Thomson Brooks/Cole), parts III and IV.

**Periodicals**

See page 6 for details of publishers of periodicals:

### STUDENT'S REFERENCE

■ **Gene Structure and Expression** Biol. Sci. Rev., 12 (5) May 2000, pp. 22-25. *An account of gene function, including a comparison of gene regulation in pro- and eukaryotes.*

■ **What is a Gene?** Biol. Sci. Rev., 15(2) Nov. 2002, pp. 9-11. *A good synopsis of genes and their role in heredity, mutations, and transcriptional control of gene expression.*

■ **Transfer RNA** Biol. Sci. Rev., 15(3) Feb. 2003, pp. 26-29. *An account of tRNA in protein synthesis.*

■ **Stuff or Nonsense** New Scientist, 1 April 2000, pp. 38-41. *The functional and evolutionary role of introns (junk DNA) in the genomes of organisms.*

### TEACHER'S REFERENCE

■ **DNA 50** SSR, 84(308), March 2003, pp. 17-80. *A special issue celebrating 50 years since the discovery of DNA. There are various articles examining the practical and theoretical aspects of teaching molecular genetics and inheritance.*

■ **DNA: 50 Years of the Double Helix** New Scientist, 15 March 2003, pp. 35-51. *A special issue on DNA: structure and function, repair, the new-found role of histones, and the functional significance of chromosome position in the nucleus.*

■ **Evolution Encoded** Scientific American, April 2004, pp. 56-63. *Genetic instructions for the manufacture of proteins are written in 3-letter codons, each specifying one of 20 amino acids or a 'stop translating' sign. Their arrangement indicates that natural selection has maintained an order that is good at minimizing errors.*

■ **The Alternative Genome** Scientific American, April, 2005, pp. 40-47. *"One gene, one protein" no longer holds true. The more com plex an organism, the more likely it became that way by extracting multiple protein meanings from individual genes.*

■ **The Unseen Genome: Gems Among the Junk** Scientific American, Nov. 2003, pp. 26-33. *98% of the DNA in humans was once dismissed as junk, but the discovery of many hidden genes that work through RNA, rather than protein, has overturned this assumption.*

■ **The Hidden Genetic Program** Scientific American, Oct. 2004, pp. 30-37. *Large portions of the DNA of complex organisms may encode RNA molecules with important regulatory functions.*

■ **The Great Inventors** New Scientist, 21 Feb. 2004, pp. 41-43. *The human genome is riddled with duplications, the engines of evolution providing raw material for mutations. Random mutation can modify one copy of a duplicated gene without upsetting existing biochemical pathways.*

■ **Junking the Genome** New Scientist, 59(2), 04 Aug 2007, pp. 42-45. *The HGP reveals new theories that junk DNA may have an important evolutionary function.*

■ **Modeling the Classic Meselson and Stahl Experiment** The Am. Biology Teacher, 63(5), May 2001, pp. 358-361. *An account of how to model the experiments of Meselson and Stahl to demonstrate semi-conservative replication of DNA.*

■ **A Working Model of Protein Synthesis using Lego™ Building Blocks** The Am. Biology Teacher, 64(9), Nov. 2002, pp. 673-678. *Using a hands-on project to demonstrate the various stages of protein synthesis.*

■ **Using Concrete & Representational Experiences to Understand the Structure of DNA** The American Biology Teacher, 67(2), February 2005, pp. 77-85. *A series of closely related activities on DNA.*

**Internet**

See pages 10-11 for details of how to access **Bio Links** from our web site: **www.thebiozone.com** From Bio Links, access sites under the topics:

**GENERAL BIOLOGY ONLINE RESOURCES** > **Online Textbooks and Lecture Notes:** • The Biology Project • Kimball's biology pages … *and others* > **General Online Biology Resources**: • AP interactive animation • Access Excellence • BioInteractive… *and others* > **Glossaries:** • Genetic glossary • Glossary of molecular biology

**GENETICS:** • Genetic Science Learning Center • MIT biology hypertextbook • Prokaryotic genetics and gene expression … *and others* > **Molecular Genetics (DNA):** • Beginners guide to molecular biology • Center for Biomolecular Modeling • DNA interactive • DNA and molecular genetics • DNA from the beginning • DNA workshop • Molecular genetics • Primer on molecular genetics • Protein synthesis • Model of Lac operon • Induction of the Lac operon

**Presentation MEDIA** to support this topic:
**GENES AND INHERITANCE**
• The Genetic Code
• Nature of Genes

*Genes & Inheritance*

# Nucleic Acids

Nucleic acids are a special group of chemicals in cells concerned with the transmission of inherited information. They have the capacity to store the information that controls cellular activity. The central nucleic acid is called **deoxyribonucleic acid** (DNA). DNA is a major component of chromosomes and is found primarily in the nucleus, although a small amount is found in mitochondria and chloroplasts. Other **ribonucleic acids** (RNA) are involved in the 'reading' of the DNA information. All nucleic acids are made up of simple repeating units called **nucleotides**, linked together to form chains or strands, often of great length (see the activity *DNA Molecules*). The strands vary in the sequence of the bases found on each nucleotide. It is this sequence which provides the 'genetic code' for the cell. In addition to nucleic acids, certain nucleotides and their derivatives are also important as suppliers of energy (**ATP**) or as hydrogen ion and electron carriers in respiration and photosynthesis (NAD, NADP, and FAD).

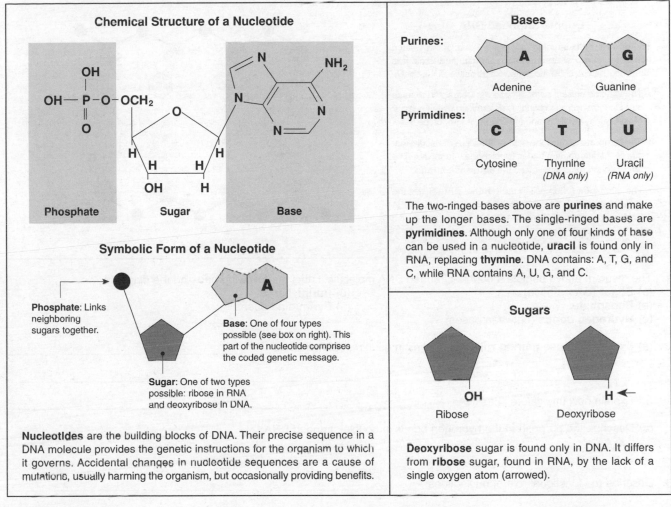

### Chemical Structure of a Nucleotide

Phosphate     Sugar     Base

### Symbolic Form of a Nucleotide

**Phosphate**: Links neighboring sugars together.

**Base**: One of four types possible (see box on right). This part of the nucleotide comprises the coded genetic message.

**Sugar**: One of two types possible: ribose in RNA and deoxyribose in DNA.

**Nucleotides** are the building blocks of DNA. Their precise sequence in a DNA molecule provides the genetic instructions for the organism to which it governs. Accidental changes in nucleotide sequences are a cause of mutations, usually harming the organism, but occasionally providing benefits.

### Bases

**Purines:**    A (Adenine)    G (Guanine)

**Pyrimidines:**    C (Cytosine)    T (Thymine) *(DNA only)*    U (Uracil) *(RNA only)*

The two-ringed bases above are **purines** and make up the longer bases. The single-ringed bases are **pyrimidines**. Although only one of four kinds of base can be used in a nucleotide, **uracil** is found only in RNA, replacing **thymine**. DNA contains: A, T, G, and C, while RNA contains A, U, G, and C.

### Sugars

Ribose     Deoxyribose

**Deoxyribose** sugar is found only in DNA. It differs from **ribose** sugar, found in RNA, by the lack of a single oxygen atom (arrowed).

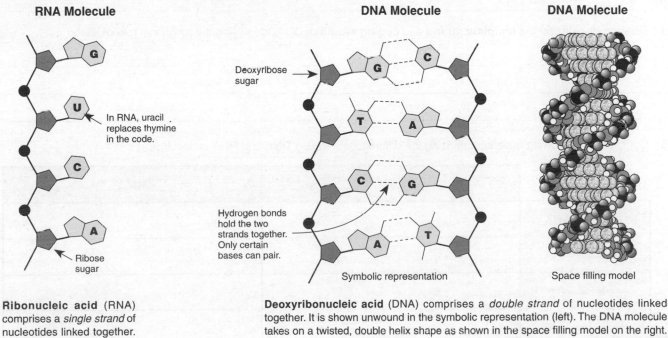

### RNA Molecule

In RNA, uracil replaces thymine in the code.

Ribose sugar

### DNA Molecule

Deoxyribose sugar

Hydrogen bonds hold the two strands together. Only certain bases can pair.

Symbolic representation

### DNA Molecule

Space filling model

**Ribonucleic acid** (RNA) comprises a *single strand* of nucleotides linked together.

**Deoxyribonucleic acid** (DNA) comprises a *double strand* of nucleotides linked together. It is shown unwound in the symbolic representation (left). The DNA molecule takes on a twisted, double helix shape as shown in the space filling model on the right.

*Molecular Genetics*

**Related activities**: DNA Molecules, Creating a DNA Molecule

A 1

## Formation of a nucleotide

## Formation of a dinucleotide

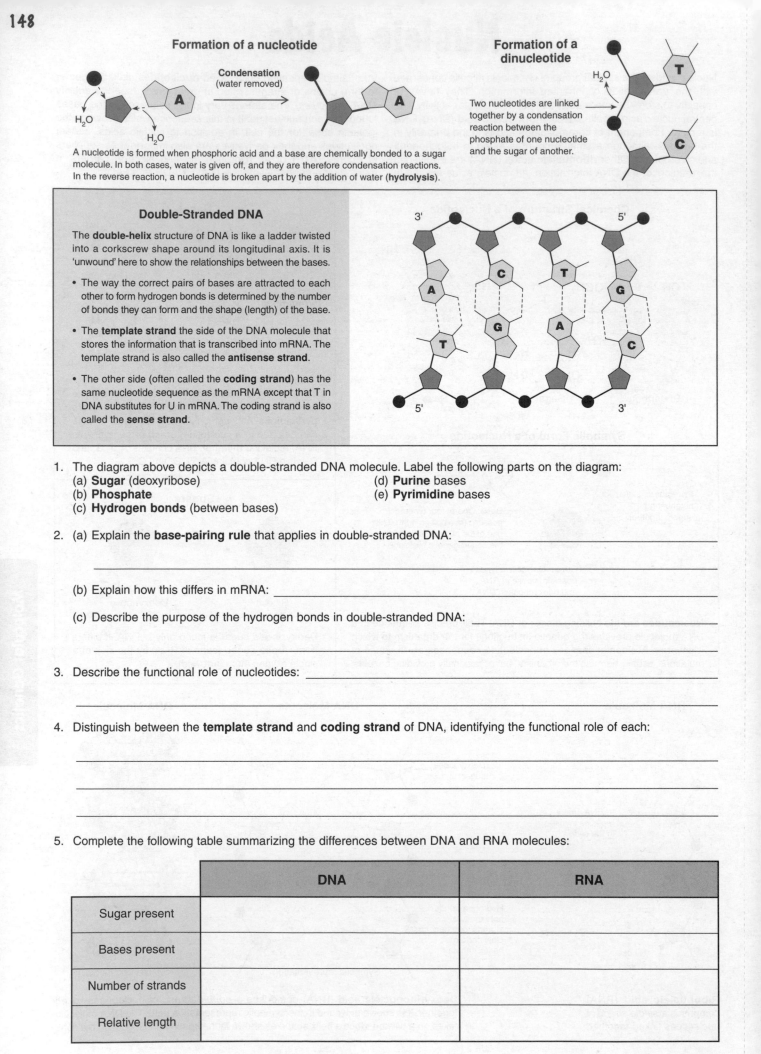

A nucleotide is formed when phosphoric acid and a base are chemically bonded to a sugar molecule. In both cases, water is given off, and they are therefore condensation reactions. In the reverse reaction, a nucleotide is broken apart by the addition of water (**hydrolysis**).

Two nucleotides are linked together by a condensation reaction between the phosphate of one nucleotide and the sugar of another.

### Double-Stranded DNA

The **double-helix** structure of DNA is like a ladder twisted into a corkscrew shape around its longitudinal axis. It is 'unwound' here to show the relationships between the bases.

- The way the correct pairs of bases are attracted to each other to form hydrogen bonds is determined by the number of bonds they can form and the shape (length) of the base.

- The **template strand** the side of the DNA molecule that stores the information that is transcribed into mRNA. The template strand is also called the **antisense strand**.

- The other side (often called the **coding strand**) has the same nucleotide sequence as the mRNA except that T in DNA substitutes for U in mRNA. The coding strand is also called the **sense strand**.

1. The diagram above depicts a double-stranded DNA molecule. Label the following parts on the diagram:
   (a) **Sugar** (deoxyribose)          (d) **Purine** bases
   (b) **Phosphate**                     (e) **Pyrimidine** bases
   (c) **Hydrogen bonds** (between bases)

2. (a) Explain the **base-pairing rule** that applies in double-stranded DNA: _____

   _____

   (b) Explain how this differs in mRNA: _____

   (c) Describe the purpose of the hydrogen bonds in double-stranded DNA: _____

   _____

3. Describe the functional role of nucleotides: _____

   _____

4. Distinguish between the **template strand** and **coding strand** of DNA, identifying the functional role of each:

   _____

   _____

   _____

5. Complete the following table summarizing the differences between DNA and RNA molecules:

| | DNA | RNA |
|---|---|---|
| Sugar present | | |
| Bases present | | |
| Number of strands | | |
| Relative length | | |

# DNA Molecules

Even the smallest DNA molecules are extremely long. The DNA from the small *Polyoma* virus, for example, is 1.7 μm long; about three times longer than the longest proteins. The DNA comprising a bacterial chromosome is 1000 times longer than the cell into which it has to fit. The amount of DNA present in the nucleus of the cells of eukaryotic organisms varies widely from one species to another. In vertebrate sex cells, the quantity of DNA ranges from 40 000 **kb** to 80 000 000 **kb**, with humans about in the middle of the range. The traditional focus of DNA research has been on those DNA sequences that code for proteins, yet protein-coding DNA accounts for less than 2% of the DNA in human chromosomes. The rest of the DNA, once dismissed as non-coding 'evolutionary junk', is now recognized as giving rise to functional RNA molecules, many of which have already been identified as having important regulatory functions. While there is no clear correspondence between the complexity of an organism and the number of protein-coding genes in its genome, this is not the case for non-protein-coding DNA. The genomes of more complex organisms contain much more of this so-called "non-coding" DNA. These RNA-only 'hidden' genes tend to be short and difficult to identify, but the sequences are highly conserved and clearly have a role in inheritance, development, and health.

## Sizes of DNA Molecules

| Group | Organism | Base pairs (in 1000s, or kb) | Length |
|-------|----------|------------------------------|--------|
| Viruses | Polyoma or SV40 | 5.1 | 1.7 μm |
| | Lambda phage | 48.6 | 17 μm |
| | T2 phage | 166 | 56 μm |
| | *Vaccinia* | 190 | 65 μm |
| Bacteria | Mycoplasma | 760 | 260 μm |
| | E. coli (from human gut) | 4600 | 1.56 mm |
| Eukaryotes | Yeast | 13 500 | 4.6 mm |
| | *Drosophila* (fruit fly) | 165 000 | 5.6 cm |
| | Human | 2 900 000 | 99 cm |

### Kilobase (kb)

A kilobase is unit of length equal to 1000 base pairs of a double-stranded nucleic acid molecule (or 1000 bases of a single-stranded molecule). One kb of double stranded DNA has a length of 0.34 μm. (1 μm = 1/1000 mm)

Exons: protein coding regions

DNA

Intron    Intron: edited out during protein synthesis    Intron

Most protein-coding genes in eukaryotic DNA are not continuous and may be interrupted by 'intrusions' of other pieces of DNA. Protein-coding regions (**exons**) are interrupted by non-protein-coding regions called **introns**. Introns range in frequency from 1 to over 30 in a single 'gene' and also in size (100 to more than 10 000 bases). Introns are edited out of the protein-coding sequence during protein synthesis, but probably, after processing, go on to serve a regulatory function.

### Giant lampbrush chromosomes

Lampbrush chromosomes are large chromosomes found in amphibian eggs, with lateral loops of DNA that produce a brushlike appearance under the microscope. The two scanning electron micrographs (below and right) show minute strands of DNA giving a fuzzy appearance in the high power view.

Loops of DNA

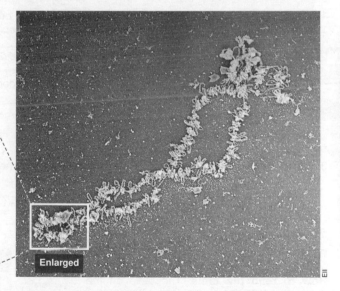

Enlarged

1. Consult the table above and make the following comparisons. Determine how much more DNA is present in:

   (a) The bacterium *E. coli* compared to the Lambda Phage virus: _____

   (b) Human cells compared to the bacteria *E. coli*: _____

2. State what proportion of DNA in a eukaryotic cell is used to code for proteins or structural RNA: _____

3. Describe two reasons why geneticists have reevaluated their traditional view that one gene codes for one polypeptide:

   (a) _____

   _____

   (b) _____

   _____

# The Genetic Code

The genetic information that codes for the assembly of amino acids is stored as three-letter codes, called **codons**. Each codon represents one of 20 amino acids used in the construction of polypeptide chains. The **mRNA-amino acid table** (below) can be used to identify the amino acid encoded by each of the mRNA codons. Note that the code is **degenerate** in that for each amino acid, there may be more than one codon. Most of this degeneracy involves the third nucleotide of a codon. The genetic code is **universal**; all living organisms on Earth, from viruses and bacteria, to plants and humans, share the same genetic code book (with a few minor exceptions representing mutations that have occurred over the long history of evolution).

| Amino acid | | Codons that code for this amino acid | No. | Amino acid | | Codons that code for this amino acid | No. |
|---|---|---|---|---|---|---|---|
| **Ala** | Alanine | GCU, GCC, GCA, GCG | 4 | **Leu** | Leucine | | |
| **Arg** | Arginine | | | **Lys** | Lysine | | |
| **Asn** | Asparagine | | | **Met** | Methionine | | |
| **Asp** | Aspartic acid | | | **Phe** | Phenylalanine | | |
| **Cys** | Cysteine | | | **Pro** | Proline | | |
| **Gln** | Glutamine | | | **Ser** | Serine | | |
| **Glu** | Glutamic acid | | | **Thr** | Threonine | | |
| **Gly** | Glycine | | | **Try** | Tryptophan | | |
| **His** | Histidine | | | **Tyr** | Tyrosine | | |
| **Iso** | Isoleucine | | | **Val** | Valine | | |

1. Use the **mRNA-amino acid table** (below) to list in the table above all the **codons** that code for each of the amino acids and the number of different codons that can code for each amino acid (the first amino acid has been done for you).

2. (a) State how many amino acids could be coded for if a codon consisted of just two bases: _____

   (b) Explain why this number of bases is inadequate to code for the 20 amino acids required to make proteins:

   _____

   _____

3. Describe the consequence of the degeneracy of the genetic code to the likely effect of **point mutations**:

   _____

   _____

## mRNA-Amino Acid Table

**How to read the table**: The table on the right is used to 'decode' the genetic code as a sequence of amino acids in a polypeptide chain, from a given mRNA sequence. To work out which amino acid is coded for by a codon (triplet of bases) look for the first letter of the codon in the row label on the left hand side. Then look for the column that intersects the same row from above that matches the second base. Finally, locate the third base in the codon by looking along the row from the right hand end that matches your codon.

**Example**: Determine **CAG**

C on the left row, A on the top column, G on the right row
**CAG** is Gln (**glutamine**)

Read second letter here

Read first letter here

Read third letter here

| | | **Second Letter** | | | | |
|---|---|---|---|---|---|---|
| | | **U** | **C** | **A** | **G** | |
| **First Letter** | **U** | UUU Phe<br>UUC Phe<br>UUA Leu<br>UUG Leu | UCU Ser<br>UCC Ser<br>UCA Ser<br>UCG Ser | UAU Tyr<br>UAC Tyr<br>UAA STOP<br>UAG STOP | UGU Cys<br>UGC Cys<br>UGA STOP<br>UGG Try | U<br>C<br>A<br>G |
| | **C** | CUU Leu<br>CUC Leu<br>CUA Leu<br>CUG Leu | CCU Pro<br>CCC Pro<br>CCA Pro<br>CCG Pro | CAU His<br>CAC His<br>CAA Gln<br>CAG Gln | CGU Arg<br>CGC Arg<br>CGA Arg<br>CGG Arg | U<br>C<br>A<br>G |
| | **A** | AUU Iso<br>AUC Iso<br>AUA Iso<br>AUG Met | ACU Thr<br>ACC Thr<br>ACA Thr<br>ACG Thr | AAU Asn<br>AAC Asn<br>AAA Lys<br>AAG Lys | AGU Ser<br>AGC Ser<br>AGA Arg<br>AGG Arg | U<br>C<br>A<br>G |
| | **G** | GUU Val<br>GUC Val<br>GUA Val<br>GUG Val | GCU Ala<br>GCC Ala<br>GCA Ala<br>GCG Ala | GAU Asp<br>GAC Asp<br>GAA Glu<br>GAG Glu | GGU Gly<br>GGC Gly<br>GGA Gly<br>GGG Gly | U<br>C<br>A<br>G |

Third Letter

# Creating a DNA Model

Although DNA molecules can be enormous in terms of their molecular size, they are made up of simple repeating units called **nucleotides**. A number of factors control the way in which these nucleotide building blocks are linked together. These factors cause the nucleotides to join together in a predictable way. This is referred to as the **base pairing rule** and can be used to construct a complementary DNA strand from a template strand, as illustrated in the exercise below:

| DNA Base Pairing Rule | | | |
|---|---|---|---|
| **Adenine** | is always attracted to | **Thymine** | A ←→ T |
| **Thymine** | is always attracted to | **Adenine** | T ←→ A |
| **Cytosine** | is always attracted to | **Guanine** | C ←→ G |
| **Guanine** | is always attracted to | **Cytosine** | G ←→ C |

1. Cut out around the nucleotides on page 149 and separate each of the 24 nucleotides by cutting along the columns and rows (see arrows indicating these cutting points). Although drawn as geometric shapes, these symbols represent chemical structures.

2. Place one of each of the four kinds of nucleotide on their correct spaces below:

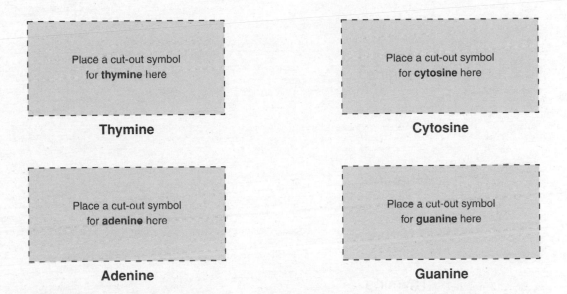

Place a cut-out symbol for **thymine** here

**Thymine**

Place a cut-out symbol for **cytosine** here

**Cytosine**

Place a cut-out symbol for **adenine** here

**Adenine**

Place a cut-out symbol for **guanine** here

**Guanine**

3. Identify and **label** each of the following features on the adenine nucleotide immediately above:
   **phosphate**, **sugar**, **base**, **hydrogen bonds**

4. Create one strand of the DNA molecule by placing the 9 correct 'cut out' nucleotides in the labeled spaces on the following page (DNA Molecule). Make sure these are the right way up (with the **P** on the left) and are aligned with the left hand edge of each box. Begin with thymine and end with guanine.

5. Create the complementary strand of DNA by using the base pairing rule above. Note that the nucleotides have to be arranged upside down.

6. Under normal circumstances, it is not possible for adenine to pair up with guanine or cytosine, nor for any other mismatches to occur. Describe the two factors that prevent a mismatch from occurring:

   (a) Factor 1: _____

   _____

   (b) Factor 2: _____

   _____

7. Once you have checked that the arrangement is correct, you may glue, paste or tape these nucleotides in place.

---

**NOTE:** There may be some value in keeping these pieces loose in order to practise the base pairing rule. For this purpose, *removable tape* would be best.

Related activities: Nucleic Acids

**PA 2**

**Molecular Genetics**

# DNA Molecule

Thymine

Cytosine

Adenine

Adenine

Guanine

Thymine

Thymine

Cytosine

Guanine

# Nucleotides

Tear out this page along the perforation and separate each of the 24 nucleotides
by cutting along the columns and rows (see arrows indicating the cutting points).

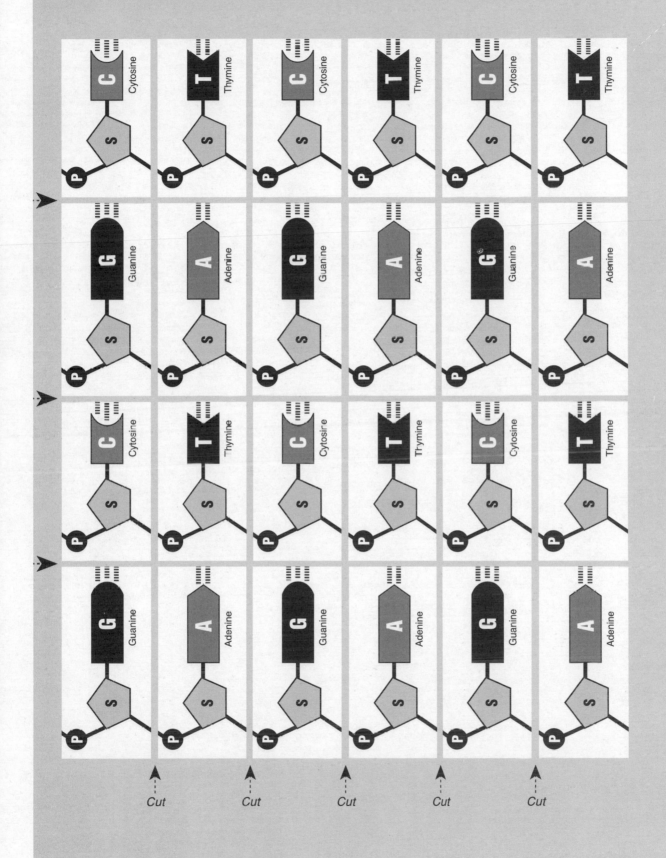

*Cut*   *Cut*   *Cut*   *Cut*   *Cut*

Molecular Genetics

# DNA Replication

The replication of DNA is a necessary preliminary step for cell division (both mitosis and meiosis). This process creates the **two chromatids** that are found in chromosomes that are preparing to divide. By this process, the whole chromosome is essentially duplicated, but is still held together by a common centromere. Enzymes are responsible for all of the key events. The diagram below shows the essential steps In the process. The diagram on the next page shows how enzymes are involved at each stage.

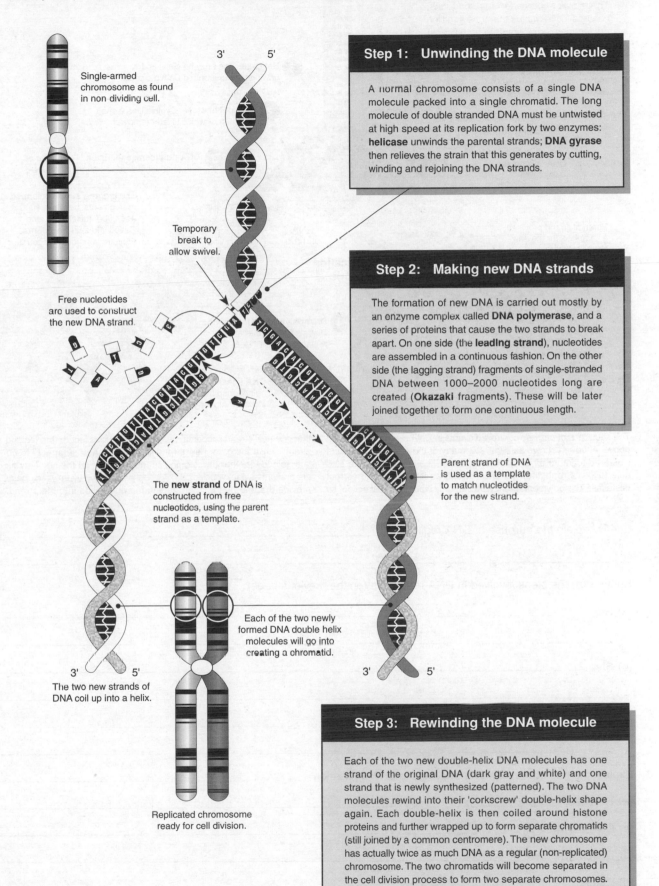

Single-armed chromosome as found in non dividing cell.

Temporary break to allow swivel.

Free nucleotides are used to construct the new DNA strand.

The **new strand** of DNA is constructed from free nucleotides, using the parent strand as a template.

Parent strand of DNA is used as a template to match nucleotides for the new strand.

Each of the two newly formed DNA double helix molecules will go into creating a chromatid.

The two new strands of DNA coil up into a helix.

Replicated chromosome ready for cell division.

## Step 1: Unwinding the DNA molecule

A normal chromosome consists of a single DNA molecule packed into a single chromatid. The long molecule of double stranded DNA must be untwisted at high speed at its replication fork by two enzymes: **helicase** unwinds the parental strands; **DNA gyrase** then relieves the strain that this generates by cutting, winding and rejoining the DNA strands.

## Step 2: Making new DNA strands

The formation of new DNA is carried out mostly by an enzyme complex called **DNA polymerase**, and a series of proteins that cause the two strands to break apart. On one side (the **leading strand**), nucleotides are assembled in a continuous fashion. On the other side (the lagging strand) fragments of single-stranded DNA between 1000–2000 nucleotides long are created (**Okazaki** fragments). These will be later joined together to form one continuous length.

## Step 3: Rewinding the DNA molecule

Each of the two new double-helix DNA molecules has one strand of the original DNA (dark gray and white) and one strand that is newly synthesized (patterned). The two DNA molecules rewind into their 'corkscrew' double-helix shape again. Each double-helix is then coiled around histone proteins and further wrapped up to form separate chromatids (still joined by a common centromere). The new chromosome has actually twice as much DNA as a regular (non-replicated) chromosome. The two chromatids will become separated in the cell division process to form two separate chromosomes.

**Molecular Genetics**

**Related activities**: Mitosis and the Cell Cycle, Meiosis, PCR
**Web links**: DNA Replication

DA 3

# Enzyme Control of DNA Replication

This process of DNA replication occurs at an astounding rate. As many as 4000 nucleotides per second are replicated. This explains how under ideal conditions, bacterial cells with as many as 4 million nucleotides, can complete a cell cycle in about 20 minutes. See the section on **polymerase chain reaction** for a useful application of this process.

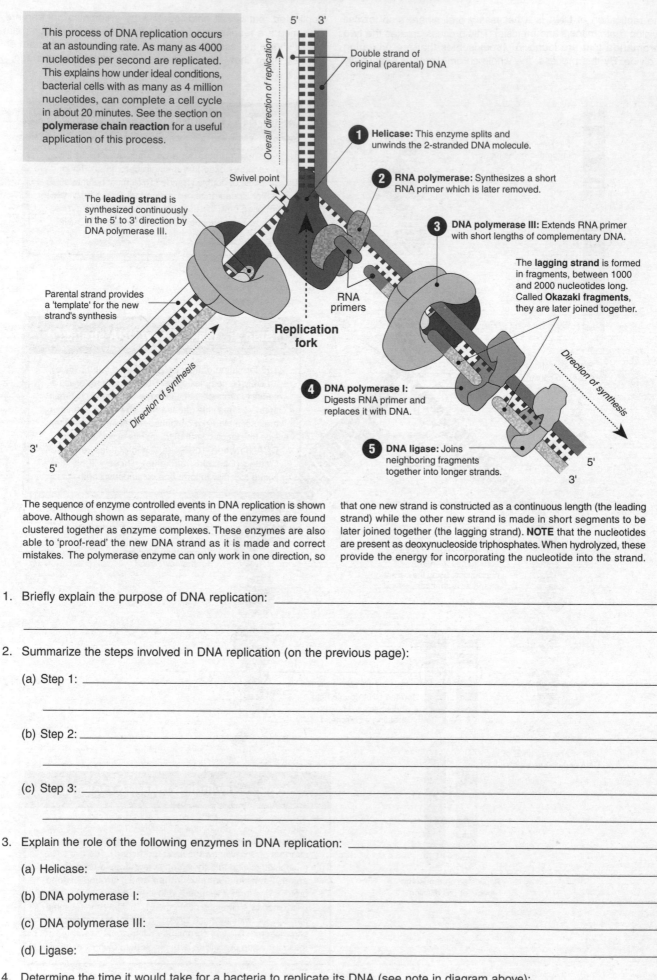

Overall direction of replication

5'  3'

Double strand of original (parental) DNA

**1** **Helicase:** This enzyme splits and unwinds the 2-stranded DNA molecule.

**2** **RNA polymerase:** Synthesizes a short RNA primer which is later removed.

**3** **DNA polymerase III:** Extends RNA primer with short lengths of complementary DNA.

The **lagging strand** is formed in fragments, between 1000 and 2000 nucleotides long. Called **Okazaki fragments**, they are later joined together.

Swivel point

The **leading strand** is synthesized continuously in the 5' to 3' direction by DNA polymerase III.

Parental strand provides a 'template' for the new strand's synthesis

RNA primers

**Replication fork**

Direction of synthesis

Direction of synthesis

**4** **DNA polymerase I:** Digests RNA primer and replaces it with DNA.

3'

5'

**5** **DNA ligase:** Joins neighboring fragments together into longer strands.

5'

3'

The sequence of enzyme controlled events in DNA replication is shown above. Although shown as separate, many of the enzymes are found clustered together as enzyme complexes. These enzymes are also able to 'proof-read' the new DNA strand as it is made and correct mistakes. The polymerase enzyme can only work in one direction, so that one new strand is constructed as a continuous length (the leading strand) while the other new strand is made in short segments to be later joined together (the lagging strand). **NOTE** that the nucleotides are present as deoxynucleoside triphosphates. When hydrolyzed, these provide the energy for incorporating the nucleotide into the strand.

1. Briefly explain the purpose of DNA replication: _____

   _____

2. Summarize the steps involved in DNA replication (on the previous page):

   (a) Step 1: _____

   _____

   (b) Step 2: _____

   _____

   (c) Step 3: _____

   _____

3. Explain the role of the following enzymes in DNA replication: _____

   (a) Helicase: _____

   (b) DNA polymerase I: _____

   (c) DNA polymerase III: _____

   (d) Ligase: _____

4. Determine the time it would take for a bacteria to replicate its DNA (see note in diagram above): _____

# The Simplest Case: Genes to Proteins

The traditionally held view of genes was as sections of DNA coding only for protein. This view has been revised in recent years with the discovery that much of the nonprotein-coding DNA encodes functional RNAs; it is not all non-coding "junk" DNA as was previously assumed. In fact, our concept of what constitutes a gene is changing rapidly and now encompasses all those segments of DNA that are transcribed (to RNA). This activity considers only the simplest scenario: one in which the gene codes for a functional protein. **Nucleotides**, the basic unit of genetic information, are read in groups of three (**triplets**). Some triplets have a special controlling function in the making of a polypeptide chain. The equivalent of the triplet on the mRNA molecule is the **codon**. Three codons can signify termination of the amino acid chain (UAG, UAA and UGA in the mRNA code). The codon AUG is found at the beginning of every gene (on mRNA) and marks the starting point for reading the gene. The genes required to form a functional end-product (in this case, a functional protein) are collectively called a **transcription unit**.

This polypeptide chain forms one part of the functional protein.

**Functional protein**

This polypeptide chain forms the other part of the functional protein.

**Polypeptide chain**

A **triplet** codes for one amino acid

**Polypeptide chain**

← Amino acids

**Translation**

← mRNA

**Transcription**

DNA: **Template** strand

START Triplet Triplet Triplet Triplet Triplet Triplet Triplet STOP START Triplet Triplet Triplet Triplet Triplet Triplet STOP

DNA: **Coding** strand

**Gene**

**Transcription unit**

**Gene**

Note: This start code is for the **coding strand** of the DNA. The template DNA strand from which the mRNA is made has the sequence: **TAC**.

*Three **nucleotides** make up a **triplet***

**Nucleotide**

In models of nucleic acids, nucleotides are denoted by their base letter. (In this case: **G** is for guanine)

1. Describe the structure in a protein that corresponds to each of the following levels of genetic information:

   (a) Triplet          codes for: _____

   (b) Gene            codes for: _____

   (c) Transcription unit   codes for: _____

2. Describe the basic building blocks for each of the following levels of genetic information:

   (a) **Nucleotide** is made up of: _____

   _____

   (b) **Triplet** is made up of: _____

   _____

   (c) **Gene** is made up of: _____

   _____

   (d) **Transcription unit** is made up of: _____

   _____

3. Describe the steps involved in forming a functional protein: _____

   _____

**Molecular Genetics**

**Related activities**: Gene Expression

A 2

# Analyzing a DNA Sample

The nucleotide (base sequence) of a section of DNA can be determined using DNA sequencing techniques (see the topic *Gene Technology* later in this workbook for a description of this technology). The base sequence determines the amino acid sequence of the resultant protein therefore the DNA tells us what type of protein that gene encodes. This exercise reviews the areas of DNA replication, transcription, and translation using an analysis of a gel electrophoresis column. **Attempt it after you have completed the rest of this topic**. Remember that the gel pattern represents the sequence in the synthesized strand.

1. Determine the amino acid sequence of a protein from the nucleotide sequence of its DNA, with the following steps:

   (a) Determine the sequence of **synthesized DNA** in the gel
   (b) Convert it to the complementary sequence of the **sample DNA**
   (c) Complete the **mRNA** sequence
   (d) Determine the **amino acid** sequence by using the *mRNA - amino acid table* in this workbook.

   NOTE: The nucleotides in the gel are read from bottom to top and the sequence is written in the spaces provided from left to right (the first four have been done for you).

Triplet | Triplet | Triplet | Triplet | Triplet | Triplet | Triplet | Triplet | Triplet | Triplet | Triplet

**C G T A** ... **Synthesised DNA**
(DNA sequence read from the gel; comprises radioactive nucleotides that bind to the coding strand DNA in the sample).

*Replication*

**G C A T** ... **DNA sample**
(This is the DNA that is being investigated)

*Transcription*

**C G U A** ... **mRNA**

*Translation*

Arginine ... **Amino acids**
Part of a polypeptide chain

Read in this direction

A
T
G
C

T  C  G  A

2. For each single strand DNA sequence below, write the base sequence for the **complementary DNA** strand:

   (a) DNA:    T A C     T A G     C C G     C G A     T T T     A C A     A T T

   DNA: _____

   (b) DNA:    T A C     G C C     T T A     A A G     G G C     C G A     A T C

   DNA: _____

   (c) Identify the cell process that this exercise represents: _____

3. For each single strand DNA sequence below, write the base sequence for the **mRNA** strand and the **amino acid** that it codes for (refer to the mRNA-amino acid table to determine the amino acid sequence):

   (a) DNA:    T A C     T A G     C C G     C G A     T T T     A C A     A T T

   mRNA: _____

   Amino
   acids: _____

   (b) DNA:    T A C     G C C     T T A     A A G     G G C     C G A     A T C

   mRNA: _____

   Amino
   acids: _____

   (c) Identify the cell process that this exercise represents: _____

**Related activities**: The Genetic Code, Gel Electrophoresis

# Gene Expression

The process of transferring the information encoded in a gene to its functional gene product is called **gene expression**. The central dogma of molecular biology for the past 50 years or so has stated that genetic information, encoded in DNA, is transcribed as molecules of RNA, which are then translated into the amino acid sequences that make up proteins. The established opinion was often stated as "one gene-one protein" and proteins were assumed to be the main regulatory agents for the cell (including its gene expression). The one gene-one protein model is supported by studies of prokaryotic genomes, where the DNA consists almost entirely of protein-coding genes and their regulatory sequences.

## Genes and Gene Expression in Prokaryotes

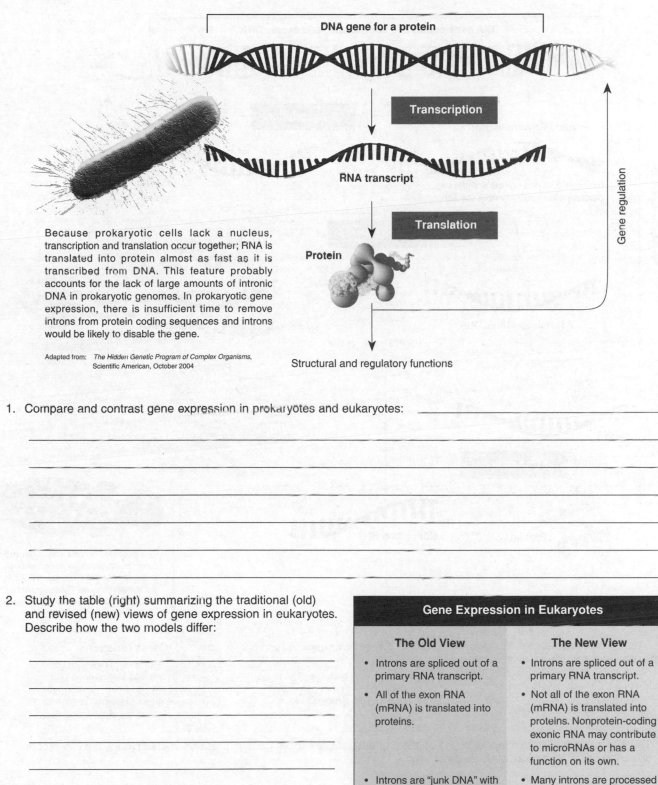

**DNA gene for a protein**

**Transcription**

**RNA transcript**

**Translation**

**Protein**

**Gene regulation**

Structural and regulatory functions

Because prokaryotic cells lack a nucleus, transcription and translation occur together; RNA is translated into protein almost as fast as it is transcribed from DNA. This feature probably accounts for the lack of large amounts of intronic DNA in prokaryotic genomes. In prokaryotic gene expression, there is insufficient time to remove introns from protein coding sequences and introns would be likely to disable the gene.

Adapted from:  *The Hidden Genetic Program of Complex Organisms,*
*Scientific American*, October 2004

1.  Compare and contrast gene expression in prokaryotes and eukaryotes: _____

    _____

    _____

    _____

    _____

    _____

    _____

2.  Study the table (right) summarizing the traditional (old) and revised (new) views of gene expression in eukaryotes. Describe how the two models differ:

    _____

    _____

    _____

    _____

    _____

    _____

    _____

    _____

    _____

    _____

### Gene Expression in Eukaryotes

| The Old View | The New View |
|---|---|
| • Introns are spliced out of a primary RNA transcript. | • Introns are spliced out of a primary RNA transcript. |
| • All of the exon RNA (mRNA) is translated into proteins. | • Not all of the exon RNA (mRNA) is translated into proteins. Nonprotein-coding exonic RNA may contribute to microRNAs or has a function on its own. |
| • Introns are "junk DNA" with no assigned function; they are degraded and recycled. | • Many introns are processed into microRNAs which appear to be involved in regulating development. |

**Molecular Genetics**

**Related activities**: The Simplest Case: Genes to Proteins

**A 3**

In contrast to prokaryotes, eukaryotic genomes contain a large amount of DNA that does not code for proteins. These DNA sequences, called **introns** or intronic DNA, were termed "junk DNA", and were assumed to have no function. However new evidence, arising as more and more diverse genomes are sequenced, suggests that this DNA may encode a vast number of RNA molecules with regulatory functions. Among the eukaryotes, an increase in complexity is associated with an increase in the proportion of nonprotein-coding DNA. This makes sense if the nonprotein-coding DNA has a role in regulating genomic function. These pages contrast gene expression in prokaryotes, where there is very little nonprotein-coding DNA, with the new view of eukaryotic gene expression, where a high proportion of the genomic DNA does not code directly for proteins.

## The New View of Gene Expression in Eukaryotes

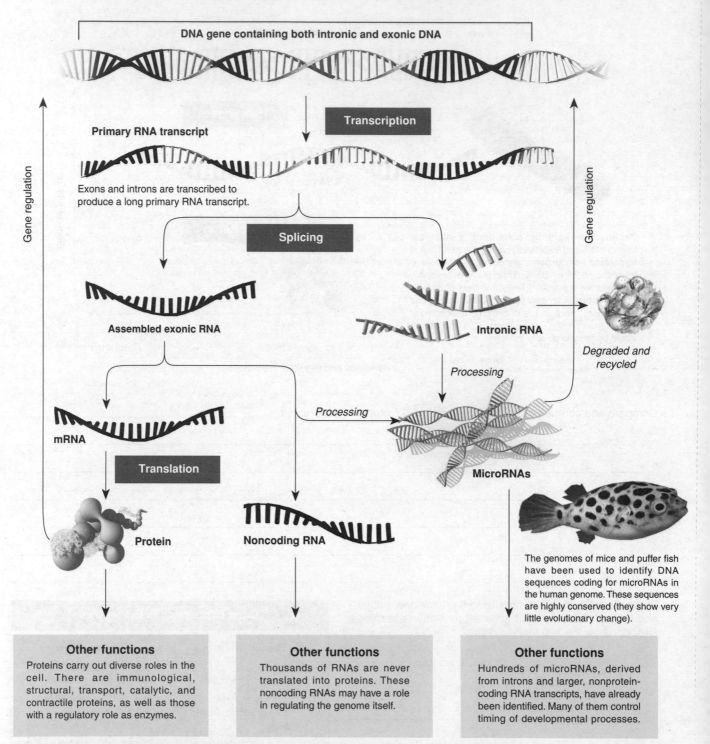

**DNA gene containing both intronic and exonic DNA**

**Transcription**

**Primary RNA transcript**

Exons and introns are transcribed to produce a long primary RNA transcript.

Gene regulation

**Splicing**

**Assembled exonic RNA**

**Intronic RNA**

*Degraded and recycled*

*Processing*

*Processing*

Gene regulation

**mRNA**

**MicroRNAs**

**Translation**

**Protein**

**Noncoding RNA**

The genomes of mice and puffer fish have been used to identify DNA sequences coding for microRNAs in the human genome. These sequences are highly conserved (they show very little evolutionary change).

### Other functions

Proteins carry out diverse roles in the cell. There are immunological, structural, transport, catalytic, and contractile proteins, as well as those with a regulatory role as enzymes.

### Other functions

Thousands of RNAs are never translated into proteins. These noncoding RNAs may have a role in regulating the genome itself.

### Other functions

Hundreds of microRNAs, derived from introns and larger, nonprotein-coding RNA transcripts, have already been identified. Many of them control timing of developmental processes.

3. The one gene-one protein model does not seem to adequately explain gene expression in eukaryotes, but it is probably still appropriate for prokaryotes. Suggest why:

_____

_____

_____

# Transcription

Transcription is the process by which the code contained in the DNA molecule is transcribed (rewritten) into a **mRNA** molecule. Transcription is under the control of the cell's metabolic processes which must activate a gene before this process can begin. The enzyme that directly controls the process is RNA polymerase, which makes a strand of mRNA using the single strand of DNA (the **template strand**) as the template (hence the term).

The enzyme transcribes only a gene length of DNA at a time and therefore recognizes start and stop signals (codes) at the beginning and end of the gene. Only RNA polymerase is involved in mRNA synthesis; it causes the unwinding of the DNA as well. It is common to find several RNA polymerase enzyme molecules on the same gene at any one time, allowing a high rate of mRNA synthesis to occur.

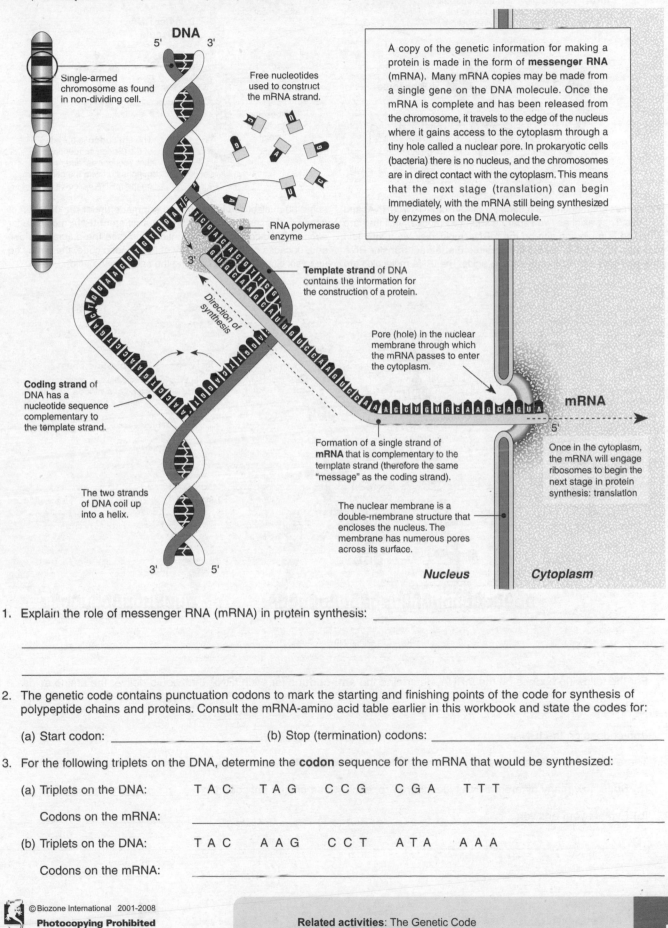

A copy of the genetic information for making a protein is made in the form of **messenger RNA** (mRNA). Many mRNA copies may be made from a single gene on the DNA molecule. Once the mRNA is complete and has been released from the chromosome, it travels to the edge of the nucleus where it gains access to the cytoplasm through a tiny hole called a nuclear pore. In prokaryotic cells (bacteria) there is no nucleus, and the chromosomes are in direct contact with the cytoplasm. This means that the next stage (translation) can begin immediately, with the mRNA still being synthesized by enzymes on the DNA molecule.

**DNA**

Single-armed chromosome as found in non-dividing cell.

Free nucleotides used to construct the mRNA strand.

RNA polymerase enzyme

Direction of synthesis

**Template strand** of DNA contains the information for the construction of a protein.

Pore (hole) in the nuclear membrane through which the mRNA passes to enter the cytoplasm.

**Coding strand** of DNA has a nucleotide sequence complementary to the template strand.

**mRNA**

Formation of a single strand of **mRNA** that is complementary to the template strand (therefore the same "message" as the coding strand).

Once in the cytoplasm, the mRNA will engage ribosomes to begin the next stage in protein synthesis: translation

The two strands of DNA coil up into a helix.

The nuclear membrane is a double-membrane structure that encloses the nucleus. The membrane has numerous pores across its surface.

**Nucleus**       **Cytoplasm**

**Molecular Genetics**

1. Explain the role of messenger RNA (mRNA) in protein synthesis: _____

_____

_____

2. The genetic code contains punctuation codons to mark the starting and finishing points of the code for synthesis of polypeptide chains and proteins. Consult the mRNA-amino acid table earlier in this workbook and state the codes for:

   (a) Start codon: _____ (b) Stop (termination) codons: _____

3. For the following triplets on the DNA, determine the **codon** sequence for the mRNA that would be synthesized:

   (a) Triplets on the DNA:       T A C      T A G      C C G      C G A      T T T

   Codons on the mRNA:      _____

   (b) Triplets on the DNA:       T A C      A A G      C C T      A T A      A A A

   Codons on the mRNA:      _____

**Related activities**: The Genetic Code
**Web links**: Transcription in Prokaryotes, Animation of Transcription

**RA 2**

# Translation

The diagram below shows the translation phase of protein synthesis. The scene shows how a single mRNA molecule can be 'serviced' by many ribosomes at the same time. The ribosome to the right (lower diagram) is in a more advanced stage of constructing a polypeptide chain because it has 'translated' more of the mRNA than the ribosome to the left. The anti-codon at the base of each tRNA must make a perfect complementary match with the codon on the mRNA before the amino acid is released. Once released, the amino acid is added to the growing polypeptide chain by enzymes.

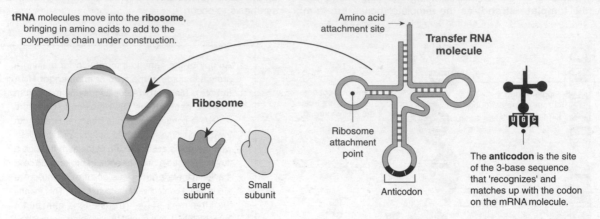

tRNA molecules move into the **ribosome**, bringing in amino acids to add to the polypeptide chain under construction.

**Ribosome**

Large subunit    Small subunit

Amino acid attachment site

**Transfer RNA molecule**

Ribosome attachment point

Anticodon

The **anticodon** is the site of the 3-base sequence that 'recognizes' and matches up with the codon on the mRNA molecule.

Ribosomes are made up of a complex of ribosomal RNA (rRNA) and proteins. They exist as two separate sub-units (above) until they are attracted to a binding site on the mRNA molecule, when they join together. Ribosomes have binding sites that attract transfer RNA (**tRNA**) molecules loaded with amino acids. The tRNA molecules are about 80 nucleotides in length and are made under the direction of genes in the chromosomes. There is a different tRNA molecule for each of the different possible anticodons (see the diagram below) and, because of the degeneracy of the genetic code, there may be up to six different tRNAs carrying the same amino acid.

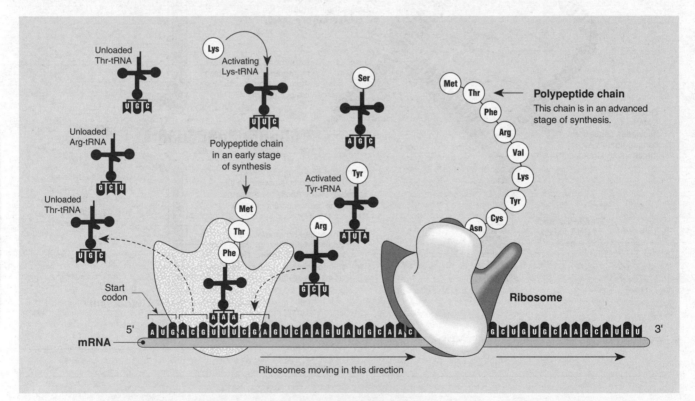

Unloaded Thr-tRNA

Activating Lys-tRNA

Unloaded Arg-tRNA

Polypeptide chain in an early stage of synthesis

Unloaded Thr-tRNA

Activated Tyr-tRNA

**Polypeptide chain**
This chain is in an advanced stage of synthesis.

Start codon

**Ribosome**

mRNA

Ribosomes moving in this direction

1. For the following codons on the mRNA, determine the **anti-codons** for each tRNA that would deliver the amino acids:

   Codons on the mRNA:          U A C    U A G    C C G    C G A    U U U

   Anti-codons on the tRNAs: _____

2. There are many different types of tRNA molecules, each with a different anti-codon (see the mRNA-amino acid table).

   (a) State how many different tRNA types there are, each with a unique anticodon: _____

   (b) Explain your answer: _____
   _____
   _____

**Related activities:** The Genetic Code
**Web links:** Polyribosomes

# Protein Synthesis Review

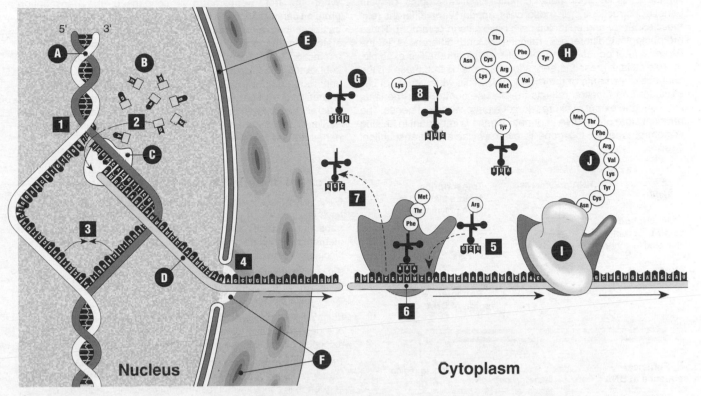

**Nucleus**

**Cytoplasm**

The diagram above shows an overview of the process of protein synthesis. It summarizes the main ideas covered in this topic. Each of the major steps in the process are numbered, while structures are labeled with letters.

1. Briefly describe each of the numbered processes in the diagram above:

   (a) Process 1: _____

   (b) Process 2: _____

   (c) Process 3: _____

   (d) Process 4: _____

   (e) Process 5: _____

   (f) Process 6: _____

   (g) Process 7: _____

   (h) Process 8: _____

2. Identify each of the structures marked with a letter and write their names below in the spaces provided:

   (a) Structure A: _____      (f) Structure F: _____

   (b) Structure B: _____      (g) Structure G: _____

   (c) Structure C: _____      (h) Structure H: _____

   (d) Structure D: _____      (i) Structure I: _____

   (e) Structure E: _____      (j) Structure J: _____

3. Describe two factors that would determine whether or not a particular protein is produced in the cell:

   (a) _____

   _____

   (b) _____

   _____

© Biozone International 2001-2008
**Photocopying Prohibited**

**Molecular Genetics**

**Related activities**: Transcription, Translation

**RA 2**

# Gene Control in Eukaryotes

All the cells in your body contain identical copies of your genetic instructions. Yet these cells appear very different (e.g. muscle, nerve, and epithelial cells have little in common). These morphological differences reflect profound differences in the expression of genes during the cell's development. For example, muscle cells express the genes for the proteins that make up the contractile elements of the muscle fiber. This wide variety of cell structure and function reflects the precise control over the time, location, and extent of expression of a huge variety of genes. The physical state of the DNA in or near a gene is important in helping to control whether the gene is even available for transcription.

When the **heterochromatin** is condensed, the transcription proteins cannot reach the DNA and the gene is not expressed. To be transcribed, a gene must first be unpacked from its condensed state. Once unpacked, control of gene expression involves the interaction of **transcription factors** with DNA sequences that control the specific gene. Initiation of transcription is the most important and universally used control point in gene expression. A simplified summary of this process is outlined below. Note the differences between this model and the operon model, described earlier, which is not applicable to eukaryotes because eukaryotic genes are not found as operons.

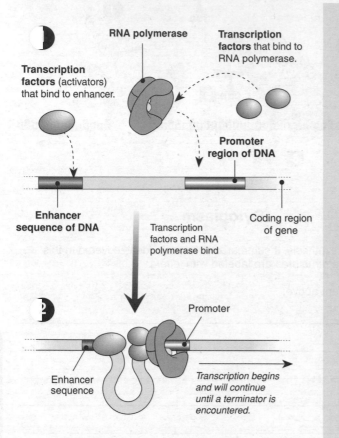

RNA polymerase

Transcription **factors** that bind to RNA polymerase.

Transcription **factors** (activators) that bind to enhancer.

Promoter region of DNA

**Enhancer sequence of DNA**

Transcription factors and RNA polymerase bind

Coding region of gene

Promoter

Enhancer sequence

*Transcription begins and will continue until a terminator is encountered.*

## Control of Gene Expression in Eukaryotes

- Eukaryotic genes are very different from prokaryotic genes: they have introns (which you recall are removed after the primary transcript is made) and a relatively large number of **control elements** (non-coding DNA that help regulate transcription by binding proteins called transcription factors).

- Each functional eukaryotic gene has a **promoter region** at the upstream end of the gene; a DNA sequence where RNA polymerase binds and starts transcription.

- Eukaryotic RNA polymerase alone cannot initiate the transcription of a gene; it is dependent on **transcription factors** in order to recognize and bind to the **promoter** (step 1).

- Transcription is activated when a hairpin loop in the DNA brings the transcription factors (activators) attached to the **enhancer sequence** in contact with the transcription factors bound to RNA polymerase at the promoter (step 2).

- Protein-protein interactions are crucial to eukaryotic transcription. Only when the complete initiation complex is assembled can the polymerase move along the DNA template strand and produce the complementary strand of RNA.

- Transcription is deactivated when a terminator sequence is encountered. Terminators are nucleotide sequences that function to stop transcription. *Do not confuse these with terminator codons, which are the stop signals for translation.*

- A range of transcription factors and enhancer sequences throughout the genome may selectively activate the expression of specific genes at appropriate stages during cell development.

1. Explain the functional role of each of the following in relation to gene regulation in a eukaryote:

   (a) Promoter: _____

   _____

   (b) Transcription factors: _____

   _____

   (c) Enhancer sequence: _____

   _____

   (d) RNA polymerase: _____

   _____

   (e) Terminator sequence: _____

   _____

2. Identify one difference between the mechanisms of gene control in eukaryotes and prokaryotes:

   _____

   _____

**Related activities**: Gene Control in Prokaryotes, Control of Metabolic Pathways

# Gene Control in Prokaryotes

The **operon** mechanism was proposed by **Jacob and Monod** to account for the regulation of gene activity in response to the needs of the cell. Their work was carried out with the bacterium *Escherichia coli* and the model is not applicable to eukaryotic cells where the genes are not found as operons. An operon consists of a group of closely linked genes that act together and code for the enzymes that control a particular **metabolic pathway**. These may be for the metabolism of an energy source (e.g. lactose) or the synthesis of a molecule such as an amino acid. The structural genes contain the information for the production of the enzymes themselves and they are transcribed as a single **transcription unit**. These structural genes are controlled by a **promoter**, which initiates the formation of the mRNA, and a region of the DNA in front of the structural genes called the **operator**. A gene outside the operon, called the **regulator gene**, produces a **repressor** molecule that can bind to the operator, and block the transcription of the structural genes. It is the repressor that switches the structural genes on or off and controls the metabolic pathway. Two mechanisms operate in the operon model: gene induction and gene repression. **Gene induction** occurs when genes are switched on by an inducer binding to the repressor molecule and deactivating it. In the **Lac operon model** based on *E.coli*, lactose acts as the **inducer**, binding to the repressor and permitting transcription of the structural genes for the utilization of lactose (an infrequently encountered substrate). **Gene repression** occurs when genes that are normally switched on (e.g. genes for synthesis of an amino acid) are switched off by activation of the repressor.

## Control of Gene Expression Through Induction: the *Lac* Operon

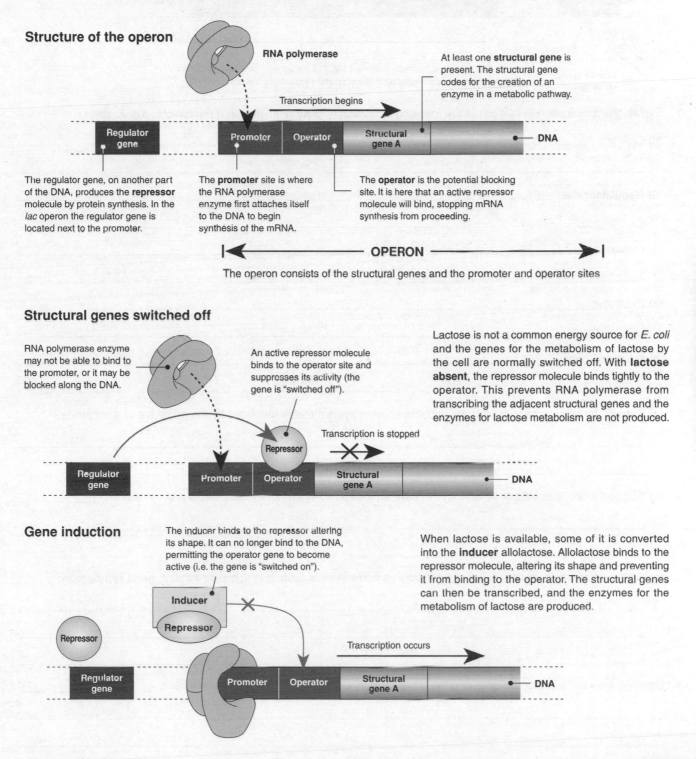

### Structure of the operon

**RNA polymerase**

At least one **structural gene** is present. The structural gene codes for the creation of an enzyme in a metabolic pathway.

Transcription begins

| Regulator gene | Promoter | Operator | Structural gene A | | DNA |

The regulator gene, on another part of the DNA, produces the **repressor** molecule by protein synthesis. In the *lac* operon the regulator gene is located next to the promoter.

The **promoter** site is where the RNA polymerase enzyme first attaches itself to the DNA to begin synthesis of the mRNA.

The **operator** is the potential blocking site. It is here that an active repressor molecule will bind, stopping mRNA synthesis from proceeding.

OPERON

The operon consists of the structural genes and the promoter and operator sites

### Structural genes switched off

RNA polymerase enzyme may not be able to bind to the promoter, or it may be blocked along the DNA.

An active repressor molecule binds to the operator site and suppresses its activity (the gene is "switched off").

Lactose is not a common energy source for *E. coli* and the genes for the metabolism of lactose by the cell are normally switched off. With **lactose absent**, the repressor molecule binds tightly to the operator. This prevents RNA polymerase from transcribing the adjacent structural genes and the enzymes for lactose metabolism are not produced.

**Repressor**

Transcription is stopped

| Regulator gene | Promoter | Operator | Structural gene A | | DNA |

### Gene induction

The inducer binds to the repressor altering its shape. It can no longer bind to the DNA, permitting the operator gene to become active (i.e. the gene is "switched on").

When lactose is available, some of it is converted into the **inducer** allolactose. Allolactose binds to the repressor molecule, altering its shape and preventing it from binding to the operator. The structural genes can then be transcribed, and the enzymes for the metabolism of lactose are produced.

**Inducer**

**Repressor**

**Repressor**

Transcription occurs

| Regulator gene | Promoter | Operator | Structural gene A | | DNA |

**Related activities**: Gene Control in Eukaryotes

A 3

Molecular Genetics

# Control of Gene Expression Through Repression

## Gene repression

**RNA polymerase**

The repressor requires the presence of an **effector**, which helps the repressor bind to the operator.

The combined effector and repressor molecule bind to the operator and block RNA polymerase, preventing any further transcription.

**Repressor**

**Repressor**

Transcription is stopped

| Regulator gene | Promoter | Operator | Structural gene A | | **DNA** |

Effector in high concentration

The operon is normally "switched on". The genes are "switched off" as a response to the **overabundance** of an **end product** of a metabolic pathway.

In *E. coli*, the enzyme **tryptophan synthetase** synthesizes the amino acid tryptophan. The gene for producing this enzyme is normally switched on. When **tryptophan** is present in excess, some of it acts as an **effector** (also called a co-repressor). The effector activates the repressor, and they bind to the operator gene, preventing any further transcription of the structural gene. Once transcription stops, the enzyme tryptophan synthetase is no longer produced. This is an example of **end-product inhibition** (feedback inhibition).

1. Explain the functional role of each of the following in relation to gene regulation in a prokaryote, e.g. *E. coli*:

   (a) Operon: _____

   _____

   (b) Regulator gene: _____

   _____

   (c) Operator: _____

   _____

   (d) Promoter: _____

   _____

   (e) Structural genes: _____

   _____

2. (a) Explain the advantage in having an inducible enzyme system that is regulated by the presence of a substrate:

   _____

   _____

   (b) Suggest when it would not be adaptive to have an inducible system for metabolism of a substrate: _____

   _____

   _____

   (c) Giving an example, outline how gene control in a non-inducible system is achieved through **gene repression**:

   _____

   _____

   _____

3. Describe how the two mechanisms of gene control described here are fundamentally different: _____

   _____

   _____

# Control of Metabolic Pathways

**Metabolism** is all the chemical activities of life. The myriad enzyme-controlled **metabolic pathways** that are described as metabolism form a tremendously complex network that is necessary in order to 'maintain' the organism. Errors in the step-wise regulation of enzyme-controlled pathways can result in metabolic disorders that in some cases can be easily identified. An example of a well studied metabolic pathway, the metabolism of **phenylalanine**, is described below.

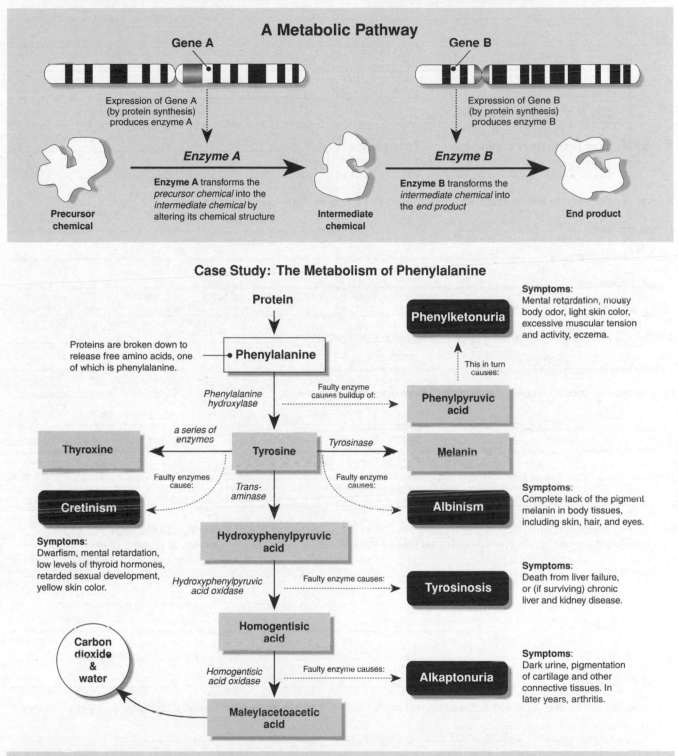

## A Metabolic Pathway

**Gene A**

Expression of Gene A (by protein synthesis) produces enzyme A

**Gene B**

Expression of Gene B (by protein synthesis) produces enzyme B

**Precursor chemical**

**Enzyme A**

**Enzyme A** transforms the *precursor chemical* into the *intermediate chemical* by altering its chemical structure

**Intermediate chemical**

**Enzyme B**

**Enzyme B** transforms the *intermediate chemical* into the *end product*

**End product**

## Case Study: The Metabolism of Phenylalanine

**Protein**

Proteins are broken down to release free amino acids, one of which is phenylalanine.

**Phenylalanine**

**Phenylketonuria**

**Symptoms:** Mental retardation, mousy body odor, light skin color, excessive muscular tension and activity, eczema.

*Phenylalanine hydroxylase*

Faulty enzyme causes buildup of:

This in turn causes:

**Phenylpyruvic acid**

*a series of enzymes*

**Thyroxine**

**Tyrosine**

*Tyrosinase*

**Melanin**

Faulty enzymes cause:

*Trans-aminase*

Faulty enzyme causes:

**Cretinism**

**Albinism**

**Symptoms:** Complete lack of the pigment melanin in body tissues, including skin, hair, and eyes.

**Symptoms:** Dwarfism, mental retardation, low levels of thyroid hormones, retarded sexual development, yellow skin color.

**Hydroxyphenylpyruvic acid**

*Hydroxyphenylpyruvic acid oxidase*

Faulty enzyme causes:

**Tyrosinosis**

**Symptoms:** Death from liver failure, or (if surviving) chronic liver and kidney disease.

**Homogentisic acid**

**Carbon dioxide & water**

*Homogentisic acid oxidase*

Faulty enzyme causes:

**Alkaptonuria**

**Symptoms:** Dark urine, pigmentation of cartilage and other connective tissues. In later years, arthritis.

**Maleylacetoacetic acid**

**Molecular Genetics**

A well studied metabolic pathway is the metabolic breakdown of the essential amino acid **phenylalanine**. The first step is carried out by an enzyme produced in the liver, called phenylalanine hydroxylase. This enzyme converts phenylalanine to the amino acid **tyrosine**. Tyrosine, in turn, through a series of intermediate steps, is converted into **melanin**, the skin pigment, and other substances. If phenylalanine hydroxylase is absent, phenylalanine is in part converted into phenylpyruvic acid, which accumulates, together with phenylalanine, in the blood stream. Phenylpyruvic acid and phenylalanine are toxic to the central nervous system

and produce some of the symptoms of the genetic disease **phenylketonuria**. Other genetic metabolic defects in the tyrosine pathway are also known. As indicated above, absence of enzymes operating between tyrosine and melanin, is a cause of **albinism**. **Tyrosinosis** is a rare defect that causes hydroxyphenylpyruvic acid to accumulate in the urine. **Alkaptonuria** makes urine turn black on exposure to air, causes pigmentation to appear in the cartilage, and produces symptoms of arthritis. A different block in another pathway from tyrosine produces thyroid deficiency leading to goiterous **cretinism** (due to lack of thyroxine).

**Related activities**: Complementary Genes, Epistasis

**RA 3**

1. Using the metabolism of phenyalanine as an example, discuss the role of enzymes in **metabolic pathways**:

_____

_____

_____

_____

_____

_____

2. Identify three **products** of the metabolism of phenylalanine: _____

_____

3. Identify the enzyme failure (faulty enzyme) responsible for each of the following conditions:

   (a) Albinism: _____

   (b) Phenylketonuria: _____

   (c) Tyrosinosis: _____

   (d) Alkaptonuria: _____

4. Explain why people with **phenylketonuria** have light skin coloring: _____

_____

5. Discuss the consequences of disorders in the metabolism of **tyrosine**: _____

_____

_____

_____

_____

6. The five conditions illustrated in the diagram are due to too much or too little of a chemical in the body. For each condition listed below, state which chemical causes the problem and whether it is absent or present in excess:

   (a) Albinism: _____

   (b) Phenylketonuria: _____

   (c) Cretinism: _____

   (d) Tyrosinosis: _____

   (e) Alkaptonuria: _____

7. If you suspected that a person suffered from phenylketonuria, how would you test for the condition if you were a doctor:

_____

_____

_____

8. The diagram at the top of the previous page represents the normal condition for a simple metabolic pathway. A starting chemical, called the **precursor**, is progressively changed into a final chemical called the **end product**.

   Consider the effect on this pathway if **gene A** underwent a mutation and the resulting **enzyme A** did not function:

   (a) Identify the chemicals that would be present in **excess**: _____

   (b) Identify the chemicals that would be **absent**: _____

# Genes and Chromosomes

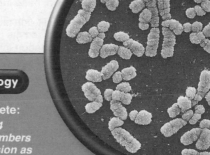

| IB SL | IB HL | IB Options | AP Biology |
|---|---|---|---|
| **Complete:** 1-2, 4-5, 7-12(a)-(c), 13, 18, 23-24(a), 25, 29-30, 32 | **Complete:** 1-2, 4-5, 7-15, 17-18, 23-24(a), 25, 29-30, 32 Ext.: 3, 6, 19-22, 33 | Not applicable to options | **Complete:** 1-34 Some numbers as extension as appropriate |

## Learning Objectives

☐ 1. Compile your own glossary from the **KEY WORDS** displayed in **bold type** in the learning objectives below.

### Chromosome Structure *(page 171-176, 210)*

☐ 2. Describe the structure and morphology of eukaryote **chromosomes**, identifying the role of **histone proteins** in packaging the DNA in the nucleus.

☐ 3. With respect to structure and organization, distinguish between prokaryote and eukaryote chromosomes.

☐ 4. Define the terms: **karyotype**, **autosomes**, and **sex chromosomes**. Explain the basis of karyotyping and describe one application of this process.

☐ 5. Appreciate that karyotyping is performed using cells collected by amniocentesis or chorionic villus sampling, for **prenatal diagnosis** of chromosome abnormalities.

☐ 6. Explain, in general terms, how a karyotype is prepared.

☐ 7. Distinguish between **gene** and **allele**. Clearly define the following terms: **genome**, **homologous chromosomes (=homologues)**, **chromatid**, and **centromere**.

### Sources of Variation *(pages 181-184)*

☐ 8. Appreciate that both genes and environment contribute to phenotypic variation. With reference to specific examples, identify sources of genetic and environmental variation.

### Meiosis *(pages 181, 185-188)*

☐ 9. Appreciate the general significance of meiosis in generating genetic variation. Identify how meiosis creates new allele combinations in the gametes.

☐ 10. Describe how chromosome numbers can vary between somatic cells (**diploid** 2N) and gametes (**haploid** 1N).

☐ 11. Recognize that meiosis, like mitosis, involves DNA replication during interphase in the parent cell, but that this is followed by two cycles of nuclear division.

☐ 12. Summarize the principal events in meiosis, including:
   (a) Pairing of **homologous chromosomes** (synapsis) and the formation of **bivalents**.
   (b) **Chiasma** formation and exchange between **chromatids** in the first, (**reduction**) **division**.
   (c) Separation of chromatids in the second division and the production of **haploid cells**.
   (d) The associated behavior of the **nuclear envelope**, plasma membrane, and **centrioles**.
   (e) Identification of the names of the main stages.

☐ 13. Describe the behavior of homologous chromosomes (and their associated alleles) during meiosis and fertilization, with reference to:

   • The **independent assortment** of maternal and paternal chromosomes. Chance governs which pole each chromosome of a bivalent moves to, ensuring random combinations of non-homologous chromosomes in the haploid nuclei.
   • The **recombination** of segments of maternal and paternal homologous chromosomes in **crossing over**.
   • The **random fusion** of gametes during fertilization.

Explain how these events in meiosis and fertilization give rise to genetic variety in the gametes.

### Linkage and recombination *(pages 181, 189-192)*

☐ 14. With respect to inheritance, explain what is meant by the terms: **linkage** and **linkage group**. Explain the consequences of linkage to the inheritance of alleles.

☐ 15. Recall that **recombination** refers to the exchange of alleles between homologous chromosomes as a result of **crossing over**. Explain the consequences of recombination to the inheritance of alleles.

☐ 16. Explain what is meant by the **crossover frequency** (frequency of recombination, **crossover value**, or COV). Describe how crossover values are used as a measure of the relative positions of genes on the same chromosome. Demonstrate the use of crossover values in chromosome (gene) mapping.

☐ 17. In general terms, explain the effect of linkage and recombination on the phenotypic ratios from dihybrid crosses (see the topic *Inheritance*).

### Mutagens and mutations *(pages 193-196)*

☐ 18. Explain what is meant by the general term **mutation** and understand the significance of mutations as the ultimate source of all new alleles.

☐ 19. Explain the term: **spontaneous mutation**. Recognize that each species has its own frequency of naturally occurring mutations (the **background mutation rate**).

☐ 20. Define the terms: **mutagen**, **induced mutation**. Identify the environmental factors that can cause mutations. Describe the effects of chemical mutagens and radiation on DNA and the rate of mutation.

☐ 21. Mutations may occur in different types of cell. The location of a mutation can have a different significance in terms of producing heritable change. Clearly define: **germ line**, **somatic mutation**, **gametic mutation**.

☐ 22. Recognize that mutations may have different survival value in different environments. Explain, with examples, how mutations may be **harmful**, **beneficial**, or **neutral** (silent) in their effect on the organism. Recognize the evolutionary importance of **neutral mutations**.

### Gene mutations *(pages 197-201)*

☐ 23. Explain what is meant by a **gene mutation** and provide examples. Distinguish between gene mutations involving change in a single nucleotide (commonly called **point** mutations), and those involving changes to a triplet (e.g. triplet deletion or repeat). Understand why gene mutations offer the greatest evolutionary potential.

24. Understand the cause and effect of gene mutations as illustrated by the following: **base substitution, base deletion, base insertion**.

25. Describe the effect of a base substitution mutation on the resulting amino acid sequence and the phenotype, as illustrated by the **sickle cell mutation** in humans.

26. Recognize other disorders that arise as a result of single gene mutations: **β-thalassemia, cystic fibrosis**, and **Huntington disease**. Describe the genetic basis of one or more of these diseases.

### Chromosome mutations *(page 202)*

27. Explain what is meant by a **chromosome mutation**, and contrast chromosome and gene mutations.

28. Using symbolic diagrams in which genes are identified, describe the nature and genetic consequences of chromosome mutations, with reference to:
    (a) **Translocation**: Movement of a group of genes between different chromosomes.
    (b) **Inversion**: Rotation and rejoining of a segment of a chromosome.
    (c) **Duplication**: One chromosome loses a segment, and the segment is added to its homologue.
    (d) **Deletion**: Loss of part of a chromosome.

### Aneuploidy *(pages 203, 205-207)*

29. Define the term **aneuploidy**. Explain how aneuploidy may arise as a result of **non-disjunction** during meiosis and occur with a predictable frequency. Recognize **polysomy** as a type of aneuploidy.

30. Explain what is meant by a **syndrome**. Explain why chromosomal abnormalities are typically characterized by a suite of abnormal phenotypic characteristics.

31. Describe examples of aneuploidy in human sex chromosomes, e.g. Turner or Klinefelter syndrome.

32. Describe examples of **polysomy** in human autosomes, e.g. the common form of Down syndrome (trisomy 21).

33. Explain what is meant by the **maternal age effect**. Describe an example of a chromosomal disorder that shows a maternal age effect.

### Genetic Counseling *(page 204)*

34. Discuss the role of **genetic counseling** in managing the occurrence of inherited genetic disorders in families. Describe the circumstances under which couples might seek genetic counseling.

See the 'Textbook Reference Grid' on pages 8-9 for textbook page references relating to material in this topic.

## Supplementary Texts

See pages 5-6 for additional details of these texts:

- Adds, J., *et al.*, 2004. **Genetics, Evolution and Biodiversity**, (NelsonThornes), chpt. 7.
- Clegg, C.J., 1999. **Genetics & Evolution**, (John Murray), pp. 19-22, 34-39, 41, 43.
- Helms, D.R. *et al.*, 1998. **Biology in the Laboratory** (W.H. Freeman), #13, #14.
- Jones, N., *et al.*, 2001. **Essentials of Genetics**, (JM), pp. 17-25, 61-73, 131-34, 157-71, 257.
- Tobin, A.J. and Morel, R.E., 1997. **Asking About Cells**, (Thomson Brooks/Cole), part III.

See page 6 for details of publishers of periodicals:

### STUDENT'S REFERENCE

- **What is a Mutation?** Biol. Sci. Rev., 20(3) Feb. 2008, pp. 6-9. *An account of the nature of mutations: what causes them, when they happen, and what they do. Sickle cell disease is one of the case examples described.*
- **Secrets of The Gene** National Geographic, Oct. 1999, pp. 42-75. *A comprehensive article covering the nature of genes and mutations, including inherited defects, screening & treatment.*
- **How do Mutations Lead to Evolution?** New Scientist, 14 June 2003, pp. 32-39, 48-51. *An account of the five most common points of discussion regarding evolution and the mechanisms by which it occurs.*
- **Radiation and Risk** New Scientist, 18 March 2000 (Inside Science). *In large doses radiation can kill you in hours. In low doses, it can lead to slow death by cancer. How do we quantify the effects?*
- **The Biological Aspects of Down Syndrome** Biol. Sci. Rev., 10(5) May 1998, pp. 11-15. *Chromosome trisomy: how it arises and its phenotypic effects. Includes methods of diagnosis.*

- **Genetic Screening - Controlling the Future** Biol. Sci. Rev., 12 (4) March 2000, pp. 36-38. *The techniques, applications, and ethical questions posed by genetic screening.*
- **MRSA: A Hospital Superbug** Biol. Sci. Rev., 19(4) April 2007, pp. 30-33. *Antibiotic resistance and the nature and significance of MRSA.*
- **Mechanisms of Meiosis** Biol. Sci. Rev., 15(4), April 2003, pp. 20-24. *A clear and thorough account of the events and mechanisms of meiosis.*

### TEACHER'S REFERENCE

- **The Great Inventors** New Scientist, 21 Feb. 2004, pp. 41-43. *The human genome is riddled with duplications and these provide the raw material for mutations and natural selection. Random mutation can modify one copy of a duplicated gene without interfering with existing biochemical pathways.*
- **Life Force** New Scientist, 4 Dec. 2004, pp. 46-49. *Experimental evidence for evolution in bacteria. The findings have implications for the battle against the rise of microbial drug resistance.*
- **Survival of the Sickest** New Scientist, 17 Feb. 2007, pp. 42-45. *Researchers hypothesise that iron overload mutations such as haemochromatosis must have conferred some kind of benefit in our recent evolutionary past.*
- **Ready, Steady, Evolve!** New Scientist, 28 Sept. 2002, pp. 28-31. *How plants and animals may evolve to create new body plans and the role of specific mutations in this process.*
- **Cystic Fibrosis** Scientific American, Dec. 1995, pp. 36-43. *The basis of the cystic fibrosis mutation: the nature of the mutation and how it brings about the symptoms of the disease.*
- **The Challenge of Antibiotic Resistance** Sci. American, March 1998, pp. 32-39. *An excellent article covering the basis of antibiotic resistance in bacteria. Such resistance confers an advantage.*
- **Life Force** New Scientist, 4 Dec. 2004, pp. 46-49. *Evidence for evolution in bacteria and implications for microbial drug resistance.*
- **Genetic Screening** The Am. Biology Teacher, 66(6), Aug. 2004, pp. 435-440. *A how-to-do-it activity generating situations where students can relate genetic information to genetic screening.*
- **Why Finish Your Antibiotics** The Am. Biology Teacher, 68(8), Oct. 2006, pp. 476-480. *Describes a simple and fun exercise that teaches the causes and consequences of antibiotic resistance.*
- **Modeling Mitosis and Meiosis** The Am. Biology Teacher, 62(3), March 2000, pp. 204-206. *A problem solving activity to develop better understanding of nuclear division.*

- **Students as 'Human Chromosomes' in role-playing Mitosis & Meiosis** The Am. Biology Teacher, 66(1), Jan. 2004, pp. 35-39. *Demonstrating difference between cell divisions, and how genetic variability arises in gametes.*
- **Your Own Book of Life.** New Scientist, 8 Sept. 2007, pp. 8-11. *A special report on how genome sequencing could soon be widely used to scan for defective health related genes.*
- **Tobacco Induced Mutations** The Am. Biology Teacher, 66(5), March 2004, pp. 370-376. *How-to-do-it: demonstrating serial dilution, plating bacteria using sterile technique, and the significance of biological assays in microbiology and toxicology.*
- **Making the Chromosome-Gene-Protein Connection** The Am. Biology Teacher, 58(6), Sept. 1996, pp. 364-366. *Sickle cell disease as a model for understanding the relationships between chromosome, gene, and protein (excellent).*

See pages 10-11 for details of how to access **Bio Links** from our web site: **www.thebiozone.com** From Bio Links, access sites under the topics:

**GENERAL BIOLOGY ONLINE RESOURCES > Online Textbooks and Lecture Notes**

**CELL BIOLOGY AND BIOCHEMISTRY:** • Cell & molecular biology online • Molecular biology web book ... *and others* > **Cell Division:** • Cell division: Meiosis and sexual reproduction • Comparison of mitosis and meiosis

**GENETICS:** • DNA basics • Gene almanac • Virtual library on genetics ... *and others* > **Molecular Genetics (DNA):** • Beginners guide to molecular biology • Basic genetics • DNA and molecular genetics • DNA from the beginning ... *and others* > **Mutations and Genetic Disorders:** • Mutant fruit flies • Mutations • Advances in cystic fibrosis • Mutations causing cystic fibrosis • The lung net: cystic fibrosis • Sickle cell disease • Sickle cell information centre ... *and others*

**Presentation MEDIA** to support this topic: **GENES & INHERITANCE**
- **Mutations**
- **Gene Interactions**

*Genes & Inheritance*
*Presentation MEDIA*

# Eukaryote Chromosome Structure

The chromosomes of eukaryotes are more complex than those of prokaryotes. Chromosomes are made up of a complex of DNA and protein called **chromatin**. The DNA is coiled at several levels so that the long DNA molecules can be packed into the nucleus. This **condensation** is achieved by wrapping the DNA around protein cores and then further folding and wrapping the chromatin fiber (as described below) around a protein scaffold. During the early stage of meiosis, a chromosome consists of two chromatids. A non-dividing cell would have chromosomes with the 'equivalent' of a single chromatid only.

A cluster of human chromosomes seen during metaphase of cell division. Individual chromatids (arrowed) are difficult to discern on these double chromatid chromosomes.

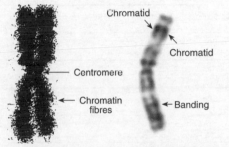

Chromosome TEM          Human chromosome 3

A human chromosome from a dividing white blood cell (above left). Note the compact organization of the chromatin in the two chromatids. The LM photograph (above right) shows the banding visible on human chromosome 3.

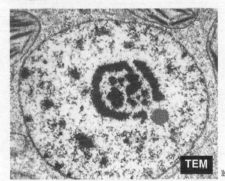

In non-dividing cells, chromosomes exist as single-armed structures. They are not visible as coiled structures, but are 'unwound' to make the genes accessible for transcription (above).

The evidence for the existence of looped domains comes from the study of giant lampbrush chromosomes in amphibian oocytes (above). Under electron microscopy, the lateral loops of the DNA-protein complex have a brushlike appearance.

## The Packaging of Chromatin

Chromatin structure is based on successive levels of DNA packing. **Histone proteins** are responsible for packing the DNA into a compact form. Without them, the DNA could not fit into the nucleus. Five types of histone proteins form a complex with DNA, in a way that resembles "beads on a string". These beads, or **nucleosomes**, form the basic unit of DNA packing.

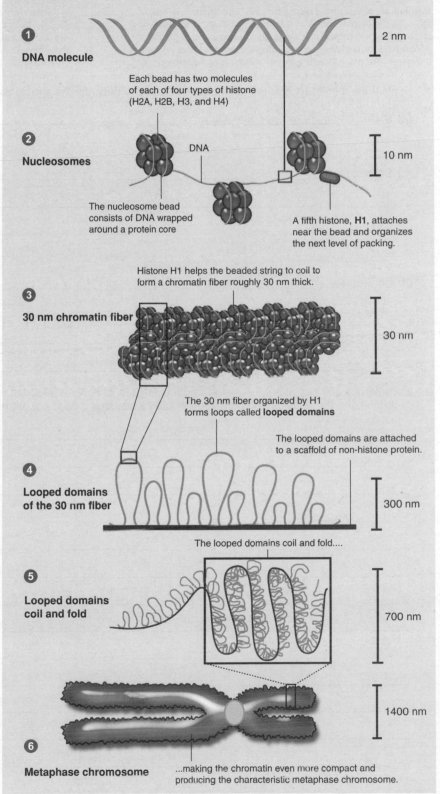

**①  DNA molecule** — 2 nm

Each bead has two molecules of each of four types of histone (H2A, H2B, H3, and H4)

**②  Nucleosomes** — DNA — 10 nm

The nucleosome bead consists of DNA wrapped around a protein core

A fifth histone, **H1**, attaches near the bead and organizes the next level of packing.

Histone H1 helps the beaded string to coil to form a chromatin fiber roughly 30 nm thick.

**③  30 nm chromatin fiber** — 30 nm

The 30 nm fiber organized by H1 forms loops called **looped domains**

The looped domains are attached to a scaffold of non-histone protein.

**④  Looped domains of the 30 nm fiber** — 300 nm

The looped domains coil and fold....

**⑤  Looped domains coil and fold** — 700 nm

**⑥  Metaphase chromosome** — 1400 nm

...making the chromatin even more compact and producing the characteristic metaphase chromosome.

Genes and Chromosomes

**Related activities**: DNA Molecules
**Web links**: Chromosome Structure

A 2

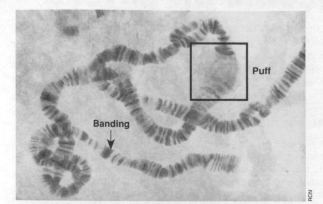

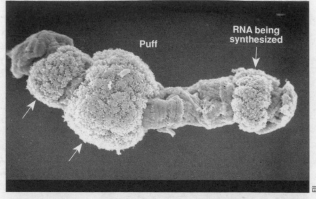

**Banded chromosome:** This light microscope photo is a view of the polytene chromosomes in a salivary gland cell of a sandfly. It shows a banding pattern that is thought to correspond to groups of genes. Regions of chromosome **puffing** are thought to occur where the genes are being transcribed into mRNA (see SEM on right).

A **polytene chromosome** viewed with a scanning electron microscope (SEM). The arrows indicate localized regions of the chromosome that are uncoiling to expose their genes (puffing) to allow transcription of those regions. Polytene chromosomes are a special type of chromosome consisting of a large bundle of chromatids bound tightly together.

1. Explain the significance of the following terms used to describe the structure of chromosomes:

(a) DNA: _____

_____

(b) Chromatin: _____

_____

(c) Histone: _____

_____

(d) Centromere: _____

_____

(e) Chromatid: _____

_____

2. Each human cell has about a 1 meter length of DNA in its nucleus. Discuss the mechanisms by which this DNA is packaged into the nucleus and organized in such a way that it does not get ripped apart during cell division:

_____

_____

_____

_____

_____

_____

_____

_____

_____

_____

_____

_____

_____

_____

# Karyotypes

The diagram below shows the **karyotype** of a normal human. Karyotypes are prepared from the nuclei of cultured white blood cells that are 'frozen' at the metaphase stage of mitosis (see the photo circled opposite). Photographs of the chromosomes are arranged on a grid so that the homologous pairs are placed together. Homologous pairs are identified by their general shape, length, and the pattern of banding produced by a special staining technique. Karyotypes for a human male and female are shown below. The **male karyotype** has 44 autosomes, a single X chromosome, and a Y chromosome (written as 44 + XY), whereas the **female karyotype** shows two X chromosomes (written as 44 + XX).

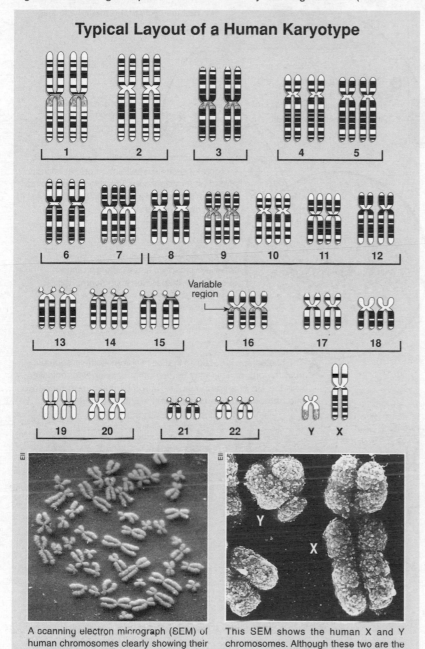

## Typical Layout of a Human Karyotype

A scanning electron micrograph (SEM) of human chromosomes clearly showing their double chromatids.

This SEM shows the human X and Y chromosomes. Although these two are the sex chromosomes, they are not homologous.

## Karyotypes for different species

The term **karyotype** refers to the chromosome complement of a cell or a whole organism. In particular, it shows the number, size, and shape of the chromosomes as seen during metaphase of mitosis. The diagram on the left depicts the human karyotype. Chromosome numbers vary considerably among organisms and may differ markedly between closely related species:

| Organism | Chromosome number (2N) |
|---|---|
| **Vertebrates** | |
| human | 46 |
| chimpanzee | 48 |
| gorilla | 48 |
| horse | 64 |
| cattle | 60 |
| dog | 78 |
| cat | 38 |
| rabbit | 44 |
| rat | 42 |
| turkey | 82 |
| goldfish | 94 |
| **Invertebrates** | |
| fruit fly, *Drosophila* | 8 |
| housefly | 12 |
| honey bee | 32 or 16 |
| *Hydra* | 32 |
| **Plants** | |
| cabbage | 18 |
| broad bean | 12 |
| potato | 48 |
| orange | 18, 27 or 36 |
| barley | 14 |
| garden pea | 14 |
| Ponderosa pine | 24 |

NOTE: The number of chromosomes is not a measure of the quantity of genetic information.

1. Explain what a **karyotype** is and comment on the information it provides: _____

_____

_____

_____

2. Distinguish between **autosomes** and **sex chromosomes**: _____

_____

_____

_____

**Related activities**: Human Karyotype Exercise

RA 1

Genes and Chromosomes

# Preparing a Karyotype

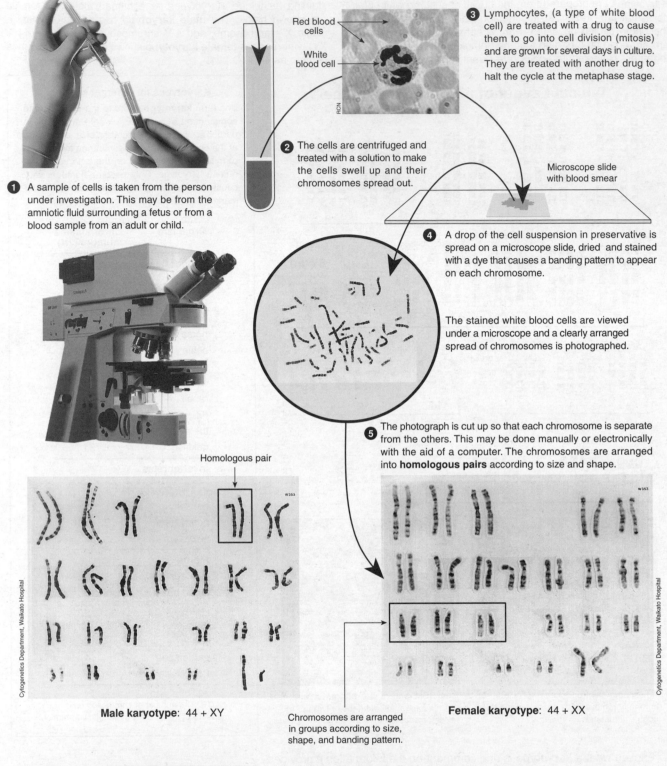

③ Lymphocytes, (a type of white blood cell) are treated with a drug to cause them to go into cell division (mitosis) and are grown for several days in culture. They are treated with another drug to halt the cycle at the metaphase stage.

Red blood cells

White blood cell

② The cells are centrifuged and treated with a solution to make the cells swell up and their chromosomes spread out.

① A sample of cells is taken from the person under investigation. This may be from the amniotic fluid surrounding a fetus or from a blood sample from an adult or child.

Microscope slide with blood smear

④ A drop of the cell suspension in preservative is spread on a microscope slide, dried and stained with a dye that causes a banding pattern to appear on each chromosome.

The stained white blood cells are viewed under a microscope and a clearly arranged spread of chromosomes is photographed.

⑤ The photograph is cut up so that each chromosome is separate from the others. This may be done manually or electronically with the aid of a computer. The chromosomes are arranged into **homologous pairs** according to size and shape.

Homologous pair

**Male karyotype:** 44 + XY

Chromosomes are arranged in groups according to size, shape, and banding pattern.

**Female karyotype:** 44 + XX

Cytogenetics Department, Waikato Hospital

3. On the male and female karyotype photographs *above* **number** each homologous pair of chromosomes using the diagram on the previous page as a guide.

4. **Circle** the sex chromosomes (**X** and **Y**) in the female karyotype and male karyotype.

5. Write down the number of *autosomes* and the arrangement of *sex chromosomes* for each sex:

   (a) **Female:**   No. of autosomes: _____   Sex chromosomes: _____

   (b) **Male:**   No. of autosomes: _____   Sex chromosomes: _____

6. State how many chromosomes are found in a:

   (a) Normal human body (**somatic**) cell: _____   (b) Normal human sperm or egg (**gametic**) cell: _____

# Prenatal Diagnosis

Technological advances in recent decades have enabled greater control over conception, gestation, and birth. There are now a number of commonly used prenatal (before birth) diagnostic tests that can be used to investigate fetal health and development, and test for genetic abnormalities. Prenatal diagnoses vary a lot in terms of how invasive they are to the pregnancy and how much information they provide. Tests of the α-fetoprotein levels in the mother's blood serum can indicate **Down syndrome** (low α-fetoprotein) or **neural tube defects** (high α-fetoprotein) without

risk to the fetus. Other prenatal procedures (e.g. **ultrasound**) carry a low risk and have become almost routine in some societies. **Amniocentesis** and **chorionic villus sampling** present a greater risk to both the mother and fetus and are usually reserved for the detection of chromosomal abnormalities in high risk pregnancies. All prenatal diagnostic procedures should involve supportive and accurate counseling regarding the benefits and risks of the procedure, and the choices available should the pregnancy prove to be abnormal.

## Candidates for Diagnosis

Before costly and potentially high-risk prenatal tests involving chromosome analysis are carried out, there must be some clinical indication of a potential problem with either of the parents or with the pregnancy. Some **clinical indications** for chromosomal analysis are:

- Family history of inherited genetic disorders or malformities.
- History of infertility, miscarriage, stillbirth, or early neonatal death.
- First pregnancy at an older age or maternal age over 38.

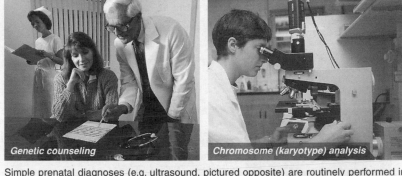

*Genetic counseling*

*Chromosome (karyotype) analysis*

Simple prenatal diagnoses (e.g. ultrasound, pictured opposite) are routinely performed in order to reassure parents that a pregnancy is normal, to check fetal growth, or to determine gender. More complex and higher risk prenatal tests involving chromosomal analysis (below and photo, above right) are not routinely performed. **Genetic counseling** (photo above, left) involves advising a patient of their risks and options and is usual practice where such tests are indicated. See the table left listing the clinical indications for chromosome analysis.

## Amniocentesis

**Performed at**: 14-16 weeks into the pregnancy. The amniotic fluid (which naturally contains some fetal cells) is centrifuged, and the cells are cultured, examined biochemically, and karyotyped.

**Used for**: Detection of nearly 300 chromosomal disorders, such as Down syndrome, neural tube defects (e.g. spina bifida), and inborn errors of metabolism.

**Recommended**: A maternal age nearing or over 40, when parents are carriers of an inherited disorder or already have a child with a chromosomal disorder.

**Associated risks**: Risk of miscarriage through damage to fetus or placenta. In women younger than 35, the risk of miscarriage through the procedure is greater than the risk of carrying a child with chromosomal abnormalities.

## Chorionic Villus Sampling (CVS)

**Performed at**: 8-10 weeks gestation. Using ultrasound guidance, a narrow tube is inserted through the cervix and a sample of the fetal chorionic villi is taken from the placenta. Compared with amniocentesis, more fetal cells are obtained so analysis can be completed earlier and more quickly.

**Used for**: As for amniocentesis: detection of chromosomal and metabolic disorders.

**Recommended**: Recommendations as for amniocentesis.

**Associated risks**: Risk of miscarriage is higher than for amniocentesis but, if abortion is recommended, this can be performed sooner. Note that both amniocentesis and CVS rely on the ultrasound to determine the position of the fetus and placenta in the uterus.

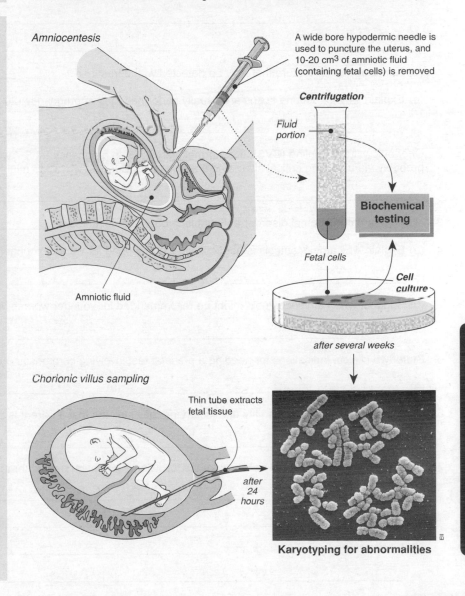

*Amniocentesis*

A wide bore hypodermic needle is used to puncture the uterus, and 10-20 cm³ of amniotic fluid (containing fetal cells) is removed

*Centrifugation*

Fluid portion

**Biochemical testing**

Fetal cells

Cell culture

after several weeks

Amniotic fluid

*Chorionic villus sampling*

Thin tube extracts fetal tissue

after 24 hours

**Karyotyping for abnormalities**

**Genes and Chromosomes**

**Related activities**: The Fate of Conceptions, Genetic Counseling

**RA 2**

## Diagnostic Ultrasound in Pregnancy

**Ultrasound** is commonly used to view the uterus and fetus during pregnancy. Scans are often performed at 18 to 20 weeks into a pregnancy, frequently as a routine procedure. They may also be performed earlier (at about 10-11 weeks) or later (after 34 weeks) if problems are indicated (e.g. severe vomiting in early pregnancy, gestational diabetes, or indications that the fetus is not growing normally). Ultrasound is used for the diagnosis of multiple pregnancies (twins) and gross fetal abnormalities (e.g. trisomy). It is also used to determine fetal age and growth, gender, conception date, and placental position. Such information aids pregnancy management. Ultrasound is *apparently* safe, but the risks associated with frequent scans are unknown.

*The reflected sound waves give a visual echo of the fetus inside the uterus.*

*In this fetus, the general shape of the body and limbs can be discerned. The operator magnifies regions of interest in order to take more accurate measurements.*

The positioning of the placenta (**P**) and umbilical cord is checked. The placenta should not lie over the entrance to the cervix (**C**), as this causes problems with delivery.

Ultrasound probe directs sound waves at the abdomen of the mother

High frequency, inaudible sound waves are reflected off the fetus and back to a receiver in the probe.

The operator takes specific measurements (on screen) of certain regions of the body e.g. limb length, head length and circumference. These are used to determine if development is normal and growth is within the expected range.

1. (a) Explain the medical reasons why an ultrasound scan might be used to examine a fetus: _____

    _____

    _____

    (b) Name one other feature that may be detected with ultrasound: _____

    (c) Explain why ultrasound scans are usually performed later in pregnancy (20 weeks): _____

    _____

2. Chorionic villus sampling (CVS), if performed very early in pregnancy (at 5-7 weeks) may cause limb abnormalities, probably via upsetting critical sites of foetal blood flow. Suggest why CVS might be performed at such an early stage:

    _____

3. Name one chromosomal disorder detectable through amniocentesis: _____

4. (a) Explain why amniocentesis is not usually recommended for women younger than 35: _____

    _____

    (b) Suggest when amniocentesis might be recommended for younger women, in spite of the risk: _____

    _____

5. State two clinical indications for needing a prenatal test involving chromosome analysis:

    (a) _____ (b) _____

6. Suggest why a history of infertility or miscarriage may indicate that a parent is carrying an inherited genetic disorder:

    _____

7. Describe some of the ethical concerns of the following information gained through prenatal diagnoses:

    (a) Gender determination: _____

    _____

    (b) Termination of a viable pregnancy: _____

    _____

# Human Karyotype Exercise

Each chromosome has distinctive features that enable it to be identified and distinguished from others. Chromosomes are stained in a special technique that gives them a banded appearance, the banding pattern representing regions of the chromosome that contains up to many hundreds of genes.

Determine the sex and chromosome condition of the individual whose chromosomes are displayed below. The karyotypes presented on the previous pages, and the hints on how to recognise chromosome pairs, can be used to help you complete this activity.

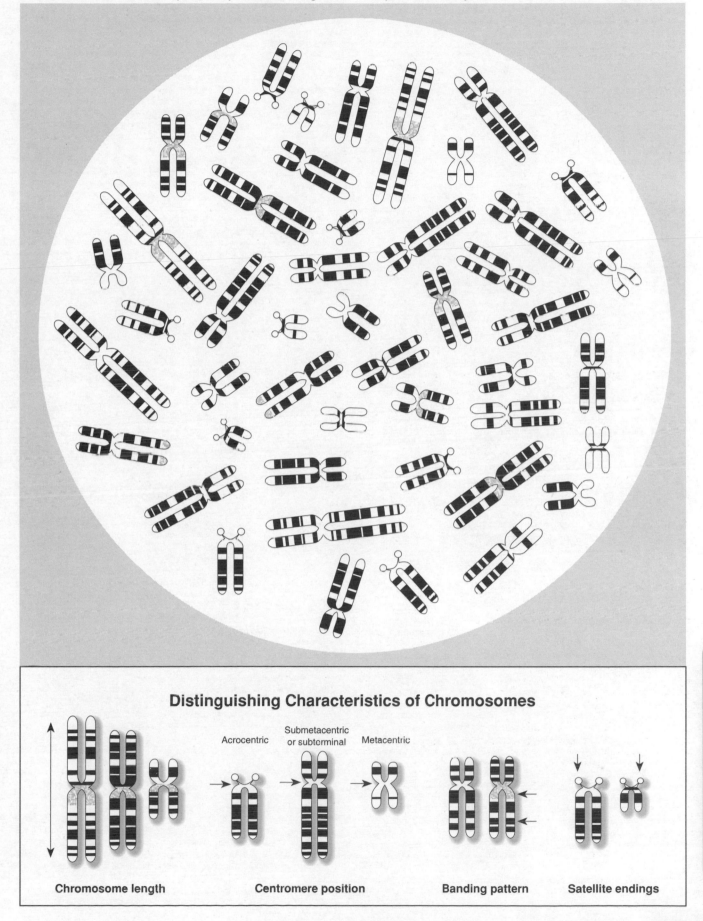

## Distinguishing Characteristics of Chromosomes

Acrocentric

Submetacentric or subterminal

Metacentric

**Chromosome length**

**Centromere position**

**Banding pattern**

**Satellite endings**

Genes and Chromosomes

**Related activities**: Karyotypes

PRA 2

1. Cut out the chromosomes on page 173 and arrange them on the record sheet below in their homologous pairs.

2. (a) Determine the sex of this individual:   **male**   or   **female**   (circle one)

   (b) State whether the individual's *chromosome arrangement* is:        **normal**   or   **abnormal**   (circle one)

   (c) If the arrangement is *abnormal*, state in what way and name the syndrome displayed: _____

   _____

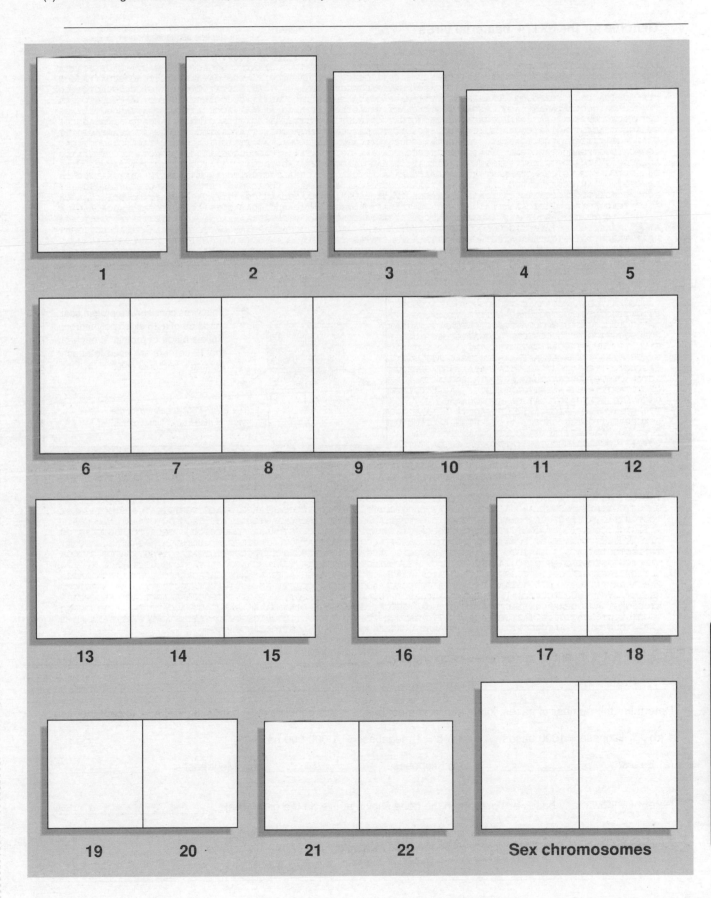

**Genes and Chromosomes**

# Genomes

Genome research has become an important field of genetics. A **genome** is the entire haploid complement of genetic material of a cell or organism. Each species has a unique genome, although there is a small amount of genetic variation between individuals within a species. For example, in humans the average genetic difference is one in every 500-1000 bases. Every cell in an individual has a complete copy of the genome. The base sequence shown below is the total DNA sequence for the genome of a virus. There are nine genes in the sequence, coding for nine different proteins. At least 2000 times this amount of DNA would be found in a single bacterial cell. Half a million times this quantity of DNA would be found in the genome of a single human cell. The first gene has been highlighted gray, while the start and stop codes are in black rectangles.

### Genome for the φX174 bacterial virus

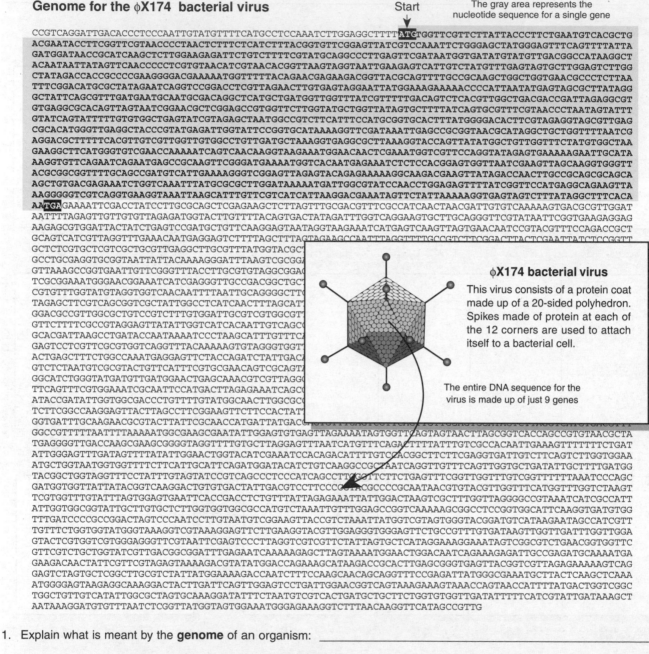

Start

The gray area represents the nucleotide sequence for a single gene

**φX174 bacterial virus**

This virus consists of a protein coat made up of a 20-sided polyhedron. Spikes made of protein at each of the 12 corners are used to attach itself to a bacterial cell.

The entire DNA sequence for the virus is made up of just 9 genes

1. Explain what is meant by the **genome** of an organism: _____

_____

2. Determine the number of bases, kilobases, and megabases in this genome (100 bases in each row, except the last):

   **1 kb** = 1 kilobase = 1000 bases      **1 Mb** = 1 megabase = 1 000 000 bases

   (a) Bases: _____   (b) Kilobases: _____   (c) Megabases: _____

3. Determine how many bases are present in the gene shown above (in the gray area): _____

4. State whether the genome of the virus above is **small, average** or **large** in size compared to those viruses listed in the table on the earlier page *DNA Molecules* (in the topic Molecular Genetics):

_____

**Related activities**: DNA Molecules, Genome Projects

# Sources of Genetic Variation

The genetic variability between individuals is what makes us all different from each other. Brothers and sisters may look similar to each other but there are always significant differences between them (unless they happen to be identical twins). The differences between close relatives is due mostly to a **shuffling** of the existing genetic material into new combinations. In addition to this is the new variation that originates from the **mutation** of existing genes. While most mutations are harmful, there are a significant number that are thought to be 'silent' and do not appear to have any effect on the individual. On rare occasions, a mutation may even prove to be beneficial. Mutations create new **alleles** and form an important part of the evolutionary process.

## Mutations

### *Gene mutations; chromosome mutations*

Mutations are the source of all **new** genetic information. Existing genes are modified by base substitutions and deletions, causing the formation of new alleles.

Mutation: Substitute **T** instead of **C**

Original DNA: A A A A T G C T T C T C

Mutant DNA: A A A A T G T T T C T C

## Gene Mutations

Mutations may cause alterations in the genetic instructions coded in the DNA of chromosomes. Most mutations are harmful, some are neutral (no effective change), while a very few may provide some improvement on the earlier version of the gene. Mutations may be accumulated (inherited) over many generations.

## Chromosome Mutations

Pieces of chromosome may be rearranged during meiosis. Pieces may be turned upside-down, duplicated, moved from one chromosome to another or lost altogether. Most instances are harmful, but occasionally they may be beneficial.

## Sexual Reproduction

### *Independent assortment; crossing over and recombination; mate selection*

Sexual reproduction provides a rearrangement and shuffling of the genetic material into new combinations.

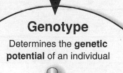

## Independent Assortment

Genes are carried on chromosomes, 23 pairs in the case of humans. Each chromosome pair is sorted independently of the other pairs during meiosis. This random shuffling produces a huge variety of gametes from a single individual (parent).

## Recombination

Pieces of chromosome are often exchanged with a chromosome's homologue (its paired chromosome with equivalent genes). This increases shuffling of allele combinations.

## Mate Selection

Variation is further enhanced by the choice of mate to produce offspring. Different combinations of genes will come together in the offspring, depending on which two parents mate together.

## Genotype

Determines the **genetic potential** of an individual

Dominant, recessive, codominant and multiple allele systems, as well as interactions between genes, combine in their effects.

## Phenotype

The phenotype expressed in an individual is the result of all the factors listed on this page. The genetic instructions for creating the individual may be modified along the way, or at least modified by environmental influences.

## Environmental Factors

Environmental factors may influence the expression of the genotype. These factors may include physical factors such as temperature, light intensity, presence of groundwater, diet or nutrients, wind exposure, and pH. The presence of other organisms may also affect the expression of the genotype.

**Genes and Chromosomes**

**Related activities**: Gene-Environment Interactions, For Harm or Benefit?

**RA 2**

1. Describe three ways in which sexual reproduction can provide genetic variation in individuals:

   (a) _____

   _____

   (b) _____

   _____

   (c) _____

   _____

2. Explain how the environment of a particular genotype can affect the phenotype: _____

   _____

   _____

   _____

3. Describe three common ways by which humans can, by choice, alter their phenotype:

   (a) _____

   _____

   (b) _____

   _____

   (c) _____

   _____

4. Explain why siblings (brothers and sisters) have a family similarity but are not identical (unless they happen to be identical twins):

   _____

   _____

   _____

   _____

   _____

5. (a) Explain what is meant by a neutral (silent) mutation: _____

   _____

   _____

   (b) Discuss how neutral mutations can be important in the evolution of populations: _____

   _____

   _____

   _____

   _____

   _____

   _____

   _____

# Gene-Environment Interactions

External environmental factors can modify the phenotype coded by genes. This can occur both in the development of the embryo and later in life. Even identical twins, which are essentially clones, have minor differences in their appearance due to environmental factors such as diet. Environmental factors that affect the phenotype of plants and animals include nutrients or diet, temperature, altitude or latitude, and the presence of other organisms.

## The Effect of Temperature

The sex of some animals is determined by the temperature at which they were incubated during their embryonic development. Examples include turtles, crocodiles, and the American alligator. In some species, high incubation temperatures produce males and low temperatures produce females. In other species, the opposite is true. The advantages of temperature regulated sex determination may arise through prevention of inbreeding (since all siblings will tend to be of the same sex).

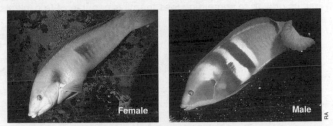

## The Effect of Other Organisms

The presence of other individuals of the same species may control the determination of sex in other individuals of the group. Some fish species, including some in the wrasse family (e.g. *Coris sandageri*, above), show such a change in phenotype. The fish live in groups consisting of a single male with attendant females and juveniles. In the presence of a male, all juvenile fish of this species grow into females. When the male dies, the dominant female will undergo physiological changes to become a male for the group. The male has distinctive vertical bands behind the gills. The female is pale in color and has very faint markings.

## The Effect of Altitude

Increasing altitude can stunt the phenotype of plants with the same genotype. In some conifers, e.g. Engelmann spruce (*Picea engelmannii*), plants at low altitude grow to their full genetic potential, but become progressively more stunted as elevation increases, forming krummholz (gnarled bushy growth forms) at the highest, most severe sites. This situation, where there is a continuous, or nearly continuous, gradation in a phenotypic character within a species, associated with a change in an environmental variable, is called a **cline**.

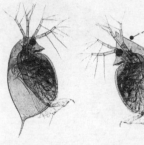

**Non-helmeted form**  **Helmeted form with long tail spine**

Some organisms respond to the presence of other, potentially harmful, organisms by changing their morphology or body shape. Invertebrates such as *Daphnia* will grow a large helmet when a predatory midge larva (*Chaoborus*) is present. Such responses are usually mediated through the action of chemicals produced by the predator (or competitor), and are common in plants as well as animals.

1. Giving appropriate examples, distinguish clearly between **genotype** and **phenotype**: _____

2. Identify some of the physical factors associated with altitude that could affect plant phenotype: _____

3. The hydrangea is a plant that exhibits a change in the color of its flowers according to the condition of the soil. Identify the physical factor that causes hydrangea flowers to be blue or pink. If you can, find out how this effect is exerted:

4. Color pointing in some breeds of cats such as the Siamese, involves the activity of a temperature sensitive enzyme that produces the pigment melanin. Explain why the darker patches of fur are found only on the face, paws and tail:

RA 2

Genes and Chromosomes

At conception (the formation of the zygote), an organism possesses a genetic potential to grow into an adult form with certain characteristics. The exact form it takes is determined largely by the genes in its chromosomes, but it is also strongly influenced by a vast range of environmental factors acting upon it. These factors may subject an organism to stresses and may limit its growth to something less than it is capable of (e.g. plants that are grown at high altitude or in very exposed locations will often have stunted growth). Changes in the phenotype due solely to environmental factors are not inherited. Traumatic events such as the loss of a limb on a tree, or the removal of the tail in a young mammal (e.g. lambs, pups), does not affect the phenotype of the next generation (trees do not grow with limbs missing, and not one lamb has been born without a tail).

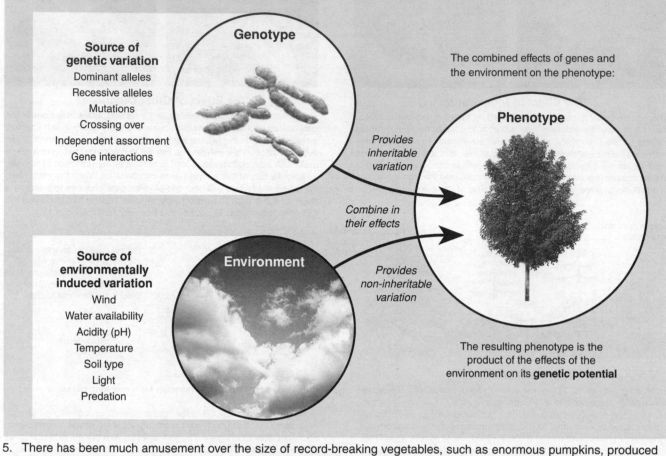

**Genotype**

**Source of genetic variation**

Dominant alleles
Recessive alleles
Mutations
Crossing over
Independent assortment
Gene interactions

*Provides inheritable variation*

*Combine in their effects*

**Source of environmentally induced variation**

Wind
Water availability
Acidity (pH)
Temperature
Soil type
Light
Predation

**Environment**

*Provides non-inheritable variation*

The combined effects of genes and the environment on the phenotype:

**Phenotype**

The resulting phenotype is the product of the effects of the environment on its **genetic potential**

5. There has been much amusement over the size of record-breaking vegetables, such as enormous pumpkins, produced for competitions. Explain how you could improve the chance that a vegetable would reach its maximum genetic potential:

_____

_____

_____

6. (a) Explain what is meant by a **cline**: _____

_____

(b) On a windswept portion of a coast, two different species of plant (species A and species B) were found growing together. Both had a low growing (prostrate) phenotype. One of each plant type was transferred to a greenhouse where "ideal" conditions were provided to allow maximum growth. In this controlled environment, species B continued to grow in its original prostrate form, but species A changed its growing pattern and became erect in form. Identify the **cause** of the prostrate phenotype in each of the coastal grown plant species and explain your answer:

Plant species A: _____

_____

_____

Plant species B: _____

_____

_____

(c) Identify which of these species (A or B) would be most likely to exhibit clinal variation: _____

# Meiosis

**Meiosis** is a special type of cell division concerned with producing sex cells (gametes) for the purpose of sexual reproduction. It involves a single chromosomal duplication followed by two successive nuclear divisions, and results in a halving of the diploid chromosome number. Meiosis occurs in the sex organs of plants and animals. If genetic mistakes (**gene** and **chromosome mutations**) occur here, they will be passed on to the offspring (they will be inherited).

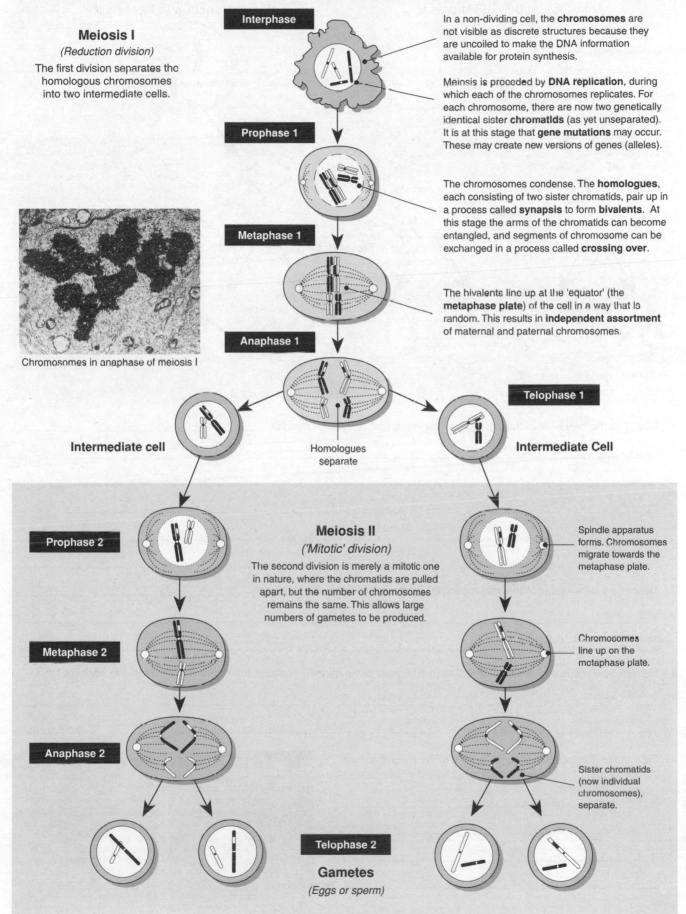

### Meiosis I
*(Reduction division)*
The first division separates the homologous chromosomes into two intermediate cells.

**Interphase**

In a non-dividing cell, the **chromosomes** are not visible as discrete structures because they are uncoiled to make the DNA information available for protein synthesis.

**Prophase 1**

Meiosis is proceded by **DNA replication**, during which each of the chromosomes replicates. For each chromosome, there are now two genetically identical sister **chromatids** (as yet unseparated). It is at this stage that **gene mutations** may occur. These may create new versions of genes (alleles).

**Metaphase 1**

The chromosomes condense. The **homologues**, each consisting of two sister chromatids, pair up in a process called **synapsis** to form **bivalents**. At this stage the arms of the chromatids can become entangled, and segments of chromosome can be exchanged in a process called **crossing over**.

**Anaphase 1**

The bivalents line up at the 'equator' (the **metaphase plate**) of the cell in a way that is random. This results in **independent assortment** of maternal and paternal chromosomes.

Chromosomes in anaphase of meiosis I

**Telophase 1**

**Intermediate cell**

Homologues separate

**Intermediate Cell**

### Meiosis II
*('Mitotic' division)*
The second division is merely a mitotic one in nature, where the chromatids are pulled apart, but the number of chromosomes remains the same. This allows large numbers of gametes to be produced.

**Prophase 2**

Spindle apparatus forms. Chromosomes migrate towards the metaphase plate.

**Metaphase 2**

Chromosomes line up on the metaphase plate.

**Anaphase 2**

Sister chromatids (now individual chromosomes), separate.

**Telophase 2**

**Gametes**
*(Eggs or sperm)*

**Genes and Chromosomes**

**Related activities**: Cell Division, Gene Mutations, Chromosome Mutations
**Web links**: Meiosis Tutorial

**RA 1**

The meiotic spindle normally distributes chromosomes to daughter cells without error. However, mistakes can occur in which the homologous chromosomes fail to separate properly at anaphase during meiosis I, or sister chromatids fail to separate during meiosis II. In these cases, one gamete receives two of the same type of chromosome and the other gamete receives no copy. This mishap, called **non-disjunction**, results in abnormal numbers of chromosomes passing to the gametes. If either of the aberrant gametes unites with a normal one at fertilization, the offspring will have an abnormal chromosome number, known as an **aneuploidy**.

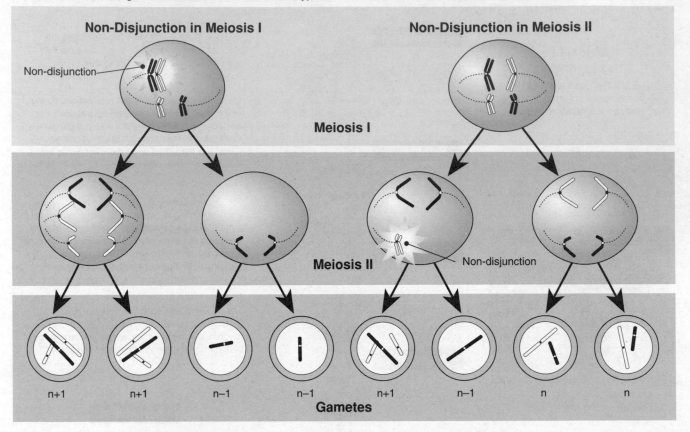

1. Describe the behavior of the chromosomes in the first division of meiosis: _____

_____

_____

_____

_____

_____

2. Describe the behavior of the chromosomes in the second division of meiosis: _____

_____

_____

3. Explain how mitosis conserves chromosome number while meiosis reduces the number from diploid to haploid:

_____

_____

4. Both these light micrographs (A and B) show chromosomes in metaphase of meiosis. State in what way they are different:

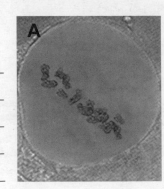
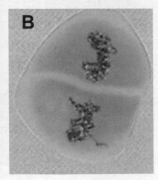

_____

_____

_____

_____

_____

# Crossing Over

Crossing over refers to the mutual exchange of pieces of chromosome and involves the swapping of whole groups of genes between the homologous chromosomes. This process can occur only during the first division of meiosis. Errors in crossing over can result in block mutations (see activity *Chromosome Mutations*), which can be very damaging to development. Crossing over can upset expected frequencies of offspring in dihybrid crosses. The frequency of crossing over (COV) for different genes (as followed by inherited, observable traits) can be used to determine the relative positions of genes on a chromosome and provide a genetic map. There has been a recent suggestion that crossing over may be necessary to ensure accurate cell division.

## Pairing of Homologous Chromosomes

Every somatic cell has a pair of each type of chromosome in its nucleus. These chromosome pairs, one from each parent, are called homologous pairs or homologues. In prophase of the first division of meiosis, the homologues pair up to form bivalents in a process called synapsis. This allows the chromatids of the homologous chromosomes to come in very close contact.

## Chiasma Formation and Crossing Over

The pairing of the homologues allows chiasmata to form between the chromatids of homologous chromosomes. These are places where the chromatids become criss-crossed and the chromosomes exchange segments. In the diagram, the chiasma are in the process of forming and the exchange of pieces of chromosome have not yet taken place. Every point where the chromatids have crossed is a chiasma.

## Separation

New combinations of genes arise from crossing over, resulting in what is called recombination. When the homologues separate at anaphase of meiosis I, each of the chromosomes pictured will have new genetic material (mixed types) that will be passed into the gametes soon to be formed. This process of recombination is an important source of variation for the gene pool of a population.

## Gamete Formation

Once the final division of meiosis is complete, the two chromatids that made up each replicated chromosome become separated and are now referred to as chromosomes. Because chromatid segments were exchanged, four chromosomes that are quite different (genetically) are produced. If no crossing over had occurred, there would have been only two types (two copies of each). Each of these chromsomes will end up in a different gamete (sperm or egg).

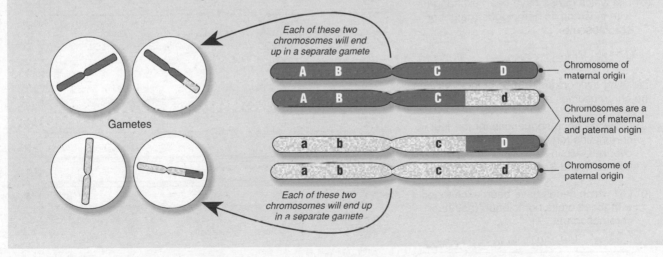

1. Briefly explain how the process of crossing over is going to alter the genotype of gametes: _____
_____

2. Describe the importance of crossing over in the process of evolution: _____
_____

**Related activities**: Chromosome Mutations, Chromosome Mapping

A 2

Genes and Chromosomes

# Crossing Over Problems

The diagram below shows a pair of homologous chromosomes about to undergo chiasma formation during the first cell division in the process of meiosis. There are known crossover points along the length of the chromatids (same on all four chromatids shown in the diagram). In the prepared spaces below, draw the gene sequences after crossing over has occurred on three unrelated and separate occasions (it would be useful to use different colored pens to represent the genes from the two different chromosomes). See the diagrams on the previous page as a guide.

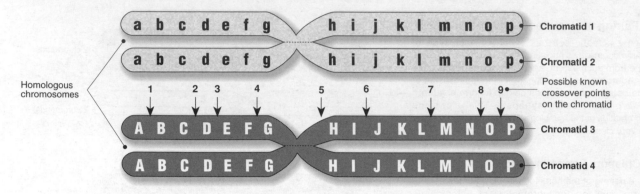

1. Crossing over occurs at a **single** point between the chromosomes above.

   (a) Draw the gene sequences for the four chromatids (on the right), after crossing over has occurred at crossover point: **2**

   (b) List which genes have been exchanged with those on its homologue (neighbor chromosome):

   _____

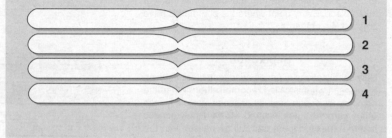

2. Crossing over occurs at **two** points between the chromosomes above.

   (a) Draw the gene sequences for the four chromatids (on the right), after crossing over has occurred between crossover points: **6** and **7**

   (b) List which genes have been exchanged with those on its homologue (neighbor chromosome):

   _____

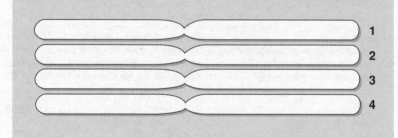

3. Crossing over occurs at **four** points between the chromosomes above.

   (a) Draw the gene sequences for the four chromatids (on the right), after crossing over has occurred between crossover points: **1** and **3**, and **5** and **7**.

   (b) List which genes have been exchanged with those on its homologue (neighbor chromosome):

   _____

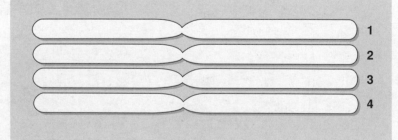

4. Explain the genetic significance of **crossing over**: _____

_____

_____

Related activities: Crossing Over

© Biozone International 2001-2008

# Linkage

**Linkage** refers to genes that are located on the same chromosome. Linked genes tend to be inherited together and fewer genetic combinations of their alleles are possible. Linkage reduces the variety of offspring that can be produced (contrast this with recombination). In genetic crosses, linkage is indicated when a greater proportion of the progeny resulting from a cross are of the parental type (than would be expected if the alleles were assorting independently). If the genes in question had been on separate chromosomes, there would have been more genetic variation in the gametes and therefore in the offspring. Note that

in the example below, wild type alleles are dominant and are denoted by an upper case symbol of the mutant phenotype (Cu or Eb). This symbology used for *Drosophila* departs from the convention of using the dominant gene to provide the symbol. This is necessary because there are many mutant alternative phenotypes to the wild type (e.g. curled and vestigial wings). A lower case symbol of the wild type (e.g. ss for straight wing), would not indicate the mutant phenotype involved. Alternatively, the wild type is sometimes denoted with a raised plus sign e.g. $cu^+cu^+$ and all symbols are in lower case.

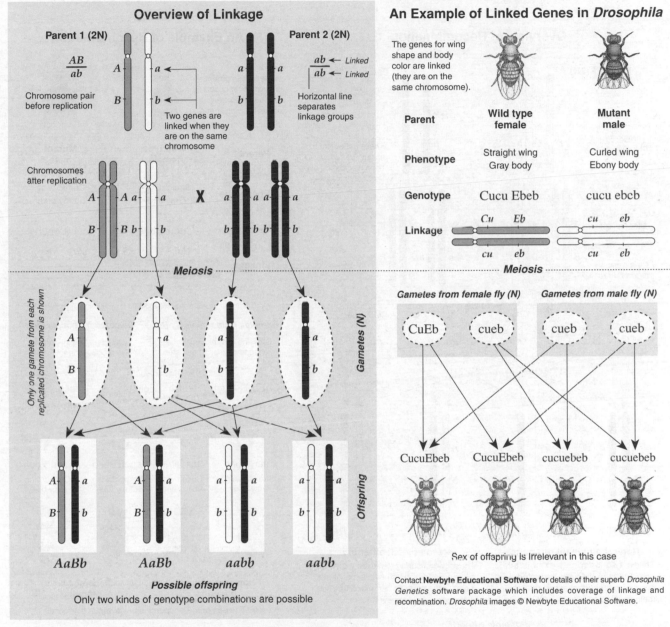

**Overview of Linkage**

Parent 1 (2N)    Parent 2 (2N)

Only two kinds of genotype combinations are possible

**An Example of Linked Genes in *Drosophila***

Sex of offspring is irrelevant in this case

Contact **Newbyte Educational Software** for details of their superb *Drosophila Genetics* software package which includes coverage of linkage and recombination. *Drosophila* images © Newbyte Educational Software.

1. Describe the effect of **linkage** on the inheritance of genes: _____

_____

2. (a) List the possible genotypes in the offspring (above, left) if genes A and B had been on **separate chromosomes**:

_____

(b) If the female *Drosophila* had been homozygous for the dominant wild type alleles (CuCu EbEb), state:

The genotype(s) of the $F_1$: _____    The phenotype(s) of the $F_1$: _____

3. Explain how linkage decreases the amount of genetic variation in the offspring: _____

_____

**Related activities**: Recombination

A 3

**Genes and Chromosomes**

# Recombination

Genetic recombination refers to the exchange of alleles between homologous chromosomes as a result of **crossing over**. The alleles of parental linkage groups separate and new associations of alleles are formed in the gametes. Offspring formed from these gametes show new combinations of characteristics and are known as **recombinants** (they are offspring with genotypes unlike either parent). The proportion of recombinants in the offspring can be used to calculate the frequency of recombination (crossover value). These values are fairly constant for any given pair of alleles and can be used to produce gene maps indicating the relative positions of genes on a chromosome. In contrast to linkage, recombination increases genetic variation. Recombination between the alleles of parental linkage groups is indicated by the appearance of recombinants in the offspring, although not in the numbers that would be expected had the alleles been on separate chromosomes (independent assortment). The example below uses the same genotypes as the previous activity, *Linkage*, but in this case crossing over occurs between the alleles in a linkage group in one parent. The symbology is the same for both activities.

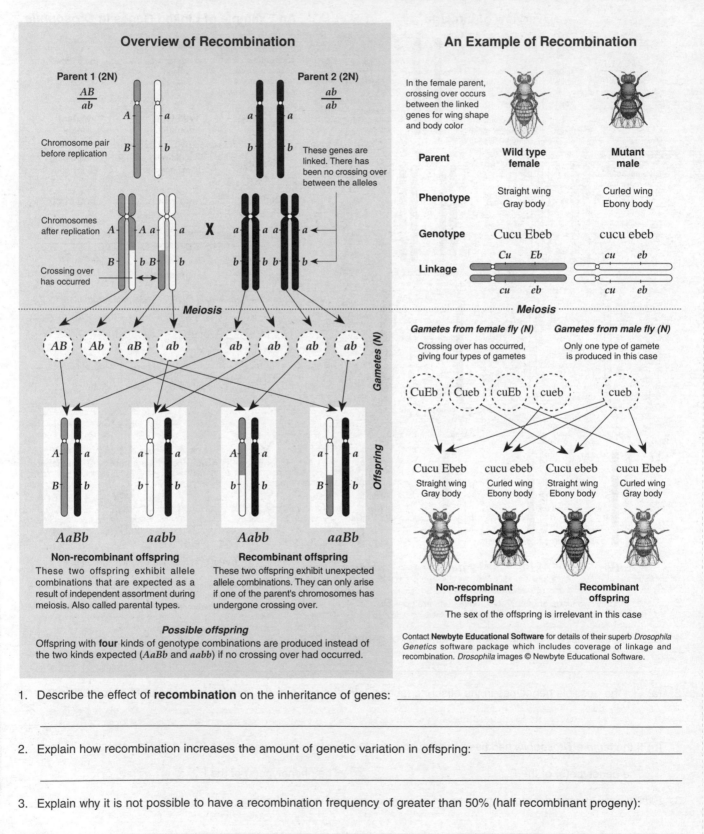

**Overview of Recombination**

**An Example of Recombination**

**Non-recombinant offspring**
These two offspring exhibit allele combinations that are expected as a result of independent assortment during meiosis. Also called parental types.

**Recombinant offspring**
These two offspring exhibit unexpected allele combinations. They can only arise if one of the parent's chromosomes has undergone crossing over.

***Possible offspring***
Offspring with **four** kinds of genotype combinations are produced instead of the two kinds expected (*AaBb* and *aabb*) if no crossing over had occurred.

The sex of the offspring is irrelevant in this case

Contact **Newbyte Educational Software** for details of their superb *Drosophila Genetics* software package which includes coverage of linkage and recombination. *Drosophila* images © Newbyte Educational Software.

1. Describe the effect of **recombination** on the inheritance of genes: _____

_____

2. Explain how recombination increases the amount of genetic variation in offspring: _____

_____

3. Explain why it is not possible to have a recombination frequency of greater than 50% (half recombinant progeny):

_____

**Related activities**: Linkage

# Chromosome Mapping

Crossover frequencies (crossover values or COV) can be used to map the relative positions of genes on a chromosome. Linked genes are genes that are located on the same chromosome, each found at a different **locus**. The amount of crossing over between linked genes is a direct measure of the distance between the genes on the chromosome. This is because genes that are further apart on the same chromosome have more potential crossing over points between them. Crossover values have traditionally been obtained as a result of test crosses for the genes concerned. A crossover value of 1% is equivalent to one unit of map distance (a *centimorgan cM*). To create a genetic map of a chromosome, two pieces of information are required: the **order** of the genes and the **relative** distances between them.

## Mapping Genes Using Crossover Values

**Step 1** **Identify the offspring genotype frequencies**

Parents with known genotypes: AaBb and aabb. *Without crossing over*, these parents can produce offspring of only two **genotypes**: AaBb and aabb. These in turn will produce only the two parental **phenotypes** (see the page on linkage).

However, if the progeny of these parents have 4 phenotypes, then crossing over must have occurred in the formation of some of the gametes. Progeny where such crossing over has occurred are called **recombinants**.

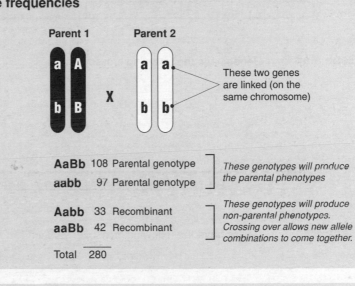

Parent 1    Parent 2

These two genes are linked (on the same chromosome)

| | | |
|---|---|---|
| **AaBb** | 108 | Parental genotype |
| **aabb** | 97 | Parental genotype |

These genotypes will produce the parental phenotypes

| | | |
|---|---|---|
| **Aabb** | 33 | Recombinant |
| **aaBb** | 42 | Recombinant |

These genotypes will produce non-parental phenotypes. Crossing over allows new allele combinations to come together.

Total    280

**Step 2** **Calculate the crossover values between genes**

The frequency of recombination between the two genes (the number of offspring showing recombination) provides an indication of the relative distance between those genes. Expressed as a crossover value, it can be calculated as follows:

$$\text{Crossover Value (\%)} = \frac{\text{No. of recombinant types}}{\text{Total no. of offspring}} \times 100$$

Using the results from the offspring above:    $\frac{33 + 42}{280} \times 100 = 26.8\%$    Crossover value between genes A and B

**Step 3** **Map the genes**

Using the crossover value determined above, a chromosome map can be created, with each percent of crossover equivalent to one genetic map unit (a **centimorgan** or **cM**).

The **centimorgan** is so named after **Thomas Hunt Morgan**, an American geneticist who confirmed the ideas of earlier geneticists such as Sutton, and established the *chromosome theory of inheritance*. He worked with *Drosophila* and, in a series of breeding experiments, established the phenomenon of sex linkage. He also discovered crossover and devised the first chromosome map.

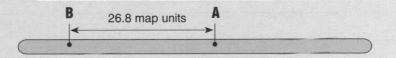

B    26.8 map units    A

Known map distances for pairs of genes may be combined to produce a more complete map for many genes. In the example below, there are three genes for which the crossing over values are known. By trial and error, the genes could be laid out in different sequences to see if the genetic mapping distances (crossover frequencies) fit, but only one combination will work:

Crossover values:

| B - A | 22% |
|---|---|
| A - C | 10% |
| B - C | 12% |

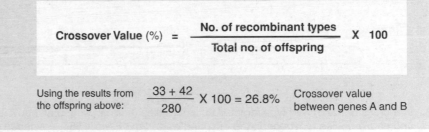

A    10    C    12    B
22

 ©Biozone International 2001-2008
**Photocopying Prohibited**

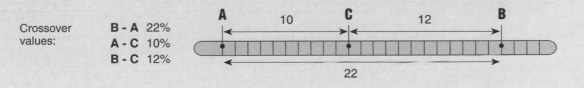

**Related activities**: Crossing Over, The Human Genome Project, Genome Projects

**ERDA 3**

Genes and Chromosomes

1. The following exercise involves some simple mapping problems. Use the procedure outlined on the previous page and the crossover values given to calculate the sequence and distance apart of the genes indicated. HINT: Always place on the map the two genes with the greatest mapping distance first, then plot the other genes relative to them.

**Gene Map 1**   Genes have the following crossover values:

| | |
|---|---|
| X – G | 18 % |
| B – G | 3 % |
| B – X | 15 % |

**Gene Map 2**   Genes have the following crossover values:

| | |
|---|---|
| P – m | 7 % |
| K – m | 28 % |
| P – K | 21 % |
| m – C | 5 % |

**Gene Map 3**   Genes have the following crossover values:

| | |
|---|---|
| Q – s | 18 % |
| X – Q | 18 % |
| X – s | 36 % |
| Z – X | 11 % |
| s – Z | 25 % |

2. In a cross between wild type female Drosophila flies (normal wing, gray body: *VgvgEbeb*) and male flies with vestigial wings and ebony bodies (*vgvgebeb*), the offspring were: *VgvgEbeb* = 585, *vgvgebeb* = 466, *vgvgEbeb* = 104, *Vgvgebeb* = 113.

(a) State the phenotypes of each genotype: _____

_____

(b) Calculate the crossover frequency (value): _____

3. Gene maps have traditionally been based on the recombinant frequencies obtained from breeding experiments. The mapping of the human genome is based on the presence of polymorphic markers (DNA with alternative forms, whose inheritance can be followed). The entire genomes of many organisms have already been mapped e.g. yeast, *E. coli,* and *Drosophila*). Describe some of the benefits to be gained from:

(a) Mapping the genome of non-human organisms: _____

_____

_____

(b) Mapping the human genome: _____

_____

_____

_____

_____

# Mutagens

Mutagens are chemicals or radiation that increase the likelihood of a mutation occurring. The rate of mutation induced by a mutagen is directly proportional to the dose received. Mutagens have a cumulative effect on an individual (i.e. small doses over a long period may be just as harmful as a single, larger dose). The four main classes of mutagens are outlined below.

RADIOACTIVE II
CONTENTS
ACTIVITY
7

| **Mutagen and Effect** | **Those Most at Risk** |
|---|---|
| ### Ionizing radiation<br>Nuclear radiation from nuclear fallout, ultraviolet radiation from the sun and tanning lamps, X-rays and gamma rays from medical diagnosis and treatment. Ionizing radiation is associated with the development of cancers, e.g. thyroid cancers and leukemia (nuclear fallout), and skin cancer (high UV exposure). | • Nuclear radiation: Those working with radioisotopes, or living near nuclear plants, waste dumps, or testing sites.<br>• UV radiation: Fair skinned people in tropical and sub-tropical regions. Those using tanning beds excessively.<br>• X-rays, gamma rays: Early workers in radiology. Today, better protection and safer equipment has considerably lowered the risks to technicians and patients. |
| ### Viruses and microorganisms<br>Some viruses integrate into the human chromosome, upsetting genes and triggering cancers. Examples include hepatitis B virus (liver cancer), HIV (Kaposi's sarcoma), and Epstein-Barr virus (Burkitt's lymphoma, Hodgkin's disease). Aflatoxins produced by the fungus *Aspergillus flavus* are potent inducers of liver cancer. | • Hepatitis B: Intravenous drug users.<br>• HIV: Intravenous drug users, those with unsafe sexual activity (i.e. unprotected sex with new partners).<br>• The development of Burkitt's lymphoma in response to infection with Epstein-Barr virus is triggered only after infection with malaria. Children in low-lying tropical regions are most at risk. |
| ### Alcohol and dietary components<br>Diets high in fat, especially those containing burned and/or fatty, highly preserved meat, slow the passage of food through the gut giving time for mutagenic irritants to form in the bowel. High alcohol intake increases the risk of some cancers and also increases susceptibility to tobacco-smoking related cancers. | • Those with a diet high in total fats (particularly saturated fat) are at higher risk of developing bowel or rectal cancers. The risks may be increased by obesity.<br>• The risks associated with specific dietary factors may be compounded by familial (inherited) susceptibility.<br>• The risks associated with specific dietary factors may be compounded by other lifestyle choices, e.g. smoking. |
| ### Environmental poisons and irritants<br>Many chemicals are mutagenic. Synthetic and natural examples include organic solvents such as benzene, asbestos, formaldehyde, tobacco tar, vinyl chlorides, coal tars, some dyes, and nitrites. | • Those working in the chemicals industries, including the glue, paint, rubber, resin, and leather industries.<br>• Those in coal and other mining industries.<br>• Petrol pump attendants exposed to petroleum volatiles and vehicle exhaust emissions.<br>• Smokers and asbestos workers. |

GASOLINE

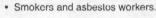
Kurchatov Inst.

**Tobacco smoking**: Tobacco tar is one of the most damaging constituents of tobacco smoke. Tobacco tars contain at least 17 known carcinogens (cancer inducing mutagens) that cause chronic irritation of the respiratory system and are a major cause of cancer in smokers. In the last 5 years, there has been acknowledgement by the tobacco-producing companies that tobacco smoke is not only addictive but also carcinogenic.

**Nuclear reactor failures**: The most famous nuclear accident is that of Chornobyl, in the Ukraine, which suffered a catastrophic explosion and fire in 1986 during routine tests. Two explosions ejected some 8 tonnes of plutonium and other highly radioactive materials from the reactor. This led to widespread contamination of food sources, an increase in radiation-linked diseases, and ongoing environmental problems throughout northern parts of western Europe.

**Ultraviolet rays from the sun**: The ultraviolet rays (UV-A and UV-B) from the sun are particularly damaging to the skin and the retina of the eyes. The development of the ozone depleted region over Antarctica each year has increased the mutagenic effect from this source. One of the main diseases caused by this radiation is a form of skin cancer called melanoma. This is often an aggressive cancer that may be fatal if left untreated.

*Genes and Chromosomes*

1. Discuss the role of **mutagens** and **carcinogens** in causing mutations: _____

_____

_____

_____

_____

**Related activities:** Cancer: Cells Out of Control

A 2

# The Effect of Mutations

Mutations add, delete, or rearrange genetic material. They can happen spontaneously, as a result of errors during DNA replication, or they can be induced by **mutagens**. Not all mutations are inherited. Only those taking place in the cells that produce gametes will be inherited. If they occur in a body cell after the organism has begun to develop beyond the zygote stage, then they may give rise to a **chimera** (an organism with a mixture of genetically different cells). In some cases, mutations trigger the onset of **cancer** through the disruption of the normal controls regulating cell division.

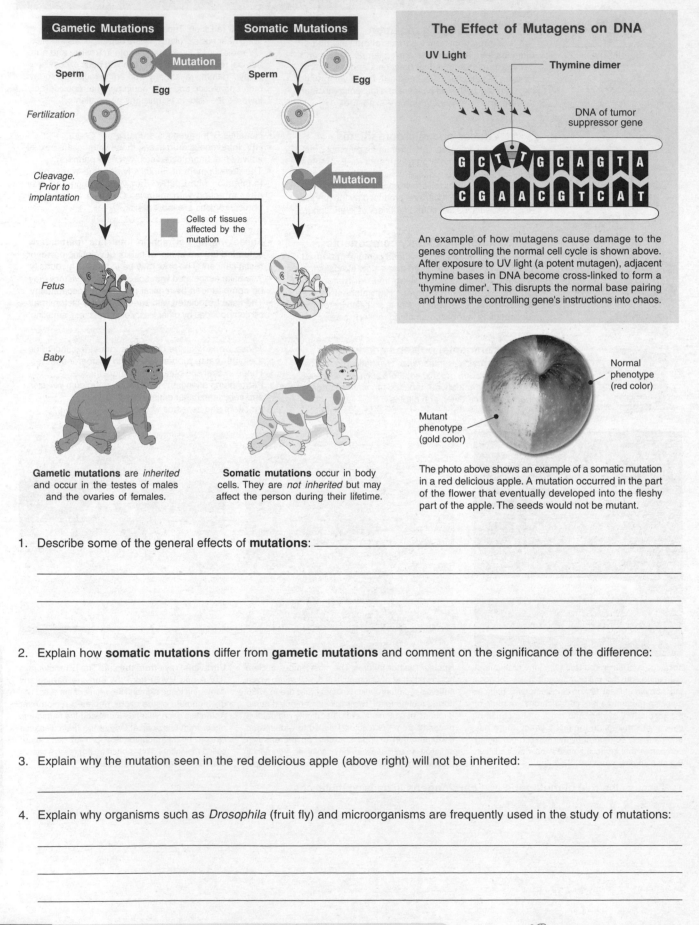

**Gametic Mutations**

Sperm

Mutation

Egg

*Fertilization*

*Cleavage. Prior to implantation*

Cells of tissues affected by the mutation

*Fetus*

*Baby*

**Gametic mutations** are *inherited* and occur in the testes of males and the ovaries of females.

**Somatic Mutations**

Sperm

Egg

Mutation

**Somatic mutations** occur in body cells. They are *not inherited* but may affect the person during their lifetime.

**The Effect of Mutagens on DNA**

UV Light

Thymine dimer

DNA of tumor suppressor gene

G C T T G C A G T A
C G A A C G T C A T

An example of how mutagens cause damage to the genes controlling the normal cell cycle is shown above. After exposure to UV light (a potent mutagen), adjacent thymine bases in DNA become cross-linked to form a 'thymine dimer'. This disrupts the normal base pairing and throws the controlling gene's instructions into chaos.

Normal phenotype (red color)

Mutant phenotype (gold color)

The photo above shows an example of a somatic mutation in a red delicious apple. A mutation occurred in the part of the flower that eventually developed into the fleshy part of the apple. The seeds would not be mutant.

1. Describe some of the general effects of **mutations**: _____

_____

_____

_____

2. Explain how **somatic mutations** differ from **gametic mutations** and comment on the significance of the difference:

_____

_____

_____

3. Explain why the mutation seen in the red delicious apple (above right) will not be inherited: _____

_____

4. Explain why organisms such as *Drosophila* (fruit fly) and microorganisms are frequently used in the study of mutations:

_____

_____

_____

# For Harm or Benefit?

It is not correct to assume that all mutations are harmful. There are many documented cases where mutations conferring a survival advantage have arisen in a population. These **beneficial mutations** occur mostly amongst viruses and bacteria, but some (such as pesticide resistance) occur in multicellular organisms (especially those, like insects, with short **generation times**).

Mutations that are neither harmful nor beneficial are called **neutral** (silent) mutations. Neutral mutations can be virtually impossible to detect because they are not associated with any observable change in phenotype. If there is no selective pressure against a mutation, it may be carried silently in the population and prove to be beneficial (or harmful) at some time in the future.

## Harmful Mutations

There are many well documented examples of mutations with harmful effects. These include the mutations giving rise to **cystic fibrosis** (CF) and **sickle cell disease**. The sickle cell mutation involves a change to only one base in a DNA sequence, whereas a common CF mutation involves the loss of a single triplet. The malformed proteins resulting from these mutations cannot carry out their normal functions. **Albinism** is caused by a mutation in the gene producing an enzyme in the metabolic pathway to **melanin**. It occurs in a large number of animals. The example above shows an albino python. Albinos are uncommon in the wild because they tend to be more vulnerable to predation and damaging UV radiation.

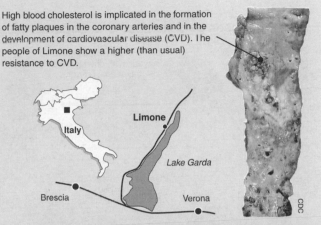

High blood cholesterol is implicated in the formation of fatty plaques in the coronary arteries and in the development of cardiovascular disease (CVD). The people of Limone show a higher (than usual) resistance to CVD.

## Beneficial Mutations

A well documented example of a beneficial mutation is the **tolerance to high cholesterol levels** in humans. In the small village of **Limone**, about 40 villagers have extraordinarily high levels of blood cholesterol, with no apparent harm to their coronary arteries. The village has 980 inhabitants and was largely isolated from the rest of the world until recently. The 40 villagers possess a mutation that alters a protein by **one amino acid** and makes it ten times more effective at mopping up excess cholesterol. Excess cholesterol is always disposed of, no matter what the dietary intake. All carriers of the mutation are related and are descended from one couple who arrived in Limone in 1636.

## Neutral Mutations

**Neutral mutations** may be important in an evolutionary sense because they can be passed from generation to generation and may directly (or indirectly through subsequent mutation) be subject to selection pressure in the future. The example below shows how a change to the DNA sequence can be silenced if there is no change to the resulting amino acid sequence.

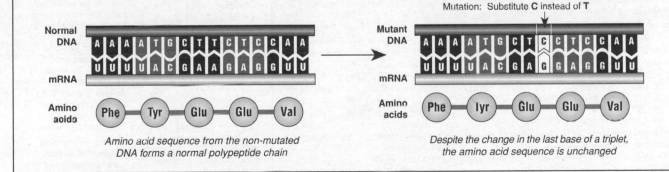

*Amino acid sequence from the non-mutated DNA forms a normal polypeptide chain*

*Despite the change in the last base of a triplet, the amino acid sequence is unchanged*

1. (a) Explain the difference between neutral (silent), beneficial, and harmful mutations: _____

_____

_____

(b) Identify which of these mutations is the most common and suggest why: _____

_____

2. Explain how the mutation that 40 of the villagers of Limone possess is beneficial under current environmental conditions:

_____

_____

**Related activities**: Control of Metabolic Pathways, Antibiotic Resistance, Cystic Fibrosis Mutation, Sickle Cell Mutation

A 2

**Genes and Chromosomes**

# Antibiotic Resistance

Antibiotics are drugs that inhibit bacterial growth and are used to treat bacterial infections. Resistance to antibiotics may arise spontaneously, as the result of a mutagenic agent, or through the transfer of genetic material between microbial sources. Over the years, more and more bacteria have developed resistance to once-effective antibiotics. Drug resistance results from an adaptive response that allows microbes to tolerate levels of antibiotic that would normally inhibit their growth. Such responses might include the production of enzymes that inactivate the drugs, or changes that prevent the antibiotic attaching or penetrating the microbial surface. With the increased antibiotic use, resistance developed quickly in microbial populations and many strains are now **multi-drug resistant**. These are particularly worrying because resistant infections are difficult to treat and increase mortality.

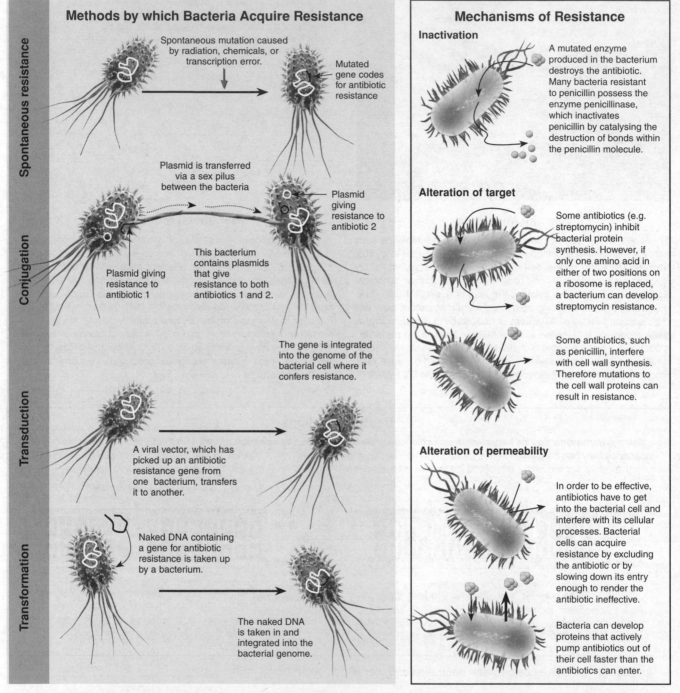

**Methods by which Bacteria Acquire Resistance**

*Spontaneous resistance*

Spontaneous mutation caused by radiation, chemicals, or transcription error.

Mutated gene codes for antibiotic resistance

*Conjugation*

Plasmid is transferred via a sex pilus between the bacteria

Plasmid giving resistance to antibiotic 2

Plasmid giving resistance to antibiotic 1

This bacterium contains plasmids that give resistance to both antibiotics 1 and 2.

The gene is integrated into the genome of the bacterial cell where it confers resistance.

*Transduction*

A viral vector, which has picked up an antibiotic resistance gene from one bacterium, transfers it to another.

*Transformation*

Naked DNA containing a gene for antibiotic resistance is taken up by a bacterium.

The naked DNA is taken in and integrated into the bacterial genome.

**Mechanisms of Resistance**

**Inactivation**

A mutated enzyme produced in the bacterium destroys the antibiotic. Many bacteria resistant to penicillin possess the enzyme penicillinase, which inactivates penicillin by catalysing the destruction of bonds within the penicillin molecule.

**Alteration of target**

Some antibiotics (e.g. streptomycin) inhibit bacterial protein synthesis. However, if only one amino acid in either of two positions on a ribosome is replaced, a bacterium can develop streptomycin resistance.

Some antibiotics, such as penicillin, interfere with cell wall synthesis. Therefore mutations to the cell wall proteins can result in resistance.

**Alteration of permeability**

In order to be effective, antibiotics have to get into the bacterial cell and interfere with its cellular processes. Bacterial cells can acquire resistance by excluding the antibiotic or by slowing down its entry enough to render the antibiotic ineffective.

Bacteria can develop proteins that actively pump antibiotics out of their cell faster than the antibiotics can enter.

1. Explain how spontaneous resistance can occur in a bacterium:

_____

_____

2. Explain how the misuse of antibiotics by patients can lead to the development of antibiotic resistant bacteria:

_____

_____

_____

# Gene Mutations

Gene mutations are small, localized changes in the structure of a DNA strand. These mutations may involve change in a single nucleotide (these are often called **point mutations**), or changes to a triplet (e.g. triplet deletion or triplet repeat). If one amino acid in a protein is wrong, the biological function of the entire protein can be disrupted. Not all mutations may result in altered proteins. Because of the degeneracy of the genetic code, a substitution of the 3rd base in a codon may code for the same amino acid. The diagrams below and on the following page show how various point mutations can occur. These alterations in the DNA are at the **nucleotide** level where individual **codons** are affected. Alteration of the precise nucleotide sequence of a coded gene in turn alters the mRNA transcribed from the mutated DNA and may affect the polypeptide chain that it normally creates.

## Base Mismatching – Tautomerism

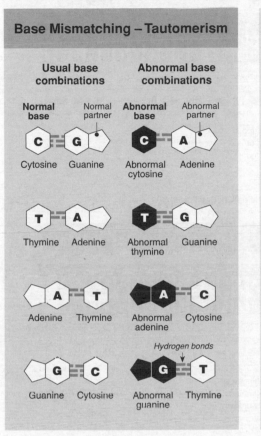

### Usual base combinations

**Normal base** — **Normal partner**

C Cytosine — G Guanine

T Thymine — A Adenine

A Adenine — T Thymine

G Guanine — C Cytosine

### Abnormal base combinations

**Abnormal base** — **Abnormal partner**

C Abnormal cytosine — A Adenine

T Abnormal thymine — G Guanine

A Abnormal adenine — C Cytosine

*Hydrogen bonds*

G Abnormal guanine — T Thymine

## Base Mismatching

Watson and Crick proposed a theory of how base mismatching could occur. The diagram on the left shows suggested changes in bases and the resulting mismatch of complementary bases. On rare occasions some bases may have altered hydrogen-bond positions. As a result, during DNA replication, such abnormal bases pair with incorrect complementary bases. This gives rise to mutations in DNA molecules, which in turn are expressed as altered forms of mRNA and often altered proteins. NOTE: The abnormal bases on the right hand side of the diagram have a different arrangement of hydrogen bonds than normal.

### A normal sequence without mutations

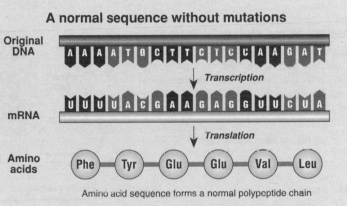

Original DNA: A A A A T G C T T C T C C A A G A T

*Transcription*

mRNA: U U U U A C G A A G A G G U U C U A

*Translation*

Amino acids: Phe — Tyr — Glu — Glu — Val — Leu

Amino acid sequence forms a normal polypeptide chain

## Missense substitution

A single base is substituted for another base which may result in a codon that codes for a different amino acid. Some substitutions, however, may still code for the same amino acid, because of the high degree of degeneracy in the genetic code (i.e. many amino acids have 4 or 6 codons coding for them). In the illustrated example, placing a T where a C should have been, results in the amino acid **lysine** appearing where **glutamic** acid should be. This could affect how this protein functions.

## Nonsense substitution

Some amino acids can be coded for by 4 or 6 different codons and are therefore less affected by substitutions. In the example illustrated, a single base substitution in the first nucleotide of the third codon has a dramatic effect on the nature of the polypeptide chain it is coding for. The codon no longer codes for an amino acid, but instead is an instruction for the termination of the translation process of protein synthesis. This results in a very short polypeptide chain that is likely to have little or no function since the **STOP** codon is introduced near the **START** codon.

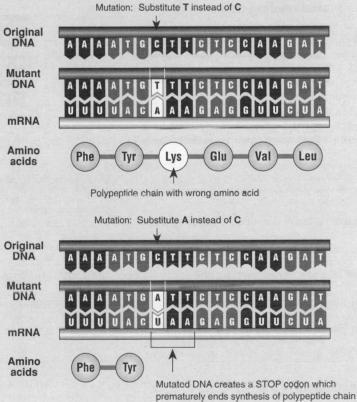

Mutation: Substitute **T** instead of **C**

Original DNA: A A A A T G C T T C T C C A A G A T

Mutant DNA: A A A A T G T T T C T C C A A G A T

mRNA: U U U U A C A A A G A G G U U C U A

Amino acids: Phe — Tyr — Lys — Glu — Val — Leu

Polypeptide chain with wrong amino acid

Mutation: Substitute **A** instead of **C**

Original DNA: A A A A T G C T T C T C C A A G A T

Mutant DNA: A A A A T G A T T C T C C A A G A T

mRNA: U U U U A C U A A G A G G U U C U A

Amino acids: Phe — Tyr

Mutated DNA creates a STOP codon which prematurely ends synthesis of polypeptide chain

**Genes and Chromosomes**

**Related activities**: For Harm or Benefit?, Examples of Gene Mutations, Sickle Cell Mutation

RA 3

Some gene mutations may have no observable effect on the phenotype of the organism; the subtle changes in the DNA sequence may still produce a chain of identical amino acids in the protein, or at least produce a protein that is unaffected by the change. Because of the degeneracy of the genetic code, many gene mutations do not cause a significant change in the biological activity of the protein, although there are notable exceptions, e.g. sickle cell disease.

## Reading frame shift by insertion

A major upset can occur when a single extra base is inserted into the DNA sequence. This has the effect of displacing all the other bases along one position and thereby creating a whole new sequence of codons. Such mutations are almost always likely to lead to a non-functional protein, but this does depend on the distance of the insertion or deletion from the START codon (i.e. the closer the insertion is to the START codon, the more the protein will be affected).

NOTE: could also lead to nonsense

## Reading frame shift by deletion

In the same way that an insertion of an extra base into the DNA sequence has a large scale damaging effect, a deletion may also cause a frame shift. Again the result is usually a polypeptide chain of doubtful biological activity.

NOTE: could also lead to nonsense

## Partial reading frame shift

Both an insertion and a deletion of bases within a gene can cause a frame shift effect where each codon no longer has the correct triplet of three bases. In this example, three codons have been affected, along with the amino acids they code for. The error is limited to the codons including and between the insertion and deletion. There is no biological activity if the amino acids altered are important to the functioning of the resulting protein.

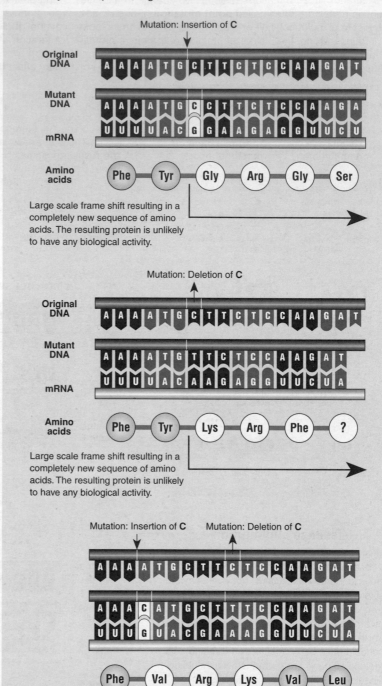

1. Explain what is meant by a **reading frame shift**: _____

_____

2. Not all gene mutations have the same effect on the organism, some are more disruptive than others.

    (a) Identify which type of gene mutations are the most damaging to an organism: _____

    (b) Explain why they are the most disruptive: _____

    _____

3. Explain why **biological activity** of a protein might be affected by a reading frame shift: _____

_____

# Examples of Gene Mutations

Humans have more than 6000 physiological diseases attributed to mutations in single genes and over one hundred syndromes known to be caused by chromosomal abnormality. The number of genetic disorders identified increases every year. The work of the Human Genome Project is enabling the identification of the genetic basis of these disorders. This will facilitate the development of new drug therapies and gene therapies. Four genetic disorders are summarized below.

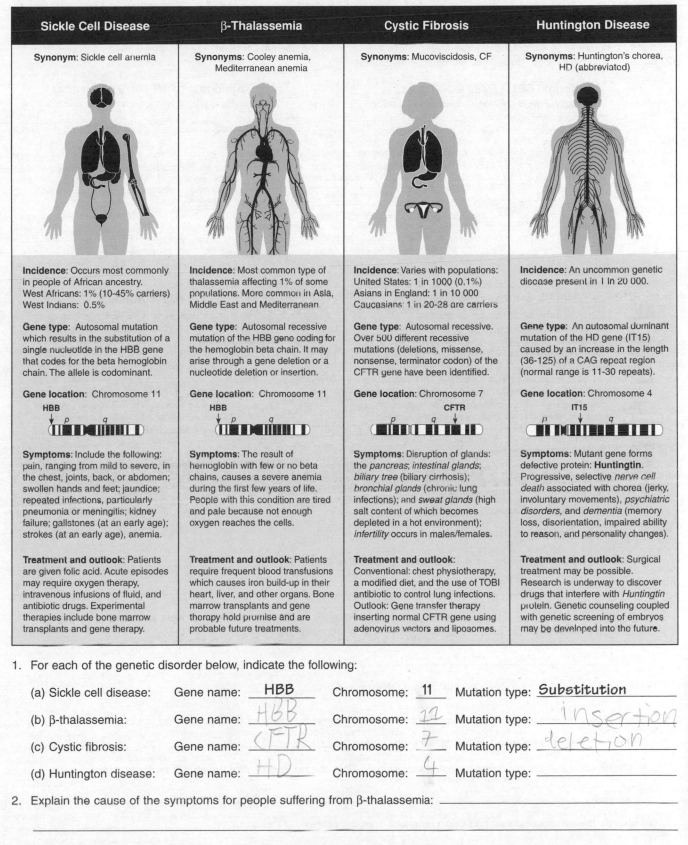

| Sickle Cell Disease | β-Thalassemia | Cystic Fibrosis | Huntington Disease |
| --- | --- | --- | --- |
| **Synonym**: Sickle cell anemia | **Synonyms**: Cooley anemia, Mediterranean anemia | **Synonyms**: Mucoviscidosis, CF | **Synonyms**: Huntington's chorea, HD (abbreviated) |
| **Incidence**: Occurs most commonly in people of African ancestry. West Africans: 1% (10-45% carriers) West Indians: 0.5% | **Incidence**: Most common type of thalassemia affecting 1% of some populations. More common in Asia, Middle East and Mediterranean. | **Incidence**: Varies with populations: United States: 1 in 1000 (0.1%) Asians in England: 1 in 10 000 Caucasians: 1 in 20-28 are carriers | **Incidence**: An uncommon genetic disease present in 1 in 20 000. |
| **Gene type**: Autosomal mutation which results in the substitution of a single nucleotide in the HBB gene that codes for the beta hemoglobin chain. The allele is codominant. | **Gene type**: Autosomal recessive mutation of the HBB gene coding for the hemoglobin beta chain. It may arise through a gene deletion or a nucleotide deletion or insertion. | **Gene type**: Autosomal recessive. Over 500 different recessive mutations (deletions, missense, nonsense, terminator codon) of the CFTR gene have been identified. | **Gene type**: An autosomal dominant mutation of the HD gene (IT15) caused by an increase in the length (36-125) of a CAG repeat region (normal range is 11-30 repeats). |
| **Gene location**: Chromosome 11 | **Gene location**: Chromosome 11 | **Gene location**: Chromosome 7 | **Gene location**: Chromosome 4 |
| **Symptoms**: Include the following: pain, ranging from mild to severe, in the chest, joints, back, or abdomen; swollen hands and feet; jaundice; repeated infections, particularly pneumonia or meningitis; kidney failure; gallstones (at an early age); strokes (at an early age), anemia. | **Symptoms**: The result of hemoglobin with few or no beta chains, causes a severe anemia during the first few years of life. People with this condition are tired and pale because not enough oxygen reaches the cells. | **Symptoms**: Disruption of glands: the *pancreas*; *intestinal glands*; *biliary tree* (biliary cirrhosis); *bronchial glands* (chronic lung infections); and *sweat glands* (high salt content of which becomes depleted in a hot environment); *infertility* occurs in males/females. | **Symptoms**: Mutant gene forms defective protein: **Huntingtin**. Progressive, selective *nerve cell death* associated with chorea (jerky, involuntary movements), *psychiatric disorders,* and *dementia* (memory loss, disorientation, impaired ability to reason, and personality changes). |
| **Treatment and outlook**: Patients are given folic acid. Acute episodes may require oxygen therapy, intravenous infusions of fluid, and antibiotic drugs. Experimental therapies include bone marrow transplants and gene therapy. | **Treatment and outlook**: Patients require frequent blood transfusions which causes iron build-up in their heart, liver, and other organs. Bone marrow transplants and gene therapy hold promise and are probable future treatments. | **Treatment and outlook**: Conventional: chest physiotherapy, a modified diet, and the use of TOBI antibiotic to control lung infections. Outlook: Gene transfer therapy inserting normal CFTR gene using adenovirus vectors and liposomes. | **Treatment and outlook**: Surgical treatment may be possible. Research is underway to discover drugs that interfere with *Huntingtin* protein. Genetic counseling coupled with genetic screening of embryos may be developed into the future. |

1. For each of the genetic disorder below, indicate the following:

   (a) Sickle cell disease:    Gene name: __HBB__    Chromosome: __11__    Mutation type: _Substitution_

   (b) β-thalassemia:    Gene name: _HBB_    Chromosome: _11_    Mutation type: _insertion_

   (c) Cystic fibrosis:    Gene name: _CFTR_    Chromosome: _7_    Mutation type: _deletion_

   (d) Huntington disease:    Gene name: _HD_    Chromosome: _4_    Mutation type: _____

2. Explain the cause of the symptoms for people suffering from β-thalassemia: _____

   _____

3. Suggest a reason for the differences in the country-specific incidence rates for some genetic disorders:

   _____

   _____

Genes and Chromosomes

**Related activities**: The Human Genome Project, Sickle Cell Mutation, Cystic Fibrosis Mutation

A 2

# Cystic Fibrosis Mutation

Cystic fibrosis an inherited disorder caused by a mutation of the **CF gene**. It is one of the most common lethal autosomal recessive conditions affecting caucasians, with an incidence in the US of 1 in 1000 live births and a **carrier frequency** of 4%. It is uncommon in Asians and Africans. The CF gene's protein product, **CFTR**, is a membrane-based protein with a function in regulating the transport of chloride across the membrane. A faulty gene in turn codes for a faulty CFTR. More than 500 mutations of the CF gene have been described, giving rise to disease symptoms of varying severity. One mutation is particularly common and accounts for more than 70% of all defective CF genes. This mutation, called δ(delta)F508, leads to the absence of CFTR from its proper position in the membrane. This mutation is described below. Another CF mutation, R117H, which is also relatively common, produces a partially functional CFTR protein. The DNA sequence below is part of the transcribing sequence for the **normal** CF gene.

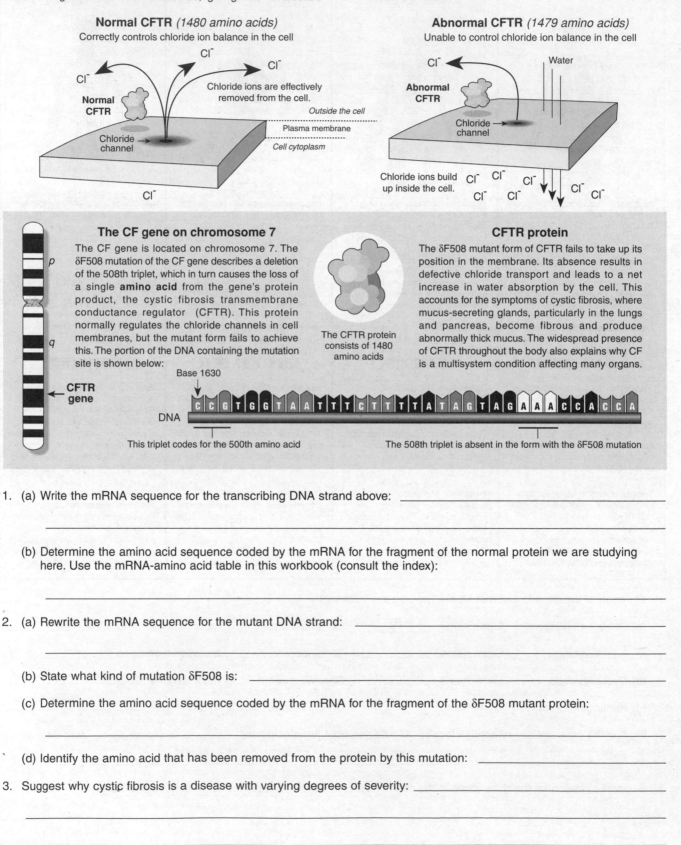

**Normal CFTR** (1480 amino acids)
Correctly controls chloride ion balance in the cell

**Abnormal CFTR** (1479 amino acids)
Unable to control chloride ion balance in the cell

## The CF gene on chromosome 7

The CF gene is located on chromosome 7. The δF508 mutation of the CF gene describes a deletion of the 508th triplet, which in turn causes the loss of a single **amino acid** from the gene's protein product, the cystic fibrosis transmembrane conductance regulator (CFTR). This protein normally regulates the chloride channels in cell membranes, but the mutant form fails to achieve this. The portion of the DNA containing the mutation site is shown below:

The CFTR protein consists of 1480 amino acids

## CFTR protein

The δF508 mutant form of CFTR fails to take up its position in the membrane. Its absence results in defective chloride transport and leads to a net increase in water absorption by the cell. This accounts for the symptoms of cystic fibrosis, where mucus-secreting glands, particularly in the lungs and pancreas, become fibrous and produce abnormally thick mucus. The widespread presence of CFTR throughout the body also explains why CF is a multisystem condition affecting many organs.

Base 1630

DNA    C C G T G G T A A T T T C T T T T T A T A G T A G A A A C C A C C A

This triplet codes for the 500th amino acid

The 508th triplet is absent in the form with the δF508 mutation

1.  (a) Write the mRNA sequence for the transcribing DNA strand above: _____

    _____

    (b) Determine the amino acid sequence coded by the mRNA for the fragment of the normal protein we are studying here. Use the mRNA-amino acid table in this workbook (consult the index):

    _____

2.  (a) Rewrite the mRNA sequence for the mutant DNA strand: _____

    _____

    (b) State what kind of mutation δF508 is: _____

    (c) Determine the amino acid sequence coded by the mRNA for the fragment of the δF508 mutant protein:

    _____

    (d) Identify the amino acid that has been removed from the protein by this mutation: _____

3.  Suggest why cystic fibrosis is a disease with varying degrees of severity: _____

    _____

    _____

**Related activities**: The Genetic Code, Examples of Gene Mutations

# Sickle Cell Mutation

**Sickle cell disease** (formerly called sickle cell anemia) is an inherited disorder caused by a gene mutation which codes for a faulty beta (β) chain hemoglobin (Hb) protein. This in turn causes the red blood cells to deform causing a whole range of medical problems. The DNA sequence below is the beginning of the transcribing sequence for the **normal** β-chain Hb molecule.

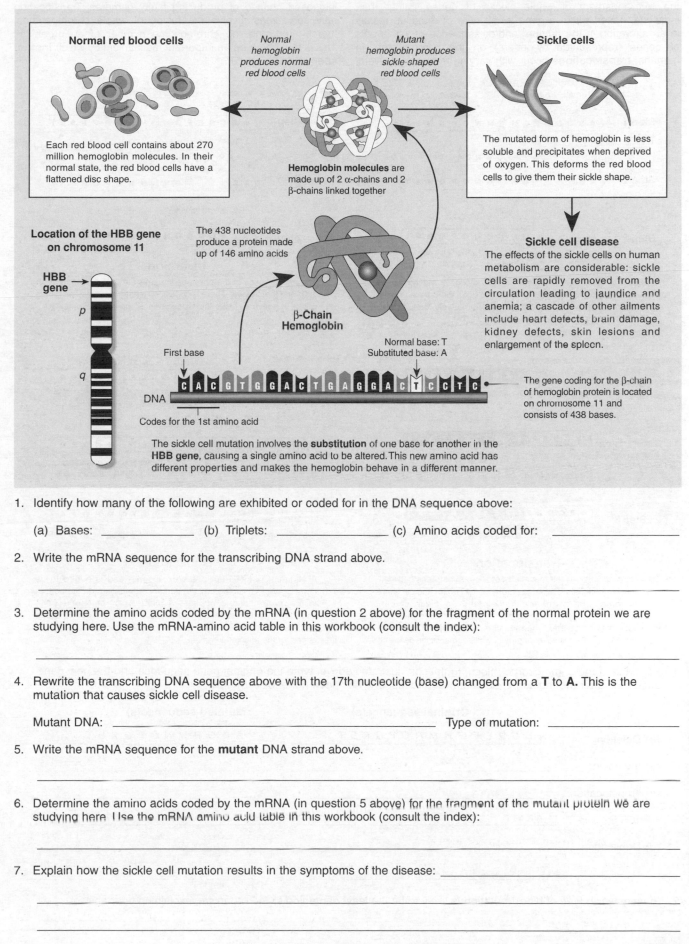

**Normal red blood cells**

Each red blood cell contains about 270 million hemoglobin molecules. In their normal state, the red blood cells have a flattened disc shape.

*Normal hemoglobin produces normal red blood cells*

*Mutant hemoglobin produces sickle-shaped red blood cells*

**Sickle cells**

The mutated form of hemoglobin is less soluble and precipitates when deprived of oxygen. This deforms the red blood cells to give them their sickle shape.

**Hemoglobin molecules** are made up of 2 α-chains and 2 β-chains linked together

**Location of the HBB gene on chromosome 11**

HBB gene

p

q

The 438 nucleotides produce a protein made up of 146 amino acids

**β-Chain Hemoglobin**

First base

Normal base: T
Substituted base: A

DNA

C A C G T G G A C T G A G G A C T C C T C

Codes for the 1st amino acid

**Sickle cell disease**
The effects of the sickle cells on human metabolism are considerable: sickle cells are rapidly removed from the circulation leading to jaundice and anemia; a cascade of other ailments include heart defects, brain damage, kidney defects, skin lesions and enlargement of the spleen.

The gene coding for the β-chain of hemoglobin protein is located on chromosome 11 and consists of 438 bases.

The sickle cell mutation involves the **substitution** of one base for another in the **HBB gene**, causing a single amino acid to be altered. This new amino acid has different properties and makes the hemoglobin behave in a different manner.

1. Identify how many of the following are exhibited or coded for in the DNA sequence above:

   (a) Bases: _____ (b) Triplets: _____ (c) Amino acids coded for: _____

2. Write the mRNA sequence for the transcribing DNA strand above.

   _____

3. Determine the amino acids coded by the mRNA (in question 2 above) for the fragment of the normal protein we are studying here. Use the mRNA-amino acid table in this workbook (consult the index):

   _____

4. Rewrite the transcribing DNA sequence above with the 17th nucleotide (base) changed from a **T** to **A.** This is the mutation that causes sickle cell disease.

   Mutant DNA: _____ Type of mutation: _____

5. Write the mRNA sequence for the **mutant** DNA strand above.

   _____

6. Determine the amino acids coded by the mRNA (in question 5 above) for the fragment of the mutant protein we are studying here. Use the mRNA amino acid table in this workbook (consult the index):

   _____

7. Explain how the sickle cell mutation results in the symptoms of the disease: _____

   _____

   _____

**Related activities**: The Genetic Code, Examples of Gene Mutations

RA 3

**Genes and Chromosomes**

# Chromosome Mutations

The diagrams below show the different types of **chromosome mutation** that can occur only during **meiosis**. These mutations (sometimes also called **block mutations**) involve the rearrangement of whole blocks of genes, rather than individual bases within a gene. Each type of mutation results in an alteration in the number and/or sequence of whole sets of genes (represented by letters) on the chromosome. In humans, **translocations** occur with varying frequency (several rare types of Down syndrome occur in this way). Individuals with a **balanced translocation** have the correct amount of genetic material and appear phenotypically normal but have an increased chance of producing faulty gametes. Translocation may sometimes involve the fusion of whole chromosomes, thereby reducing the chromosome number of an organism. This is thought to be an important mechanism by which **instant speciation** can occur.

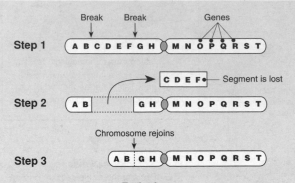

### Deletion

A break may occur at two points on the chromosome and the middle piece of the chromosome falls out. The two ends then rejoin to form a chromosome deficient in some genes. Alternatively, the end of a chromosome may break off and is lost.

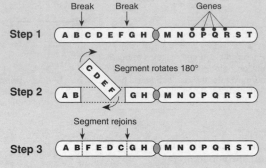

### Inversion

The middle piece of the chromosome falls out and rotates through 180° and then rejoins. There is no loss of genetic material. The genes will be in a reverse order for this segment of the chromosome.

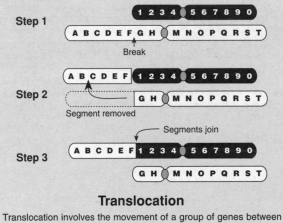

### Translocation

Translocation involves the movement of a group of genes between different chromosomes. The large chromosome (white) and the small chromosome (black) are not homologous. A piece of one chromosome breaks off and joins onto another chromosome. This will cause major problems when the chromosomes are passed to gametes. Some will receive extra genes, while some will be deficient.

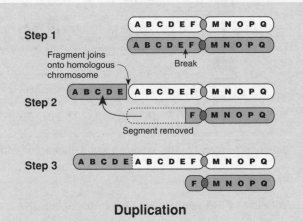

### Duplication

A segment is lost from one chromosome and is added to its homologue. In this diagram, the darker chromosome on the bottom is the 'donor' of the duplicated piece of chromosome. The chromosome with the segment removed is deficient in genes. Some gametes will receive double the genes while others will have no genes for the affected segment.

1. For each of the chromosome (block) mutations illustrated above, write the original gene sequence and the new gene sequence after the mutation has occurred (the first one has been done for you):

|  | Original sequence(s) | Mutated sequence(s) |
|---|---|---|
| (a) Deletion: | A B C D E F G H M N O P Q R S T | A B G H M N O P Q R S T |
| (b) Inversion: | | |
| (c) Translocation: | | |
| (d) Duplication: | | |

2. Identify which type of block mutation is likely to be the least damaging to the organism, explaining your answer:

# The Fate of Conceptions

A significant number of conceptions do not end in live births. A large proportion of miscarriages, which are spontaneous natural abortions, are caused by **chromosome disorders** such as trisomy and polyploidy. Some of these disorders are less severe than others and those affected survive into childhood or beyond.

There is a good correlation between the age of the mother and the incidence in chromosome abnormalities, called the **maternal age effect**. Prospective mothers older than 35-40 years are encouraged to have a prenatal test (e.g. **amniocentesis** or **CVS**) to determine the **karyotype** of the fetus.

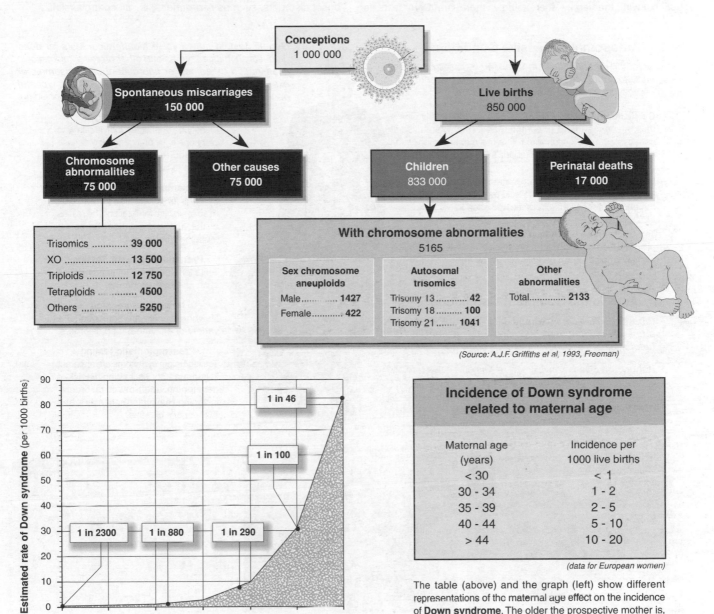

**Conceptions**
1 000 000

**Spontaneous miscarriages**
150 000

**Live births**
850 000

**Chromosome abnormalities**
75 000

**Other causes**
75 000

**Children**
833 000

**Perinatal deaths**
17 000

Trisomics ............. 39 000
XO ...................... 13 500
Triploids .............. 12 750
Tetraploids ........... 4500
Others .................. 5250

**With chromosome abnormalities**
5165

| Sex chromosome aneuploids | Autosomal trisomics | Other abnormalities |
|---|---|---|
| Male............. 1427 | Trisomy 13 ............ 42 | Total.............. 2133 |
| Female........... 422 | Trisomy 18 .......... 100 | |
| | Trisomy 21 ........ 1041 | |

(Source: A.J.F. Griffiths et al, 1993, Freeman)

**Estimated rate of Down syndrome (per 1000 births)** vs **Maternal age (years)**

1 in 46
1 in 100
1 in 2300
1 in 880
1 in 290

### Incidence of Down syndrome related to maternal age

| Maternal age (years) | Incidence per 1000 live births |
|---|---|
| < 30 | < 1 |
| 30 - 34 | 1 - 2 |
| 35 - 39 | 2 - 5 |
| 40 - 44 | 5 - 10 |
| > 44 | 10 - 20 |

(data for European women)

The table (above) and the graph (left) show different representations of the maternal age effect on the incidence of **Down syndrome**. The older the prospective mother is, the more likely it is that she will have an affected child.

1. Discuss the role of the **maternal age effect** in the incidence rate of Down syndrome and other trisomic syndromes:

_____

_____

_____

_____

2. Explain the role of **amniocentesis** in detecting trisomic disorders: _____

_____

_____

3. Explain why, in recent times, most Down syndrome babies are born to younger mothers: _____

_____

_____

**Related activities:** Prenatal Diagnosis, Aneuploidy in Humans, Down Syndrome

**RA 2**

**Genes and Chromosomes**

# Genetic Counseling

Genetic counselling is an analysis of the risk of producing offspring with known gene defects within a family. Counsellors identify families at risk, investigate the problem present in the family, interpret information about the disorder, analyze inheritance patterns and risks of recurrence, and review available options with the family. Increasingly, there are DNA tests for the identification of specific defective genes. People usually consider genetic counselling if they have a family history of a genetic disorder, or if a routine prenatal screening test yields an unexpected result. While screening for many genetic disorders is now recommended, the use of presymptomatic tests for adult-onset disorders, such as Alzheimer's, is still controversial.

## Autosomal Recessive Conditions

*Common inherited disorders caused by recessive alleles on autosomes. Recessive conditions are evident only in homozygous recessive genotypes.*

**Cystic fibrosis**: Malfunction of the pancreas and other glands; thick mucus leads to pneumonia and emphysema. Death usually occurs in childhood. CF is the most frequent lethal genetic disorder in childhood (about 1 case in 3700 live births).

**Maple syrup urine disease**: Mental and physical retardation produced by a block in amino acid metabolism. Isoleucine in the urine produces the characteristic odor.

**Tay-Sachs disease**: A lipid storage disease which causes progressive developmental paralysis, mental deterioration, and blindness. Death usually occurs by three years of age.

## Autosomal Dominant Conditions

*Inherited disorders caused by dominant alleles on autosomes. Dominant conditions are evident both in heterozygotes and in homozygous dominant individuals.*

**Huntington disease**: Involuntary movements of the face and limbs with later general mental deterioration. The beginning of symptoms is highly variable, but occurs usually between 30 to 40 years of age.

*Genetic testing may involve biochemical tests for gene products such as enzymes and other proteins, microscopic examination of stained or fluorescent chromosomes, or examination of the DNA molecule itself. Various types of genetic tests are performed for various reasons, including:*

**Carrier Screening**
Identifying unaffected individuals who carry one copy of a gene for a disease that requires two copies for the disease to be expressed.

**Preimplantation Genetic Diagnosis**
Screens for genetic flaws in embryos used for *in vitro* fertilization. The results of the analysis are used to select mutation-free embryos.

**Prenatal Diagnostic Testing**
Tests for chromosomal abnormalities such as Down syndrome.

**Newborn Screening**
Newborn babies are screened for a variety of enzyme-based disorders.

**Presymptomatic Testing**
Testing before symptoms are apparent is important for estimating the risk of developing adult-onset disorders, including Huntington's, cancers, and Alzheimer's disease.

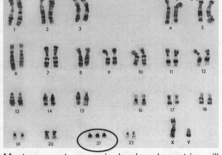

Cytogenetics Dept., Waikato Hospital

About half of the cases of childhood deafness are the result of an autosomal recessive disorder. Early identification of the problem prepares families and allows early appropriate treatment.

Genetic counseling provides information to families who have members with birth defects or genetic disorders, and to families who may be at risk for a variety of inherited conditions.

Most pregnant women in developed countries will have a prenatal test to detect chromosomal abnormalities such as Down syndrome and developmental anomalies such as neural defects.

1. Outline the benefits of **carrier screening** to a couple with a family history of a genetic disorder:

_____

_____

2. (a) Suggest why Huntington disease persists in the human population when it is caused by a lethal, dominant allele:

_____

_____

(b) Explain how presymptomatic genetic testing could change this: _____

_____

_____

**Related activities**: Prenatal Diagnosis, Examples of Gene Mutations, Aneuploidy in Humans, Down Syndrome, Lethal Alleles

# Aneuploidy in Humans

**Euploidy** is the condition of having an exact multiple of the haploid number of chromosomes. Normal euploid humans have 46 chromosomes (2N). **Aneuploidy** is the condition where the chromosome number is not an exact multiple of the normal haploid set for the species (the number may be more, e.g. 2N+2, or less, e.g. 2N–1). **Polysomy** is aneuploidy involving reduplication of some of the chromosomes beyond the normal diploid number (e.g. 2N+1). Aneuploidy usually results from the **non-disjunction** (failure to separate) of homologous chromosomes during meiosis. The two most common forms are monosomy (e.g. Turner syndrome) and trisomy (e.g. Down and Klinefelter syndrome) as outlined on the following pages.

## Faulty Egg Production

The male has produced normal gametes, but the female has not. The two X-sex chromosomes failed to separate during the first division of meiosis.

## Faulty Sperm Production

The female has produced normal gametes, while the male has had an error during the first division of meiosis. The two sex chromosomes (**X** and **Y**) failed to separate during the first division.

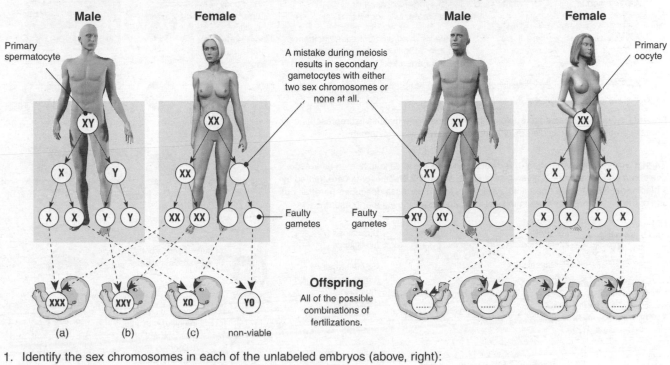

1. Identify the sex chromosomes in each of the unlabeled embryos (above, right):

2. Using the table on the next page, identify the syndrome for each of the offspring labeled (a) to (c) above:

   (a) _____  (b) _____  (c) _____

3. Explain why the YO configuration (above) is non-viable (i.e. there is no embryonic development): _____

   _____

4. (a) For karyotype **A**, below, circle the sex chromosomes and state:

   Chromosome configuration: _____ Sex of individual (M/F): ____ Syndrome: _____

   (b) For karyotype **B**, below, circle the sex chromosomes and state:

   Chromosome configuration: _____ Sex of individual (M/F): ____ Syndrome: _____

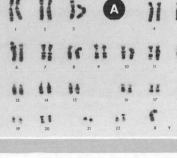

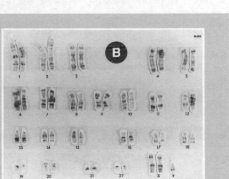

**Related activities:** Down Syndrome

RA 2

Genes and Chromosomes

## Examples of Aneuploidy in Human Sex Chromosomes

| Sex chromosomes and chromosome condition | Apparent sex | Phenotype |
|---|---|---|
| **XO**, monosomic | Female | Turner syndrome |
| **XX**, disomic | Female | **Normal female** |
| **XXX**, trisomic | Female | Metafemale. Most appear normal; they have a greater tendency to criminality |
| **XXXX**, tetrasomic | Female | Rather like Down syndrome, low fertility and intelligence |
| **XY**, disomic | Male | **Normal male** |
| **XYY**, trisomic | Male | Jacob syndrome, apparently normal male, tall, aggressive |
| **XXY**, trisomic | Male | Klinefelter syndrome (infertile). Incidence rate 1 in 1000 live male births, with a maternal age effect. |
| **XXXY**, tetrasomic | Male | Extreme Klinefelter, mentally retarded |

**Above**: Features of selected aneuploidies in humans. Note that this list represents only a small sample of the possible sex chromosome aneuploidies in humans.

**Right**: Symbolic representation of Barr body occurrence in various human karyotypes. The chromosome number is given first, and the inactive X chromosomes are framed by a black box. Note that in aneuploid syndromes, such as those described here, all but one of the X chromosomes are inactivated, regardless of the number present.

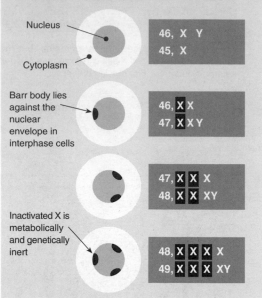

### Barr Bodies

In the nucleus of any non-dividing somatic cell, one of the X chromosomes condenses to form a visible piece of chromatin, called a **Barr body**. This chromosome is inactivated, so that only one X chromosome in a cell ever has its genes expressed. The inactivation is random, and the inactive X may be either the maternal homologue (from the mother) or the paternal homologue (from the father).

Nucleus

Cytoplasm

46, X  Y
45, X

Barr body lies against the nuclear envelope in interphase cells

46, X X
47, X X Y

47, X X  X
48, X X  XY

Inactivated X is metabolically and genetically inert

48, X X X  X
49, X X X  XY

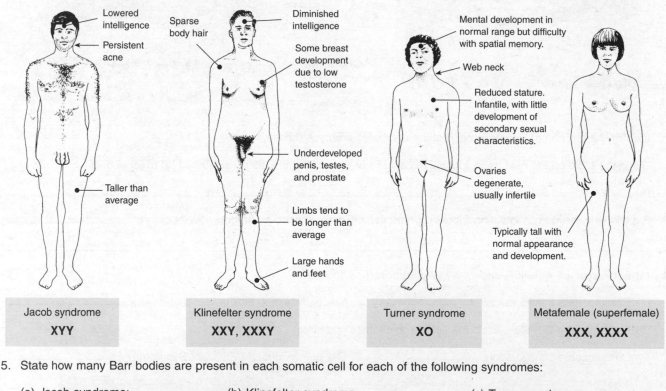

Lowered intelligence

Persistent acne

Taller than average

**Jacob syndrome
XYY**

Sparse body hair

Diminished intelligence

Some breast development due to low testosterone

Underdeveloped penis, testes, and prostate

Limbs tend to be longer than average

Large hands and feet

**Klinefelter syndrome
XXY, XXXY**

Mental development in normal range but difficulty with spatial memory.

Web neck

Reduced stature. Infantile, with little development of secondary sexual characteristics.

Ovaries degenerate, usually infertile

**Turner syndrome
XO**

Typically tall with normal appearance and development.

**Metafemale (superfemale)
XXX, XXXX**

5. State how many Barr bodies are present in each somatic cell for each of the following syndromes:

(a) Jacob syndrome: _____ (b) Klinefelter syndrome: _____ (c) Turner syndrome: _____

6. Explain the consequence of X-chromosome inactivation in terms of the proteins encoded by the X chromosome genes:

_____

_____

7. State how many chromosomes for each set of homologues are present for the following forms of aneuploidy:

(a) Nullisomy: _____ (c) Trisomy: _____

(b) Monosomy: _____ (d) Polysomy: _____

# Down Syndrome

**Trisomy** is a form of **polysomy** where the nucleus of the cells have one chromosome pair represented by three chromosomes (2N+1). The extra chromosome disturbs the overall chromosomal balance causing abnormalities or death. In humans, about 50% of all spontaneous abortions result from chromosomal abnormalities, and trisomies are responsible for about half of these (25% of all spontaneous abortions). About 6% of live births involve children with chromosomal abnormalities. Autosomal trisomies make up only 0.1% of all pregnancies. Of the three autosomal trisomies surviving to birth, trisomy 21 (**Down** syndrome) is the most common. The other two, **Edward** and **Patau**, show severe physical and mental abnormalities. Trisomies in other autosomes are rare.

## Down Syndrome (Trisomy 21)

Down syndrome is the most common of the human aneuploidies. The incidence rate in humans is about 1 in 800 births for women aged 30 to 31 years, with a maternal age effect (the rate increases rapidly with maternal age). The most common form of this condition arises when meiosis fails to separate the pair of chromosome number 21s in the eggs that are forming in the woman's ovaries (it is apparently rare for males to be the cause of this condition). In addition to growth failure and mental retardation, there are a number of well known phenotypic traits (see diagram right).

Down syndrome may arise from several causes:

**Non-disjunction**: Nearly all cases (approximately 95%) result from **non-disjunction** of chromosome 21 during **meiosis**. When this happens, a gamete (usually the oocyte) ends up with 24 rather than 23 chromosomes, and fertilization produces a trisomic offspring (see the karyotype photo, above right).

**Translocation**: One in twenty cases of Down syndrome (fewer than 3-4%) arise from a **translocation** mutation where one parent is a translocation carrier (chromosome 21 is fused to another chromosome, usually number 14).

**Mitotic errors**: A very small proportion of cases (fewer than 3%) arise from the failure of the pair of chromosomes 21 to separate during **mitosis** at an early embryonic stage. The resulting individual is a **mosaic** in which two cell lines exist, one of which is trisomic. If the mitotic abnormality occurs very early in development, a large number of cells are affected and the full Down syndrome is expressed. If only a few cells are affected, there are only mild expressions of the syndrome.

A child showing features of the Down syndrome phenotype.

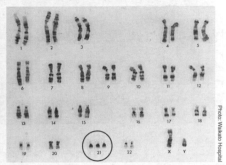

The karyotype of a trisomic 21 individual that produces the phenotype known as Down syndrome.

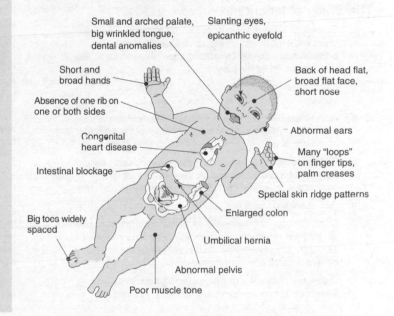

Small and arched palate, big wrinkled tongue, dental anomalies

Slanting eyes, epicanthic eyefold

Short and broad hands

Absence of one rib on one or both sides

Congenital heart disease

Intestinal blockage

Big toes widely spaced

Back of head flat, broad flat face, short nose

Abnormal ears

Many "loops" on finger tips, palm creases

Special skin ridge patterns

Enlarged colon

Umbilical hernia

Abnormal pelvis

Poor muscle tone

1. Distinguish between an autosomal aneuploidy and one involving the sex chromosomes: _____

_____

2. (a) Suggest a possible reason why the presence of an extra chromosome causes such a profound effect on the development of a person's phenotype:

_____

(b) With reference to Down syndrome, explain what you understand by the term **syndrome**: _____

_____

3. (a) Describe the main cause of Down syndrome: _____

_____

(b) Describe the features of the Down phenotype: _____

_____

4. Describe one other cause of Down syndrome: _____

_____

5. State how many chromosomes would be present in the somatic cells of an individual with Down syndrome: _____

**Related activities**: Prenatal Diagnosis, Aneuploidy in Humans

RA 2

Genes and Chromosomes

# Inheritance

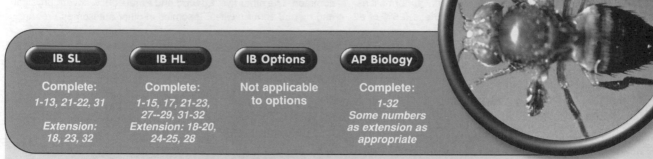

**IB SL**
Complete:
1-13, 21-22, 31

Extension:
18, 23, 32

**IB HL**
Complete:
1-15, 17, 21-23,
27--29, 31-32
Extension: 18-20,
24-25, 28

**IB Options**
Not applicable
to options

**AP Biology**
Complete:
1-32
Some numbers
as extension as
appropriate

## Learning Objectives

☐ 1. Compile your own glossary from the **KEY WORDS** displayed in **bold type** in the learning objectives below.

### The Study of Inheritance  *(pages 210-213)*

☐ 2. Summarize the outcomes of Gregor **Mendel**'s historical breeding experiments with peas. Outline Mendel's principles of inheritance, stating their importance to the understanding of heredity.

☐ 3. Explain the relationship between Mendel's law of segregation and meiosis.

☐ 4. Appreciate that Mendelian principles were important in providing a mechanism through which natural selection could act upon the genetic variation in populations.

☐ 5. Define the terms: **allele** and **locus**. Distinguish between **dominant**, **recessive**, and **codominant** alleles. Appreciate how new alleles are formed.

☐ 6. Define the term **trait** with respect to the study of genetics.

☐ 7. Describe how genes, and their dominant and recessive alleles, are represented symbolically by letters of the alphabet. Explain clearly what is meant by the terms: **heterozygous** and **homozygous**.

☐ 8. Distinguish between **genotype** and **phenotype** and use these terms appropriately when discussing the outcomes of genetic crosses.

☐ 9. Demonstrate an ability to use a **Punnett square** in the solution of different inheritance problems. Define the terms: **monohybrid**, and **dihybrid cross**.

☐ 10. Define and demonstrate an understanding of the terms commonly used in inheritance studies: **cross, carrier, selfing, pure-breeding, test-cross, back-cross, offspring** (progeny), **$F_1$ generation, $F_2$ generation.**

### Inheritance Patterns  *(pages 213-220, 222-28, 240-42)*

For each case below, use a Punnett square through to the $F_2$ generation and determine the probability of the occurrence of a particular genetic outcome (genotype and phenotype ratios).

☐ 11. Describe **monohybrid inheritance** involving a single trait or gene locus. Solve problems involving the inheritance of phenotypic traits that follow a simple **dominant-recessive** pattern.

☐ 12. Solve problems involving the inheritance of phenotypic traits that follow a pattern of **codominance**.

☐ 13. Recognize that **multiple alleles** (alternative alleles) may exist for a single gene, e.g. ABO blood groups. Solve problems involving the inheritance of phenotypic traits involving multiple alleles.

☐ 14. Describe **dihybrid inheritance** involving **unlinked, autosomal genes** for two traits. Solve problems involving dihybrid inheritance of unlinked genes.

☐ 15. Describe **dihybrid inheritance** involving **linked, autosomal genes** for two traits (where the genes described are carried on the same chromosome). Explain how, from the results of a cross, you would decide whether or not genes are linked. Solve problems involving dihybrid inheritance of linked genes, demonstrating proper notation in your working.

☐ 16. Demonstrate an ability to use the **chi-squared test** to test the significance of differences observed between the observed and expected results of genetic crosses.

☐ 17. Explain why experimental results may be expected only to approximate Mendelian ratios.

☐ 18. Describe examples of recessive and/or dominant **lethal alleles**. Recognize how lethal alleles modify the ratio of progeny resulting from a cross. If required, explain the mechanisms by which the lethal allele operates.

☐ 19. Discuss the phenomenon of **genomic imprinting** (parental imprinting). Recognise genomic imprinting as part of **epigenetic inheritance**: the heritable changes in gene function that occur without involving changes to the DNA sequence. Describe an example in which genomic imprinting accounts for the different expression of the same genetic disorder in humans, e.g. Prader-Willi syndrome and Angelman syndrome.

☐ 20. Explain how genomic imprinting is achieved, e.g. by **DNA methylation**. Appreciate that DNA methylation is also important in the X-inactivation of chromosomes.

### Sex Determination in Humans  *(page 221)*

☐ 21. Understand the basis of **sex determination** in humans. Recognize humans as being of the **XX / XY** type. Distinguish **sex chromosomes** from **autosomes**.

### Sex Linkage  *(pages 229-231)*

☐ 22. Define the term: **sex linked**. Describe examples and solve problems involving different patterns of sex linked inheritance involving sex linked genes (e.g. red-green color-blindness or hemophilia).

☐ 23. Contrast the pattern of inheritance of **sex linked recessive traits** and **sex linked dominant traits**.

### Gene Interactions  *(pages 234-239)*

☐ 24. Describe examples of a simple interaction between two genes, e.g. **collaboration** in the determination of **comb shape** of domestic hens. Show how genes that show collaboration influence the same trait, but produce a phenotype that could not result from the action of either gene independently. Solve problems involving the inheritance of phenotypic traits involving collaboration.

☐ 25. Explain what is meant by **pleiotropy** and describe an example of a gene with pleiotropic effects, e.g. **sickle cell gene mutation**. Describe how the phenotype is affected by the presence of the sickle cell mutation.

□ 26. Explain what is meant by **epistasis**, **epistatic gene**, and **hypostatic gene**. Solve problems involving the inheritance of phenotypic traits involving epistasis.

**Example of epistasis 1**: coat color in mice. Several genes determine coat color in mice. Mice that are homozygous recessive for the albino gene are white regardless of their genotype for coat color.

**Example of epistasis 2**: Where one gene can only be expressed in the presence of another. Such **complementary genes** control some flower colors (e.g. in sweet peas): one gene controls the production of a colorless intermediate (for a pigment) and another gene controls the transformation of that intermediate into the pigment. Both genes need to have a dominant allele present for the pigmented phenotype to be expressed.

□ 27. Describe the distribution pattern of phenotypic variation produced by **polygenic inheritance**. Understand why **polygenes** are also called multiple genes. Provide examples of traits that follow this type of **quantitative inheritance** pattern.

□ 28. Demonstrate genetic crosses for the inheritance of a polygenic trait (e.g. skin color) using a Punnett square

through to the F2 generation and determine the probability of the occurrence of a particular genetic outcome (i.e. genotype and phenotype ratios).

□ 29. Distinguish between **continuous** and **discontinuous variation** in phenotypes and explain the genetic basis for each pattern.

□ 30. Collect data related to a continuous phenotypic variable in your class. Plot the data, and calculate the mean and standard deviation for the sample. Describe the distribution obtained.

## Pedigree Analysis *(pages 204, 232-233)*

□ 31. Describe the symbols and notation used in **pedigree analysis** charts. Use pedigree analysis charts to illustrate the inheritance of genetically determined traits in a 'family tree'. Use the charts to determine the probability of certain offspring having particular traits.

□ 32. Appreciate the importance of **genetic counseling**. Describe the circumstances under which couples seek genetic counseling. Explain how this field has been expanded in the light of new technologies.

---

**Textbooks**

See the 'Textbook Reference Grid' on pages 8-9 for textbook page references relating to material in this topic.

### Supplementary Texts

See pages 5-6 for additional details of these texts:

■ Adds, J., *et al.*, 2004. **Genetics, Evolution and Biodiversity**, (NelsonThornes), chpt. 6 as reqd.

■ Clegg, C.J., 1999. **Genetics and Evolution**, (John Murray), pp. 4-39 (in part).

■ Helms, D.R. *et al.*, 1998. **Biology in the Laboratory** (W.H. Freeman), #15.

■ Jones, N., *et al.*, 2001. **Essentials of Genetics**, pp. 29-56, 61-74 (review), 77-110.

**Periodicals**

See page 6 for details of publishers of periodicals:

### STUDENT'S REFERENCE

■ **What is a Gene?** Biol. Sci. Rev., 15(2) Nov. 2002, pp. 9-11. *A good introduction to genes and their role in heredity. This article provides a useful overview and an historical perspective.*

■ **What is Variation?** Biol. Sci. Rev., 13(1) Sept. 2000, pp. 30-31. *The nature of continuous and discontinuous variation in particular characters. The distribution pattern of traits that show continuous variation as a result of polygeny is discussed.*

■ **It Takes Two** New Scientist, 5 Oct. 2002, pp. 34-37. *The relative influence of genes and environment. Studies of twins may help to clarify the nature versus nurture debate.*

■ **Boy Meets Girl / The Gender Police** New Scientist, 12 May 2001, pp. 28-35, 38-41. *Two part special report examining the nature of gender.*

**Presentation MEDIA** to support this topic: **GENES AND INHERITANCE**
• Inheritance
• Gene Interactions

■ **Secrets of The Gene** National Geographic, 196(4) Oct. 1999, pp. 42-75. *Thorough coverage of the nature of genes and the inheritance of particular genetic traits through certain populations.*

■ **The Subtle Key to Human Diversity** New Scientist, 13 Jan. 2007, p. 8. *Although genomic differences between races are small, each group may have distinctive patterns of gene activity.*

### TEACHER'S REFERENCE

■ **Going Beyond X and Y** Scientific American, Jun. 2007, pp. 22-23. *Genetic of sex determination, including the actions of the SRY gene.*

■ **Why the Y is so Weird** Scientific American, Feb. 2001, pp. 42-47. *A comparison of the physical features of the X and Y chromosomes: why they look so different and behavior during division.*

■ **The Double Life of Women** New Scientist, 10 May 2003, pp. 42-45. *Two X chromosomes make you a girl, but why are women not overloaded by having two. A good account of the role of X inactivation in embryonic development.*

■ **Decoding the Ys and Wherefores of Males** New Scientist, 21 June 2003, p. 15. *The publication of the genetic sequence of the Y chromosome has unveiled surprising information; the Y chromosome contains about 78 genes, and has mechanisms by which it can repair itself, generation to generation.*

■ **Illustrating Probability** The Am. Biology Teacher, 69(9). 2007, pp. 544-551. *A hands on activity, illustrating probability and other genetic maths concepts, such as chi-squared, in an effective manner using simple tools.*

■ **Fair Enough** New Scientist, 12 Oct. 2002, pp. 34-37. *The inheritance of skin color in humans. This article examines why humans have such varied skin pigmentation and looks at the argument for there being a selective benefit to being dark or pale in different environments.*

■ **The Unseen Genome: Beyond DNA** Scientific American, Dec. 2003, pp. 78-85. *Most traits are transmitted by genes in DNA that encode proteins, but a separate code, written in chemical signatures outside DNA sequences, also influences health and appearance. This epigenetic code may explain why some diseases skip generations.*

■ **Relating Enzyme Function to Concepts of Dominance and Recessiveness** The Am. Biology Teacher, 63(6), Aug. 2001, pp. 432-436. *Integrating concepts related to genes and inheritance in an experiment imitating the action of functional and non-functional enzymes.*

■ **Does Race Exist?** Scientific American, Dec. 2003, pp. 50-57. *The outward signs on which most definitions of race are based are dictated by only a handful of genes. But the other genes of two people of the same 'race' can be very different,*

*and two people of different race can share more genetic similarity than two of the 'same race'.*

■ **Inheritance of Kernel Color in Corn** The Am. Biology Teacher, 62(3), March 2000, pp. 181-188. *A class practical using corn can enhance understanding of basic Mendelian inheritance.*

■ **Back to Your Roots** New Scientist, 16 March 2002, 32-36. *Genetic profiling is used to determine family lineages and establish accurate genealogies.*

■ **Mending Mendelism** The Am. Biology Teacher, 62(9), Nov. 2000, pp. 633-639. *An examination of the concepts proposed by Mendel, including his laws of segregation and independent assortment, and the concept of dominance.*

■ **A Simulation of X-Linked Inheritance** The Am. Biology Teacher, 59(4), April 1997, pp. 224-228. *A simulation of X-linked inheritance in humans using examples of commonly occurring sex linked disorders in humans.*

■ **An Interdisciplinary Approach to Teaching Dihybrid and Multifactorial Crosses** The Am. Biology Teacher, 63(9), Nov. 2001, pp. 655-659. *An integration of mathematics and biology in the teaching of Mendelian inheritance.*

■ **Where Did You Get Your Brains?** New Scientist, 3 May 1997, pp. 34-39. *What features do we inherit from our mothers and which from our fathers? A better understanding of epigenetic inheritance may help to answer this question.*

**Internet** WWW

See pages 10-11 for details of how to access **Bio Links** from our web site: **www.thebiozone.com** From Bio Links, access sites under the topics:

**GENERAL BIOLOGY ONLINE RESOURCES > Online Textbooks and Lecture Notes:** • Kimball's biology pages ... *and others* > **General Online Biology resources:** • Ken's Bioweb resources ... *and others* > **Glossaries:** • DNA glossary • Genetics glossary... *and others*

**GENETICS:** • Genetest • Gene Almanac ... *and others* > **Molecular Genetics:** • DNA from the beginning ... *and others* > **Inheritance:** • Coat color and pattern genetics of the domestic cat • Cat color genetics • Drag and drop genetics • Funny types of gene interactions • Gene interactions • MendelWeb homework sets • Online Mendelian inheritance in man • Patterns of inheritance • The role of genes ... *and others* > **Mutations & Genetic Disorders:** • Fragile X syndrome • PKU fact sheet • Sickle cell disease • What are metabolic disorders?... *and others*

# Alleles

Sexually reproducing organisms in nearly all cases have paired sets of chromosomes, one set coming from each parent. The equivalent chromosomes that form a pair are termed **homologues**. They contain equivalent sets of genes on them. But there is the potential for different versions of a gene to exist in a population and these are termed **alleles**.

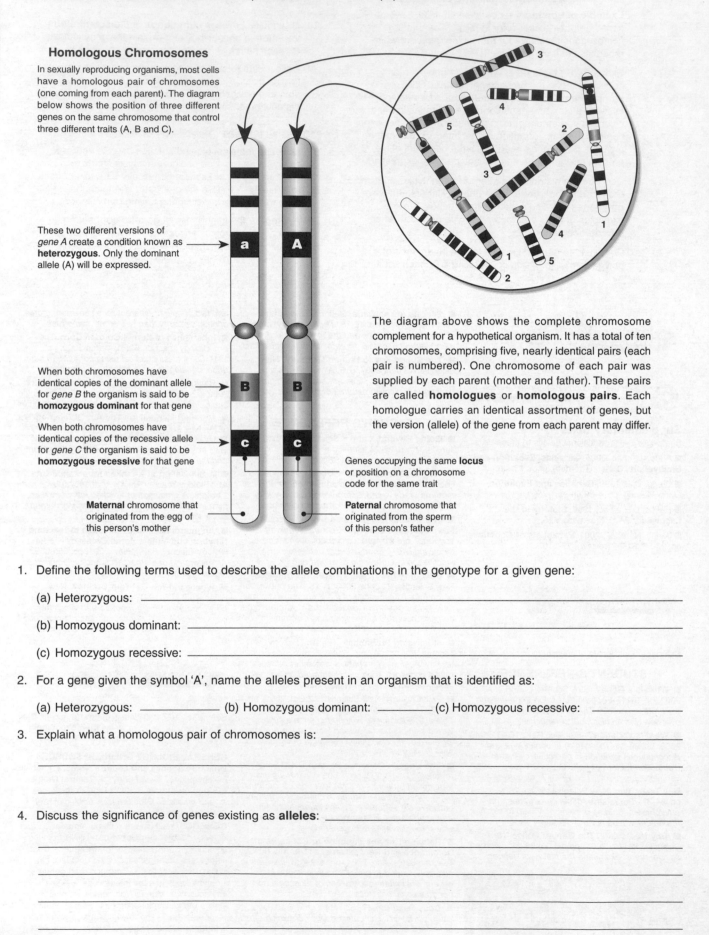

## Homologous Chromosomes

In sexually reproducing organisms, most cells have a homologous pair of chromosomes (one coming from each parent). The diagram below shows the position of three different genes on the same chromosome that control three different traits (A, B and C).

These two different versions of *gene A* create a condition known as **heterozygous**. Only the dominant allele (A) will be expressed.

When both chromosomes have identical copies of the dominant allele for *gene B* the organism is said to be **homozygous dominant** for that gene

When both chromosomes have identical copies of the recessive allele for *gene C* the organism is said to be **homozygous recessive** for that gene

Genes occupying the same **locus** or position on a chromosome code for the same trait

**Maternal** chromosome that originated from the egg of this person's mother

**Paternal** chromosome that originated from the sperm of this person's father

The diagram above shows the complete chromosome complement for a hypothetical organism. It has a total of ten chromosomes, comprising five, nearly identical pairs (each pair is numbered). One chromosome of each pair was supplied by each parent (mother and father). These pairs are called **homologues** or **homologous pairs**. Each homologue carries an identical assortment of genes, but the version (allele) of the gene from each parent may differ.

1. Define the following terms used to describe the allele combinations in the genotype for a given gene:

   (a) Heterozygous: _____

   (b) Homozygous dominant: _____

   (c) Homozygous recessive: _____

2. For a gene given the symbol 'A', name the alleles present in an organism that is identified as:

   (a) Heterozygous: _____ (b) Homozygous dominant: _____ (c) Homozygous recessive: _____

3. Explain what a homologous pair of chromosomes is: _____

   _____

   _____

4. Discuss the significance of genes existing as **alleles**: _____

   _____

   _____

   _____

   _____

**Related activities**: Meiosis

# Mendel's Pea Plant Experiments

**Gregor Mendel** (1822-1884), pictured on the right, was an Austrian monk who is regarded as the 'father of genetics'. He carried out some pioneering work using pea plants to study the inheritance patterns of a number of **traits** (characteristics). Mendel observed that characters could be masked in one generation of peas but could reappear in later generations. He showed that inheritance involved the passing on to offspring of discrete units of inheritance; what we now call genes. Mendel examined a number of phenotypic traits and found that they were inherited in predictable ratios, depending on the phenotype of the parents. Below are some of his results from crossing heterozygous plants (e.g. tall plants that were the offspring of tall and dwarf parent plants: Tt x Tt). The numbers in the results column represent how many offspring had those phenotypic features.

1. Study the **results** for each of the six experiments below. Determine which of the two phenotypes is the dominant one, and which is the recessive. Place your answers in the spaces in the **dominance** column in the table below.

2. Calculate the ratio of dominant phenotypes to recessive phenotypes (to two decimal places). The first one (for seed shape) has been done for you (5474 ÷ 1850 = 2.96). Place your answers in the spaces provided in the table below:

| Trait | Possible Phenotypes | | Results | | Dominance | Ratio |
|---|---|---|---|---|---|---|
| Seed shape | *Wrinkled* | *Round* | Wrinkled 1850 <br> Round 5474 <br> **TOTAL 7324** | | Dominant: Round <br><br> Recessive: Wrinkled | 2.96 : 1 |
| Seed color | *Green* | *Yellow* | Green 2001 <br> Yellow 6022 <br> **TOTAL 8023** | | Dominant: <br><br> Recessive: | |
| Pod color | *Green* | *Yellow* | Green 428 <br> Yellow 152 <br> **TOTAL 580** | | Dominant: <br><br> Recessive: | |
| Flower position | *Axial* | *Terminal* | Axial 651 <br> Terminal 207 <br> **TOTAL 858** | | Dominant: <br><br> Recessive: | |
| Pod shape | *Constricted* | *Inflated* | Constricted 299 <br> Inflated 882 <br> **TOTAL 1181** | | Dominant: <br><br> Recessive: | |
| Stem length | *Tall* | *Dwarf* | Tall 787 <br> Dwarf 277 <br> **TOTAL 1064** | | Dominant: <br><br> Recessive: | |

3. Mendel's experiments identified that two heterozygous parents should produce offspring in the ratio of three times as many dominant offspring to those showing the recessive phenotype.

   (a) State which three of Mendel's experiments provided ratios closest to the theoretical 3:1 ratio:

   _____

   (b) Suggest a possible reason why these results deviated less from the theoretical ratio than the others:

   _____

# Mendel's Laws of Inheritance

From his work on the inheritance of phenotypic traits in peas, Mendel formulated a number of ideas about the inheritance of characters. These were later given formal recognition as Mendel's laws of inheritance. These are outlined below.

## The Theory of Particulate Inheritance

Mendel recognized that characters are determined by discrete units that are inherited intact down through the generations. This model explained many observations that could not be explained by the idea of blending inheritance that was universally accepted prior to this. The diagram on the right illustrates this principle, showing that the trait for flower color appears to take on the appearance of only one parent plant in the first generation, but reappears in later generations.

White X Purple **Parent plants**

X **Generation 1**

The offspring are inbred (self-pollinated)

**Generation 2**

## Law of Segregation

The diagram on the right illustrates how, during meiosis, the two members of any pair of alleles segregate unchanged by passing into different gametes. These gametes are eggs and sperm in animals, and pollen grains and ova in plants. The allele in the gamete will be passed on to the offspring.

Homologous pair of chromosomes, each has a copy of the gene on it (A or a)

**Oocyte**

*Meiosis*

A Egg | A Egg | a Egg | a Egg

NOTE: This diagram has been simplified, omitting the stage where the second chromatid is produced for each chromosome.

## Law of Independent Assortment

The diagram on the right illustrates how genes are carried on chromosomes. There are two genes shown (A and B) that code for different traits. Each of these genes is represented twice, one copy (allele) on each of two homologous chromosomes. The genes A and B are located on different chromosomes and, because of this, they will be inherited independently of each other, i.e. the gametes may contain any combination of the parental alleles.

**Oocyte**

Genotype: AaBb

**Intermediate cell**

**Intermediate cell**

**Eggs**

Ab | Ab | aB | aB

1. Briefly state what **property of genetic inheritance** allows parent pea plants that differ in flower color to give rise to flowers of a single color in the first generation, with both parental flower colors reappearing in the following generation:

   _____

2. The oocyte is the egg producing cell in the ovary of an animal. In the diagram illustrating the **law of segregation** above:

   (a) State the genotype for the oocyte (adult organism): _____

   (b) State the genotype of each of the **four** gametes: _____

   (c) State how many different kinds of gamete can be produced by this oocyte: _____

3. The diagram illustrating the **law of independent assortment** (above) shows only one possible result of the random sorting of the chromosomes to produce: Ab and aB in the gametes.

   (a) List another possible combination of genes (on the chromosomes) ending up in gametes from the same oocyte:

   _____

   (b) State how many different gene combinations are possible for the oocyte: _____

**A 2** **Related activities**: Alleles, Mendel's Pea Plant Experiments

# Basic Genetic Crosses

For revision purposes, examine the diagrams below on monohybrid crosses and complete the exercise for dihybrid (two gene) inheritance. A **test cross** is also provided to show how the genotype of a dominant phenotype can be determined. A test cross will yield one of two different results, depending on the genotype of the dominant individual. A **back cross** (not shown) refers to any cross between an offspring and one of its parents (or an individual genetically identical to one of its parents).

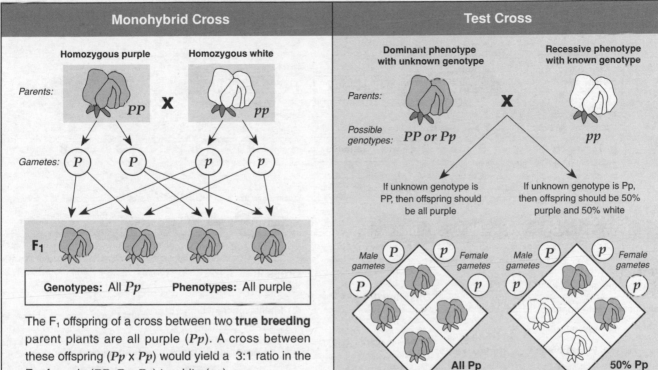

## Monohybrid Cross

Homozygous purple    Homozygous white

Parents:    $PP$    X    $pp$

Gametes:    P    P    p    p

$F_1$

Genotypes: All $Pp$    Phenotypes: All purple

The $F_1$ offspring of a cross between two **true breeding** parent plants are all purple ($Pp$). A cross between these offspring ($Pp$ x $Pp$) would yield a 3:1 ratio in the $F_2$ of purple ($PP$, $Pp$, $Pp$) to white ($pp$).

## Test Cross

Dominant phenotype with unknown genotype    X    Recessive phenotype with known genotype

Parents:

Possible genotypes: $PP$ or $Pp$    $pp$

If unknown genotype is PP, then offspring should be all purple

If unknown genotype is Pp, then offspring should be 50% purple and 50% white

Male gametes    P    p    Female gametes
P    p

Male gametes    P    p    Female gametes
p    p

All Pp    50% Pp
50% pp

## Dihybrid Cross

In pea seeds, yellow color ($Y$) is dominant to green ($y$) and round shape ($R$) is dominant to wrinkled ($r$). Each **true breeding** parental plant has matching alleles for each of these characters ($YYRR$ or $yyrr$). $F_1$ offspring will all have the same genotype and phenotype (yellow-round: $YyRr$).

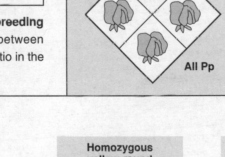

Parents:    Homozygous yellow-round    X    Homozygous green-wrinkled

Gametes:    $YR$    $yr$

$F_1$ all yellow-round    $YyRr$ X $YyRr$ for the $F_2$

1. Fill in the Punnett square (below right) to show the genotypes of the $F_2$ generation.

2. In the boxes below, use fractions to indicate the numbers of each phenotype produced from this cross.

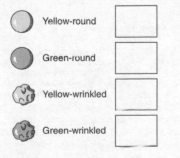

- Yellow-round
- Green-round
- Yellow-wrinkled
- Green-wrinkled

3. Express these numbers as a ratio:

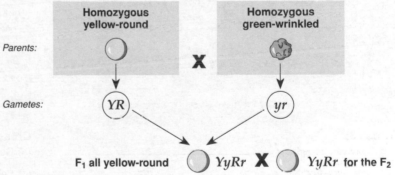

Offspring ($F_2$)    Female gametes

Possible fertilizations    $YR$    $Yr$    $yR$    $yr$

Male gametes    $YR$    $Yr$    $yR$    $yr$

# Monohybrid Cross

The study of **single-gene inheritance** is achieved by performing **monohybrid crosses**. The six basic types of matings possible among the three genotypes can be observed by studying a pair of alleles that govern coat color in the guinea pig. A dominant allele: given the symbol **B** produces **black** hair, and its recessive allele: **b**, produces white. Each of the parents can produce two types of gamete by the process of **meiosis** (in reality there are four, but you get identical pairs). Determine the **genotype** and **phenotype frequencies** for the crosses below (enter the frequencies in the spaces provided). For crosses 3 to 6, you must also determine gametes produced by each parent (write these in the circles), and offspring (F₁) genotypes and phenotypes (write in the genotype inside the offspring and state if black or white).

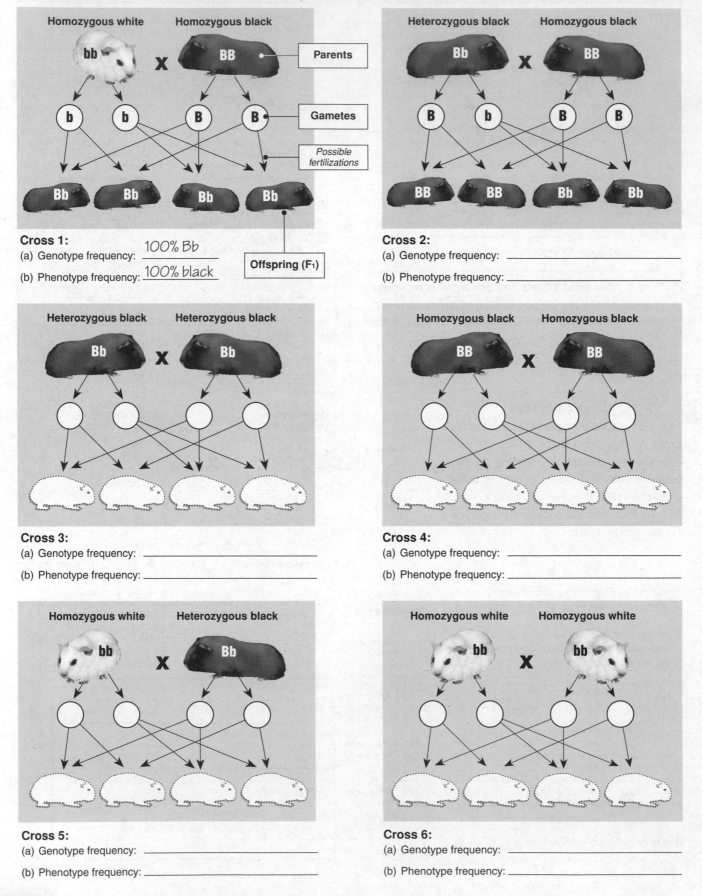

**Cross 1:**

(a) Genotype frequency: _100% Bb_

(b) Phenotype frequency: _100% black_

Parents

Gametes

*Possible fertilizations*

Offspring (F₁)

**Cross 2:**

(a) Genotype frequency: _____

(b) Phenotype frequency: _____

**Cross 3:**

(a) Genotype frequency: _____

(b) Phenotype frequency: _____

**Cross 4:**

(a) Genotype frequency: _____

(b) Phenotype frequency: _____

**Cross 5:**

(a) Genotype frequency: _____

(b) Phenotype frequency: _____

**Cross 6:**

(a) Genotype frequency: _____

(b) Phenotype frequency: _____

**Related activities**: Basic Genetic Crosses

# Dominance of Alleles

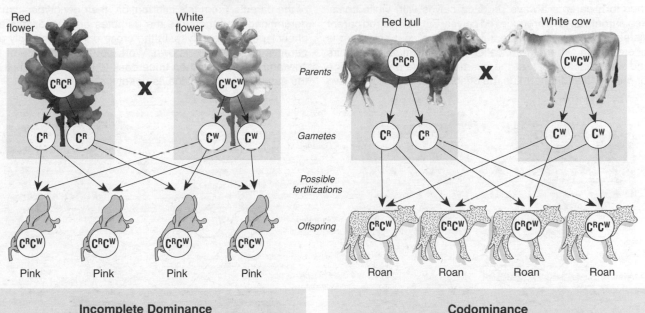

**Incomplete Dominance**

Incomplete dominance refers to the situation where the action of one allele does not completely mask the action of the other and neither allele has dominant control over the trait. The heterozygous offspring is **intermediate** in phenotype between the contrasting homozygous parental phenotypes. In crosses involving incomplete dominance the phenotype and genotype ratios are identical. Examples include snapdragons (*Antirrhinum*), where red and white-flowered parent plants are crossed to produce pink-flowered offspring. In this type of inheritance the phenotype of the offspring results from the partial influence of both alleles.

**Codominance**

Codominance refers to inheritance patterns when both alleles in a heterozygous organism contribute to the phenotype. Both alleles are **independently** and **equally expressed**. One example includes the human blood group AB which is the result of two alleles: A and B, both being equally expressed. Other examples include certain coat colors in horses and cattle. Reddish coat color is not completely dominant to white. Animals that have both alleles have coats that are **roan**-colored (coats with a mix of red and white hairs). The red hairs and white hairs are expressed equally and independently (not blended to produce pink).

1. In incomplete and codominance, two parents of differing phenotype produce offspring different from either parent. Explain the mechanism by which this occurs in:

   (a) Incomplete dominance: _____

   _____

   (b) Codominance: _____

   _____

2. For each situation below, explain how the heterozygous individuals differ in their phenotype from homozygous ones:

   (a) Incomplete dominance: _____

   (b) Codominance: _____

3. Describe the classical phenotypic ratio for a codominant gene resulting from the cross of two heterozygous parents (in the case of the cattle described above, this would be a cross between two roan cattle). Use the Punnett square (provided right) to help you:

   _____

   _____

   _____

   Gametes from male

   Gametes from female

4. A plant breeder wanted to produce flowers for sale that were only pink or white (i.e. no red). Determine the phenotypes of the two parents necessary to produce these desired offspring. Use the Punnett square (provided right) to help you:

   _____

   _____

   Gametes from male

   Gametes from female

In the shorthorn cattle breed coat color is inherited. White shorthorn parents always produce calves with white coats. Red parents always produce red calves. But when a red parent mates with a white one the calves have a coat color that is different from either parent, called roan (a mixture of red hairs and white hairs). Look at the example on the previous page for guidance and determine the offspring for the following two crosses. In the cross on the left, you are given the phenotype of the parents. From this information, their genotypes can be determined, and therefore the gametes and genotypes and phenotypes of the calves. In the cross on the right, only one parent's phenotype is known. Work out the genotype of the cow and calves first, then trace back to the unknown bull via the gametes, to determine its genotype.

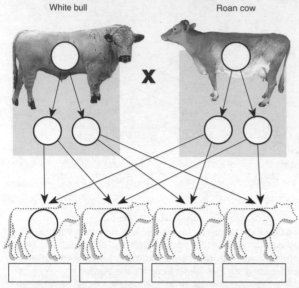

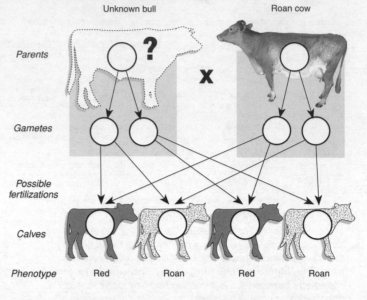

5.  A white bull is mated with a roan cow (above, left).

    (a) Fill in the spaces on the diagram (above, left) to show the genotype and phenotype for parents and calves.

    (b) State the phenotype ratio for this cross: _____

    (c) Suggest how the farmer who owns these cattle could control the breeding so that the herd ultimately consisted of red colored cattle only:

    _____

    _____

    _____

6.  A unknown bull is mated with a roan cow (above, right). A farmer has only roan shorthorn cows on his farm. He suspects that one of the bulls from his next door neighbors may have jumped the fence to mate with his cows earlier in the year. All the calves born were either red or roan. One neighbor has a red bull, the other has a roan bull.

    (a) Fill in the spaces on the diagram (above, right) to show the genotype and phenotype for parents and calves.

    (b) State which of the neighbor's bulls must have mated with the cows: **red** or **white**   (*delete one*)

7.  A plant breeder crossed two plants of the plant variety known as Japanese four o'clock. This plant is known to have its flower color controlled by a gene which possesses incomplete dominant alleles. Pollen from a pink flowered plant was placed on the stigma of a red flowered plant.

    (a) Fill in the spaces on the diagram on the right to show the genotype and phenotype for parents and offspring.

    (b) State the phenotype ratio:

    _____

    _____

    _____

# Multiple Alleles in Blood Groups

The four common blood groups of the human 'ABO blood group system' are determined by three alleles: *A*, *B*, and *O* (also represented in some textbooks as: I^A, I^B, and i^O or just i). This is an example of a **multiple allele** system for a gene. The ABO antigens consist of sugars attached to the surface of red blood cells. The alleles code for enzymes (proteins) that join together these sugars. The allele *O* produces a non-functioning enzyme that is unable to make any changes to the basic antigen (sugar) molecule. The other two alleles *(A, B)* are **codominant** and are expressed equally. They each produce a different functional enzyme that adds a different, specific sugar to the basic sugar molecule. The blood group A and B antigens are able to react with antibodies present in the blood from other people and must be matched for transfusion.

| Recessive allele: | *O* | produces a non-functioning protein |
| Dominant allele: | *A* | produces an enzyme which forms **A antigen** |
| Dominant allele: | *B* | produces an enzyme which forms **B antigen** |

If a person has the *AO* allele combination then their blood group will be group **A**. The presence of the recessive allele has no effect on the blood group in the presence of a dominant allele. Another possible allele combination that can create the same blood group is *AA*.

| Blood group (phenotype) | Possible genotypes | Frequency* | | |
|---|---|---|---|---|
| | | White | Black | Native American |
| **O** | *OO* | 45% | 49% | 79% |
| **A** | *AA AO* | 40% | 27% | 16% |
| **B** | | 11% | 20% | 4% |
| **AB** | | 4% | 4% | 1% |

\* Frequency is based on North American population
Source: www.kcom.edu/faculty/chamberlain/Website/MSTUART/Lect13.htm

1. Use the information above to complete the table for the possible genotypes for blood group B and group AB.

2. Below are six crosses possible between couples of various blood group types. The first example has been completed for you. Complete the genotype and phenotype for the other five crosses shown:

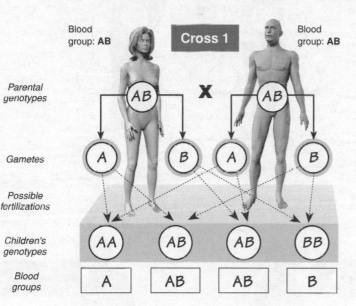

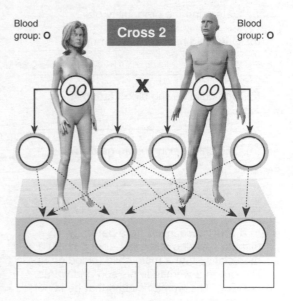

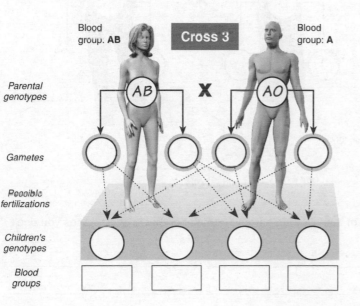

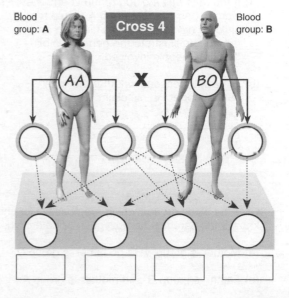

**Related activities**: Dominance of Alleles

A 2

218

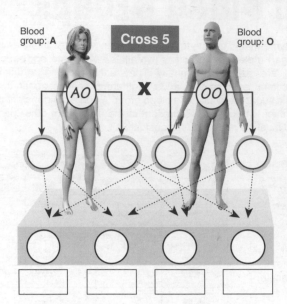

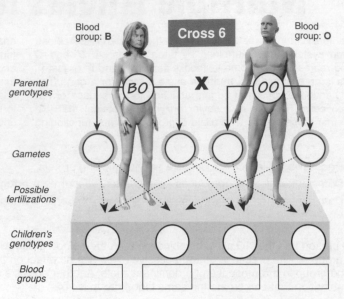

3. A wife is heterozygous for blood group **A** and the husband has blood group **O**.

(a) Give the genotypes of each parent (fill in spaces on the diagram on the right).

Determine the probability of:

(b) One child having blood group **O**:

_____

(c) One child having blood group **A**:

_____

(d) One child having blood group **AB**:

_____

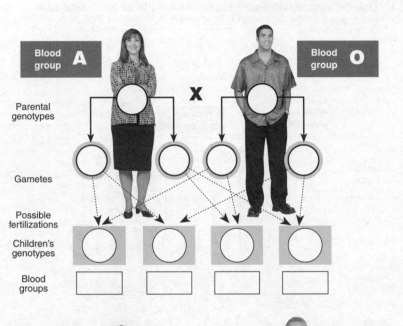

4. In a court case involving a paternity dispute (i.e. who is the father of a child) a man claims that a male child (blood group **B**) born to a woman is his son and wants custody. The woman claims that he is not the father.

(a) If the man has a blood group **O** and the woman has a blood group **A**, could the child be his son? Use the diagram on the right to illustrate the genotypes of the three people involved.

(b) State with reasons whether the man can be correct in his claim:

_____

_____

_____

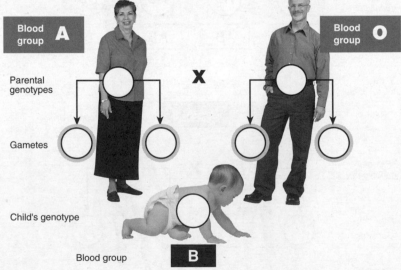

5. Give the blood groups which are possible for children of the following parents (remember that in some cases you don't know if the parent is homozygous or heterozygous).

(a) Mother is group **AB** and father is group **O**: _____

(b) Father is group **B** and mother is group **A**: _____

# Dihybrid Cross

A cross (or mating) between two organisms where the inheritance patterns of **two genes** are studied is called a **dihybrid cross** (compared with the study of one gene in a monohybrid cross). There are a greater number of gamete types (four) produced when two genes are considered. Remember that the genes described are being carried by separate chromosomes and are sorted independently of each other during meiosis (that is why you get four kinds of gamete). The two genes below control two unrelated characteristics **hair color** and **coat length**. Black and short are dominant.

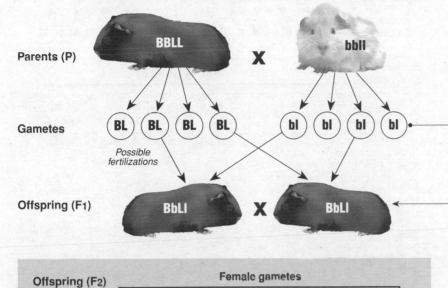

**Homozygous black, short hair**     **Homozygous white, long hair**

Parents (P)     BBLL     X     bbll

Gametes     BL  BL  BL  BL     bl  bl  bl  bl

*Possible fertilizations*

Offspring (F1)     BbLl     X     BbLl

**Parents:** The notation P, is only used for a cross between **true breeding** (homozygous) parents.

**Gametes:** Only one type of gamete is produced from each parent (although they will produce four gametes from each oocyte or spermatocyte). This is because each parent is homozygous for both traits.

**F1 offspring:** There is only one **kind** of gamete from each parent, therefore only one kind of offspring produced in the first generation. The notation **F1** is only used to denote the heterozygous offspring of a cross between two true breeding parents.

**F2 offspring:** The F1 were mated with each other (**selfed**). Each individual from the F1 is able to produce four different kinds of gamete. Using a grid called a **Punnett square** (left), it is possible to determine the expected genotype and phenotype ratios in the F2 offspring. The notation **F2** is only used to denote the offspring produced by crossing F1 heterozygotes.

Each of the 16 animals shown here represents the possible zygotes formed by different combinations of gametes coming together at fertilization.

**Offspring (F2)**

*Possible fertilizations*

**Female gametes**

BL    Bl    bL    bl

**Male gametes**

BL →    BBLL    BBLl    BbLL    BbLl

Bl →    BBLl    BBll    BbLl    Bbll

bL →    BbLL    BbLl    bbLL    bbLl

bl →    BbLl    Bbll    bbLl    bbll

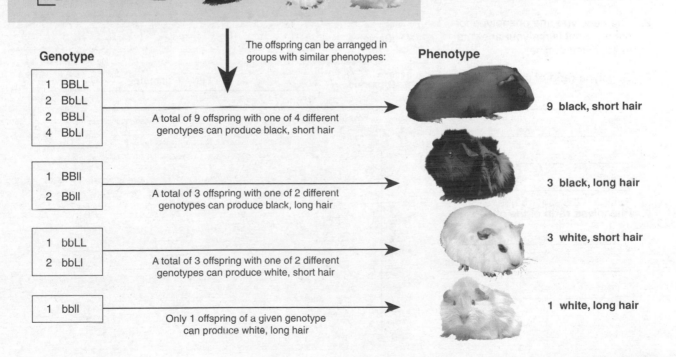

The offspring can be arranged in groups with similar phenotypes:

**Genotype**

| 1 | BBLL |
| 2 | BbLL |
| 2 | BBLl |
| 4 | BbLl |

A total of 9 offspring with one of 4 different genotypes can produce black, short hair

| 1 | BBll |
| 2 | Bbll |

A total of 3 offspring with one of 2 different genotypes can produce black, long hair

| 1 | bbLL |
| 2 | bbLl |

A total of 3 offspring with one of 2 different genotypes can produce white, short hair

| 1 | bbll |

Only 1 offspring of a given genotype can produce white, long hair

**Phenotype**

9 black, short hair

3 black, long hair

3 white, short hair

1 white, long hair

**Related activities:** Basic Genetic Crosses, Dihybrid Cross with Linkage

A 2

## Cross N⁰· 1

The dihybrid cross on the right has been partly worked out for you. You must determine:

1. The genotype and phenotype for each animal (write your answers in its dotted outline).

2. Genotype **ratio** of the offspring:

_____

_____

_____

_____

_____

_____

3. Phenotype **ratio** of the offspring:

_____

_____

_____

_____

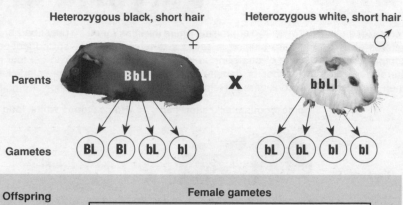

**Heterozygous black, short hair** ♀

**Heterozygous white, short hair** ♂

Parents    **BbLl**    X    **bbLl**

Gametes    BL  Bl  bL  bl        bL  bL  bl  bl

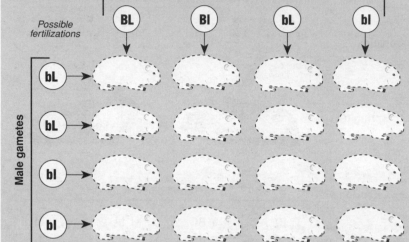

Offspring                    **Female gametes**

*Possible fertilizations*        BL    Bl    bL    bl

Male gametes    bL    bL    bl    bl

## Cross N⁰· 2

For the dihybrid cross on the right, determine:

1. Gametes produced by each parent (write these in the circles).

2. The genotype and phenotype for each animal (write your answers in its dotted outline).

3. Genotype **ratio** of the offspring:

_____

_____

_____

_____

4. Phenotype **ratio** of the offspring:

_____

_____

_____

_____

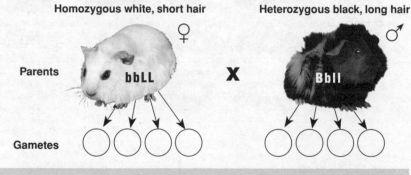

**Homozygous white, short hair** ♀

**Heterozygous black, long hair** ♂

Parents    **bbLL**    X    **Bbll**

Gametes

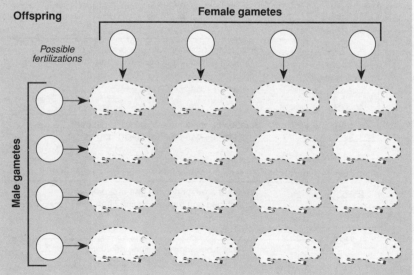

Offspring                    **Female gametes**

*Possible fertilizations*

Male gametes

# Sex Determination

The determination of the sex (gender) of an organism is controlled in most cases by the sex chromosomes provided by each parent. These have evolved to regulate the ratios of males and females produced and preserve the genetic differences between the sexes. In humans, males are referred to as the **heterogametic sex** because each somatic cell has one X chromosome and one Y chromosome. The determination of sex is based on the presence or absence of the Y chromosome. Without the Y chromosome, an individual will develop into a **homogametic** female (each somatic cell with two X chromosomes). In mammals, the male is always the heterogametic sex, but this is not necessarily the case in other taxa. In birds and butterflies, the female is the heterogametic sex, and in some insects the male is simply X whereas the female is XX.

## Sex Determination in Humans

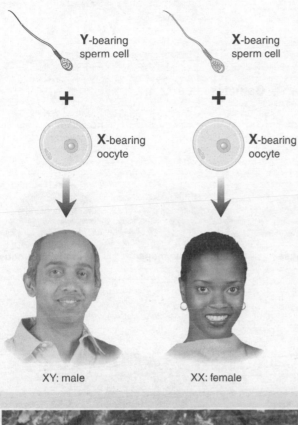

Y-bearing sperm cell    X-bearing sperm cell

+    +

X-bearing oocyte    X-bearing oocyte

XY: male    XX: female

## The Sex Determining Region of the Y Chromosome

Scientists have known since 1959 that the Y chromosome is associated with being male. However, it was not until 1990 that a group of researchers, working for the Medical Research Council in London, discovered the gene on the Y chromosome that determines maleness. It was named **SRY**, for **Sex Determining Region of the Y**. The SRY gene produces a type of protein called a **transcription factor**. This transcription factor switches on the genes that direct the development of male structures in the embryo.

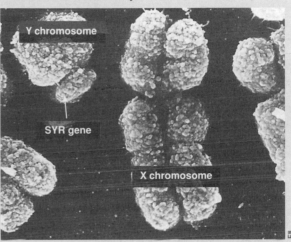

Y chromosome

SYR gene

X chromosome

Smaller and darker female half

Larger and lighter male half

**Gynandromorphism** occurs when an animal is a genetic mosaic and possesses both male and female characteristics (i.e. some of its cells are genetically male and others are female). This phenomenon is found particularly in insects, but also appears in birds and mammals. Gynandromorphism occurs due to the loss of an X chromosome in a stem cell of a female (XX), so that all the tissues derived from that cell are phenotypically male.

In the pill woodlouse, *Armadillium vulgare*, sex determination is characterized by female heterogamety (ZW) and male homogamety (ZZ). However, in several wild populations this system is overridden by an infectious bacterium. This bacterium causes genetically male woodlice to change into females. The bacteria are transmitted through the egg cytoplasm of the woodlouse. Therefore the conversion of males to females increases the propagation of the bacterium.

1. Explain what determines the sex of the offspring at the moment of conception in humans: _____

_____

2. Explain why human males are called the heterogametic sex: _____

_____

# Lethal Alleles

Lethal alleles are mutations of a gene that produce a gene product, which is not only nonfunctional, but may affect the organism's survival. Some lethal alleles are fully dominant and kill in one dose in the heterozygote. Others, such as in the **Manx** cat and yellow mice (below), produce viable offspring with a recognizable phenotype in the heterozygote. In some lethal alleles, the lethality is fully recessive and the alleles confer no detectable effect in the heterozygote at all. Furthermore, lethal alleles may take effect at different stages in development (e.g. in juveniles or, as in **Huntington disease**, in adults).

When **Lucien Cuenot** investigated inheritance of coat color in yellow mice in 1905, he reported a peculiar pattern. When he mated two yellow mice, about $^2/_3$ of their offspring were yellow, and $^1/_3$ were non-yellow. This was a departure from the expected Mendelian ratio of 3:1. A test cross of the yellow offspring showed that they were all heterozygous.

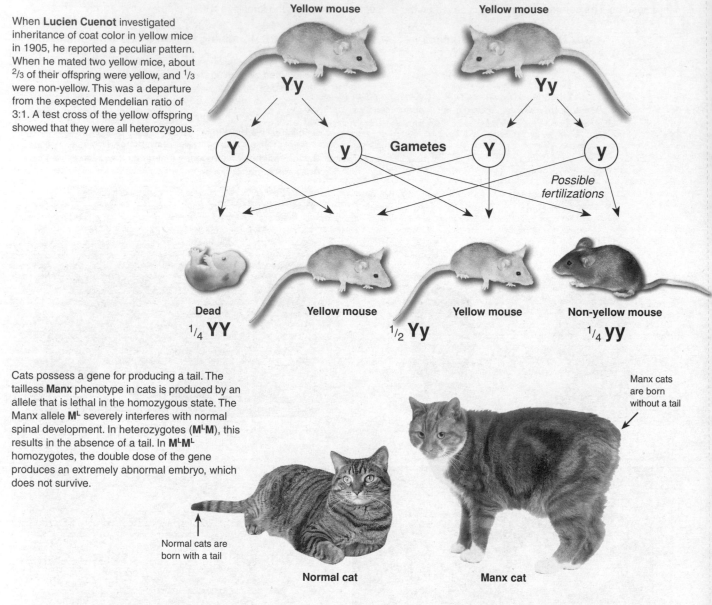

Yellow mouse — **Yy**    Yellow mouse — **Yy**

Gametes: **Y**  **y**   **Y**  **y**

Possible fertilizations

Dead — $^1/_4$ **YY**    Yellow mouse / Yellow mouse — $^1/_2$ **Yy**    Non-yellow mouse — $^1/_4$ **yy**

Cats possess a gene for producing a tail. The tailless **Manx** phenotype in cats is produced by an allele that is lethal in the homozygous state. The Manx allele **M$^L$** severely interferes with normal spinal development. In heterozygotes (**M$^L$M**), this results in the absence of a tail. In **M$^L$M$^L$** homozygotes, the double dose of the gene produces an extremely abnormal embryo, which does not survive.

Manx cats are born without a tail

Normal cats are born with a tail

Normal cat    Manx cat

1. Distinguish between recessive lethal alleles and dominant lethal alleles: _____

_____

_____

2. In Manx cats, the allele for taillessness (**M$^L$**) is incompletely dominant over the recessive allele for normal tail (**M**). Tailless Manx cats are heterozygous (**M$^L$M**) and carry a recessive allele for normal tail. Normal tailed cats are **MM**. A cross between two Manx (tailless) cats, produces two Manx to every one normal tailed cat (not a regular 3 to 1 Mendelian ratio).

(a) State the genotypes arising from this type of cross: _____

(b) State the phenotype ratio of Manx to normal cats and explain why it is not the expected 3:1 ratio: _____

_____

3. Explain why Huntington disease persists in the human population when it is caused by a lethal, dominant allele:

_____

_____

**Related activities**: Dominance of Alleles, Examples of Gene Mutations, Genetic Counseling

 © Biozone International 2001-2008
**Photocopying Prohibited**

# Problems in Mendelian Genetics

The following problems involve Mendelian crosses through to the $F_2$ generation. The alleles involved are associated with various phenotypic traits in domestic breeds. See *Basic Genetic Crosses* if you need to review test crosses and back crosses.

1. The Himalayan color-pointed, long-haired cat is a breed developed by crossing a pedigree (true-breeding), uniform-colored, long-haired Persian with a pedigree color-pointed (darker face, ears, paws, and tail) short-haired Siamese.
   The genes controlling hair coloring and length are on separate chromosomes: uniform color **U**, color pointed **u**, short hair **S**, long hair **s**.

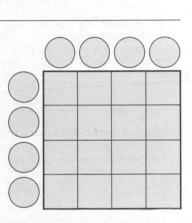

Persian          Siamese          Himalayan

   (a) Using the symbols above, indicate the genotype of each breed below its photograph (above, right). _____ _____ _____

   (b) State the genotype of the $F_1$ (Siamese X Persian): _____

   (c) State the phenotype of the $F_1$: _____

   (d) Use the Punnett square to show the outcome of a cross between the $F_1$ (the $F_2$):

   (e) State the ratio of the $F_2$ that would be Himalayan: _____

   (f) State whether the Himalayan would be true breeding: _____

   (g) State the ratio of the $F_2$ that would be color-point, short-haired cats: _____

   (h) Explain how two $F_2$ cats of the same phenotype could have different genotypes:

   _____

   _____

   (i) Explain how you could determine which of the $F_2$ color-point, short-hairs were true breeding for these characters:

   _____

   _____

2. In rabbits, spotted coat **S** is dominant to solid color **s**, while for coat color: black **B** is dominant to brown **b**. A brown spotted rabbit is mated with a solid black one and all the offspring are black spotted (the genes are not linked).

   (a) State the genotypes: Male parent: _____ Female parent: _____ Offspring: _____

   (b) Use the Punnett square to show the outcome of a cross between the $F_1$ (the $F_2$):

   (c) Using ratios, state the phenotypes of the $F_2$ generation: _____

   _____

   (d) State the name given to this type of cross: _____

3. In guinea pigs, rough coat **R** is dominant over smooth coat **r** and black coat **B** is dominant over white **b**. The genes for coat texture and color are not linked. In a cross of a homozygous rough black animal with a homozygous smooth white:

   (a) State the genotype of the $F_1$: _____

   (b) State the phenotype of the $F_1$: _____

   (c) Use the Punnett square to show the outcome of a cross between the $F_1$ (the $F_2$):

   (d) Using ratios, state the phenotypes of the $F_2$ generation:

   _____

   _____

   _____

**Related activities**: Basic Genetic Crosses, Dominance of Alleles, Lethal Alleles
**Web links**: Drag and Drop Genetics

RA 3

(e) Use the Punnett square (right) to show the outcome of a cross between the offspring of a **back cross** of the $F_1$ to the rough, black parent:

(f) Using ratios, state the phenotype of the $F_2$ generation:

_____

(g) Use the Punnett square to show the outcome of a cross between the offspring of a **test cross** of the $F_1$ to the smooth, white parent:

(h) Using ratios, state the phenotypes of the $F_2$ generation:

_____

_____

_____

(i) A rough black guinea pig was crossed with a rough white one produced the following offspring: 28 rough black, 31 rough white, 11 smooth black, and 10 smooth white. Determine the genotypes of the parents:

_____

_____

4. Chickens with shortened wings and legs are called creepers. When creepers are mated to normal birds, they produce creepers and normals with equal frequency. When creepers are mated to creepers they produce two creepers to one normal. Crosses between normal birds produce only normal progeny. Explain these results:

_____

_____

5. Black wool of sheep is due to a recessive allele (**b**), and white wool to its dominant allele (**B**). A white ram is crossed to a white ewe. Both animals carry the allele for black (b). They produce a white ram lamb, which is then back crossed to the female parent. Determine the probability of the **back cross** offspring being black:

_____

6. Mallard ducks have their plumage color controlled by a gene with three alleles: $M^R$ restricted mallard pattern, **M** mallard pattern, and **m** dusky mallard pattern. The dominance hierarchy is: $M^R > M > m$ (i.e. $M^R$ is more dominant than **M**, which is more dominant than **m**). Determine the genotypic and phenotypic ratios expected in the $F_1$ of the following crosses:

(a) $M^R M^R$ X $M^R M$: Genotypes: _____

Phenotypes: _____

(b) $M^R M^R$ X $M^R m$: Genotypes: _____

Phenotypes: _____

(c) $M^R M$ X $M^R m$: Genotypes: _____

Phenotypes: _____

(d) $M^R m$ X Mm: Genotypes: _____

Phenotypes: _____

(e) Mm X mm: Genotypes: _____

Phenotypes: _____

7. A dominant gene (**W**) produces wire-haired texture in dogs; its recessive allele (**w**) produces smooth hair. A group of heterozygous wire-haired individuals are crossed and their $F_1$ progeny are then test-crossed. Determine the expected genotypic and phenotypic ratios among the **test cross** progeny:

_____

_____

# Dihybrid Cross with Linkage

In a normal case of Mendelian dihybrid inheritance with independent assortment of alleles, a cross between two heterozygotes produces the expected 9:3:3:1 ratio in the offspring. In cases of dihybrid inheritance involving linkage, the offspring of a cross between two heterozygotes produces a 3:1 ratio of the parental types with no recombinants. However, because total linkage is uncommon, this 3:1 ratio is rarely achieved. Most dihybrid crosses involving linkage produce equal numbers of parental types and a significantly smaller number of recombinants. The examples below show the inheritance of body color and wing shape in *Drosophila*. The genes for these two characters are linked and do not assort independently. The example on the left shows the expected phenotype ratios from a mating between heterozygotes without crossing over. The example on the right shows the results of a test cross involving recombination of alleles. A test cross reveals the frequency of recombination for the gene involved (see the activity: *Chromosome Mapping*).

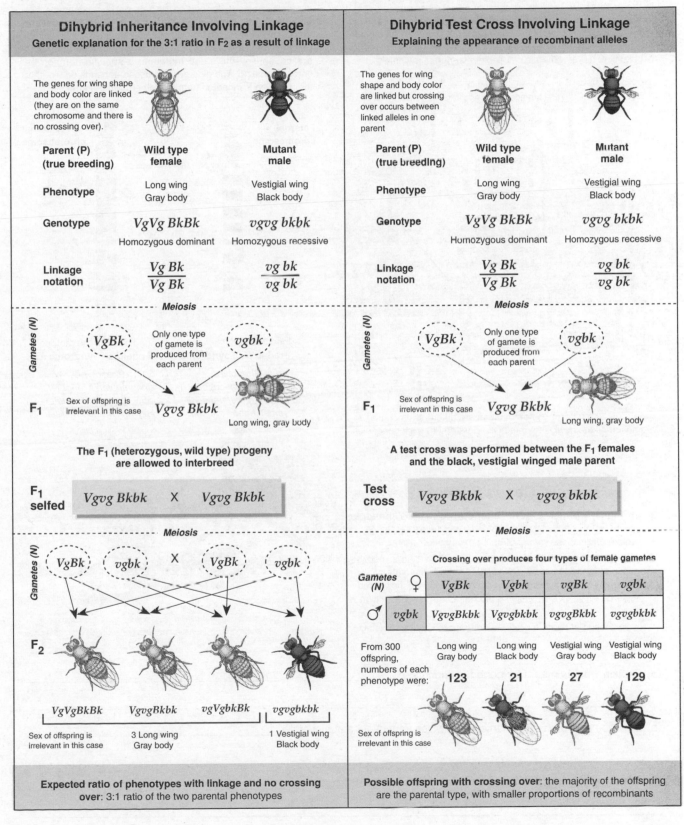

## Dihybrid Inheritance Involving Linkage
### Genetic explanation for the 3:1 ratio in F₂ as a result of linkage

The genes for wing shape and body color are linked (they are on the same chromosome and there is no crossing over).

| | Wild type female | Mutant male |
|---|---|---|
| **Parent (P)** (true breeding) | | |
| **Phenotype** | Long wing Gray body | Vestigial wing Black body |
| **Genotype** | *VgVg BkBk* Homozygous dominant | *vgvg bkbk* Homozygous recessive |
| **Linkage notation** | $\frac{Vg\ Bk}{Vg\ Bk}$ | $\frac{vg\ bk}{vg\ bk}$ |

- - - Meiosis - - -

**Gametes (N):** *VgBk* ... *vgbk*

Only one type of gamete is produced from each parent

**F₁** — Sex of offspring is irrelevant in this case — *Vgvg Bkbk*

Long wing, gray body

**The F₁ (heterozygous, wild type) progeny are allowed to interbreed**

**F₁ selfed:** *Vgvg Bkbk* X *Vgvg Bkbk*

- - - Meiosis - - -

**Gametes (N):** *VgBk* *vgbk* X *VgBk* *vgbk*

**F₂:**

*VgVgBkBk* — *VgvgBkbk* — *vgVgbkBk* — *vgvgbkbk*

Sex of offspring is irrelevant in this case | 3 Long wing Gray body | 1 Vestigial wing Black body

**Expected ratio of phenotypes with linkage and no crossing over:** 3:1 ratio of the two parental phenotypes

## Dihybrid Test Cross Involving Linkage
### Explaining the appearance of recombinant alleles

The genes for wing shape and body color are linked but crossing over occurs between linked alleles in one parent

| | Wild type female | Mutant male |
|---|---|---|
| **Parent (P)** (true breeding) | | |
| **Phenotype** | Long wing Gray body | Vestigial wing Black body |
| **Genotype** | *VgVg BkBk* Homozygous dominant | *vgvg bkbk* Homozygous recessive |
| **Linkage notation** | $\frac{Vg\ Bk}{Vg\ Bk}$ | $\frac{vg\ bk}{vg\ bk}$ |

- - - Meiosis - - -

**Gametes (N):** *VgBk* ... *vgbk*

Only one type of gamete is produced from each parent

**F₁** — Sex of offspring is irrelevant in this case — *Vgvg Bkbk*

Long wing, gray body

**A test cross was performed between the F₁ females and the black, vestigial winged male parent**

**Test cross:** *Vgvg Bkbk* X *vgvg bkbk*

- - - Meiosis - - -

**Crossing over produces four types of female gametes**

| Gametes (N) ♀ | *VgBk* | *Vgbk* | *vgBk* | *vgbk* |
|---|---|---|---|---|
| ♂ *vgbk* | *VgvgBkbk* | *Vgvgbkbk* | *vgvgBkbk* | *vgvgbkbk* |

From 300 offspring, numbers of each phenotype were:

| | Long wing Gray body | Long wing Black body | Vestigial wing Gray body | Vestigial wing Black body |
|---|---|---|---|---|
| | **123** | **21** | **27** | **129** |

Sex of offspring is irrelevant in this case

**Possible offspring with crossing over:** the majority of the offspring are the parental type, with smaller proportions of recombinants

1. Calculate the crossover (value) for the offspring of the test cross, above: _____

**Related activities:** Dihybrid Cross, Recombination, Chromosome Mapping

**RDA 2**

# Genomic Imprinting

The phenotypic effects of some mammalian genes depend on whether they were inherited from the mother or the father. This phenomenon, called **genomic imprinting** (or parental imprinting), is part of **epigenetics**, the study of the heritable changes in gene function that occur without involving changes in the DNA sequence. Just as cells inherit genes, they also inherit the instructions that communicate to the genes when to become active, in which tissue, and to what extent. Epigenetic phenomena are important because they regulate when and at what level genes are expressed.

## Genomic Imprinting

**Genomic imprinting** describes how a small subset of the genes in the genome are expressed according to their parent of origin. 'Imprints' can act as silencers or activators for imprinted genes. A mammal inherits two sets of chromosomes, one from the mother and one from the father. In this way the imprinted gene expression is balanced; a prerequisite for a viable offspring in mammals.

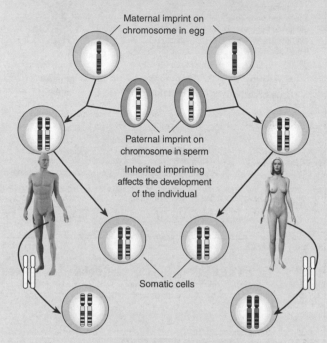

Maternal imprint on chromosome in egg

Paternal imprint on chromosome in sperm

Inherited imprinting affects the development of the individual

Somatic cells

Maternal and paternal chromosomes are differently imprinted. Chromosomes are newly imprinted (reprogrammed) each generation.

## Imprinted Genes Are Different

Some imprinted genes are expressed from a maternally inherited chromosome and **silenced** on the paternal chromosome, while other imprinted genes show the opposite expression pattern and are only expressed from a paternally inherited chromosome. Evidence of this is seen in two human genetic disorders. Both are caused by the same mutation; a specific deletion on chromosome 15. The disorder expressed depends on whether the mutation is inherited from the father or the mother.

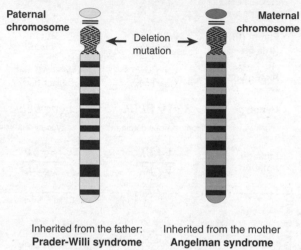

Paternal chromosome ← Deletion mutation → Maternal chromosome

Inherited from the father: **Prader-Willi syndrome**

*Phenotype:*
*Mental retardation, obesity, short stature, unusually small hands and feet*

Inherited from the mother **Angelman syndrome**

*Phenotype Uncontrollable laughter, jerky movements, motor and mental abnormalities*

## How Are Genes Silenced?

- In many instances, **gene silencing** achieved through **methylation** of the DNA of genes or regulatory sequences, which results in the gene not being expressed.

- **Methylation** turns off gene expression by adding a methyl group to cytosines in the DNA. This changes the state of the chromatin so that the expression of any genes in the methylated region is inhibited. Methylation is also important in X-inactivation.

- In other instances, phosphorylation or other chemical modification of histone proteins appears to lead to silencing.

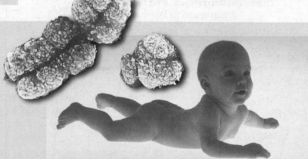

*Which genes did you inherit from your mother and which from your father? For some genes, imprinting will affect phenotypic expression.*

1. (a) Explain what is meant by genomic imprinting: _____

_____

(b) Describe one of the mechanisms by which imprinting is achieved: _____

_____

2. Explain the significance of imprinting to the inheritance of genes: _____

_____

_____

# Human Genotypes

An estimated 25 000 genes determine all human **traits**. While most traits are determined by more than one gene, a number are determined by a single gene system, with dominant/recessive, codominant, or multiple allele inheritance. Single gene traits (below) show **discontinuous variation** in a population, with individuals showing only one of a limited number of phenotypes (usually two or three). Single gene traits may, however, show variable **penetrance**. Penetrance describes the extent to which the properties controlled by a gene will be expressed. Highly penetrant genes will be expressed regardless of the effects of the environment, whereas a gene with low penetrance will only sometimes produce the trait with which it is associated.

## Trait: Handedness

| Dominant | Recessive |
| --- | --- |

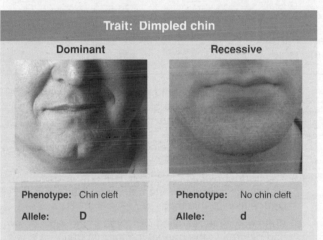

| | |
| --- | --- |
| Phenotype: Right-handed | Phenotype: Left-handed |
| Allele: **R** | Allele: **r** |

The trait of left or right handedness is genetically determined. Right-handed people have the dominant allele, while left handedness is recessive. People that consider themselves ambidextrous can assume they have the dominant allele for this trait.

## Trait: Hand clasp

| Dominant | Recessive |
| --- | --- |

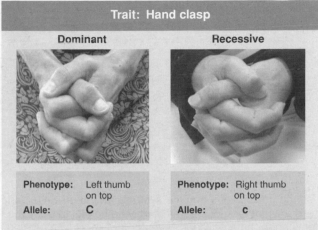

| | |
| --- | --- |
| Phenotype: Left thumb on top | Phenotype: Right thumb on top |
| Allele: **C** | Allele: **c** |

Like handedness, hand clasping shows dominance/recessiveness. When the hands are clasped together, either the left or the right thumb will naturally come to rest on top. The left thumb on top is the dominant trait (C), while the right thumb on top is recessive (c).

## Trait: Dimpled chin

| Dominant | Recessive |
| --- | --- |

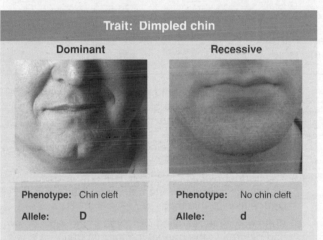

| | |
| --- | --- |
| Phenotype: Chin cleft | Phenotype: No chin cleft |
| Allele: **D** | Allele: **d** |

A cleft or dimple on the chin is inherited. A cleft is dominant (D), while the absence of a cleft is recessive (d), although this gene shows **variable penetrance**, probably as a result of modifier genes.

## Trait: Middle digit hair

| Dominant | Recessive |
| --- | --- |

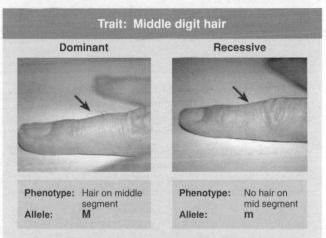

| | |
| --- | --- |
| Phenotype: Hair on middle segment | Phenotype: No hair on mid segment |
| Allele: **M** | Allele: **m** |

Some people have a dominant allele that causes hair to grow on the middle segment of their fingers. It may not be present on all fingers, and in some cases may be very fine and hard to see.

## Trait: Ear lobe shape

| Dominant | Recessive |
| --- | --- |

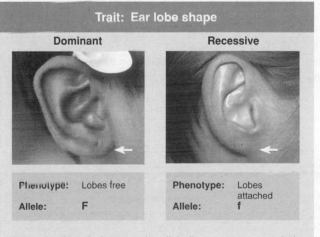

| | |
| --- | --- |
| Phenotype: Lobes free | Phenotype: Lobes attached |
| Allele: **F** | Allele: **f** |

In people with only the recessive allele (homozygous recessive), ear lobes are attached to the side of the face. The presence of a dominant allele causes the ear lobe to hang freely.

## Trait: Thumb hyperextension

| Dominant | Recessive |
| --- | --- |

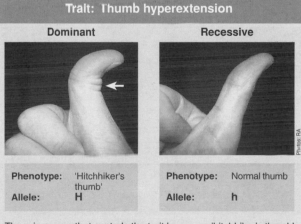

| | |
| --- | --- |
| Phenotype: 'Hitchhiker's thumb' | Phenotype: Normal thumb |
| Allele: **H** | Allele: **h** |

There is a gene that controls the trait known as 'hitchhiker's thumb' which is technically termed distal hyperextensibility. People with the dominant phenotype are able to curve their thumb backwards without assistance, so that it forms an arc shape.

**Related activities**: Polygenes

# Your Genotype Profile

Use the descriptions and the symbols on the previous page to determine your own genotype. In situations where you exhibit the dominant form of the trait, it may be helpful to study the features of your family to determine whether you are homozygous dominant or heterozygous. If you do not know whether you are heterozygous for a given trait, assume you are.

| Your traits: | Thumb | Ear lobes | Chin cleft | Middle digit hair | Handedness | Hand clasp |
|---|---|---|---|---|---|---|
| Phenotype: | | | | | | |
| Genotype: | | | | | | |

1. Enter the details of your own genotype in the table above. The row: 'Phenotype' requires that you write down the version of the trait that is expressed in you (e.g. chin cleft). Each genotype should contain two alleles.

2. Use a piece of paper and cut out 12 squares. Write the symbols for your alleles listed in the table above (each of the two alleles on two separate squares for the six traits) and write your initials on the back.

3. Move about the class, shaking hands with other class members to simulate mating (this interaction does not have to be with a member of the opposite sex).

4. Proceed to determine the possible genotypes and phenotypes for your offspring with this other person by:

   (a) Selecting each of the six characters in turn

   (b) Where a genotype for a person is known to be

homozygous (dominant or recessive) that person will simply place down one of the pieces of paper with their allele for that gene. If they are heterozygous for this trait, toss a coin to determine which gets 'donated' with heads being the dominant allele and tails being the recessive.

   (c) The partner places their allele using the same method as in (b) above to determine their contribution to this trait.

   (d) Write down the resulting genotype in the table below and determine the phenotype for that trait.

   (e) Proceed on to the next trait.

5. Try another mating with a different partner or the same partner and see if you end up with a child of the same phenotype.

| Child 1 | Thumb | Ear lobes | Chin cleft | Middle digit hair | Handedness | Hand clasp |
|---|---|---|---|---|---|---|
| Phenotype: | | | | | | |
| Genotype: | | | | | | |

| Child 2 | Thumb | Ear lobes | Chin cleft | Middle digit hair | Handedness | Hand clasp |
|---|---|---|---|---|---|---|
| Phenotype: | | | | | | |
| Genotype: | | | | | | |

# Sex Linkage

**Sex linkage** is a special case of linkage occurring when a gene is located on a sex chromosome (usually the X). The result of this is that the character encoded by the gene is usually seen only in one sex (the heterogametic sex) and occurs rarely in the homogametic sex. In humans, recessive sex linked genes are responsible for a number of heritable disorders in males, e.g. hemophilia. Women who have the recessive allele are said to be **carriers**. One of the gene loci controlling coat color in cats is sex-linked. The two alleles, red (for orange color) and non-red (for black color), are found only on the X-chromosome.

| Allele types | Genotypes | Phenotypes |
|---|---|---|
| $X_o$ = Non-red (=black) | $X_oX_o$, $X_oY$ = | Black coated female, male |
| $X_O$ = Red | $X_OX_O$, $X_OY$ = | Orange coated female, male |
| | $X_oX_O$ = | Tortoiseshell (intermingled black and orange in fur) in female cats only |

1. An owner of a cat is thinking of mating her black female cat with an orange male cat. Before she does this, she would like to know what possible coat colors could result from such a cross. Use the symbols above to fill in the diagram on the right. Summarize the possible genotypes and phenotypes of the kittens in the tables below.

|  | **Genotypes** | **Phenotypes** |
|---|---|---|
| Male kittens | | |
| Female kittens | | |

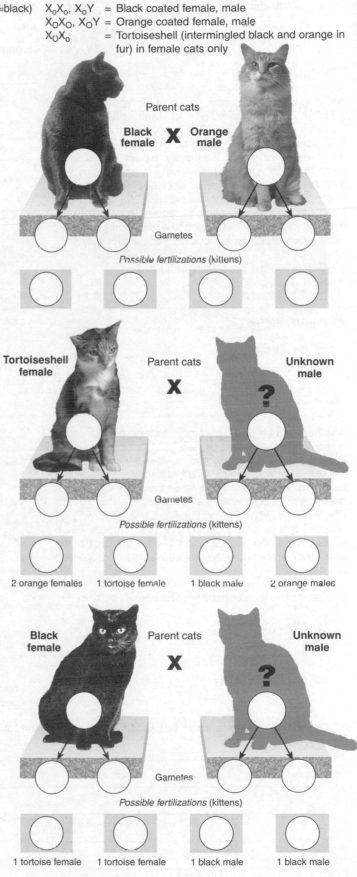

Parent cats

**Black female** X **Orange male**

Gametes

*Possible fertilizations* (kittens)

2. A female tortoiseshell cat mated with an unknown male cat in the neighborhood and has given birth to a litter of six kittens. The owner of this female cat wants to know what the appearance and the genotype of the father was of these kittens. Use the symbols above to fill in the diagram on the right. Also show the possible fertilizations by placing appropriate arrows.

Describe the father cat's:

(a) Genotype: _____

(b) Phenotype: _____

**Tortoiseshell female** Parent cats **Unknown male**

**X** **?**

Gametes

*Possible fertilizations* (kittens)

2 orange females    1 tortoise female    1 black male    2 orange males

3. The owner of another cat, a black female, also wants to know which cat fathered her two tortoiseshell female and two black male kittens. Use the symbols above to fill in the diagram on the right. Show the possible fertilizations by placing appropriate arrows.

Describe the father cat's:

(a) Genotype: _____

(b) Phenotype: _____

(c) Was it the same male cat that fathered both this litter and the one above?
**YES / NO** *(delete one)*

**Black female** Parent cats **Unknown male**

**X** **?**

Gametes

*Possible fertilizations* (kittens)

1 tortoise female    1 tortoise female    1 black male    1 black male

### Dominant allele in humans

A rare form of rickets in humans is determined by a **dominant** allele of a gene on the **X chromosome** (it is not found on the Y chromosome). This condition is not successfully treated with vitamin D therapy. The allele types, genotypes, and phenotypes are as follows:

| Allele types | Genotypes | Phenotypes |
|---|---|---|
| $X_R$ = affected by rickets | $X_R X_R$, $X_R X$ = | Affected female |
| X = normal | $X_R Y$ = | Affected male |
| | XX, XY = | Normal female, male |

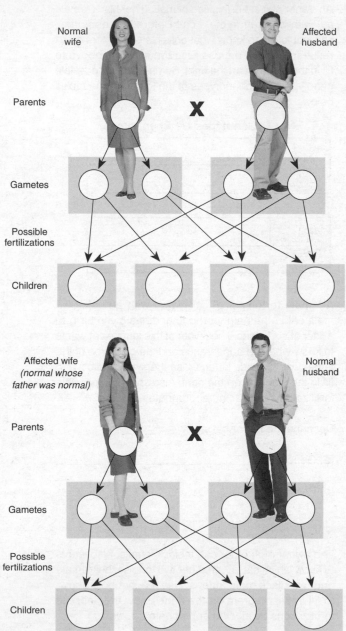

As a genetic counselor you are presented with a married couple where one of them has a family history of this disease. The husband is affected by this disease and the wife is normal. The couple, who are thinking of starting a family, would like to know what their chances are of having a child born with this condition. They would also like to know what the probabilities are of having an affected boy or affected girl. Use the symbols above to complete the diagram right and determine the probabilities stated below (expressed as a proportion or percentage).

4. Determine the probability of having:

   (a) Affected children: _____

   (b) An affected girl: _____

   (c) An affected boy: _____

Another couple with a family history of the same disease also come in to see you to obtain genetic counseling. In this case the husband is normal and the wife is affected. The wife's father was not affected by this disease. Determine what their chances are of having a child born with this condition. They would also like to know what the probabilities are of having an affected boy or affected girl. Use the symbols above to complete the diagram right and determine the probabilities stated below (expressed as a proportion or percentage).

5. Determine the probability of having:

   (a) Affected children: _____

   (b) An affected girl: _____

   (c) An affected boy: _____

6. Describing examples other than those above, discuss the role of **sex linkage** in the inheritance of genetic disorders:

_____

_____

_____

_____

_____

# Inheritance Patterns

Complete the following monohybrid crosses for different types of inheritance patterns in humans: autosomal recessive, autosomal dominant, sex linked recessive, and sex linked dominant inheritance.

1. **Inheritance of autosomal recessive traits**
   Example: *Albinism*

   Albinism (lack of pigment in hair, eyes and skin) is inherited as an autosomal recessive allele (not sex-linked).

   Using the codes: **PP** (normal)
   **Pp** (carrier)
   **pp** (albino)

   (a) Enter the parent phenotypes and complete the Punnett square for a cross between two carrier genotypes.

   (b) Give the ratios for the phenotypes from this cross.

   Phenotype ratios: _____

   _____

2. **Inheritance of autosomal dominant traits**
   Example: *Woolly hair*

   Woolly hair is inherited as an autosomal dominant allele. Each affected individual will have at least one affected parent.

   Using the codes: **WW** (woolly hair)
   **Ww** (woolly hair, heterozygous)
   **ww** (normal hair)

   (a) Enter the parent phenotypes and complete the Punnett square for a cross between two heterozygous individuals.

   (b) Give the ratios for the phenotypes from this cross.

   Phenotype ratios: _____

   _____

3. **Inheritance of sex linked recessive traits**
   Example: *Hemophilia*

   Inheritance of hemophilia is sex linked. Males with the recessive (hemophilia) allele, are affected. Females can be carriers.

   Using the codes: **XX** (normal female)
   **XX_h** (carrier female)
   **X_hX_h** (hemophiliac female)
   **XY** (normal male)
   **X_hY** (hemophiliac male)

   (a) Enter the parent phenotypes and complete the Punnett square for a cross between a normal male and a carrier female.

   (b) Give the ratios for the phenotypes from this cross:

   Phenotype ratios: _____

   _____

4. **Inheritance of sex linked dominant traits**
   Example: *Sex linked form of rickets*

   A rare form of rickets is inherited on the X chromosome.

   Using the codes: **XX** (normal female); **XY** (normal male)
   **X_RX** (affected heterozygote female)
   **X_RX_R** (affected female)
   **X_RY** (affected male)

   (a) Enter the parent phenotypes and complete the Punnett square for a cross between an affected male and heterozygous female.

   (b) Give the ratios for the phenotypes from this cross.

   Phenotype ratios: _____

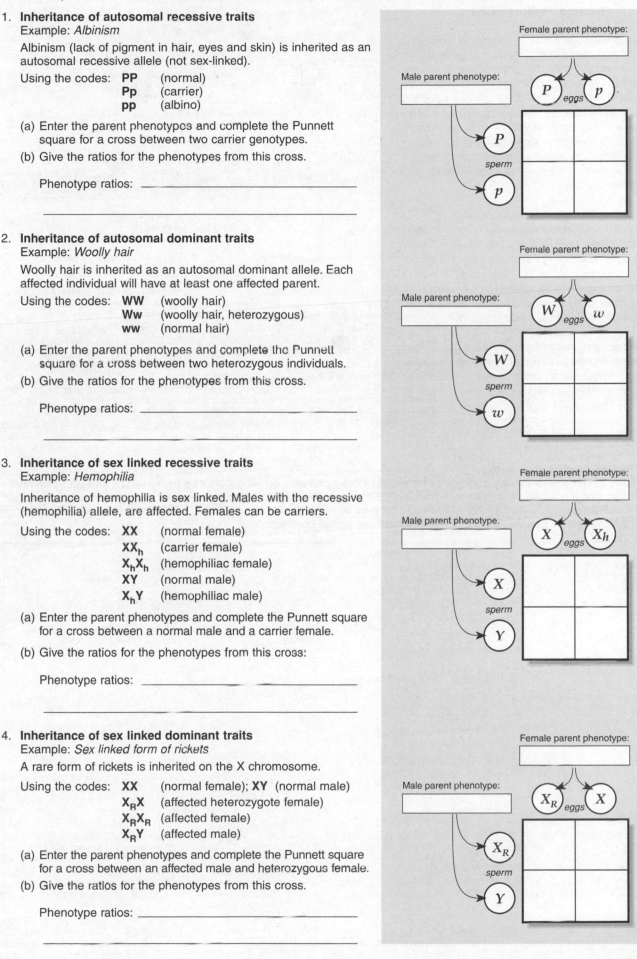

**Related activities**: Monohybrid Cross, Sex Linkage

# Pedigree Analysis

## Sample Pedigree Chart

Pedigree charts are a way of graphically illustrating inheritance patterns over a number of generations. They are used to study the inheritance of genetic disorders. The key (below the chart) should be consulted to make sense of the various symbols. Particular individuals are identified by their generation number and their order number in that generation. For example, **II-6** is the sixth person in the second row. The arrow indicates the **propositus**; the person through whom the pedigree was discovered (i.e. who reported the condition).

If the chart on the right were illustrating a human family tree, it would represent three generations: grandparents (I-1 and I-2) with three sons and one daughter. Two of the sons (II-3 and II-4) are identical twins, but did not marry or have any children. The other son (II-1) married and had a daughter and another child (sex unknown). The daughter (II-5) married and had two sons and two daughters (plus a child that died in infancy).

For the particular trait being studied, the grandfather was expressing the phenotype (showing the trait) and the grandmother was a carrier. One of their sons and one of their daughters also show the trait, together with one of their granddaughters.

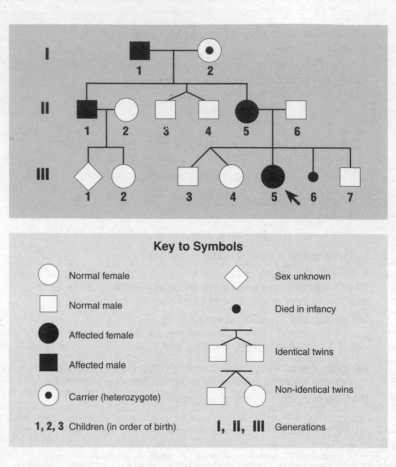

### Key to Symbols

- ○ Normal female
- □ Normal male
- ● Affected female
- ■ Affected male
- ⊙ Carrier (heterozygote)
- ◇ Sex unknown
- • Died in infancy
- Identical twins
- Non-identical twins
- **1, 2, 3** Children (in order of birth)
- **I, II, III** Generations

1. **Pedigree chart of your family**

   Using the symbols in the key above and the example illustrated as a guide, construct a pedigree chart of your own family (or one that you know of) starting with the parents of your mother and/or father on the first line. Your parents will appear on the second line (II) and you will appear on the third line (III). There may be a fourth generation line (IV) if one of your brothers or sisters has had a child. Use a ruler to draw up the chart carefully.

**Related activities**: Sex Linkage, Inheritance Patterns

2. The pedigree chart below illustrates the inheritance of a trait (darker symbols) in two families joined in marriage.

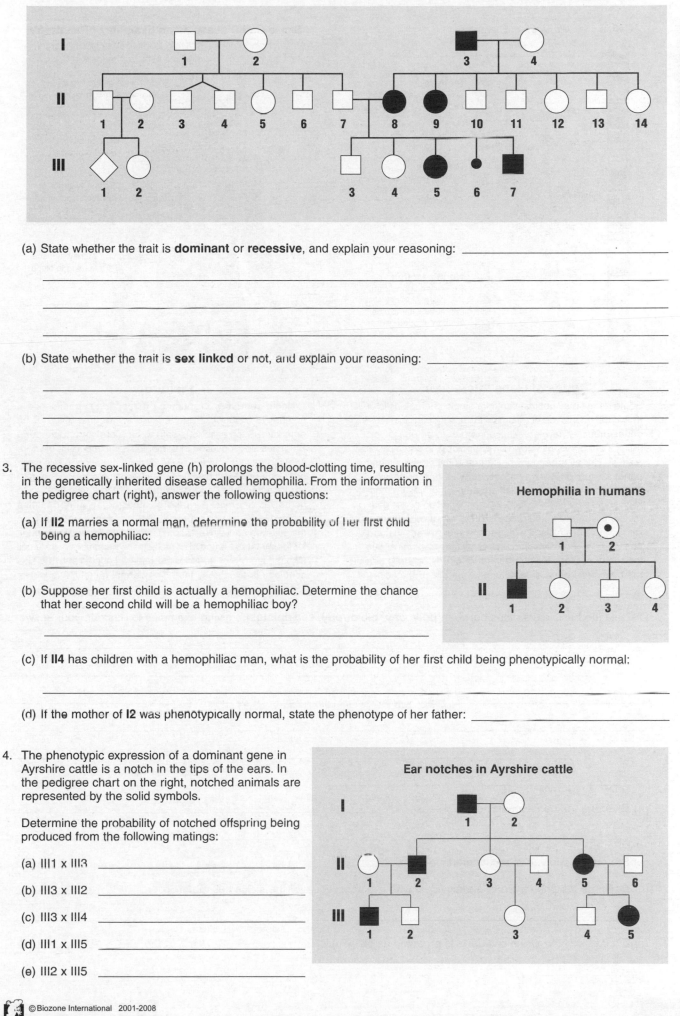

(a) State whether the trait is **dominant** or **recessive**, and explain your reasoning: _____

_____

_____

_____

(b) State whether the trait is **sex linked** or not, and explain your reasoning: _____

_____

_____

_____

3. The recessive sex-linked gene (h) prolongs the blood-clotting time, resulting in the genetically inherited disease called hemophilia. From the information in the pedigree chart (right), answer the following questions:

**Hemophilia in humans**

(a) If **II2** marries a normal man, determine the probability of her first child being a hemophiliac:

_____

(b) Suppose her first child is actually a hemophiliac. Determine the chance that her second child will be a hemophiliac boy?

_____

(c) If **II4** has children with a hemophiliac man, what is the probability of her first child being phenotypically normal:

_____

(d) If the mother of **I2** was phenotypically normal, state the phenotype of her father: _____

4. The phenotypic expression of a dominant gene in Ayrshire cattle is a notch in the tips of the ears. In the pedigree chart on the right, notched animals are represented by the solid symbols.

**Ear notches in Ayrshire cattle**

Determine the probability of notched offspring being produced from the following matings:

(a) III1 x III3 _____

(b) III3 x III2 _____

(c) III3 x III4 _____

(d) III1 x III5 _____

(e) III2 x III5 _____

# Interactions Between Genes

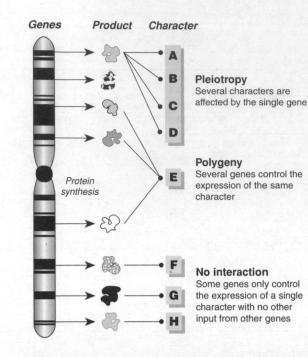

Genes    Product    Character

A
B    **Pleiotropy**
C     Several characters are
D     affected by the single gene

Protein synthesis

E    **Polygeny**
    Several genes control the
    expression of the same
    character

F
G    **No interaction**
H     Some genes only control
    the expression of a single
    character with no other
    input from other genes

### Sickle Cell Disease as an Example of Pleiotropy

A person homozygous ($Hb^SHb^S$) for the sickle cell allele produces mutant hemoglobin. This affects a number of organs.

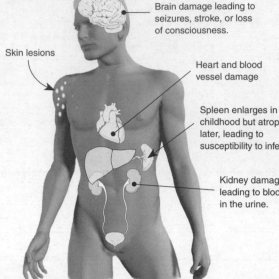

Skin lesions

Brain damage leading to seizures, stroke, or loss of consciousness.

Heart and blood vessel damage

Spleen enlarges in childhood but atrophies later, leading to susceptibility to infection.

Kidney damage leading to blood in the urine.

## Types of Gene Interaction

Some genes may not just control a single characteristic or trait in the phenotype of an organism. It is thought that most genes probably have an effect on one or more phenotypic traits, a phenomenon known as **pleiotropy**. In some cases a single characteristic may be controlled by more than one gene; a situation known as **polygeny**. A further possible type of gene interaction, called **epistasis**, involves two non-allelic genes (at different loci), where the action of one gene masks or otherwise alters the expression of other genes. An example is albinism, which appears in rodents that are homozygous recessive for color even if they have the alleles for agouti or black fur (the gene for color is epistatic and the hypostatic gene determines the nature of the color).

## Pleiotropy

A single gene may produce a product that can influence a number of traits or characteristics in the phenotype of an organism. Such a gene is said to be **pleiotropic**. The gene Hb codes for production of hemoglobin, an important oxygen-carrying molecule in the blood. A point mutation to this gene produces sickle cell disease. The phenotype has poor oxygen-carrying capability and deformed red blood cells leading to hemolytic anemia. A range of other organ abnormalities (above) also occur as a result of the mutant hemoglobin. In the diagram above, $Hb^S$ stands for the single gene that codes for the mutated hemoglobin molecule. A person with sickle cell disease is homozygous for the mutated allele $Hb^SHb^S$. This condition is eventually fatal. The normal genotype is HbHb.

1. Discuss the basic differences between **polygeny**, **pleiotropy**, and **epistasis**, giving examples to illustrate your answer:

_____

_____

_____

_____

_____

_____

2. (a) Describe the cause of sickle cell disease: _____

_____

(b) State the genotype of an affected individual: _____

(c) Describe the phenotype of an individual who is homozygous for the sickle cell mutation: _____

_____

(d) Explain why the sickle cell gene is regarded as pleiotropic: _____

_____

**Related activities**: Sickle Cell Mutation, Polygenes, Epistasis
**Web links**: Summary of Gene Interactions

# Collaboration

There are genes that may influence the same trait, but produce a phenotype that could not result from the action of either gene independently. These are termed collaborative genes (they show collaboration). There are typically four possible phenotypes for this condition. An example of this type of interaction can be found in the comb shape of domestic hens.

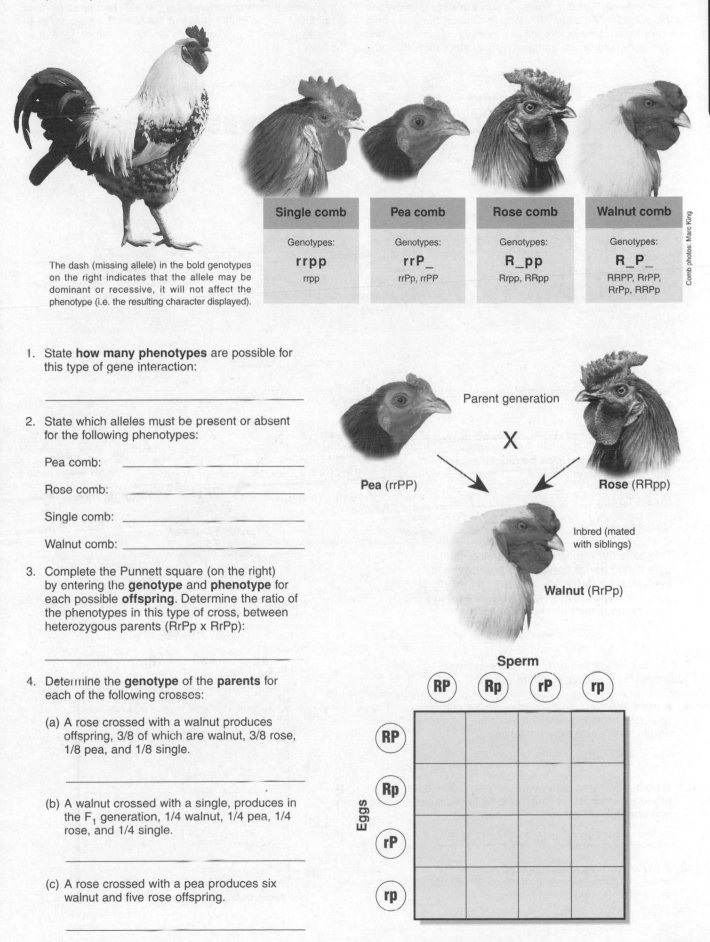

The dash (missing allele) in the bold genotypes on the right indicates that the allele may be dominant or recessive, it will not affect the phenotype (i.e. the resulting character displayed).

| Single comb | Pea comb | Rose comb | Walnut comb |
|---|---|---|---|
| Genotypes: **rrpp** | Genotypes: **rrP_** | Genotypes: **R_pp** | Genotypes: **R_P_** |
| rrpp | rrPp, rrPP | Rrpp, RRpp | RRPP, RrPP, RrPp, RRPp |

Comb photos: Marc King

1. State **how many phenotypes** are possible for this type of gene interaction:

   _____

2. State which alleles must be present or absent for the following phenotypes:

   Pea comb: _____

   Rose comb: _____

   Single comb: _____

   Walnut comb: _____

3. Complete the Punnett square (on the right) by entering the **genotype** and **phenotype** for each possible **offspring**. Determine the ratio of the phenotypes in this type of cross, between heterozygous parents (RrPp x RrPp):

   _____

4. Determine the **genotype** of the **parents** for each of the following crosses:

   (a) A rose crossed with a walnut produces offspring, 3/8 of which are walnut, 3/8 rose, 1/8 pea, and 1/8 single.

   _____

   (b) A walnut crossed with a single, produces in the F₁ generation, 1/4 walnut, 1/4 pea, 1/4 rose, and 1/4 single.

   _____

   (c) A rose crossed with a pea produces six walnut and five rose offspring.

   _____

Parent generation

X

**Pea** (rrPP)        **Rose** (RRpp)

Inbred (mated with siblings)

**Walnut** (RrPp)

**Sperm**

RP    Rp    rP    rp

Eggs: RP, Rp, rP, rp

**Related activities**: Dihybrid Cross
**Web links**: Summary of Gene Interactions

A 3

# Complementary Genes

Some genes can only be expressed in the presence of other genes: they are **complementary**. Both genes have to have a dominant allele present for the final end product of the phenotype to be expressed. Typically, there are **two possible phenotypes** for this condition. An example of such an interaction would be if one gene controls the production of a pigment (intermediate) and another gene controls the transformation of that intermediate into the pigment (by producing a controlling enzyme). Such genes have been found to control some flower colors. The diagram below right illustrates how one kind of flower color in sweet peas is controlled by two complementary genes. The purple pigment is produced only in the presence of the dominant allele for each of the two genes. If a dominant is absent for either gene, then the flower is white.

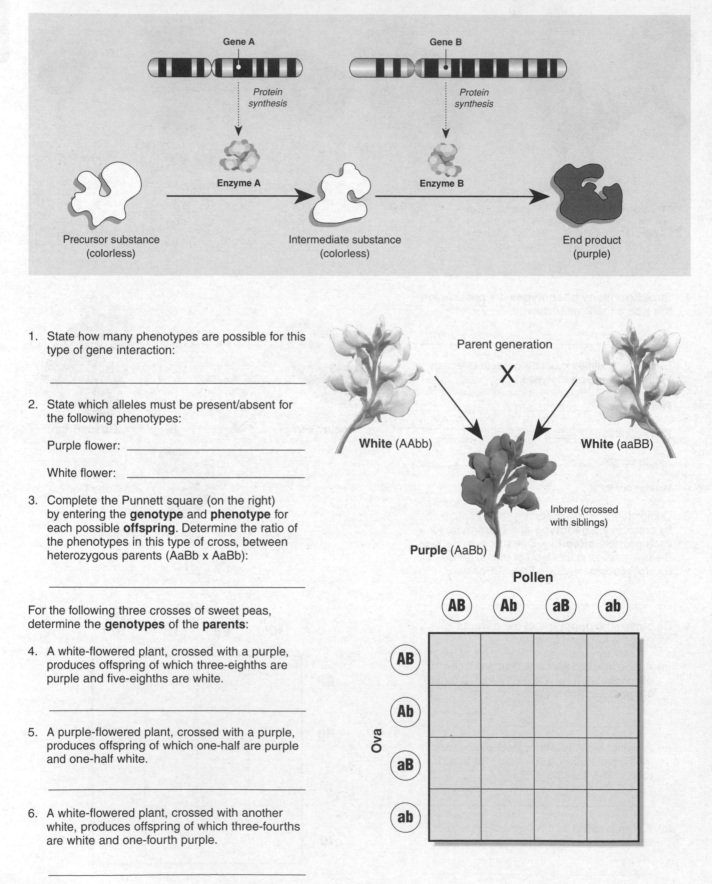

1. State how many phenotypes are possible for this type of gene interaction:

   _____

2. State which alleles must be present/absent for the following phenotypes:

   Purple flower: _____

   White flower: _____

3. Complete the Punnett square (on the right) by entering the **genotype** and **phenotype** for each possible **offspring**. Determine the ratio of the phenotypes in this type of cross, between heterozygous parents (AaBb x AaBb):

   _____

For the following three crosses of sweet peas, determine the **genotypes** of the **parents**:

4. A white-flowered plant, crossed with a purple, produces offspring of which three-eighths are purple and five-eighths are white.

   _____

5. A purple-flowered plant, crossed with a purple, produces offspring of which one-half are purple and one-half white.

   _____

6. A white-flowered plant, crossed with another white, produces offspring of which three-fourths are white and one-fourth purple.

   _____

Parent generation

X

White (AAbb)   White (aaBB)

Purple (AaBb)

Inbred (crossed with siblings)

**Pollen**

AB   Ab   aB   ab

Ova: AB, Ab, aB, ab

**Related activities**: Control of Metabolic Pathways, Dihybrid Cross
**Web links**: Summary of Gene Interactions

© Biozone International  2001-2008
**Photocopying Prohibited**

# Polygenes

A single phenotype may be influenced, or determined, by more than one gene. Such phenotypes exhibit continuous variation in a population. Examples are skin color and height, although the latter has been found to be influenced primarily by one gene.

A light-skinned person

A dark-skinned person

In the diagram (right), the five possible phenotypes for skin color are represented by nine genotypes. The production of the skin pigment melanin is controlled by two genes. The amount of pigment produced is directly proportional to the number of dominant alleles for either gene. No dominant allele results in an **albino** (aabb). Full pigmentation (black) requires four dominant alleles (AABB).

| White | Light | Medium | Dark | Black |
|-------|-------|--------|------|-------|
| **aabb** | **Aabb** **aaBb** | **AAbb** **AaBb** **aaBB** | **AaBB** **AABb** | **AABB** |

1. State how many phenotypes are possible for this type of gene interaction:

   _____

2. State which alleles must be present/absent for the following phenotypes:

   Black: _____

   Medium: _____

   White: _____

3. Complete the Punnett square (on the right) by entering the **genotype** and **phenotype** for each possible offspring. Determine the **ratio** of the phenotypes in this type of cross, between heterozygous parents (AaBb x AaBb):

   _____

   _____

   _____

   _____

For the following two crosses between humans, determine the phenotypes of the offspring:

4. A mating of white with black:

   _____

5. A mating between two individuals of medium skin color:

   _____

6. In a polygenic inheritance illustrated above, two genes (A and B) are able to produce five phenotypes. Determine how many possible phenotypes could be produced if **three** genes were involved (i.e. genes A, B and C produce genotypes aabbcc, Aabbcc, etc.):

Parent generation

X

**Black** (AABB)

$F_1$ generation

**White** (aabb)

Breeding with an identical phenotype

**Medium** (AaBb)

$F_2$ generation

Sperm

AB    Ab    aB    ab

Eggs

AB

Ab

aB

ab

_____

_____

_____

**Related activities**: Descriptive Statistics, Dihybrid Cross, Human Genotypes
**Web links**: Summary of Gene Interactions

7. Discuss the differences between **continuous** and **discontinuous** variation, giving examples to illustrate your answer:

_____

_____

_____

_____

8. From a sample of no less than 30 adults, collect data (by request or measurement) for one continuous variable (e.g. height, weight, shoe size, or hand span). Record and tabulate your results in the space below, and then plot a frequency histogram of the data on the grid below:

**Raw data**

**Tally Chart (frequency table)**

**Variable:** _____

Frequency

(a) Calculate each of the following for your data. See *Descriptive Statistics* if you need help and attach your working:

**Mean**: _____  **Mode**: _____  **Median**: _____

**Standard deviation**: _____

(b) Describe the pattern of distribution shown by the graph, giving a reason for your answer: _____

_____

(c) Explain the genetic basis of this distribution: _____

_____

(d) Explain the importance of a large sample size when gathering data relating to a continuous variable:

_____

# Epistasis

In its narrowest definition, **epistatic genes** are those that mask the effect of other genes. Typically there are **three possible phenotypes** for a dihybrid cross involving this type of gene interaction. One well studied example of epistasis occurs between the genes controlling coat color in rodents and other mammals. Skin and hair color is the result of melanin, a pigment which may be either black/brown (eumelanin) or reddish/yellow (phaeomelanin). Melanin itself is made up through several biochemical steps from the amino acid tyrosine. The control of coat color and patterning in mammals is complex and involves at least five major interacting genes. One of these genes (gene C), controls the production of the pigment melanin, while another gene (gene B), is responsible for whether the color is black or brown. The interaction between these genes in determining coat color in mice is illustrated below. Epistasis literally means "standing upon". In albinism, the homozygous recessive condition, cc, "stands upon" the other coat color genes, blocking their expression.

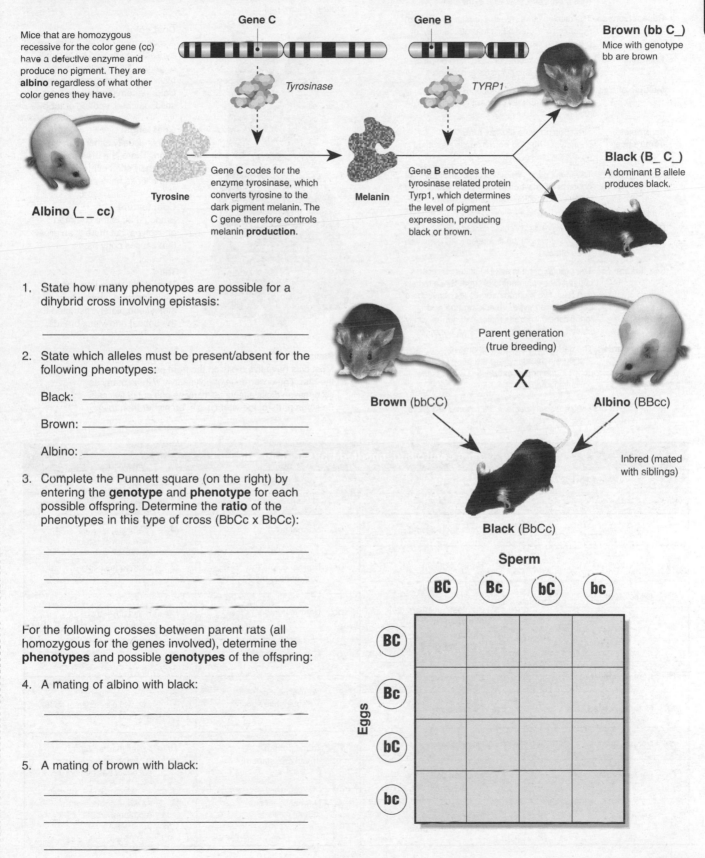

Mice that are homozygous recessive for the color gene (cc) have a defective enzyme and produce no pigment. They are **albino** regardless of what other color genes they have.

**Gene C**

*Tyrosinase*

**Gene B**

*TYRP1*

**Tyrosine**

Gene **C** codes for the enzyme tyrosinase, which converts tyrosine to the dark pigment melanin. The C gene therefore controls melanin **production**.

**Melanin**

Gene **B** encodes the tyrosine related protein Tyrp1, which determines the level of pigment expression, producing black or brown.

**Brown (bb C_)**
Mice with genotype bb are brown

**Black (B_ C_)**
A dominant B allele produces black.

**Albino (_ _ cc)**

1. State how many phenotypes are possible for a dihybrid cross involving epistasis:

   _____

2. State which alleles must be present/absent for the following phenotypes:

   Black: _____

   Brown: _____

   Albino: _____

3. Complete the Punnett square (on the right) by entering the **genotype** and **phenotype** for each possible offspring. Determine the **ratio** of the phenotypes in this type of cross (BbCc x BbCc):

   _____

   _____

   _____

**Brown** (bbCC)

Parent generation
(true breeding)

X

**Albino** (BBcc)

Inbred (mated with siblings)

**Black** (BbCc)

For the following crosses between parent rats (all homozygous for the genes involved), determine the **phenotypes** and possible **genotypes** of the offspring:

4. A mating of albino with black:

   _____

   _____

5. A mating of brown with black:

   _____

   _____

   _____

**Sperm**

| | BC | Bc | bC | bc |
|---|---|---|---|---|
| **BC** | | | | |
| **Bc** | | | | |
| **bC** | | | | |
| **bc** | | | | |

Eggs

# Inheritance in Domestic Cats

Cats have been domesticated for thousands of years. During this time, certain traits or characteristics have been considered fashionable or desirable in a cat by people in different parts of the world. In the domestic cat, the 'wild type' is the short-haired tabby. All the other coat colors found in cats are modifications of this ancestral tabby pattern. Inheritance of coat characteristics and a few other features in cats is interesting because they exhibit the most common genetic phenomena. Some selected traits for domestic cats are identified below, together with a list of the kinds of genetic phenomena easily demonstrated in cats.

## Inheritance Patterns in Domestic Cats

**Dominance** — The polydactylism gene with the dominant allele (Pd) produces a paw with extra digits.

**Recessiveness** — The dilution gene with the recessive allele (d) produces a diluted black to produce gray, or orange to cream.

**Epistasis** — The dominant agouti gene (A) must be present for the tabby gene (T) to be expressed.

**Multiple alleles** — The albino series (C) produces a range of phenotypes from full pigment intensity to true albino.

**Incomplete dominance** — The spotting gene (S) has three phenotypes ranging from extensive spotting to no spotting at all.

**Lethal genes** — The Manx gene (M) that produces a stubby or no tail is lethal when in the homozygous dominant condition (MM causes death in the womb).

**Pleiotropy** — The white gene (W) also affects eye color and can cause congenital deafness (one gene with three effects).

**Sex linkage** — The orange gene is sex (X) linked and can convert black pigment to orange. Since female cats have two X chromosomes they have three possible phenotypes (black, orange and tortoiseshell) whereas males can normally only exhibit two phenotypes (black and orange).

**Environmental effects** — The dark color pointing in Siamese and Burmese cats where the gene (cs) is only active in the cooler extremities such as the paws, tail and face.

*(NOTE: Some of these genetic phenomena are covered elsewhere)*

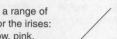

**Eyes**
May have a range of coloring for the irises: blue, yellow, pink.

**Ears**
May be normal pointed ears, or the ears may be folded.

**Coat color**
A wide range of coat colors are available, controlled by a variety of genes. Basic colors include black, white, orange and agouti. Color patterns can range from solid, patched, spotted or tabby.

**Coat length**
Hair is usually either long or short. There is a breed with extremely short hair; so much so that it looks hairless (sphynx).

**Coat texture**
Smooth hair is the common phenotype, but there is an allele that causes curly hair.

**Tail**
Most cats have a long tail. An allele for short, stubby tails is almost completely restricted to the bobcat and Manx breeds.

**Paws**
Most cats have five digits on the front paw and four on the rear. The occurrence of polydactyly with as many as six or seven digits affects as many as one out of five cats (in some parts of the world it is even higher than this).

## Genes controlling inherited traits in domestic cats

| Wild forms | | Mutant forms | | Wild forms | | Mutant forms | |
|---|---|---|---|---|---|---|---|
| *Allele* | *Phenotype* | *Allele* | *Phenotype* | *Allele* | *Phenotype* | *Allele* | *Phenotype* |
| **A** | Agouti | **a** | Black (non-agouti) | **m** | Normal tail | **M** | Manx tail, shorter than normal (stubby) |
| **B** | Black pigment | **b** | Brown pigment | **o** | Normal colors (no red, usually black) | **O** | Orange (sex linked) |
| **C** | Unicolored | **cch** Silver<br>**cs** Siamese (pointing: dark at extremities)<br>**ca** Albino with blue eyes<br>**c** Albino with pink eyes | **pd** | Normal number of toes | **Pd** | Polydactylism; has extra toes |
| | | | | **R** | Normal, smooth hair | **R** | Rex hair, curly |
| **D** | Dense pigment | **d** | Dilute pigment | **s** | Normal coat color without white spots | **S** | Color interspersed with white patches or spots (piebald white spotting) |
| **fd** | Normal, pointed ears | **Fd** | Folded ears | | | | |
| **Hr** | Normal, full coat | **h** | Hairlessness | **T** | Tabby pattern (mackerel striped) | **Ta** Abyssinian tabby<br>**tb** Blotched tabby, classic pattern of patches or stripes |
| **i** | Fur colored all over | **I** | Inhibitor: part of the hair is not colored (silver) | | | | |
| **L** | Short hair | **l** | Long hair, longer than normal | **w** | Normal coat color, not all white | **W** All white coat color (dominant white)<br>**Wh** Wirehair |

# Variation in Coat Color in Domestic Cats

### Non-agouti

A completely jet black cat has no markings on it whatsoever. It would have the genotype: ***aaB–D–*** since no dominant agouti allele must be present, and the black pigment is not diluted.

### Siamese

The color pointing of Siamese cats is caused by warm temperature deactivation of a gene that produces melanin pigment. Cooler parts of the body are not affected and appear dark.

### Tortoiseshell

Because this is a sex linked trait, it is normally found only in female cats (***XO, Xo***). The coat is a mixture of orange and black fur irregularly blended together.

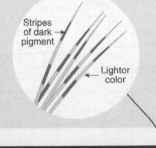

### Agouti hair

Enlarged view of agouti hair. Note that the number of darkly pigmented stripes can vary on the same animal.

Stripes of dark pigment

Lighter color

### Sex linked orange

The orange (***XO, XO***) cat has an orange coat with little or no patterns such as tabby showing.

### Blotched tabby

Lacks stripes but has broad, irregular bands arranged in whorls (***tb***).

### Wild type

Mackerel (striped) tabby (***A–B–T–***) with evenly spaced, well-defined, vertical stripes. The background color is **agouti** with the stripes being areas of completely black hairs.

Orange

White

Black

### Calico

Similar to a tortoiseshell, but with substantial amounts of white fur present as well. Black, orange and white fur.

Golden yellow coat

Deeper colour stripes

### Marmalade

The orange color (***XO, XO***) is expressed, along with the alleles for the tabby pattern. The allele for orange color shows epistatic dominance and overrides the expression of the agouti color so that the tabby pattern appears dark orange.

# Other Inherited Features In Domestic Cats

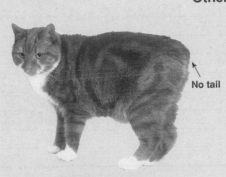

No tail

### Manx tail (Mm)

The Manx breed of cat has little or no tail. This dominant allele is lethal if it occurs in the homozygous condition.

6 digits on the paw

### Polydactylism (Pd–)

This is a dominant mutation. The number of digits on the front paw should be five, with four digits on the rear paw.

Ears folded forwards

### Ear fold (Fd–)

Most cats have normal pointed ears. A dominant mutation exists where the ear is permanently folded forwards.

# What Genotype Has That Cat?

Consult the table of genes listed on the previous pages and enter the allele symbols associated with each of the phenotypes in the column headed 'Allele'. For this exercise, study the appearance of real cats around your home or look at color photographs of different cats. For each cat, complete the checklist of traits listed below by simply placing a tick in the appropriate spaces. These traits are listed in the same order as the genes for **wild forms** and **mutant forms** on page 236. On a piece of paper, write each of the cat's genotypes. Use a dash (-) for the second allele for characteristics that could be either heterozygous or homozygous dominant (see the sample at the bottom of the page).

**NOTES:**
1. *Agouti* fur coloring is used to describe black **hairs** with a light band of pigment close to its tip.
2. Patches of silver fur (called chinchilla) produces the silver tabby phenotype in agouti cats. Can also produce "smoke" phenotype in Persian long-haired cats, causing reduced intensity of the black.
3. Describes the dark extremities (face, tail and paws) with lighter body (e.g. Siamese).
4. The recessive allele makes black cats blue-gray in color and yellow cats cream.
5. Spottiness involving less than half the surface area is likely to be heterozygous.

| Phenotype Record Sheet for Domestic Cats | | | | | | | |
|---|---|---|---|---|---|---|---|
| **Gene** | **Phenotype** | **Allele** | **Sample** | **Cat 1** | **Cat 2** | **Cat 3** | **Cat 4** |
| Agouti color | Agouti[1] | | | | | | |
| | Non-agouti | | ✔ | | | | |
| Pigment color | Black | | ✔ | | | | |
| | Brown | | | | | | |
| Color present | Uncolored | | ✔ | | | | |
| | Silver patches[2] | | | | | | |
| | Pointed[3] | | | | | | |
| | Albino with blue eyes | | | | | | |
| | Albino with pink eyes | | | | | | |
| Pigment density | Dense pigment | | | | | | |
| | Dilute pigment[4] | | ✔ | | | | |
| Ear shape | Pointed ears | | ✔ | | | | |
| | Folded ears | | | | | | |
| Hairiness | Normal, full coat | | ✔ | | | | |
| | Hairlessness | | | | | | |
| Hair length | Short hair | | ✔ | | | | |
| | Long hair | | | | | | |
| Tail length | Normal tail (long) | | ✔ | | | | |
| | Stubby tail or no tail at all | | | | | | |
| Orange color | Normal colors (non-orange) | | ✔ | | | | |
| | Orange | | | | | | |
| Number of digits | Normal number of toes | | ✔ | | | | |
| | Polydactylism (extra toes) | | | | | | |
| Hair curliness | Normal, smooth hair | | ✔ | | | | |
| | Curly hair (rex) | | | | | | |
| Spottiness | No white spots | | | | | | |
| | White spots (less than half)[5] | | ✔ | | | | |
| | White spots (more than half) | | | | | | |
| Stripes | Mackerel striped (tabby) | | | | | | |
| | Blotched stripes | | | | | | |
| White coat | Not all white | | ✔ | | | | |
| | All white coat color | | | | | | |

**Sample cat:** (see ticks in chart above)

To give you an idea of how to read the chart you have created, here is an example genotype of the author's cat with the following features: *A smoky gray uniform-colored cat, with short smooth hair, normal tail and ears, with 5 digits on the front paws and 4 on the rear paws, small patches of white on the feet and chest. (Note that the stripe genotype is completely unknown since there is no agouti allele present).*

**GENOTYPE:**  aa  B–  C–  dd  fdfd  Hr–  ii  L–  mm  oo  pdpd  R–  Ss  ww

**Related activities:** Inheritance in Domestic Cats

# Aspects of Biotechnology

## Learning Objectives

☐ 1. Compile your own glossary from the **KEY WORDS** displayed in **bold type** in the learning objectives below.

### Introduction to Gene Technology *(pages 245-246)*

☐ 2. Explain what is meant by **gene technology** and distinguish it from **biotechnology**. Distinguish between **genetic engineering** and **genetic modification** in general. Recognise one as a subset of the other.

☐ 3. Recognise that a small number of basic techniques (restriction digestion, DNA ligation, gel electrophoresis, and PCR) are used in a number of different processes (e.g. gene cloning, transgenesis, DNA profiling). Appreciate that these processes have wide application.

☐ 4. Provide an outline of the various applications of gene technology in modern medicine, agriculture, and industry. Appreciate the pivotal role of microorganisms in the development and application of this technology.

### Techniques in Gene Technology *(pages 247-252, 255-260 and the TRC: Biotechnology Supplement)*

☐ 5. Explain how **restriction enzymes** work, including the role of the **recognition site**. Distinguish between **sticky end** and **blunt end** DNA fragments.

☐ 6. Identify the role of restriction enzymes in **recombinant DNA technology**. List some commonly used restriction enzymes and give their recognition sites.

☐ 7. Explain the technique and purpose of **DNA ligation** and **annealing**, including the role of **DNA ligase**.

☐ 8. Understand how **recombinant DNA** is produced by the ligation of DNA from different sources.

☐ 9. Explain the role of **gel electrophoresis** (of DNA) in gene technology. Outline the basic principles, including the role of **restriction digestion**. Identify properties of the **gel** that facilitate the separation of DNA fragments.

☐ 10. Explain how the DNA fragments on a gel are made visible. Describe the role of **DNA markers** in identifying DNA fragments of different size.

☐ 11. Explain the role of **polymerase chain reaction (PCR)** in **DNA amplification**. Explain why PCR is an essential tool for many procedures in gene technology. Describe the basic technique of PCR, including the role of **primers**, **nucleotides**, and **DNA polymerase**.

☐ 12. Describe the use of **PCR**, **radioactive labeling**, and **gel electrophoresis** in **DNA sequencing**. Distinguish between **manual** and **automated** sequencing. Discuss how these techniques are used in **genome analysis**.

☐ 13. Describe the construction of a **DNA chip (microarray)**, identifying the principles by which the chip operates. Discuss some of the current and potential applications of this relatively new technology in gene research.

## Processes & Applications in Gene Technology

### DNA profiling *(pages 204, 253-254, 271-273)*

☐ 14. Explain what is meant **DNA profiling** (also called genetic profiling or DNA fingerprinting). Distinguish clearly between DNA profiling and DNA sequencing.

☐ 15. Describe DNA profiling using **PCR**, including the role of **microsatellites**, **PCR**, and **gel electrophoresis**.

☐ 16. Describe applications of DNA profiling, e.g. in **forensic** analysis, in establishing paternity or pedigree, and as a tool in diagnostic medicine.

☐ 17. Describe the basic principles involved in **genetic screening** and discuss the advantages and/or disadvantages with the application of this technology.

### Gene cloning *(pages 255-256)*

☐ 18. Describe applications of **gene cloning** and recognize the stages involved, including preparation of the clone (#20) and the actual cloning of the gene itself (#21).

☐ 19. Outline the steps in preparing a gene for cloning:
   (a) Explain how the gene is **isolated** from cells.
   (b) Describe the role of **reverse transcriptase** in creating the gene to be inserted into the vector.
   (c) The creation of a **molecular clone**.

☐ 20. Explain how the prepared molecular clone is introduced into the host cells. Describe how bacterial colonies with the desired gene are identified, isolated, and grown in culture (to produce multiple copies of the gene).

### Transgenesis *(pages 245, 261-264)*

☐ 21. Explain clearly what is meant by a **transgenic organism**. Note: **transformation** refers to the acquisition of genetic material by the uptake of **naked DNA**. It is a term most often used with respect to bacteria, but increasingly applied to other organisms.

☐ 22. Describe the techniques involved in transgenesis, including the role of viral or **plasmid vectors** in integrating foreign DNA into the genome of another organism. Explain how **recombinant vectors** are made using **restriction enzymes** and **DNA ligation**.

### Genome analysis *(pages 257-258, 271-273)*

☐ 23. Describe **genome analysis**, identifying the role of the techniques involved, including restriction digestion, DNA ligation, PCR, and gel electrophoresis.

☐ 24. Appreciate the role of rapid automated sequencing in the feasibility of the **Human Genome Project** (HGP) and discuss possible outcomes of the HGP.

☐ 25. Identify areas of further development in sequence analysis of both mitochondrial DNA (mtDNA) and nuclear DNA, for example in determining when and where genes are expressed, investigating gene products (**proteomics**), and establishing **phylogenies**.

## Meeting Human Demands with Biotechnology
### *(pages 123-124, 246, 265-270, 275-278)*

☐ 26. Discuss the use or potential use of genetically modified organisms (GMOs) to meet human demands, e.g.:
   (a) Crop resistance to herbicides and/or insect pests.
   (b) Expansion of crop growing range (e.g. salt tolerance, frost tolerance).
   (c) Improved storage and/or crop quality.
   (d) Sense/antisense technology (**Flvr Savr tomatoes**).
   (e) Production of α-1-antitrypsin in milk.
   (f) Microbial production human proteins (e.g. human insulin, factor VIII), antibiotics, and enzymes.
   (g) Gene therapy (see #27-29 below)

### Gene therapy

☐ 27. Outline the principles of **gene therapy**. Identify the criteria that must be met before gene therapy can be considered as a potentially viable treatment. Distinguish between using gene therapy to cure a disease and its use to relieve symptoms of a disease.

☐ 28. Using an appropriate example, explain the techniques involved in **gene therapy**, including the **vectors** used, and delivery systems for these vectors. Discuss the difficulties currently encountered in improving the success of gene therapy and explain why successful gene therapy has, to date, been largely unsuccessful.

☐ 29. Identify types of **vectors** used in gene therapy and discuss the advantages and disadvantages of each. Include reference to **viral vectors** and **liposomes**.

### Cloning and transplant technology

☐ 30. Appreciate that cloning of animals has traditionally been achieved through **embryo splitting**. Contrast embryo splitting with **nuclear transfer** (using differentiated cells). Recognize forms of cloning as techniques in their own right, with wider applications.

☐ 31. Identify the current and potential uses of **cloning** technology, including the cloning of transgenic organisms. Describe the benefits, disadvantages, and ethical and welfare issues associated with nuclear transfer techniques and with cloning in general.

☐ 32. Discuss aspects of organ transplantation and xenotransplantation technology including reference to any of the following:
   (a) The source of animal organs.
   (b) Transplantation from transgenic animals.
   (c) Cloning to produce immune-compatible tissues and organs in quantities to meet demand.
   (d) The use of animals bred solely for organ supply.
   (e) The risk of **zoonotic** infections.

☐ 33. Discuss the relevant biological, ethical, and social issues associated with the use of genetic manipulation technology in agriculture, industry, and medicine.

---

 **Textbooks**

 See the 'Textbook Reference Grid' on pages 8-9 for textbook page references relating to material in this topic.

### Supplementary Texts

See pages 5-6 for additional details of these texts:

■ Adds, J. *et al.*, 1999. **Tools, Techniques and Assessment in Biology** (NelsonThornes), pp. 56-71.

■ Adds, J., *et al.*, 2004. **Genetics, Evolution and Biodiversity**, (NelsonThornes), chpt. 9.

■ Barnum, S.R., 2005. **Biotechnology: An Introduction** (Thomson Brooks/Cole).

■ Clegg, C.J., 1999. **Genetics and Evolution** (John Murray), pp. 48-59.

■ Helms, D.R. *et al.*, 1998. **Biology in the Laboratory** (W.H. Freeman), #18.

■ Jones, N., *et al.*, 2001. **Essentials of Genetics** (John Murray), pp. 235-260.

**Periodicals**

See page 6 for details of publishers of periodicals:

### STUDENT'S REFERENCE

■ **Agro-Biotech** Biol. Sci. Rev., 16(1) Sept. 2003, pp. 21-24. *Genetic engineering provides a tool to improving crops and meeting consumer demand. What is being developed and what are the risks?*

■ **The Polymerase Chain Reaction** Biol. Sci. Rev., 16(3) Feb. 2004, pp. 10-13. *This account explains the techniques and applications of PCR.*

■ **Rice, Risk and Regulations** Biol. Sci. Rev., 20(2) Nov. 2007, pp. 17-20. *The genetic engineering of one of the world's most important cereal crops is an ethical concern for many.*

■ **Birds, Bees, and Superweeds** Biol. Sci. Rev., 17(2) Nov. 2004, pp. 24-27. *Genetically modified crops: their advantages and commercial applications, as well as some of the risks and concerns associated with their use.*

■ **What is Genomics?** Biol. Sci. Rev., 20(2) Nov. 2007, pp. 38-41. *The techniques involved in genomic studies and their medical applications .*

■ **Liver Transplantation and Ethical Issues** Biol. Sci. Rev., 20(3) Feb. 2008, pp. 26-29. *The technical and ethical issues associated with liver transplants.*

### TEACHER'S REFERENCE

■ **Back to the Future of Cereals** Scientific American, Aug. 2004, pp. 26-33. *An excellent, up-to-date account of the state of crop technology. Fuelled by genomic studies, a new green revolution is predicted to increase crop yields ever further.*

■ **Genes Can Come True** New Scientist, 30 Nov. 2002, pp. 30-33. *An overview of the recent state of gene therapy, and a note about future directions in this controversial new area of medicine.*

■ **Human Gene Therapy** The Am. Biology Teacher, 64(4), April 2002, pp. 264-270. *Some of the latest advances and setbacks in gene therapy.*

■ **The Land of Milk and Honey** Scientific American, Nov. 2005, pp. 72-75. *Alternative forms of protein manufacture are nearing completion, including an animal genetically engineered to produce a therapeutic protein in its milk.*

■ **Make me a Hipporoo** New Scientist, 11 Feb. 2006, pp. 25-38. *In the future, designing genomes with do-it-yourself kits could become a very personal thing, even an art form. Discussion of the changing role of evolution as a result of this.*

■ **Why the Long Wait for Tailored Drugs?** New Scientist, 27 Oct. 2007, pp. 6-7. *How gene technology can be used to tailor drugs suited exactly to an individual's genetic profile.*

■ **The Magic of Microarrays** Scientific American, Feb. 2002, pp. 34-41. *DNA chips (microarrays) and their use in identifying health and disease, along with implications for drug treatment.*

■ **GM Food Safety Special Report** Scientific American, April 2001. *Special issue examining aspects of the GM food debate (excellent).*

■ **Understanding the Human Genome Project** The Am. Biology Teacher, 67(8), Oct. 2005, pp. 475-484. *Lessons designed to introduce some of the techniques used to study and manipulate DNA.*

■ **Teaching Molecular Biological Techniques in a Research Context** The Am. Biology Teacher, 68(1), Jan. 2006, p. 36-42. *The design of a research-based laboratory course that employs 'environmental PCR' to investigate planktonic community composition.*

■ **A DNA Fingerprinting Simulation Laboratory** The Am. Biology Teacher, 63(8), Oct. 2001, pp. 596-605. *How-to-do-it; using a DNA fingerprinting simulation to solve a mock forensic investigation.*

■ **A Paternity Testing Simulation Laboratory** The Am. Biology Teacher, 64(3), March 2002, pp. 212-218. *Simulation involving PCR amplification, DNA profiling, and blood group analysis.*

■ **Microarrays Made Simple: 'DNA chips' Paper Activity** The Am. Biology Teacher, 68(3), March 2006, p. 139. *Visualizing differences in gene expression using a DNA microarray.*

 **Internet**

See pages 10-11 for details of how to access **Bio Links** from our web site: **www.thebiozone.com** From Bio Links, access sites under the topics:
**BIOTECHNOLOGY** > General Biotechnology Sites: • ABelgoBiotech ... *and others* > **Biotechnology Techniques:** • Interactive biotechnology • Recombinant DNA • Restriction enzymes • Principle of the PCR ... *and others* > **Biotechnology Processes:** • Animal and plant transformation • Basics of DNA fingerprinting • DNA workshop • Transgenic organisms ... *and others* > **Applications in Biotechnology:** access sites under > *Food biotechnology* > *Medical biotechnology* > *Industrial biotechnology* > **Cloning and Tissue Culture:** • Conceiving a clone • Cloning and stem cell technology ... *and others* > **The Human Genome Project:** • A users guide to the human genome • Genome FAQs file • Primer on molecular genetics ... *and others* > **Genome Projects:** • Genomes OnLine • Genome News Network ... *and others* **Issues & Ethics in Biotechnology:** • Bioethics for beginners • Ethical, legal, and social issues-HGP • Genetic engineering and its dangers ... *& others*

**Presentation MEDIA** to support this topic: **GENES AND INHERITANCE** • Gene Technology

*Genes & Inheritance*

# What is Genetic Modification?

The genetic modification of organisms is a vast industry, and the applications of the technology are exciting and far reaching. It brings new hope for medical cures, promises to increase yields in agriculture, and has the potential to help solve the world's pollution and resource crises. Organisms with artificially altered DNA are referred to as **genetically modified organisms** or **GMOs**. They may be modified in one of three ways (outlined below). Some of the current and proposed applications of gene technology raise complex ethical and safety issues, where the benefits of their use must be carefully weighed against the risks to human health, as well as the health and well-being of other organisms and the environment as a whole.

## Producing Genetically Modified Organisms (GMOs)

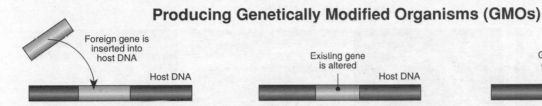

Aspects of Biotechnology

### Add a foreign gene

A novel (foreign) gene is inserted from another species. This will enable the GMO to express the trait coded by the new gene. Organisms genetically altered in this way are referred to as **transgenic**.

Human insulin, used to treat diabetic patients, is now produced using transgenic bacteria.

### Alter an existing gene

An existing gene may be altered to make it express at a higher level (e.g. growth hormone) or in a different way (in tissue that would not normally express it). This method is also used for gene therapy.

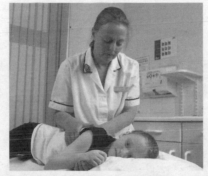

Gene therapy could be used treat genetic disrorders, such as cystic fibrosis.

### Delete or 'turn off' a gene

An existing gene may be deleted or deactivated (switched off) to prevent the expression of a trait (e.g. the deactivation of the ripening gene in tomatoes produced the Flavr-Savr tomato).

Manipulating gene action is one way in which to control processes such as ripening in fruit.

1. Using examples, discuss the ways in which an organism may be genetically modified (to produce a GMO):

   _____

   _____

   _____

   _____

   _____

   _____

2. Explain how human needs or desires have provided a stimulus for the development of the following biotechnologies:

   (a) Gene therapy: _____

   _____

   _____

   (b) The production and use of transgenic organisms: _____

   _____

   _____

   (c) Plant micropropagation (tissue culture): _____

   _____

   _____

**Related activities**: Genetically Modified Plants, Transgenic Organisms, The Ethics of GMO Technology

RA 2

# Applications of GMOs

Techniques for genetic manipulation are now widely applied throughout modern biotechnology: in food and enzyme technology, in industry and medicine, and in agriculture and horticulture. Microorganisms are among the most widely used GMOs, with applications ranging from pharmaceutical production and vaccine development to environmental clean-up. Crop plants are also popular candidates for genetic modification although their use, as with much of genetic engineering of higher organisms, is controversial and sometimes problematic.

## Applications of GMOs

### Extending shelf life

Some fresh produce (e.g. tomatoes) have been engineered to have an extended keeping quality. In the case of tomatoes, the gene for ripening has been switched off, delaying the natural process of softening in the fruit.

### Pest or herbicide resistance

Plants can be engineered to produce their own insecticide and become pest resistant. Genetically engineered herbicide resistance is also common. In this case, chemical weed killers can be used freely without crop damage.

### Crop improvement

Gene technology is now an integral part of the development of new crop varieties. Crops can be engineered to produce higher protein levels or to grow in inhospitable conditions (e.g. salty or arid conditions).

### Environmental clean-up

Some bacteria have been engineered to thrive on waste products, such as liquefied newspaper pulp or oil. As well as degrading pollutants and wastes, the bacteria may be harvested as a commercial protein source.

### Biofactories

Transgenic bacteria are widely used to produce desirable products: often hormones or proteins. Large quantities of a product can be produced using bioreactors (above). Examples: insulin production by recombinant yeast, production of bovine growth hormone.

### Vaccine development

The potential exists for multipurpose vaccines to be made using gene technology. Genes coding for vaccine components (e.g. viral protein coat) are inserted into an unrelated live vaccine (e.g. polio vaccine), and deliver proteins to stimulate an immune response.

### Livestock improvement using transgenic animals

Transgenic sheep have been used to enhance wool production in flocks (above, left). The keratin protein of wool is largely made of a single amino acid, cysteine. Injecting developing sheep with the genes for the enzymes that generate cysteine produces woollier transgenic sheep. In some cases, transgenic animals have been used as biofactories. Transgenic sheep carrying the human gene for a protein, α-1-antitrypsin produce the protein in their milk. The antitrypsin is extracted from the milk and used to treat hereditary emphysema.

1. In a short account discuss one of the applications of GMOs described above: _____

_____

_____

_____

_____

_____

_____

_____

_____

_____

_____

_____

# Restriction Enzymes

One of the essential tools of genetic engineering is a group of special **restriction enzymes** (also known as restriction endonucleases). These have the ability to cut DNA molecules at very precise sequences of 4 to 8 base pairs called **recognition sites**. These enzymes are the "molecular scalpels" that allow genetic engineers to cut up DNA in a controlled way. Although first isolated in 1970, these enzymes were discovered earlier in many bacteria (see panel on the next page). The purified forms of these bacterial restriction enzymes are used today as tools to cut DNA (see table on the next page for examples). Enzymes are named according to the bacterial species from which they were first isolated. By using a 'tool kit' of over 400 restriction enzymes recognizing about 100 recognition sites, genetic engineers can isolate, sequence, and manipulate individual genes derived from any type of organism. The sites at which the fragments of DNA are cut may result in overhanging "sticky ends" or non-overhanging "blunt ends". Pieces may later be joined together using an enzyme called **DNA ligase** in a process called **ligation**.

## Sticky End Restriction Enzymes

**1** A **restriction enzyme** cuts the double-stranded DNA molecule at its specific **recognition site** (see the table opposite for a representative list of restriction enzymes and their recognition sites).

**2** The cuts produce a DNA fragment with two **sticky ends** (ends with exposed nucleotide bases at each end). The piece it is removed from is also left with sticky ends.

Restriction enzymes may cut DNA leaving an overhang or sticky end, without its complementary sequence opposite. DNA cut in such a way is able to be joined to other exposed end fragments of DNA with matching sticky ends. Such joins are specific to their recognition sites.

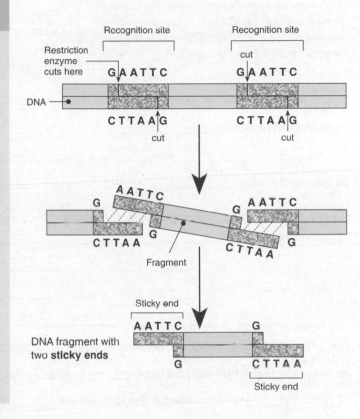

## Blunt End Restriction Enzymes

**1** A **restriction enzyme** cuts the double-stranded DNA molecule at its specific **recognition site** (see the table opposite for a representative list of restriction enzymes and their recognition sites).

**2** The cuts produce a DNA fragment with two **blunt ends** (ends with no exposed nucleotide bases at each end). The piece it is removed from is also left with blunt ends.

It is possible to use restriction enzymes that cut leaving no overhang. DNA cut in such a way is able to be joined to any other blunt end fragment, but tends to be nonspecific because there are no sticky ends as recognition sites.

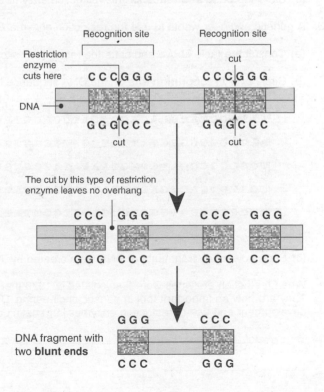

## Origin of Restriction Enzymes

Restriction enzymes have been isolated from many bacteria. It was observed that certain *bacteriophages* (viruses that infect bacteria) could not infect bacteria other than their usual hosts. The reason was found to be that other potential hosts could destroy almost all of the phage DNA using *restriction enzymes* present naturally in their cells; a defense mechanism against the entry of foreign DNA. Restriction enzymes are named according to the species they were first isolated from, followed by a number to distinguish different enzymes isolated from the same organism.

### Recognition sites for selected restriction enzymes

| Enzyme | Source | Recognition Sites |
|--------|--------|-------------------|
| *Eco*RI | *Escherichia coli* RY13 | G A A T T C |
| *Bam*HI | *Bacillus amyloliquefaciens* H | G G A T C C |
| *Hae*III | *Haemophilus aegyptius* | G G C C |
| *Hind*III | *Haemophilus influenzae* Rd | A A G C T T |
| *Hpa*I | *Haemophilus parainfluenzae* | G T T A A C |
| *Hpa*II | *Haemophilus parainfluenzae* | C C G G |
| *Mbo*I | *Moraxella bovis* | G A T C |
| *Not*I | *Norcardia otitidis-caviarum* | G C G G C C G C |
| *Taq*I | *Thermus aquaticus* | T C G A |

1. Explain the following terms, identifying their role in recombinant DNA technology:

   (a) Restriction enzyme: _____

   _____

   (b) Recognition site: _____

   _____

   (c) Sticky end: _____

   _____

   (d) Blunt end: _____

   _____

2. The action of a specific sticky end restriction enzyme is illustrated on the previous page (top). Use the table above to:

   (a) Name the **restriction enzyme** used: _____

   (b) Name the organism from which it was first isolated: _____

   (c) State the **base sequence** for this restriction enzyme's recognition site: _____

3. A genetic engineer wants to use the restriction enzyme *Bam*HI to cut the DNA sequence below:

   (a) Consult the table above and state the recognition site for this enzyme: _____

   (b) Circle every **recognition site** on the DNA sequence below that could be cut by the enzyme *Bam*HI:

   ```
             10              20              30              40              50              60
   |AATGGGTACG|CACAGTGGAT|CCACGTAGTA|TGCGATGCGT|AGTGTTTATG|GAGAGAAGAA|
             70              80              90             100             110             120
   |AACGCGTCGC|CTTTTATCGA|TGCTGTACGG|ATGCGGAAGT|GGCGATGAGG|ATCCATGCAA|
            130             140             150             160             170             180
   |TCGCGGCCGA|TCGXGTAATA|TATCGTGGCT|GCGTTTATTA|TCGTGACTAG|TAGCAGTATG|
            190             200             210             220             230             240
   |CGATGTGACT|GATGCTATGC|TGACTATGCT|ATGTTTTTAT|GCTGGATCCA|GCGTAAGCAT|
            250             260             270             280             290             300
   |TTCGCTGCGT|GGATCCCATA|TCCTTATATG|CATATATTCT|TATACGGATC|GCGCACGTTT|
   ```

   (c) State how many fragments of DNA were created by this action: _____

4. When restriction enzymes were first isolated in 1970 there were not many applications to which they could be put to use. They are now an important tool in genetic engineering. Describe the human needs and demands that have driven the development and use of restriction enzymes in genetic engineering:

   _____

   _____

   _____

# Ligation

DNA fragments produced using restriction enzymes may be reassembled by a process called **ligation**. Pieces are joined together using an enzyme called **DNA ligase**. DNA of different origins produced in this way is called **recombinant DNA** (because it is DNA that has been recombined from different sources). The combined techniques of using restriction enzymes and ligation are the basic tools of genetic engineering (also known as recombinant DNA technology).

## Creating a Recombinant DNA Plasmid

**1** If two pieces of DNA are cut by the same restriction enzyme, they will produce fragments with matching **sticky ends** (ends with exposed nucleotide bases at each end).

**2** When two such matching sticky ends come together, they can join by base-pairing. This process is called **annealing**. This can allow DNA fragments from a different source, perhaps a **plasmid**, to be joined to the DNA fragment.

**3** The joined fragments will usually form either a linear molecule or a circular one, as shown here for a **plasmid**. However, other combinations of fragments can occur.

**4** The fragments of DNA are joined together by the enzyme **DNA ligase**, producing a molecule of **recombinant DNA**.

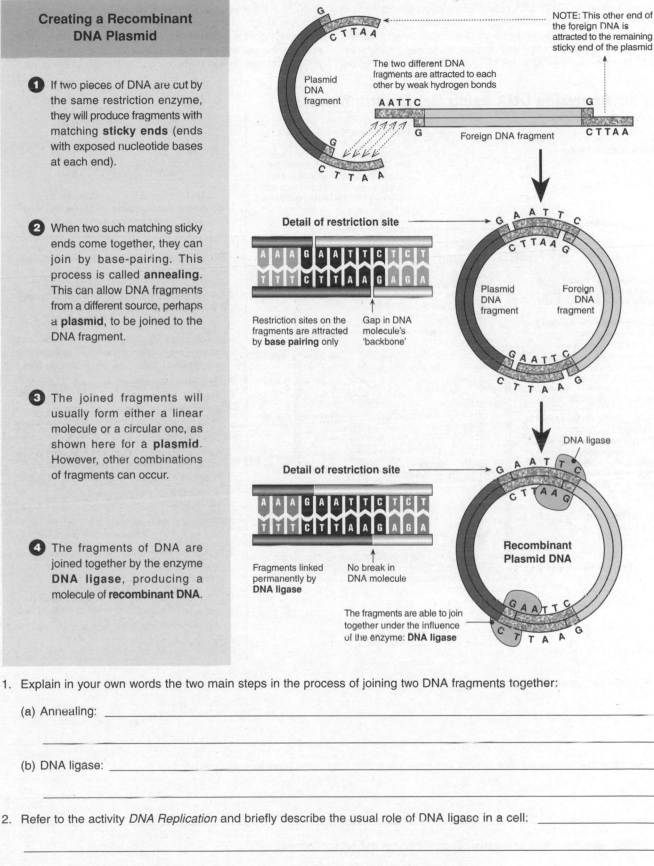

NOTE: This other end of the foreign DNA is attracted to the remaining sticky end of the plasmid

The two different DNA fragments are attracted to each other by weak hydrogen bonds

Plasmid DNA fragment

Foreign DNA fragment

**Detail of restriction site**

Restriction sites on the fragments are attracted by **base pairing** only

Gap in DNA molecule's 'backbone'

Plasmid DNA fragment

Foreign DNA fragment

**Detail of restriction site**

Fragments linked permanently by **DNA ligase**

No break in DNA molecule

DNA ligase

**Recombinant Plasmid DNA**

The fragments are able to join together under the influence of the enzyme: **DNA ligase**

Aspects of Biotechnology

1. Explain in your own words the two main steps in the process of joining two DNA fragments together:

(a) Annealing: _____

_____

(b) DNA ligase: _____

_____

2. Refer to the activity *DNA Replication* and briefly describe the usual role of DNA ligase in a cell: _____

_____

3. Explain why ligation can be considered the *reverse* of the restriction enzyme process: _____

_____

**Related activities**: Restriction Enzymes, DNA Replication

RA 3

# Gel Electrophoresis

**Gel electrophoresis** is a method that separates large molecules (including nucleic acids or proteins) on the basis of size, electric charge, and other physical properties. Such molecules possess a slight electric charge (see DNA below). To prepare DNA for gel electrophoresis the DNA is often cut up into smaller pieces. This is done by mixing DNA with restriction enzymes in controlled conditions for about an hour. Called **restriction digestion**, it produces a range of DNA fragments of different lengths. During electrophoresis, molecules are forced to move through the pores of a **gel** (a jelly-like material), when the electrical current is applied. Active electrodes at each end of the gel provide the driving force. The electrical current from one electrode repels the molecules while the other electrode simultaneously attracts the molecules. The frictional force of the gel material resists the flow of the molecules, separating them by size. Their rate of migration through the gel depends on the strength of the electric field, size and shape of the molecules, and on the ionic strength and temperature of the buffer in which the molecules are moving. After staining, the separated molecules in each lane can be seen as a series of bands spread from one end of the gel to the other.

## Analyzing DNA using Gel Electrophoresis

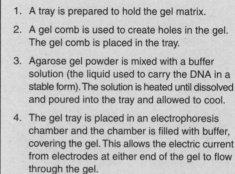

DNA is negatively charged because the phosphates (black) that form part of the backbone of a DNA molecule have a negative charge.

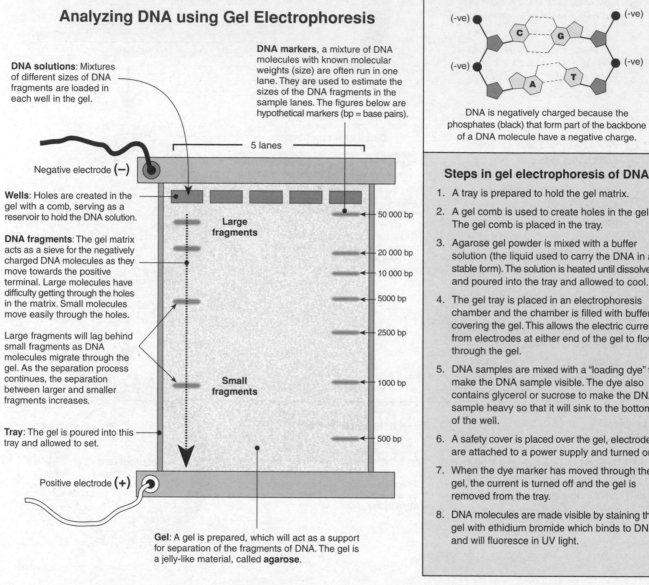

**DNA solutions**: Mixtures of different sizes of DNA fragments are loaded in each well in the gel.

**DNA markers**, a mixture of DNA molecules with known molecular weights (size) are often run in one lane. They are used to estimate the sizes of the DNA fragments in the sample lanes. The figures below are hypothetical markers (bp = base pairs).

5 lanes

Negative electrode (−)

**Wells**: Holes are created in the gel with a comb, serving as a reservoir to hold the DNA solution.

**DNA fragments**: The gel matrix acts as a sieve for the negatively charged DNA molecules as they move towards the positive terminal. Large molecules have difficulty getting through the holes in the matrix. Small molecules move easily through the holes.

Large fragments will lag behind small fragments as DNA molecules migrate through the gel. As the separation process continues, the separation between larger and smaller fragments increases.

**Tray**: The gel is poured into this tray and allowed to set.

Large fragments

Small fragments

← 50 000 bp
← 20 000 bp
← 10 000 bp
← 5000 bp
← 2500 bp
← 1000 bp
← 500 bp

Positive electrode (+)

**Gel**: A gel is prepared, which will act as a support for separation of the fragments of DNA. The gel is a jelly-like material, called **agarose**.

### Steps in gel electrophoresis of DNA

1. A tray is prepared to hold the gel matrix.

2. A gel comb is used to create holes in the gel. The gel comb is placed in the tray.

3. Agarose gel powder is mixed with a buffer solution (the liquid used to carry the DNA in a stable form). The solution is heated until dissolved and poured into the tray and allowed to cool.

4. The gel tray is placed in an electrophoresis chamber and the chamber is filled with buffer, covering the gel. This allows the electric current from electrodes at either end of the gel to flow through the gel.

5. DNA samples are mixed with a "loading dye" to make the DNA sample visible. The dye also contains glycerol or sucrose to make the DNA sample heavy so that it will sink to the bottom of the well.

6. A safety cover is placed over the gel, electrodes are attached to a power supply and turned on.

7. When the dye marker has moved through the gel, the current is turned off and the gel is removed from the tray.

8. DNA molecules are made visible by staining the gel with ethidium bromide which binds to DNA and will fluoresce in UV light.

1. Explain the purpose of gel electrophoresis: _____

_____

_____

2. Describe the two forces that control the speed at which fragments pass through the gel:

   (a) _____

   (b) _____

3. Explain why the smallest fragments travel through the gel the fastest: _____

_____

_____

**Related activities**: Analyzing a DNA Sample
**Web links**: DNA Extraction, Gel Electrophoresis

A 3

# Polymerase Chain Reaction

Many procedures in DNA technology (such as DNA sequencing and DNA profiling) require substantial amounts of DNA to work with. Some samples, such as those from a crime scene or fragments of DNA from a long extinct organism, may be difficult to get in any quantity. The diagram below describes the laboratory technique called **polymerase chain reaction** (PCR). Using this technique, vast quantities of DNA identical to trace samples can

be created. This process is often termed **DNA amplification**. Although only one cycle of replication is shown below, following cycles replicate DNA at an exponential rate. PCR can be used to make literally billions of copies in only a few hours. **Linear PCR** differs from regular PCR in that the same original DNA templates are used repeatedly. It is used to make many radio-labeled DNA fragments for DNA sequencing.

## A Single Cycle of the Polymerase Chain Reaction

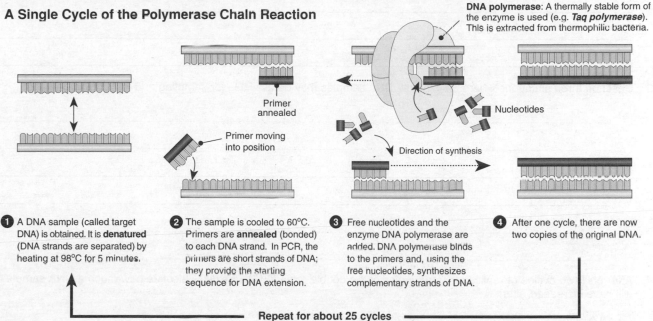

**DNA polymerase**: A thermally stable form of the enzyme is used (e.g. *Taq polymerase*). This is extracted from thermophilic bacteria.

Primer annealed

Primer moving into position

Nucleotides

Direction of synthesis

**1** A DNA sample (called target DNA) is obtained. It is **denatured** (DNA strands are separated) by heating at 98°C for 5 minutes.

**2** The sample is cooled to 60°C. Primers are **annealed** (bonded) to each DNA strand. In PCR, the primers are short strands of DNA; they provide the starting sequence for DNA extension.

**3** Free nucleotides and the enzyme DNA polymerase are added. DNA polymerase binds to the primers and, using the free nucleotides, synthesizes complementary strands of DNA.

**4** After one cycle, there are now two copies of the original DNA.

**Repeat for about 25 cycles**

Repeat cycle of heating and cooling until enough copies of the target DNA have been produced

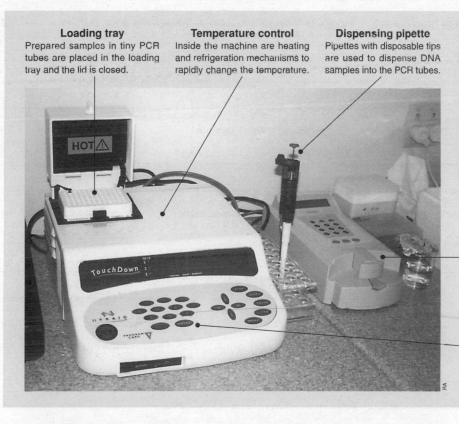

**Loading tray**
Prepared samples in tiny PCR tubes are placed in the loading tray and the lid is closed.

**Temperature control**
Inside the machine are heating and refrigeration mechanisms to rapidly change the temperature.

**Dispensing pipette**
Pipettes with disposable tips are used to dispense DNA samples into the PCR tubes.

### Thermal Cycler

Amplification of DNA can be carried out with simple-to-use machines called **thermal cyclers**. Once a DNA sample has been prepared, in just a few hours the amount of DNA can be increased billions of times. Thermal cyclers are in common use in the biology departments of universities, as well as other kinds of research and analytical laboratories. The one pictured on the left is typical of this modern piece of equipment.

#### DNA quantitation
The amount of DNA in a sample can be determined by placing a known volume in this quantitation machine. For many genetic engineering processes, a minimum amount of DNA is required.

#### Controls
The control panel allows a number of different PCR programs to be stored in the machine's memory. Carrying out a PCR run usually just involves starting one of the stored programs.

1. Explain the purpose of PCR: _____

_____

_____

_____

Aspects of Biotechnology

**Related activities**: Automated DNA Sequencing, DNA Profiling Using PCR

**RDA 3**

2. Briefly describe how the **polymerase chain reaction** (PCR) works: _____

_____

_____

_____

_____

_____

_____

3. Describe three situations where only minute DNA samples may be available for sampling and PCR could be used:

(a) _____

_____

(b) _____

_____

(c) _____

_____

4. After only two cycles of replication, four copies of the double-stranded DNA exist. Calculate how much a DNA sample will have increased after:

(a) 10 cycles: _____     (b) 25 cycles: _____

5. The risk of contamination in the preparation for PCR is considerable.

(a) Explain what the effect would be of having a single molecule of unwanted DNA in the sample prior to PCR:

_____

_____

_____

(b) Describe two possible sources of DNA contamination in preparing a PCR sample:

Source 1: _____

Source 2: _____

(c) Describe two precautions that could be taken to reduce the risk of DNA contamination:

Precaution 1: _____

_____

Precaution 2: _____

_____

6. Describe two other genetic engineering/genetic manipulation procedures that require PCR amplification of DNA:

(a) _____

_____

_____

(b) _____

_____

_____

# DNA Profiling Using PCR

In chromosomes, some of the DNA contains simple, repetitive sequences. These *noncoding* nucleotide sequences repeat themselves over and over again and are found scattered throughout the genome. Some repeating sequences are short (2-6 base pairs) called **microsatellites** or **short tandem repeats** (STRs) and can repeat up to 100 times. The human genome has numerous different microsatellites. Equivalent sequences in different people vary considerably in the numbers of the repeating unit. This phenomenon has been used to develop **DNA profiling**, which identifies the natural variations found in every person's DNA. Identifying such differences in the DNA of individuals is a useful tool for forensic investigations.

In 1998, the FBI's Combined Offender DNA Index System (CODIS) was established, providing a national database of DNA samples from convicted criminals, suspects, and crime scenes. In the USA, there are many laboratories approved for forensic DNA testing. Increasingly, these are targeting the 13 core STR loci recommended by the FBI; enough to guarantee that the odds of someone else sharing the same result are extremely unlikely (less than one in a thousand million). The CODIS may be used to solve previously unsolved crimes and to assist in current or future investigations. DNA profiling can also be used to establish genetic relatedness (e.g. in paternity or pedigree disputes), or when searching for a specific gene (e.g. screening for disease).

## Microsatellites (Short Tandem Repeats)

Microsatellites consist of a variable number of tandem repeats of a 2 to 6 base pair sequence. In the example below it is a two base sequence (CA) that is repeated.

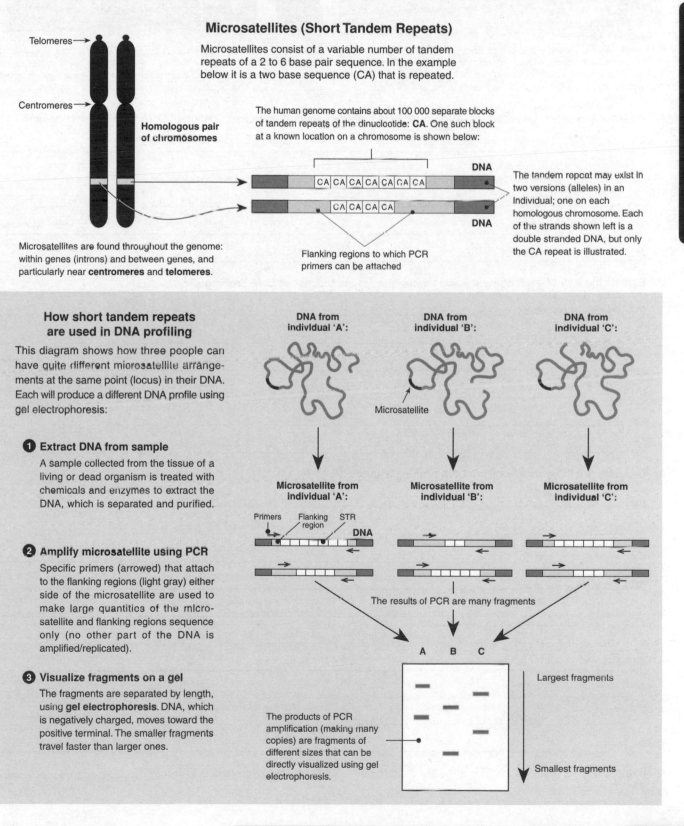

Telomeres
Centromeres

**Homologous pair of chromosomes**

Microsatellites are found throughout the genome: within genes (introns) and between genes, and particularly near **centromeres** and **telomeres**.

The human genome contains about 100 000 separate blocks of tandem repeats of the dinucleotide: **CA**. One such block at a known location on a chromosome is shown below:

DNA
DNA

Flanking regions to which PCR primers can be attached

The tandem repeat may exist in two versions (alleles) in an individual; one on each homologous chromosome. Each of the strands shown left is a double stranded DNA, but only the CA repeat is illustrated.

### How short tandem repeats are used in DNA profiling

This diagram shows how three people can have quite different microsatellite arrangements at the same point (locus) in their DNA. Each will produce a different DNA profile using gel electrophoresis:

**1 Extract DNA from sample**

A sample collected from the tissue of a living or dead organism is treated with chemicals and enzymes to extract the DNA, which is separated and purified.

**2 Amplify microsatellite using PCR**

Specific primers (arrowed) that attach to the flanking regions (light gray) either side of the microsatellite are used to make large quantities of the microsatellite and flanking regions sequence only (no other part of the DNA is amplified/replicated).

**3 Visualize fragments on a gel**

The fragments are separated by length, using **gel electrophoresis**. DNA, which is negatively charged, moves toward the positive terminal. The smaller fragments travel faster than larger ones.

DNA from individual 'A':
DNA from individual 'B':
DNA from individual 'C':

Microsatellite

Microsatellite from individual 'A':
Microsatellite from individual 'B':
Microsatellite from individual 'C':

Primers   Flanking region   STR
DNA

The results of PCR are many fragments

A   B   C

The products of PCR amplification (making many copies) are fragments of different sizes that can be directly visualized using gel electrophoresis.

Largest fragments
Smallest fragments

**Related activities**: Polymerase Chain Reaction, Gel Electrophoresis

A 3

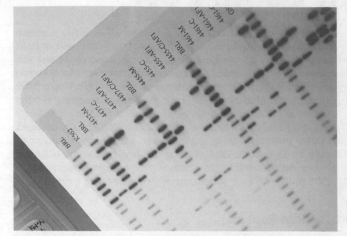

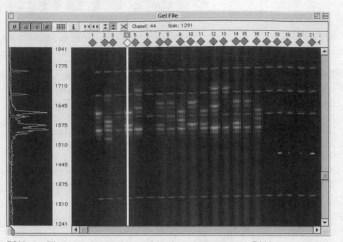

The photo above shows a film output from a DNA profiling procedure. Those lanes with many regular bands are used for calibration; they contain DNA fragment sizes of known length. These calibration lanes can be used to determine the length of fragments in the unknown samples.

DNA profiling can be automated in the same way as DNA sequencing. Computer software is able to display the results of many samples run at the same time. In the photo above, the sample in lane 4 has been selected. It displays fragments of different length on the left of the screen.

1. Describe the properties of **short tandem repeats** that are important to the application of **DNA profiling** technology:

_____

_____

_____

_____

_____

2. Explain the role of each of the following techniques in the process of DNA profiling:

(a) Gel electrophoresis: _____

_____

_____

(b) PCR: _____

_____

_____

3. Describe the three main steps in DNA profiling using PCR:

(a) _____

_____

_____

(b) _____

_____

_____

(c) _____

_____

_____

4. Explain why as many as 10 STR sites are used to gain a DNA profile for forensic evidence: _____

_____

# DNA Chips

Microarrays (DNA chips or gene chips) are relatively recent tools in gene research. Their development a decade ago built on earlier DNA probe technology and provided a tool to quickly compare the (known) DNA on a chip with (unknown) DNA to determine which genes were present in a sample or to determine the code of an unsequenced string of DNA. Microarrays have also provided a tool which, increasingly, is being used to investigate the activity level (the expression) of those genes. Microarrays rely on **nucleic acid hybridization**, in which a known DNA fragment is used as a **probe** to find complementary sequences. In a microarray, DNA fragments, corresponding to known genes, are fixed to a solid support in an orderly pattern, usually as a series of dots. The fragments are tested for hybridization with samples of labeled cDNA molecules. Computer analysis then reveals which genes are active in different tissues, in different stages of development, or in tissues in different states of health.

**Aspects of Biotechnology**

## What is a DNA Chip?

A **microarray** (DNA chip) consists of DNA probes fixed to a small solid support such as a glass slide or a nylon filter. Each spot on the microarray has thousands to millions of copies of a different **DNA probe**. The probes are single stranded DNA molecules, each representing a gene.

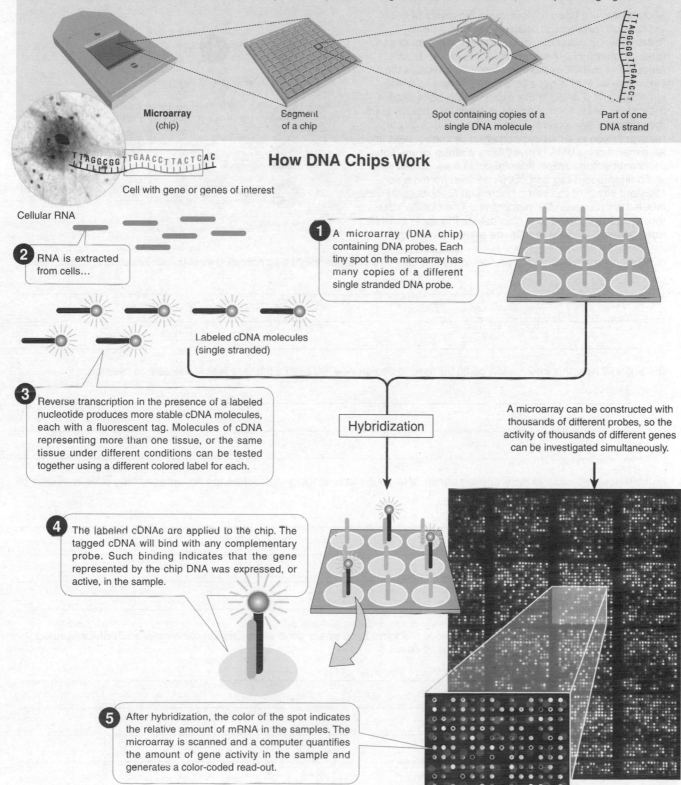

**Microarray** (chip)

**Segment** of a chip

**Spot containing copies of a single DNA molecule**

**Part of one DNA strand**

## How DNA Chips Work

Cell with gene or genes of interest

Cellular RNA

**2** RNA is extracted from cells...

**1** A microarray (DNA chip) containing DNA probes. Each tiny spot on the microarray has many copies of a different single stranded DNA probe.

Labeled cDNA molecules (single stranded)

**3** Reverse transcription in the presence of a labeled nucleotide produces more stable cDNA molecules, each with a fluorescent tag. Molecules of cDNA representing more than one tissue, or the same tissue under different conditions can be tested together using a different colored label for each.

Hybridization

A microarray can be constructed with thousands of different probes, so the activity of thousands of different genes can be investigated simultaneously.

**4** The labeled cDNAs are applied to the chip. The tagged cDNA will bind with any complementary probe. Such binding indicates that the gene represented by the chip DNA was expressed, or active, in the sample.

**5** After hybridization, the color of the spot indicates the relative amount of mRNA in the samples. The microarray is scanned and a computer quantifies the amount of gene activity in the sample and generates a color-coded read-out.

**Related activities**: Gene Cloning Using Plasmids
**Web links**: Genomics, DNA Microarray

**RA 3**

1. Describe one purpose of microarrays: _____

_____

_____

2. (a) Identify the basic principle by which microarrays work: _____

_____

_____

   (b) Identify the role of reverse transcription in microarray technology: _____

_____

3. Microarrays are used to determine the levels of gene expression (expression analysis). In one type of microarray, hybridization of the red (experimental) and green (control) cDNAs is proportional to the relative amounts of mRNA in the samples. Red indicates the overexpression of a gene and green indicates under-expression of a gene in the experimental cells relative the control cells, yellow indicates equal expression in the experimental and control cells, and no color indicates no expression in either experimental or control cells. In an experiment, cDNA derived from a strain of antibiotic resistant bacteria (experimental cells) was labeled with a red fluorescent tag and cDNA derived from a a non-resistant strain of the same bacterium (control cells) was labeled with a green fluorescent tag. The cDNAs were mixed and hybridized to a chip containing spots of DNA from genes 1-25. The results are shown on the right.

   No colour (no expression)

   Red (overexpression)

   Green (underexpression)

   Yellow (equal expression)

   (a) Discuss the conclusions you could make about which genes might be implicated in antibiotic resistance in this case:

_____

_____

_____

   (b) Suggest how this information could be used to design new antibiotics that are less vulnerable to resistance:

_____

_____

_____

4. Explain how microarrays have built on earlier DNA probe technology and describe the advantages they offer in studies of gene expression:

_____

_____

_____

_____

5. Microarrays are frequently used in diagnostic medicine to compare gene expression in cancerous and non-cancerous tissue. Suggest how this information could be used:

_____

_____

_____

_____

_____

# Automated DNA Sequencing

DNA sequencing can be automated using **gel electrophoresis** machines that can sequence up to 600 bases at a time. Automation improves the speed at which samples can be sequenced and has made large scale sequencing projects (such as the **Human Genome Project**) possible. Automated sequencing uses nucleotides labeled with **fluorescent dyes**. With this technique, the entire base sequence for a sample can be determined from a single lane on the gel. Computer software automatically interprets the data from the gel and produces a base sequence.

Aspects of Biotechnology

All photos are RA (unless indicated otherwise)

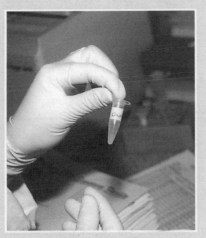

### 1. DNA sample arrives

Purified DNA samples may contain linear DNA or plasmids. The sample should contain about $1 \times 10^{11}$ DNA molecules. The sample is checked to ensure that there is enough DNA present in the sample to work with.

### 2. Primer and reaction mix added

A **DNA primer** is added to the sample which provides a starting sequence for synthesis. Also added is the **sequencing reaction mix** containing the *polymerase enzyme* and free nucleotides, some which are labeled with dye.

### 3. Create dye-labeled fragments

A PCR machine creates fragments of DNA complementary to the original template DNA. Each fragment is tagged with a fluorescent dye-labeled nucleotide. Running for 25 cycles, it creates $25 \times 10^{11}$ single-stranded DNA molecules.

### 4. Centrifuge to create DNA pellet

The sample is chemically precipitated and centrifuged to settle the DNA fragments as a solid pellet at the bottom of the tube. Unused nucleotides, still in the liquid, are discarded.

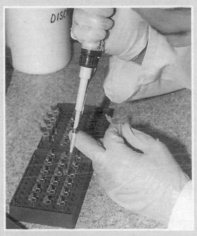

### 5. DNA pellet washed, buffer added

The pellet is washed with ethanol, dried, and a gel loading buffer is added. All that remains now is single stranded DNA with one dye-labeled nucleotide at the end of each molecule.

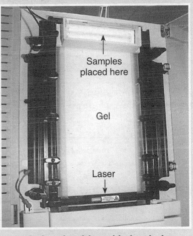

Samples placed here

Gel

Laser

### 6. Acrylamide gel is loaded

The DNA sequencer is prepared by placing the gel (sandwiched between two sheets of glass) into position. A 36 channel 'comb' for receiving the samples is placed at the top of the gel.

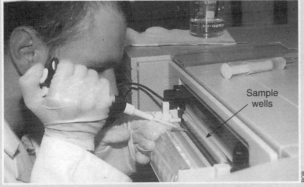

Sample wells

### 7. Loading DNA samples onto gel

Different samples can be placed in each of the 36 wells (funnel shaped receptacles) above the gel. A control DNA sample of known sequence is applied to the first lane of the sequencer. If there are problems with the control sequence then results for all other lanes are considered invalid.

### 8. Running the DNA sequencer

Powerful computer software controls the activity of the DNA sequencer. The gel is left to run for up to 10 hours. During this time an argon laser is constantly scanning across the bottom of the gel to detect the passing of dye-labeled nucleotides attached to DNA fragments.

**Related activities**: The Human Genome Project, Polymerase Chain Reaction, DNA Profiling Using PCR

**RA 3**

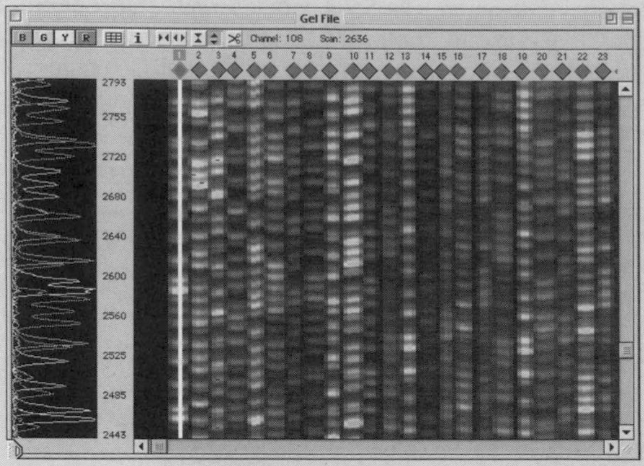

**9. Data collection**

The data from the digital camera are collected by computer software. The first of 23 samples is highlighted above in lane 1 with base sequences appearing on the far left.

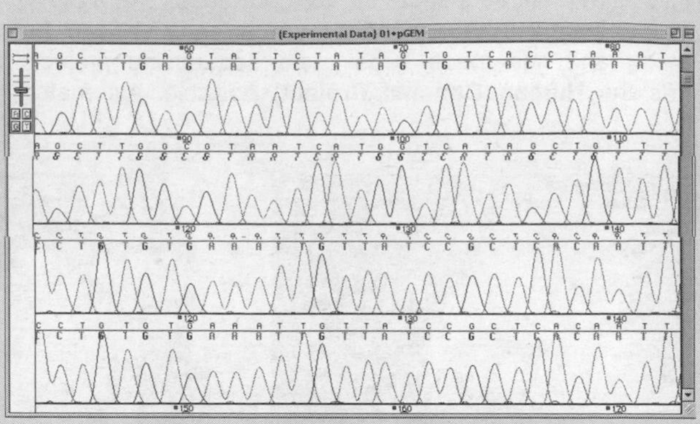

**10. Computer analysis**

The data can be saved as a file for analysis by other computer software. Such software can provide a printout of the base sequence and perform comparisons with other DNA sequences (e.g. when looking for mutations).

1. Briefly describe how PCR, DNA sequencing, DNA profiling, and/or DNA screening may assist the following areas of study:

(a) Forensic science: _____

_____

_____

(b) Legal disputes: _____

_____

_____

(c) Medical applications: _____

_____

_____

(d) Investigations into evolutionary relationships and taxonomy: _____

_____

_____

(e) Archaeology and anthropology: _____

_____

_____

(f) Conservation of endangered species: _____

_____

_____

(g) Management of livestock breeding programs: _____

_____

_____

2. Explain why the Human Genome Project provided a large stimulus for the automation of DNA sequencing technology:

_____

_____

# Gene Cloning Using Plasmids

**Gene cloning** is a process of making large quantities of a desired piece of DNA once it has been isolated. The purpose of this process is often to yield large quantities of either an individual gene or its protein product when the gene is expressed. Methods have been developed to insert a DNA fragment of interest (e.g. a human gene for a desired protein) into the DNA of a vector, resulting in a **recombinant DNA molecule** or **molecular clone**. A **vector** is a self-replicating DNA molecule (e.g. plasmid or viral DNA) used to transmit a gene from one organism into another. To be useful, all vectors must be able to replicate inside their host

organism, they must have one or more sites at which a restriction enzyme can cut, and they must have some kind of **genetic marker** that allows them to be easily identified. Organisms such as bacteria, viruses and yeasts have DNA that behaves in this way. Large quantities of the desired gene can be obtained if the recombinant molecule is allowed to replicate in an appropriate host. The host (e.g. bacterium) may then go on to express the gene and produce the desired protein. Two types of vector are **plasmids** (illustrated below) and **bacteriophages** (viruses that infect bacteria).

## Cloning a Human Gene

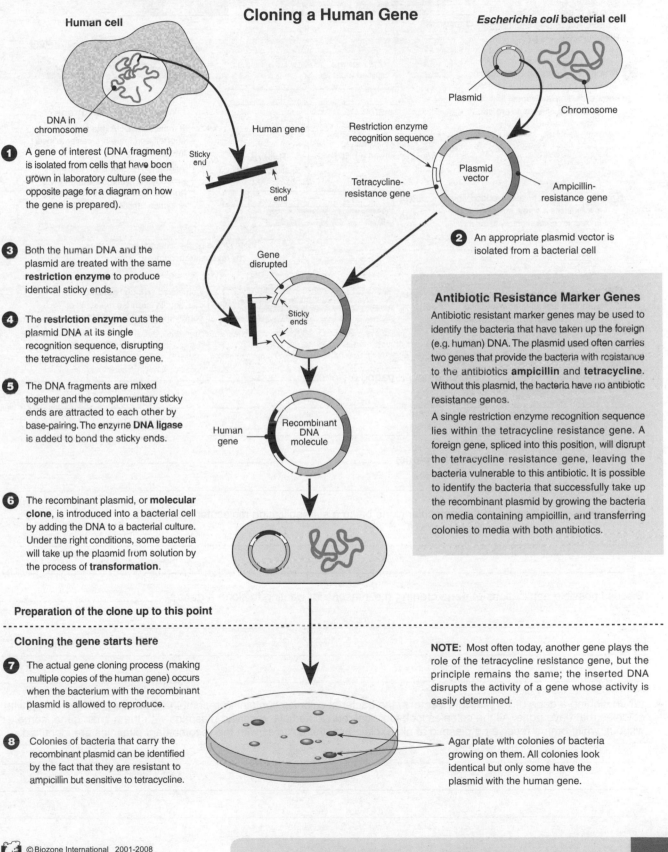

**Human cell**

DNA in chromosome

**1** A gene of interest (DNA fragment) is isolated from cells that have been grown in laboratory culture (see the opposite page for a diagram on how the gene is prepared).

Human gene

Sticky end

Sticky end

**3** Both the human DNA and the plasmid are treated with the same **restriction enzyme** to produce identical sticky ends.

**4** The **restriction enzyme** cuts the plasmid DNA at its single recognition sequence, disrupting the tetracycline resistance gene.

**5** The DNA fragments are mixed together and the complementary sticky ends are attracted to each other by base-pairing. The enzyme **DNA ligase** is added to bond the sticky ends.

Gene disrupted

Sticky ends

Human gene

Recombinant DNA molecule

**6** The recombinant plasmid, or **molecular clone**, is introduced into a bacterial cell by adding the DNA to a bacterial culture. Under the right conditions, some bacteria will take up the plasmid from solution by the process of **transformation**.

*Escherichia coli* **bacterial cell**

Plasmid

Chromosome

Restriction enzyme recognition sequence

Plasmid vector

Tetracycline-resistance gene

Ampicillin-resistance gene

**2** An appropriate plasmid vector is isolated from a bacterial cell

### Antibiotic Resistance Marker Genes

Antibiotic resistant marker genes may be used to identify the bacteria that have taken up the foreign (e.g. human) DNA. The plasmid used often carries two genes that provide the bacteria with resistance to the antibiotics **ampicillin** and **tetracycline**. Without this plasmid, the bacteria have no antibiotic resistance genes.

A single restriction enzyme recognition sequence lies within the tetracycline resistance gene. A foreign gene, spliced into this position, will disrupt the tetracycline resistance gene, leaving the bacteria vulnerable to this antibiotic. It is possible to identify the bacteria that successfully take up the recombinant plasmid by growing the bacteria on media containing ampicillin, and transferring colonies to media with both antibiotics.

**Preparation of the clone up to this point**

- - - - - - - - - - - - - - - - - - - - - - - - - - - - - - - -

**Cloning the gene starts here**

**7** The actual gene cloning process (making multiple copies of the human gene) occurs when the bacterium with the recombinant plasmid is allowed to reproduce.

**8** Colonies of bacteria that carry the recombinant plasmid can be identified by the fact that they are resistant to ampicillin but sensitive to tetracycline.

**NOTE**: Most often today, another gene plays the role of the tetracycline resistance gene, but the principle remains the same; the inserted DNA disrupts the activity of a gene whose activity is easily determined.

Agar plate with colonies of bacteria growing on them. All colonies look identical but only some have the plasmid with the human gene.

**Related activities**: Restriction Enzymes, Transgenic Organisms
**Web links**: Gene Cloning

**RA 3**

## Preparing a Gene For Cloning

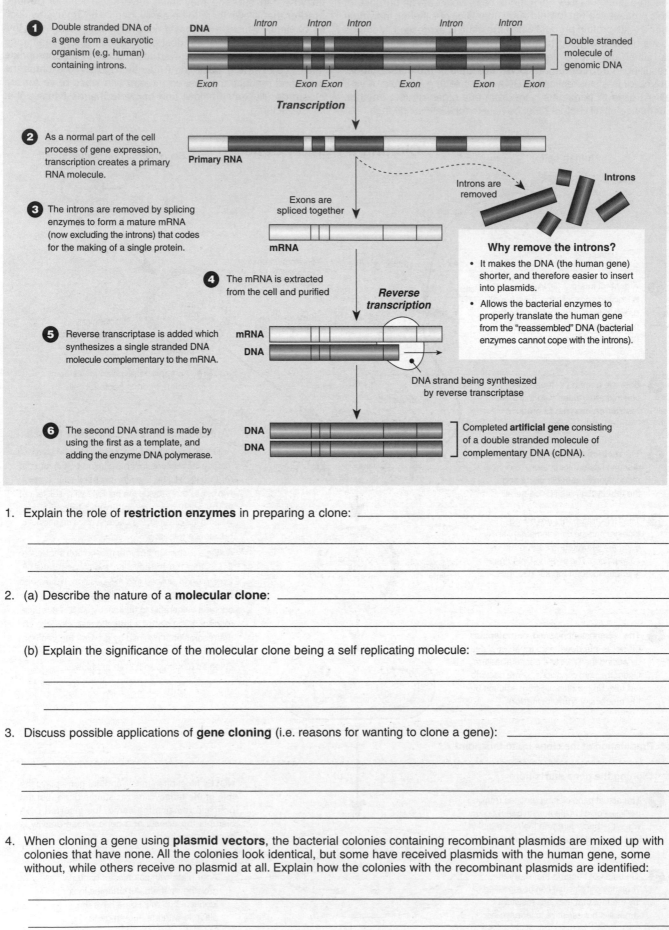

1. Double stranded DNA of a gene from a eukaryotic organism (e.g. human) containing introns.

DNA — *Intron* *Intron* *Intron* *Intron* *Intron*

*Exon* *Exon* *Exon* *Exon* *Exon* *Exon*

Double stranded molecule of genomic DNA

**Transcription**

2. As a normal part of the cell process of gene expression, transcription creates a primary RNA molecule.

**Primary RNA**

3. The introns are removed by splicing enzymes to form a mature mRNA (now excluding the introns) that codes for the making of a single protein.

Exons are spliced together

**mRNA**

Introns are removed

**Introns**

### Why remove the introns?

- It makes the DNA (the human gene) shorter, and therefore easier to insert into plasmids.
- Allows the bacterial enzymes to properly translate the human gene from the "reassembled" DNA (bacterial enzymes cannot cope with the introns).

4. The mRNA is extracted from the cell and purified

*Reverse transcription*

5. Reverse transcriptase is added which synthesizes a single stranded DNA molecule complementary to the mRNA.

**mRNA**

**DNA**

DNA strand being synthesized by reverse transcriptase

6. The second DNA strand is made by using the first as a template, and adding the enzyme DNA polymerase.

**DNA**

**DNA**

Completed **artificial gene** consisting of a double stranded molecule of complementary DNA (cDNA).

1. Explain the role of **restriction enzymes** in preparing a clone: _____

_____

_____

2. (a) Describe the nature of a **molecular clone**: _____

_____

(b) Explain the significance of the molecular clone being a self replicating molecule: _____

_____

_____

3. Discuss possible applications of **gene cloning** (i.e. reasons for wanting to clone a gene): _____

_____

_____

_____

4. When cloning a gene using **plasmid vectors**, the bacterial colonies containing recombinant plasmids are mixed up with colonies that have none. All the colonies look identical, but some have received plasmids with the human gene, some without, while others receive no plasmid at all. Explain how the colonies with the recombinant plasmids are identified:

_____

_____

_____

# Genetically Modified Plants

Plants with **novel traits** may be produced by traditional methods, such as accelerated mutagenesis or hybridization. More recently, recombinant DNA techniques and **marker assisted breeding** have allowed a much more controlled and directed approach to introducing new genetic material into plants. Genomic studies of plants, particularly the major crop plants such as rice and wheat, have enabled scientists to identify the genes for particular traits (below) and apply these new technologies to rapidly develop new, high yielding crop varieties. A large number of plants, including many crop plants, have now been genetically modified using recombinant DNA techniques, and the methodology for this (called **transformation**) is now well established (see the next page). Scientists are also developing marker assisted breeding technology to move beneficial alleles into modern crop breeding lines through conventional cross breeding. In this method, the allele itself serves as a traceable marker for the trait and seedlings can be scanned for the allele's presence at every round of breeding. This shortens the time it takes to develop a new crop variety. The genetic manipulation of plants through these methods has enabled important agricultural crops to be endowed with new traits that increase yield, improve pest resistance, and reduce the need for agrichemicals.

## Matching Traits to Genes in Crop Plants

In crop research, standard mapping techniques can be used to identify the possible location of a gene on a chromosome. Sequencing the DNA in that region enables the gene to then be identified. To find out the gene's function in the plant, scientists can use any one of the techniques described below (A-C).

### A Database search

To compare a new desirable gene with those already sequenced in other organisms.

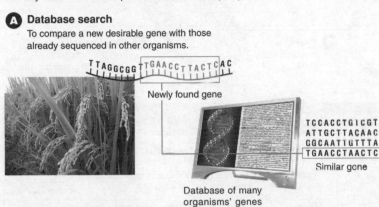

Newly found gene

TCCACCTGICGT
ATTGCTTACAAC
GGCAATTGTTTA
TGAACCTAACTC

Similar gene

Database of many organisms' genes

The genes responsible for basic cellular activities are often nearly identical in different organisms. A newly found gene can be compared with known genes in existing databases to reveal close matches. 20 000 of the 30 000-50 000 predicted genes in rice have sequence similarity (homology) to previously discovered genes whose function is known.

### B Expression profile

To determine when the newly found gene is expressed, hence its probable function.

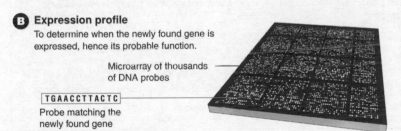

Microarray of thousands of DNA probes

TGAACCTTACTC

Probe matching the newly found gene

A microarray contains thousands of DNA fragments called probes. Each one matches a mRNA, which acts as a signature for gene activity. When plant cell samples are washed across the microarray, any mRNAs present will stick to their matching probes and fluoresce. If a gene is activated (expressed) at one particular stage of plant development, it is assumed to play a role in that stage.

### C Mutant library

To compare the expression of a gene in a normal and a mutant plant in order to determine the function of the newly found gene.

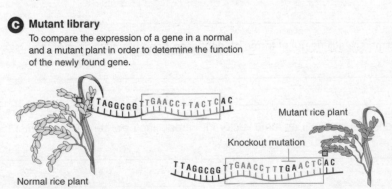

Mutant rice plant

Knockout mutation

Normal rice plant

A small piece of DNA inserted into a gene of interest can "knock out," or silence, that gene in the developing plant. Screening the mutant for differences from normal plants can reveal the gene's usual role.

### Desirable Traits

Plant breeders seek to modify traits that lead to increases in yield or improved nutritional value.

**Growth**
Grain size or number
Size of seed head
Maturation rate

**Architecture**
Height
Branching
Flowering

**Stress tolerance**
Drought
Pests and diseases
Herbicides
Intensive fertilizer
  application

**Nutrient content/quality**
Starch
Proteins
Lipids
Vitamins

## Predicted Classification of Rice Genes

Rice has a relatively small genome compared with other crop plants (430 million bp compared with 3 billion bp in corn and 16 billion bp in wheat). Because of this, it has been the easiest of all the cereals to work with and is the first to have had its entire genome sequenced. The methods described (left) have been already been used to determine (or predict) the functions of a large fraction of the genes in rice.

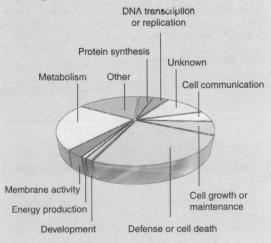

DNA transcription or replication

Protein synthesis

Unknown

Metabolism

Other

Cell communication

Membrane activity

Cell growth or maintenance

Energy production

Development

Defense or cell death

Adapted from: Goff and Salmeron (2004). Back to the future of cereals. Scientific American 291(2), August 2004, pp. 26-33.

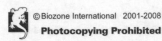

**Related activities**: Genome Projects
**Web links**: DNA Microarray

RA 2

# Transformation using a *Ti* Plasmid in *Agrobacterium*

The *Ti* plasmid from the soil bacteria, *Agrobacterium tumefaciens*, causes tumors (galls) in plants. It can be successfully transferred to plant cells where a segment of its DNA can be integrated into the plant's chromosome.

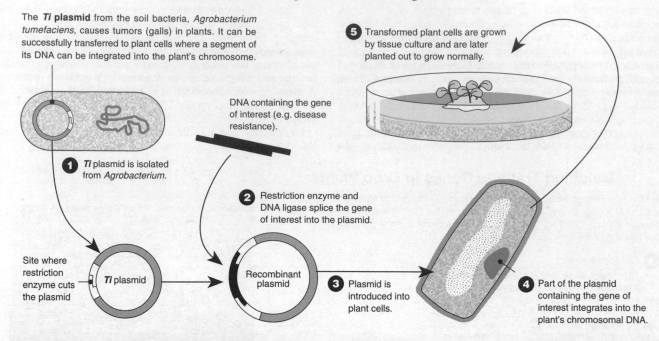

**① ** *Ti* plasmid is isolated from *Agrobacterium*.

DNA containing the gene of interest (e.g. disease resistance).

**② ** Restriction enzyme and DNA ligase splice the gene of interest into the plasmid.

Site where restriction enzyme cuts the plasmid

*Ti* plasmid

Recombinant plasmid

**③ ** Plasmid is introduced into plant cells.

**④ ** Part of the plasmid containing the gene of interest integrates into the plant's chromosomal DNA.

**⑤ ** Transformed plant cells are grown by tissue culture and are later planted out to grow normally.

## Examples of Genetically Modified Plants

| Crop | Phenotypic trait altered | Crop | Phenotypic trait altered |
|---|---|---|---|
| **Argentine canola** | Herbicide tolerance, modified seed fatty acid content (high oleic acid/low linolenic acid expression), pollination control system (male sterility, fertility restoration). | **Potato** | Resistance to: Colorado potato beetle, leafroll *luteovirus*, potato virus Y. |
| | | **Rice** | Herbicide resistance, adding provitamin A. |
| **Carnation** | Increased shelf-life (delayed senescence), herbicide tolerance, modified flower color. | **Soybean** | Herbicide resistance, modified fatty acid content (high oleic acid/low linolenic acid expression), herbicide tolerance. |
| **Chicory** | Male sterility, herbicide tolerance. | **Squash** | Resistance to infection: cucumber mosaic virus, watermelon mosaic virus, zucchini yellow mosaic virus. |
| **Cotton** | Herbicide tolerance, resistance to lepidopteran pests (e.g. cotton worm, pink bollworm, tobacco budworm). | | |
| **Flax** (linseed) | Herbicide tolerance. | **Sugar beet** | Herbicide tolerance. |
| **Maize** | Herbicide tolerance, male sterility, resistance to European corn borer. | **Tobacco** | Herbicide tolerance. |
| | | **Tomato** | Increased shelf-life through delayed ripening and delayed softening. Resistance to lepidopteran pests. |
| **Melon** | Delayed ripening. | | |
| **Papaya** | Resistance to infection by papaya ringspot virus. | **Wheat** | Herbicide tolerance. |

1. For each of the following traits, suggest features that could be desirable in terms of increasing yield:

   (a) Grain size or number: _____

   (b) Maturation rate: _____

   (c) Pest resistance: _____

2. Suggest why the genomic studies of other organisms are still useful in terms of identifying gene functions in crop plants:

   _____

   _____

3. Describe the property of *Agrobacterium tumefaciens* that makes it an ideal vector for introducing new genes into plants:

   _____

   _____

4. Suggest why a modified protein content might be desirable in a food crop: _____

   _____

# Transgenic Organisms

**Transgenesis** is concerned with the movement of genes from one species to another. An organism developing from a cell into which foreign DNA has been inserted is called a **transgenic organism**. Transgenic techniques have been applied to plants, animals, and bacteria. They allow direct modification of a genome and enable traits to be introduced that are not naturally present in a species. This technology can be applied to improving crops and livestock, producing human proteins, and treating genetic defects through **gene therapy**. Cloning technology can be used to propagate transgenic organisms so that introduced genes quickly become part of the germ line (and are inherited). Some methods involved in transgenesis are shown below:

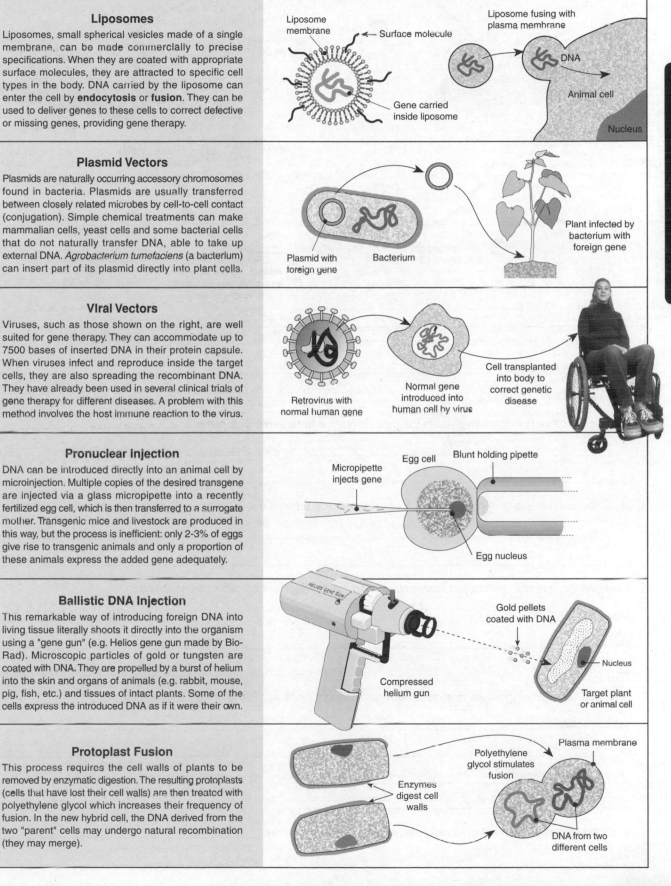

## Liposomes

Liposomes, small spherical vesicles made of a single membrane, can be made commercially to precise specifications. When they are coated with appropriate surface molecules, they are attracted to specific cell types in the body. DNA carried by the liposome can enter the cell by **endocytosis** or **fusion**. They can be used to deliver genes to these cells to correct defective or missing genes, providing gene therapy.

Liposome membrane — Surface molecule
Liposome fusing with plasma membrane
DNA
Animal cell
Nucleus
Gene carried inside liposome

## Plasmid Vectors

Plasmids are naturally occurring accessory chromosomes found in bacteria. Plasmids are usually transferred between closely related microbes by cell-to-cell contact (conjugation). Simple chemical treatments can make mammalian cells, yeast cells and some bacterial cells that do not naturally transfer DNA, able to take up external DNA. *Agrobacterium tumefaciens* (a bacterium) can insert part of its plasmid directly into plant cells.

Plasmid with foreign gene    Bacterium
Plant infected by bacterium with foreign gene

## Viral Vectors

Viruses, such as those shown on the right, are well suited for gene therapy. They can accommodate up to 7500 bases of inserted DNA in their protein capsule. When viruses infect and reproduce inside the target cells, they are also spreading the recombinant DNA. They have already been used in several clinical trials of gene therapy for different diseases. A problem with this method involves the host immune reaction to the virus.

Retrovirus with normal human gene
Normal gene introduced into human cell by virus
Cell transplanted into body to correct genetic disease

## Pronuclear Injection

DNA can be introduced directly into an animal cell by microinjection. Multiple copies of the desired transgene are injected via a glass micropipette into a recently fertilized egg cell, which is then transferred to a surrogate mother. Transgenic mice and livestock are produced in this way, but the process is inefficient: only 2-3% of eggs give rise to transgenic animals and only a proportion of these animals express the added gene adequately.

Micropipette injects gene    Egg cell    Blunt holding pipette
Egg nucleus

## Ballistic DNA Injection

This remarkable way of introducing foreign DNA into living tissue literally shoots it directly into the organism using a "gene gun" (e.g. Helios gene gun made by Bio-Rad). Microscopic particles of gold or tungsten are coated with DNA. They are propelled by a burst of helium into the skin and organs of animals (e.g. rabbit, mouse, pig, fish, etc.) and tissues of intact plants. Some of the cells express the introduced DNA as if it were their own.

HELIOS GENE GUN
Compressed helium gun
Gold pellets coated with DNA
Nucleus
Target plant or animal cell

## Protoplast Fusion

This process requires the cell walls of plants to be removed by enzymatic digestion. The resulting protoplasts (cells that have lost their cell walls) are then treated with polyethylene glycol which increases their frequency of fusion. In the new hybrid cell, the DNA derived from the two "parent" cells may undergo natural recombination (they may merge).

Enzymes digest cell walls
Polyethylene glycol stimulates fusion
Plasma membrane
DNA from two different cells

Aspects of Biotechnology

**Related activities**: Applications of GMOs, Genetically Modified Plants

RA 2

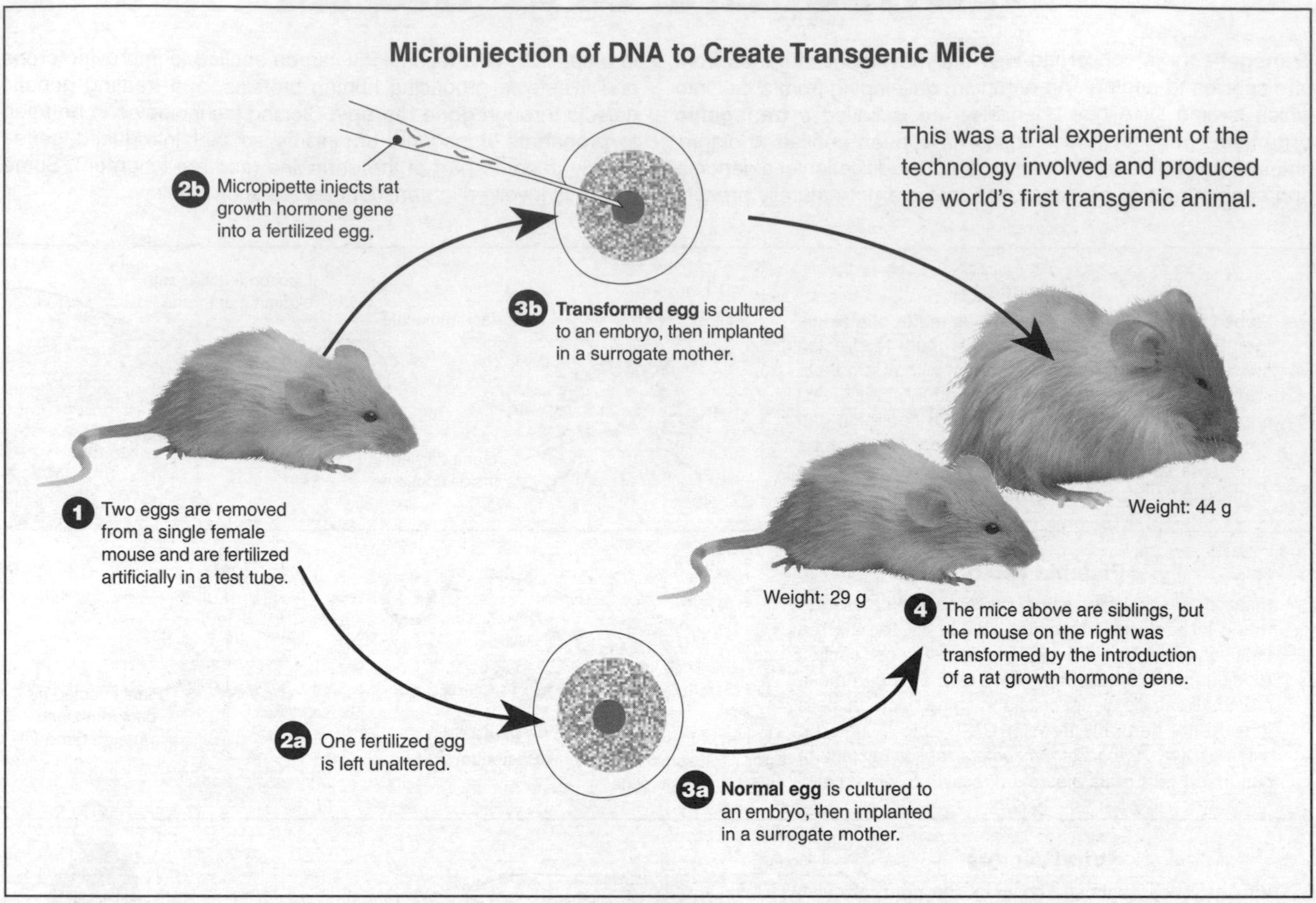

## Microinjection of DNA to Create Transgenic Mice

**2b** Micropipette injects rat growth hormone gene into a fertilized egg.

This was a trial experiment of the technology involved and produced the world's first transgenic animal.

**3b** **Transformed egg** is cultured to an embryo, then implanted in a surrogate mother.

**1** Two eggs are removed from a single female mouse and are fertilized artificially in a test tube.

**2a** One fertilized egg is left unaltered.

**3a** **Normal egg** is cultured to an embryo, then implanted in a surrogate mother.

Weight: 44 g

Weight: 29 g

**4** The mice above are siblings, but the mouse on the right was transformed by the introduction of a rat growth hormone gene.

1. In the context of recombinant DNA technology, define the terms:

   (a) **Transgenesis**: _____

   (b) Foreign DNA: _____

2. Outline the basic principles involved in the production of a **transgenic organism**: _____

   _____

   _____

3. Describe an example of improvement in a commercial crop brought about by the application of transgenic techniques:

   _____

   _____

4. Describe three human needs that have encouraged the development of transgenic techniques:

   (a) _____

   (b) _____

   (c) _____

5. Describe two advantages and one disadvantage of using viruses as vectors for gene delivery:

   (a) Advantages: _____

   _____

   _____

   (b) Disadvantage: _____

6. Explain the purpose behind the transgenic mice experiment (above): _____

   _____

# Gene Therapy

**Gene therapy** refers to the application of gene technology to correct or replace defective genes. It was first envisioned as a treatment, or even a cure, for genetic disorders, but it could also be used to treat a wide range of diseases, including those that resist conventional treatments. Gene therapy may operate by providing a correctly working version of a faulty gene or by adding a **novel gene** to perform a corrective role. In other cases, gene expression may be blocked in order to control cellular (or viral) activity. About two thirds of currently approved gene therapy procedures are targeting cancer, about one quarter aim to treat genetic disorders, such as cystic fibrosis, and the remainder are attempting to provide relief for infectious diseases. Gene therapy requires a **gene delivery system**; a way to transfer the gene to the patient's cells. This may be achieved using a infectious agent such as a virus; a technique called **transfection**. A promising development has been the recent approval for gene therapy to be used in treating tumors in cancer patients. Severe combined immune deficiency syndrome (SCIDS) has also shown improvement after gene therapy. Infants treated for this inherited, normally lethal condition have become healthy young adults (see below). Gene therapy involving **somatic cells** may be therapeutic, but the genetic changes are not inherited. The transfection of **stem cells**, rather than mature somatic cells, achieves a longer persistence of therapy in patients. In the future, the introduction of corrective genes into **germline cells** will enable genetic corrections to be inherited.

## Gene Delivery Using Extracted Cells

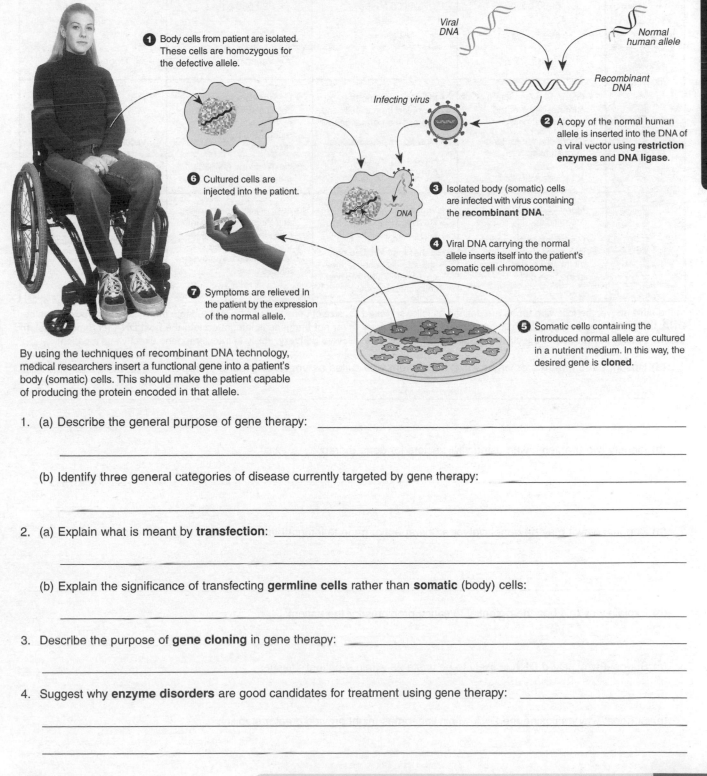

1 Body cells from patient are isolated. These cells are homozygous for the defective allele.

*Viral DNA*

*Normal human allele*

*Recombinant DNA*

*Infecting virus*

2 A copy of the normal human allele is inserted into the DNA of a viral vector using **restriction enzymes** and **DNA ligase**.

6 Cultured cells are injected into the patient.

3 Isolated body (somatic) cells are infected with virus containing the **recombinant DNA**.

*DNA*

4 Viral DNA carrying the normal allele inserts itself into the patient's somatic cell chromosome.

7 Symptoms are relieved in the patient by the expression of the normal allele.

5 Somatic cells containing the introduced normal allele are cultured in a nutrient medium. In this way, the desired gene is **cloned**.

By using the techniques of recombinant DNA technology, medical researchers insert a functional gene into a patient's body (somatic) cells. This should make the patient capable of producing the protein encoded in that allele.

1.  (a) Describe the general purpose of gene therapy: _____

    _____

    (b) Identify three general categories of disease currently targeted by gene therapy: _____

    _____

2.  (a) Explain what is meant by **transfection**: _____

    _____

    (b) Explain the significance of transfecting **germline cells** rather than **somatic** (body) cells:

    _____

3.  Describe the purpose of **gene cloning** in gene therapy: _____

    _____

4.  Suggest why **enzyme disorders** are good candidates for treatment using gene therapy: _____

    _____

    _____

**Related activities**: Gene Delivery Systems, Vectors for Gene Therapy
**Web links**: Gene Therapy

RA 2

# Vectors for Gene Therapy

Gene therapy usually requires a **vector** (carrier) to introduce the DNA. The majority of approved clinical gene therapy protocols (63%) employ **retroviral vectors** to deliver the selected gene to the target cells, although there is considerable risk in using these vectors (below). Other widely used vectors include adenoviral vectors (16%), and liposomes (13%). The remaining 8% employ a variety of vector systems, the majority of which include injection of naked plasmid DNA.

| Vectors That Can Be Used For Gene Therapy | | | |
|---|---|---|---|
| **Retrovirus** | **Adenovirus** | **Liposome** | **Naked DNA** |
| **Insert size:** 8000 bases | 8000 bases | >20 000 bases | >20 000 bases |
| **Integration:** Yes | No | No | No |
| ***In vivo* delivery:** Poor | High | Variable | Poor |
| **Advantages** • Integrate genes into the chromosomes of the human host cell. • Offers chance for long-term stability. | • Modified for gene therapy, they infect human cells and express the normal gene. • Most do not cause disease. • Have a large capacity to carry foreign genes. | • Liposomes seek out target cells using sugars in their membranes that are recognized by cell receptors. • Have no viral genes that may cause disease. | • Have no viral genes that may cause disease. • Expected to be useful for vaccination. |
| **Disadvantages** • Many infect only cells that are dividing. • Genes integrate randomly into chromosomes, so might disrupt useful genes in the host cell. | • Viruses may have poor survival due to attack by the host's immune system. • Genes may function only sporadically because they are not integrated into host cell's chromosome. | • Less efficient than viruses at transferring genes into cells, but recent work on using sugars to aid targeting have improved success rate. | • Unstable in most tissues of the body. • Inefficient at gene transfer. |

In the table above, the following terms are defined as follows: **Naked DNA**: the genes are applied by ballistic injection (firing using a gene gun) or by regular hypodermic injection of plasmid DNA. **Insert size**: size of gene that can be inserted into the vector. **Integration**: whether or not the gene is integrated into the host DNA (chromosomes). **In vivo delivery**: ability to transfer a gene directly into a patient.

1. (a) Describe the features of viruses that make them well suited as **vectors** for gene therapy: _____

_____

_____

(b) Identify two problems with using viral vectors for gene therapy: _____

_____

_____

2. (a) Suggest why it may be beneficial for a (therapeutic) gene to integrate into the patient's chromosome: _____

_____

_____

(b) Explain why this has the potential to cause problems for the patient: _____

_____

3. (a) Suggest why naked DNA is likely to be unstable within a patient's tissues: _____

_____

(b) Suggest why enclosing the DNA within liposomes might provide greater stability: _____

_____

**Related activities**: Gene Therapy, Gene Delivery Systems
**Web links**: Gene Therapy Primer

# Gene Delivery Systems

The mapping of the human genome has improved the feasibility of gene therapy as a option for treating an increasingly wide range of diseases, but it remains technically difficult to deliver genes successfully to a patient. Even after a gene has been identified, cloned, and transferred to a patient, it must be expressed normally. To date, the success of gene therapy has been generally poor, and improvements have been short-lived or counteracted by adverse side effects. Inserted genes may reach only about 1% of target cells and those that reach their destination may work inefficiently and produce too little protein, too slowly to be of benefit. In addition, many patients react immunologically to the vectors used in gene transfer. Much of the current research is focused on improving the efficiency of gene transfer and expression. One of the first gene therapy trials was for **cystic fibrosis** (CF). CF was an obvious candidate for gene therapy because, in most cases, the disease is caused by a single, known gene mutation. However, despite its early promise, gene therapy for this disease has been disappointing (below).

## Gene Therapy as a Potential Treatment for Cystic Fibrosis (CF)

In cystic fibrosis, a gene mutation causes the body to produce an abnormally thick, sticky mucus that accumulates in the lungs and intestines. The identification and isolation of the CF gene in 1989 meant that scientists could look for ways in which to correct the genetic defect rather than just treating the symptoms using traditional therapies.

In trials, normal genes were isolated and inserted into patients using vectors such as **adenoviruses** and **liposomes**.

In order to prevent the progressive and ultimately lethal lung damage, the main target of CF gene therapy is the lung. The viral vector was piped directly into the lung, whereas the liposomes were inhaled in a spray formulation. The results of these trials were disappointing; on average, there was only a 25% correction, the effects were short lived, and the benefits were quickly reversed. Alarmingly, the adenovirus used in one of the trials led to the death of one patient.

Source: Cystic Fibrosis Trust, UK.

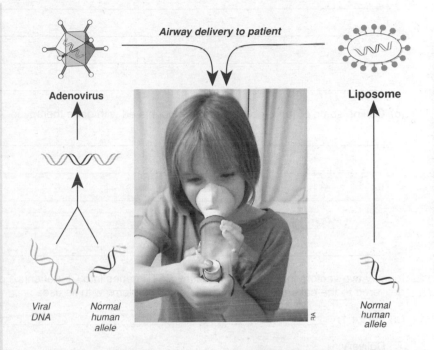

**Airway delivery to patient**

**Adenovirus**

**Liposome**

*Viral DNA*  *Normal human allele*

*Normal human allele*

An **adenovirus** that normally causes colds is genetically modified to make it safe and to carry the normal (unmutated) CFTR ('cystic fibrosis') gene.

**Liposomes** are tiny fat globules. Normal CF genes are enclosed in liposomes, which fuse with plasma membranes and deliver the genes into the cells.

## Gene Delivery Systems Used In Human Patients

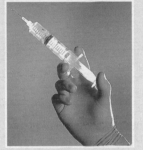

### Hypodermic needle injection

▶ Injection of the vectors directly into the bloodstream or organs of the patient. Vectors injected into the blood travel through the body and may be taken up by the target cells.

▶ Injections of plasmid DNA into thymus, skin, cardiac muscle and skeletal muscle have already proved successful in non-human trials (mice and primates).

### Aerosol delivery

▶ Aerosols and nebulizers offer an effective spread and efficient delivery of the vector to the site of certain target cells (especially in the respiratory tract).

▶ Used in trials of gene therapy for cystic fibrosis, but effective only on epithelial cells that can be reached by the aerosol.

### Ballistic DNA injection

▶ Plasmid DNA with the gene of interest is coated onto microbeads. These are 'fired' at the target cells using gas pressure or a high voltage discharge.

▶ Used to transfer genes to a wide variety of cell lines (*ex vivo*) or directly into surgically exposed tissue (*in vivo*).

▶ May be used in DNA-based vaccines to prevent infectious diseases or cancer.

▶ Allows precise DNA dosages to be delivered, but the genes are expressed transiently and there is considerable cell damage at the delivery site.

*Ballistic DNA injection is also called microprojectile gene transfer, the gene-gun, or particle bombardment method.*

### Gene delivery to extracted cells and cell culture

▶ Target cells are isolated from tissue. Genes are delivered non-specifically to the cell population or as a microinjection of DNA into the nucleus of a single cell.

▶ Cells that have taken up the normal allele are cultured outside the body and re-injected into the patient.

▶ The expression of the normal allele relieves symptoms of the disease.

*An incubator for culturing cell lines (ex-vivo).*

©1999 University of Kansas Office of University Relations

**Related activities**: Vectors for Gene Therapy

**RA 2**

1. A great deal of current research is being devoted to discovering a gene therapy solution to treat **cystic fibrosis** (CF):

(a) Describe the symptoms of CF: _____

_____

_____

(b) Explain why this genetic disease has been so eagerly targeted by gene therapy researchers: _____

_____

_____

_____

_____

(c) Outline some of the problems so far encountered with gene therapy for CF: _____

_____

_____

_____

_____

_____

2. Identify two vectors for introducing healthy CFTR genes into CF patients. For each vector, outline how it might be delivered to the patient and describe potential problems with its use:

(a) Vector 1: _____

Delivery: _____

Problems: _____

_____

_____

(b) Vector 2: _____

Delivery: _____

Problems: _____

_____

_____

3. Changes made to chromosomes as a result of gene therapy involving somatic cells are not inherited. Germline gene therapy has the potential to cure disease, but the risks and benefits are still not clear. For each of the points outlined below, evaluate the risk of germline gene therapy relative to somatic cell gene therapy and explain your answer:

(a) Chance of interfering with an essential gene function: _____

_____

_____

_____

(b) Misuse of the therapy to selectively alter phenotype: _____

_____

_____

# Production of Human Proteins

Transgenic microorganisms are now widely used as **biofactories** for the production of human proteins. These proteins are often used to treat metabolic protein-deficiency disorders. **Type 1 diabetes mellitus** is a metabolic disease caused by a lack of insulin and is treatable only with insulin injection. Before the advent of genetic engineering, insulin was extracted from the pancreatic tissue of pigs or cattle. This method was expensive and problematic in that the insulin caused various side effects and was often contaminated. Since the 1980s, human insulin has been mass produced using genetically modified (GM) bacteria (*Escherichia coli*) and yeast (*Saccharomyces cerevisiae*). Similar methods are used for the genetic manipulation of both microorganisms, although the size of the bacterial plasmid requires that the human gene be inserted as two, separately expressed, nucleotide sequences (see below). The use of insulin from GM sources has greatly improved the management of Type 1 diabetes, and the range of formulations now available has allowed diabetics to live much more normal lives than previously.

## Synthesis of human insulin using recombinant DNA technology

Type I diabetes is treated with regular injections of insulin according to daily needs (right). Since the 1980s, human insulin has been mass produced using genetically modified (GM) microorganisms and marketed under various trade names. Various methodologies are employed to produce the insulin, but all involve inserting a human gene into a plasmid (bacterial or yeast), followed by secretion of a protein product from which the active insulin can be derived.

**❶ Identify and synthesize the human gene**

Insulin is a small, simple protein. It comprises a total of 51 amino acids in two polypeptide chains (A and B). The two chains are linked by disulfide bonds. The nucleotide sequence of the gene for human insulin has been determined from the amino acid sequence. The first step in insulin production is to chemically synthesize the DNA chains that carry the specific nucleotide sequences for the A and B chains of insulin (the A and B 'genes').

**❷ Insert the synthetic DNA into plasmids**

Using a tool kit of restriction enzymes and DNA ligase, the synthetic A and B nucleotide sequences are separately inserted into the gene for the bacterial enzyme, β-galactosidase, which is carried on the bacterial plasmid. In *E. coli*, β-galactosidase controls the transcription of genes. To make the bacteria produce insulin, the insulin gene needs to be tied to the gene for this enzyme.

**❸ Insert plasmid into the bacterial cell**

The recombinant plasmids are then introduced to *E. coli* cells in culture conditions that favor the bacterial uptake of plasmid DNA. In practical terms, the synthesis of human insulin requires millions of copies of bacteria whose plasmid has been combined with the insulin gene. The insulin gene is expressed as it replicates with the β-galactosidase in the cell undergoing mitosis.

**❹ Make the functional protein**

The protein formed consists partly of β-galactosidase, joined either to the A or B chain of insulin. The A and B chains are then extracted from the β-galactosidase fragment and purified. The two chains are then mixed and reconnected in a reaction that forms the disulfide cross bridges and the functional human protein, insulin. The final purified product is made suitable for injection and provided in a number of different formulations.

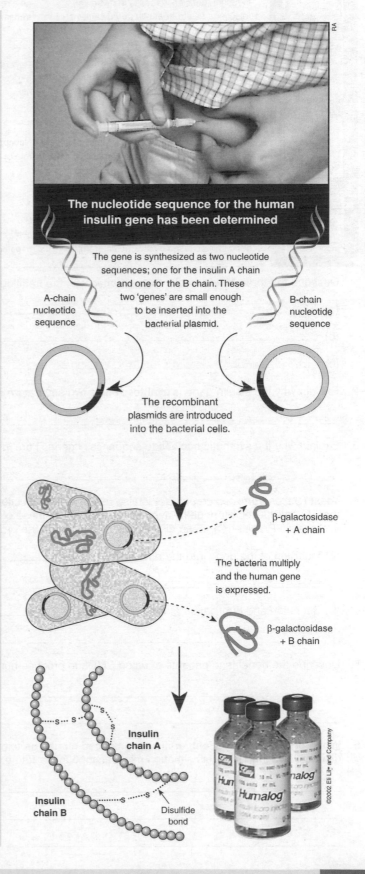

The nucleotide sequence for the human insulin gene has been determined

The gene is synthesized as two nucleotide sequences; one for the insulin A chain and one for the B chain. These two 'genes' are small enough to be inserted into the bacterial plasmid.

A-chain nucleotide sequence

B-chain nucleotide sequence

The recombinant plasmids are introduced into the bacterial cells.

The bacteria multiply and the human gene is expressed.

β-galactosidase + A chain

β-galactosidase + B chain

Insulin chain A

Insulin chain B

Disulfide bond

Aspects of Biotechnology

## Human Proteins Produced Using Genetic Engineering

| Human protein and biological role | Traditional production method | Current production |
|---|---|---|
| **Erythropoetin** <br> A hormone, produced by kidneys, which stimulates red blood cell production. Used to treat anemia in patients with kidney failure. | Not applicable. Previous methods to treat anemia in patients with kidney failure was through repeated blood transfusions. | Cloned gene grown in hamster ovary cells |
| **Human Growth Hormone** <br> Pituitary hormone promoting normal growth in height (deficiency results in dwarfism). Injection used to treat pituitary dwarfism. | Extracted from the pituitary glands of corpses. Many patients developed Creutzfeldt-Jacob disease (CJD) as a result. CJD is a degenerative brain disease, transmitted via infected tissues or their extracts. | Genetically engineered bacteria |
| **Insulin** <br> Regulates the uptake of glucose by cells. Used (via injection) in the treatment of Type 1 (insulin-dependent) diabetes mellitus. | Physical extraction from the pancreatic tissue of pigs or cattle. Problems included high cost, sample contamination, and severe side effects. | Genetically engineered bacteria or yeast |
| **Interferon** <br> Anti-viral substance produced by virus-infected cells. Used in the treatment of hepatitis B and C, some cancers, and multiple sclerosis. | Not applicable. Relatively recent discovery of the role of these proteins in human physiology. | Genetically engineered bacteria |
| **Factor VIII** <br> One of the blood clotting factors normally present in blood. Used in the treatment of hemophilia caused by lack of factor VIII. | Blood donation. Risks of receiving blood contaminated with infective viruses (HIV, hepatitis), despite better screening procedures. | Genetically engineered bacteria |

1. Describe the three major problems associated with the traditional method of obtaining insulin to treat diabetes:

   (a) _____

   (b) _____

   (c) _____

2. Explain why the insulin gene is synthesized as two separate A and B chain nucleotide sequences: _____
   _____

3. Explain why the synthetic nucleotide sequences ('genes') are inserted into the β-galactosidase gene: _____
   _____

4. Yeast (*Saccharomyces cerevisiae*) is also used in the production of human insulin. It is a eukaryote with a larger plasmid than *E. coli*. Its secretory pathways are more similar to those of humans and β-galactosidase is not involved in gene expression. Predict how these differences might change the procedure for insulin production with respect to:

   (a) Insertion of the gene into the plasmid: _____
   _____

   (b) Secretion and purification of the protein product: _____
   _____

5. Describe the benefits to patients of using GMOs to produce human proteins: _____
   _____
   _____

6. When delivered to a patient, artificially produced human proteins only alleviate disease symptoms; they cannot cure the disease. Describe how this situation might change in the future:

   _____
   _____
   _____

# The Human Genome Project

The **Human Genome Project** (HGP) is a publicly funded venture involving many different organizations throughout the world. In 1998, Celera Genomics in the USA began a competing project, as a commercial venture, in a race to be the first to determine the human genome sequence. In 2000, both organizations reached the first draft stage, and the entire genome is now available as a high quality (golden standard) sequence. In addition to determining the order of bases in the human genome, genes are being identified, sequenced, and mapped (their specific chromosomal location identified). The next challenge is to assign functions to the identified genes. By identifying and studying the protein products of genes (a field known as **proteomics**),

scientists can develop a better understanding of genetic disorders. Long term benefits of the HGP are both medical and non-medical (see next page). Many biotechnology companies have taken out patents on gene sequences. This practice is controversial because it restricts the use of the sequence information to the patent holders. Other genome sequencing projects have arisen as a result of the initiative to sequence the human one. In 2002 the International HapMap Project was started with the aim of developing a haplotype map (HapMap) of the human genome. Initially data was gathered from four populations with African, Asian and European ancestry and additional populations may be included as analysis of human genetic variation continues.

## Gene Mapping

This process involves determining the precise position of a gene on a chromosome. Once the position is known, it can be shown on a diagram.

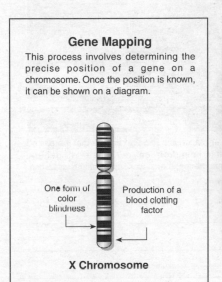

One form of color blindness

Production of a blood clotting factor

**X Chromosome**

## Equipment used for DNA Sequencing

Banks of PCR machines prepare DNA for the sequencing gel stage. The DNA is amplified and chemically tagged (to make the DNA fluoresce and enable visualization on a gel).

Banks of DNA sequencing gels and powerful computers are used to determine the base order in DNA.

## Count of Mapped Genes

The length and number of mapped genes to date for each chromosome are tabulated below. The entire human genome contains approximately 20 000-25 000 genes.

| Chromosome | Length (Mb) | No. of Mapped Genes |
|---|---|---|
| 1 | 263 | 1873 |
| 2 | 255 | 1113 |
| 3 | 214 | 965 |
| 4 | 203 | 614 |
| 5 | 194 | 782 |
| 6 | 183 | 1217 |
| 7 | 171 | 995 |
| 8 | 155 | 591 |
| 9 | 145 | 804 |
| 10 | 144 | 872 |
| 11 | 144 | 1162 |
| 12 | 143 | 894 |
| 13 | 114 | 290 |
| 14 | 109 | 1013 |
| 15 | 106 | 510 |
| 16 | 98 | 658 |
| 17 | 92 | 1034 |
| 18 | 85 | 302 |
| 19 | 67 | 1129 |
| 20 | 72 | 599 |
| 21 | 50 | 386 |
| 22 | 56 | 501 |
| X | 164 | 1021 |
| Y | 59 | 122 |
| | **Total:** | **19 447** |

As at: 28 March 2008  For an update see:
http://gdbwww.gdb.org/gdbreports/
CountGeneByChromosome.html

## Examples of Mapped Genes

The positions of an increasing number of genes have been mapped onto human chromosomes (see below). Sequence variations can cause or contribute to identifiable disorders. Note that chromosome 21 (the smallest human chromosome) has a relatively low gene density, while others are gene rich. This is possibly why trisomy 21 (Down syndrome) is one of the few viable human autosomal trisomies.

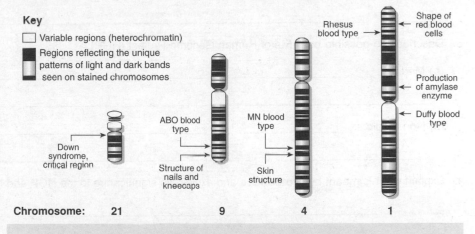

**Key**

☐ Variable regions (heterochromatin)

▨ Regions reflecting the unique patterns of light and dark bands seen on stained chromosomes

Down syndrome, critical region

ABO blood type

Structure of nails and kneecaps

MN blood type

Skin structure

Rhesus blood type

Shape of red blood cells

Production of amylase enzyme

Duffy blood type

**Chromosome:** 21    9    4    1

The aim of the HGP was to produce a continuous block of sequence information for each chromosome. Initially the sequence information was obtained to draft quality, with an error rate of 1 in 1000 bases. The **Gold Standard sequence**, with an error rate of <1 per 100 000 bases, was completed in October 2004. Key results of the research are:

- The analysis suggests that there are perhaps only 20 000-25 000 protein-coding genes in our human genome.
- The number of gaps has been reduced 400-fold to only 341
- It covers 99% of the gene containing parts of the genome and is 99.999% accurate.
- The new sequence correctly identifies almost all known genes (99.74%).
- Its accuracy and completeness allows systematic searches for causes of disease.

Related activities: Genome Projects    RA 2

## Benefits and ethical issues arising from the Human Genome Project

### Medical benefits

- Improved **diagnosis** of disease and predisposition to disease by genetic testing.
- Better identification of disease carriers, through genetic testing.
- Better **drugs** can be designed using knowledge of protein structure (from gene sequence information) rather than by trial and error.
- Greater possibility of successfully using **gene therapy** to correct genetic disorders.

### Non-medical benefits

- Greater knowledge of **family relationships** through genetic testing, e.g. paternity testing in family courts.
- Advances **forensic science** through analysis of DNA at crime scenes.
- Improved knowledge of the evolutionary relationships between humans and other organisms, which will help to develop better, more accurate classification systems.

### Possible ethical issues

- It is unclear whether third parties, e.g. health insurers, have rights to genetic test results.
- If treatment is unavailable for a disease, genetic knowledge about it may have no use.
- Genetic tests are costly, and there is no easy answer as to who should pay for them.
- Genetic information is hereditary so knowledge of an individual's own genome has implications for members of their family.

Couples can already have a limited range of genetic tests to determine the risk of having offspring with some disease-causing mutations.

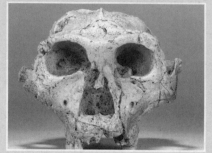

When DNA sequences are available for humans and their ancestors, comparative analysis may provide clues about human evolution.

Legislation is needed to ensure that there is no discrimination on the basis of genetic information, e.g. at work or for health insurance.

1. Briefly describe the objectives of the Human Genome Project (HGP): _____

_____

_____

_____

2. Suggest a reason for developing a HapMap of the human genome: _____

_____

_____

3. Describe two possible **benefits** of Human Genome Project (HGP):

(a) Medical: _____

_____

(b) Non-medical: _____

_____

4. Explain what is meant by **proteomics** and explain its significance to the HGP and the ongoing benefits arising from it:

_____

_____

_____

_____

5. Suggest two possible points of view for one of the **ethical issues** described in the list above (top right):

(a) _____

_____

(b) _____

_____

# Genome Projects

There are many genome projects underway around the world, including the Human Genome Project. The aim of most genome projects is to determine the DNA sequence of the organism's entire genome. Over one hundred bacterial and viral genomes, as well as a number of larger genomes (including honeybee, nematode worm, African clawed frog, pufferfish, zebra fish, rice, cow, dog, and rat) have already been sequenced. Genomes that are, for a variety of reasons, high priority for DNA sequencing include the sea urchin, kangaroo, pig, cat, baboon, silkworm,

rhesus monkey, turkey and even Neanderthals (prehumans). Genome sequencing is costly, so candidates are carefully chosen. Important factors in this choice include the value of the knowledge to practical applications, the degree of technical difficulty involved, and the size of the genome (very large genomes are generally avoided). Genome sizes and the number of genes per genome vary, and are not necessarily correlated with the size and structural complexity of the organism itself. Once completed, genome sequences are analyzed by computer to identify genes.

Artist's impression

MPI

### Yeast (*Saccharomyces cerevisiae*)
**Status:** Completed in 1996
**Number of genes:** 6000
**Genome size:** 13 Mb

The first eukaryotic genome to be completely sequenced. Yeast is used as a model organism to study human cancer.

### Bacteria (*Escherichia coli*)
**Status:** Completed in 1997
**Number of genes:** 4403
**Genome size:** 4.6 Mb

*E. coli* has been used as a laboratory organism for over 70 years. Various strains of *E. coli* are responsible for several human diseases.

### Fruit fly (*Drosophila melanogaster*)
**Status:** Completed in 2000
**Number of genes:** 14 000
**Genome size:** 150 Mb

*Drosophila* has been used extensively for genetic studies for many years. About 50% of all fly proteins show similarities to mammalian proteins.

### Mouse (*Mus musculus*)
**Status:** Completed in 2002
**Number of genes:** 30 000
**Genome size:** 2500 Mb

New drugs destined for human use are often tested on mice because more than 90% of their proteins show similarities to human proteins.

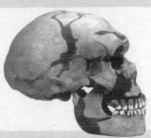

### Chimpanzee (*Pan troglodytes*)
**Status:** Draft, Dec. 2003, Completed, Sept. 2005
**Genome size:** 3000 Mb

Chimp and human genomes differ by <2%. Identifying differences could provide clues to the genetics of diseases such as cancer, to which chimps are less prone.

### Banana (*Musa acuminata*)
**Status:** In progress. Due 2006
**Genome size:** 500-600 Mb

The first tropical crop to be sequenced. Bananas have high economic importance. Knowledge of the genome will assist in producing disease resistant varieties of banana.

### Neanderthal (*H. neanderthalensis*)
**Status:** In progress
**Genome size:** 3000 Mb

This ambitious project is attempting to reconstruct the genome of a Neanderthal. Already more than 1 000 000 base pairs have been sequenced from fossil remains.

### Chicken (*Gallus gallus*)
**Status:** Completed in Feb. 2004
**Genome size:** 1200 Mb

Various human viruses were first found in chickens making this species important for the study of human disease and cross-species transfers. It was the first bird genome to be sequenced.

1. Calculate the number of genes per megabase (Mb) of DNA for the organisms above:

   (a) Yeast: _____ (b) *E. coli*: _____ (c) Fruit fly: _____ (d) Mouse: _____

2. Suggest why the number of genes per Mb of DNA varies between organisms (hint: consider relative sizes of introns):

   _____

   _____

3. Suggest why researchers want to sequence the genomes of plants such as wheat, rice, and maize:

   _____

   _____

4. Use a web engine search to find:

   (a) First **multicellular animal genome** to be sequenced: _____ Date: _____

   (b) First **plant genome** to be sequenced: _____ Date: _____

**Related activities:** Genomes, The Human Genome Project

**RDA 2**

Aspects of Biotechnology

# Cloning by Embryo Splitting

Livestock breeds frequently produce only one individual per pregnancy and all individuals in a herd will have different traits. Cloning (by embryo splitting or other means) makes it possible to produce high value herds with identical traits more quickly. Developed in the 1980s, and adopted by livestock breeders, embryo splitting, or artificial twinning, is the simplest way in which to create a clone. Embryo splitting simply replicates the natural twinning process. A fertilized egg is grown into eight cells before being split into four individual embryos, each consisting of just two cells. The four genetically identical embryos are then implanted into surrogate mothers. While this technique produces multiple clones, the clones are derived from an embryo whose physical characteristics are not completely known. This represents a serious limitation for practical applications when the purpose of the procedure is to produce high value livestock. In 2000, a rhesus macaque was cloned in this manner, with the goal of producing identical individuals that could be used to perfect new therapies for human disease. Cloning technology can also be used to produce early embryos from which undifferentiated **stem cells** can be isolated for use in tissue and cell engineering.

Livestock are selected for cloning on the basis of desirable qualities such as wool, meat, or milk productivity.

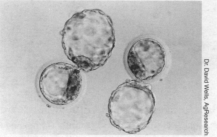

Cloned embryos immediately prior to implantation into a surrogate. These are at the blastocyst stage (a mass of cells that have begun to differentiate).

The individuals produced by embryo splitting have the same characteristics as the parents.

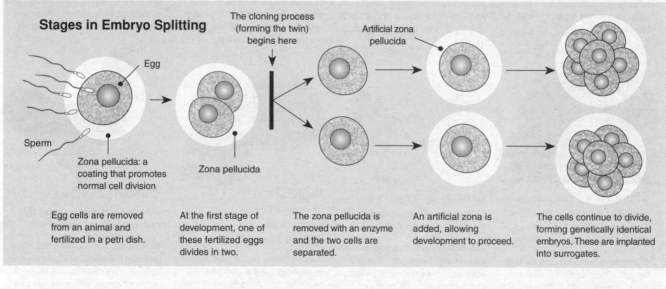

**Stages in Embryo Splitting**

The cloning process (forming the twin) begins here

Artificial zona pellucida

Egg

Sperm

Zona pellucida: a coating that promotes normal cell division

Zona pellucida

Egg cells are removed from an animal and fertilized in a petri dish.

At the first stage of development, one of these fertilized eggs divides in two.

The zona pellucida is removed with an enzyme and the two cells are separated.

An artificial zona is added, allowing development to proceed.

The cells continue to divide, forming genetically identical embryos. These are implanted into surrogates.

1. Explain how **embryo splitting** differs from adult cloning: _____

_____

_____

2. Briefly describe the possible benefits to be gained from cloning the following:

   (a) Stem cells for medical use: _____

   _____

   _____

   (b) High milk yielding cows: _____

   _____

   _____

3. Suggest one reason why it would undesirable to produce all livestock using embryo splitting: _____

_____

_____

**Related activities**: Cloning by Nuclear Transfer, Stem Cells & Tissue Engineering
**Web links**: What is Cloning?

# Cloning by Nuclear Transfer

Clones are genetically identical individuals produced from one parent. Cloning is not new; it has been used in plant breeding for years. In recent years clones have been produced from both embryonic and non-embryonic cells using standard **nuclear transfer techniques** (below). In 2004, Australian genetic researchers successfully cloned a cow (called Brandy) using **serial nuclear transfer** (SNT) which involves an extra round of nuclear transfer to improve the reprograming of the fused donor cells. In animal reproductive technology, cloning has facilitated the rapid production of genetically superior stock. These animals may then be dispersed among commercial herds. The **primary focus** of the new cloning technologies is to provide an economically viable way to rapidly produce transgenic animals with very precise genetic modifications.

## Creating Dolly Using Nuclear Transfer

Dolly, the Finn Dorset lamb born at the Roslin Institute (near Edinburgh) in July 1996, was the first mammal to be cloned from **non-embryonic cells**. Nuclear transfer has been used successfully to clone cells from embryonic tissue, but Dolly was created from a fully differentiated udder cell from a six year old ewe. This cell was made quiescent and then 'tricked' into re-entering an embryonic state. Dolly's birth was a breakthrough, because it showed that the processes leading to cell specialization are not irreversible; even specialized cells can be 'reprogramed' into an embryonic state. The steps involved in creating Dolly are outlined below. While cloning seems relatively easy to achieve using this method, Dolly's early death (right) has raised concerns that the techniques could have caused premature aging. Although there is, as yet, no evidence for this, the long term viability of animals cloned from non-embryonic cells has still to be established.

### Dolly Dies

Dolly the sheep was euthanased (put to sleep) on **February 14th, 2003** after examinations showed she had developed progressive lung disease. Dolly was six years old; half the normal life expectancy of sheep. A post mortem examination showed that her demise was due to a viral infection, not uncommon in older sheep, especially those housed inside. Despite the concerns of some scientists, there is no evidence that cloning was a factor in Dolly contracting the disease.

**1** **Donor cells taken from udder:** Cells from the udder of a Finn Dorset ewe were cultured in low nutrient medium for a week. The nutrient deprived cells stopped dividing, switched off their active genes, and became dormant.

**2** **Unfertilized egg has nucleus removed:** In preparation for the nuclear transfer, an **unfertilized** egg cell was taken from a Scottish blackface ewe. Using micromanipulation techniques, the nucleus containing the DNA, was removed. This left a recipient egg cell with no nucleus, but an intact cytoplasm and the cellular machinery for producing an embryo.

Donor cell

Finn Dorset ewe

Egg cell

Blunt "holding pipette"

Nucleus is sucked up micropipette

micropipette

Nucleus of egg cell

First electric pulse

Donor cell with nucleus intact

**3** **Cells are fused:** The two cells (the dormant donor cell and the recipient egg cell) were placed next to each other and a gentle electric pulse causes them to fuse together (like soap bubbles).

Egg cell without nucleus

A time delay improves the process by allowing as yet unknown factors in the cytoplasm to activate the chromatin.

Second electric pulse

Fused cells

Blackface ewe

Dolly

**4** **Cell division is triggered:** A second electric pulse triggers cellular activity and cell division, effectively jump-starting the cell into production of an embryo. This reaction can also be triggered by chemical means.

**5** After six days, the resulting embryo was surgically implanted into the uterus of the surrogate mother; another Scottish blackface ewe. Of the hundreds of reconstructed eggs, only 29 successfully formed embryos, and only Dolly survived to birth.

**6** **Birth:** After a gestation of 148 days, the pregnant blackface ewe gave birth to Dolly, the Finn Dorset lamb that is genetically identical to the original donor.

**Related activities**: Transgenic Organisms
**Web links**: Click and Clone

A 2

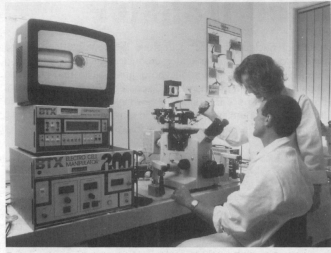

Embryo micromanipulation laboratory in Hamilton, New Zealand. Such labs use sophisticated equipment to manipulate ova (monitor's image is enlarged, right).

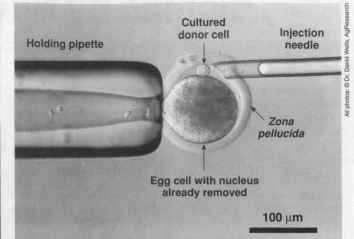

Holding pipette

Cultured donor cell

Injection needle

Zona pellucida

Egg cell with nucleus already removed

100 µm

A single cultured cell is injected underneath the *zona pellucida* (the outer membrane) and positioned next to the egg cell (step 3 of diagram on the left).

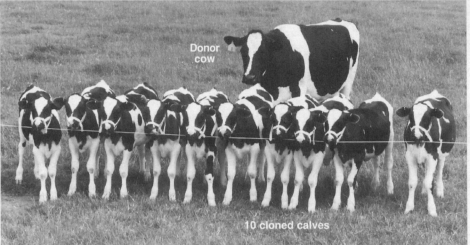

Donor cow

10 cloned calves

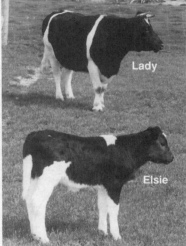

Lady

Elsie

Adult cloning heralds a new chapter in the breeding of livestock. Traditional breeding methods are slow, unpredictable, and suffer from a time delay in waiting to see what the phenotype is like before breeding the next generation. Adult cloning methods now allow a rapid spread of valuable livestock into commercial use among farmers. It will also allow the livestock industry to respond rapidly to market changes in the demand for certain traits in livestock products. In New Zealand, 10 healthy clones were produced from a single cow (the differences in coat color patterns arise from the random migration of pigment cells in early embryonic development).

Lady is the last surviving cow of the rare Enderby Island (south of NZ) cattle breed. Adult cloning was used to produce her genetic duplicate, Elsie (born 31 July 1998). This result represents the first demonstration of the use of adult cloning in animal conservation.

1. Explain what is meant by **cloning** as it relates to **nuclear transfer** techniques involving adult animals:

_____

_____

2. Explain how each of the following events is controlled in the **nuclear transfer** process:

(a) The switching off of all genes in the donor cell: _____

_____

(b) The fusion (combining) of donor cell with enucleated egg cell: _____

_____

(c) The activation of the cloned cell into producing an embryo: _____

_____

3. Describe two potential applications of nuclear transfer technology for the cloning of animals:

(a) _____

_____

(b) _____

_____

# Organ Transplants

Transplant surgery involves the replacement of a diseased tissue or organ with a healthy, living substitute. The tissue or organ is usually taken from a person who has just died, although some (e.g. blood, kidneys, bone marrow) can be taken from living donors. Around the world, more than 100 000 major organs have been transplanted, mostly in the past few decades. About 80% of patients are alive and well one year after the transplantation, and most survive at least five years. There is always a great shortage of donors for organ transplants. Recently, there has been much concern over an emerging black market in body organs and tissue. Attempts to carry out transplants of organs from other species into humans (**xenotransplantation**) have not

been very successful due to rejection, although there are hopes that **genetically modified** pigs may be used to produce organs especially altered to overcome immune rejection in human recipients. The success of organ transplants today has been the result of more effective **immunosuppressant drugs**, improved **tissue-typing**, and better techniques for organ preservation and transport. With the advent of **tissue engineering** and stem cell technology, researchers are rapidly moving towards creating semisynthetic, living organs that may be used as human replacement parts. Artificial skin has already been successfully developed, and more complex organs, such as the liver, may be possible using the same technology within 20 years.

## Organ Transplants

Currently, there are five organs that are routinely transplanted. In addition to organs, whole hand transplants and, recently, **face transplants** are now possible. These transplants require careful connection of blood vessels, skin, muscles, and bone, tendons, and other connective tissues. Performing face transplants, for example on burn victims, also involves addressing a number of ethical concerns.

**Heart (H):** Replacement after heart failure due to heart attack, viral infections of the heart, or congenital, irreparable defects.

**Lungs (Ls):** Replace organs damaged by cystic fibrosis or emphysema. Typically, lungs are transplanted together, but single lung transplants and heart-lung transplants are also possible.

**Liver (Li):** Substitute for a liver destroyed by cirrhosis, congenital defects, or hepatitis.

**Pancreas (P):** Restores insulin production in Type I diabetics (caused by autoimmune destruction of the insulin producing cells of the pancreas).

**Kidneys (K):** Eliminates need for dialysis in patients suffering from renal failure, diabetes, high blood pressure, inherited illnesses, and infection.

**Hands:** On the 24th January 1999, Matthew Scott was America's first hand transplant patient. A year and a half after the operation, he could sense temperature, pressure and pain, and could write, turn the pages of a newspaper, tie shoelaces and throw a baseball.

## Tissue Transplants

A large number of tissues are currently used in transplant procedures. An estimated 200 patients can potentially benefit from the organs and tissues donated from a single body.

**Cornea:** Transplants can restore impaired vision.

**Dental powder:** This tissue is prepared to help rebuild defects in the mandible (which supports the teeth).

**Jaw:** The mandible is used in facial reconstruction.

**Ear bones:** The three bones of the inner ear can be transplanted to improve some forms of deafness.

**Pericardium:** The pericardium surrounding the heart is made of tough tissue that can be used to cover the brain after surgery. Transplants of the brain coverings themselves are no longer performed because of the risk of transmitting prion infections.

**Blood and blood vessels:** Blood transfusions are transplants of blood tissue. Blood vessels, mostly veins, can be transplanted to reroute blood around blockages in the body.

**Bone marrow:** Marrow is extracted from living donors and used to help people with a wide variety of illnesses, such as leukemia.

**Bones:** Long bones of the arms and legs can be used in limb reconstruction; ribs can be used for spinal fusions and facial repair.

**Cartilage and ligaments:** Orthopedic surgeons use these materials to rebuild ankle, knee, hip, elbow and shoulder joints.

**Hip joints:** Joints can be reconstructed by transplanting the head of the femur.

**Skin:** Skin can be used as a temporary covering for burn injuries until the patient's own skin grows back.

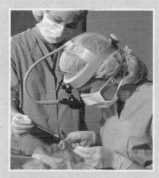

**Corneal transplants** can be used to restore sight in patients with damaged vision. The cornea naturally has a poor blood supply so rejection is less of a problem than with some other tissues

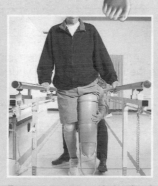

For many amputees, being fitted with an artificial limb is the first step towards mobility. In the future, such prostheses may be replaced with limb transplants, in much the same way of current hand transplants.

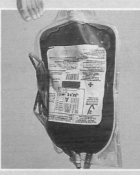

Transplants of whole blood, blood plasma, platelets, and other blood components are crucial to many medical procedures. The donor blood is carefully typed to ensure compatibility with the recipient.

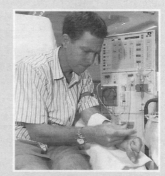

Many patients with kidney failure rely on regular dialysis in order to function. This is expensive and inconvenient, and carries health risks. Such patients are usually waiting for a kidney transplant.

Related activities: Stem Cells and Tissue Engineering, The Ethics of GMO Technology

## Xenotransplantation

| | |
|---|---|
| 1963 | Chimpanzee kidneys were transplanted into 13 patients at Tulane University, Louisianna. One patient survived 9 months. |
| 1964 | First cardiac transplant attempted to put the heart of a chimpanzee into a human. |
| 1984 | Baby Fae, born with a malformed heart, received a heart from a baboon, and lived only 20 more days. |
| 1992 | Liver transplants from baboons to humans, with one patient surviving more than two months. The massive immunosuppression necessary to avoid rejection eventually resulted in a fatal infection. |
| 1995 | Jeff Getty received immune cells from a baboon in an attempt to combat his severe AIDS. His condition mysteriously appeared to improve. |
| 1997 | Clinical trial using foetal pig nerve cells in patients with Parkinson's disease indicated some success. |

Chimpanzee

Baboon

Pig

Xenotransplantation is an attempt to overcome the shortage of human donor organs by using equivalent organs from other mammals, such as baboons, chimpanzees, and pigs (pig heart valves are in common use). It has not been widely adopted or successful. There is a considerable ethical debate surrounding its use and some justified concern over the possibility of accidentally introducing new diseases into the human population. Known as **zoonoses**, such cross-species infections by viruses have already been observed (e.g. HIV and SARS).

1. Describe three major technical advances that have improved the success rate of organ transplantation:

   (a) _____

   (b) _____

   (c) _____

2. (a) Explain the basis for organ and tissue rejection: _____

   _____

   _____

   (b) Discuss the role of **tissue typing** and **immunosuppressant drugs** in reducing or preventing this response:

   _____

   _____

   _____

   (c) Describe one of the major undesirable side-effects of using immunosuppressant drugs in transplant recipients:

   _____

3. Briefly describe the following technologies that are being developed in response to the shortage of donor organs:

   (a) Xenotransplantation: _____

   _____

   (b) Tissue engineering: _____

   _____

4. In point form, outline the ethical issues associated with organ and tissue transplants. Consider costs, benefits, source of tissue, and criteria for choosing recipients. If required, debate the issue, or develop your arguments as a separate report:

   _____

   _____

   _____

   _____

   _____

   _____

   _____

# The Ethics of GMO Technology

The risks of using **genetically modified organisms** (GMOs) have been the subject of considerable debate in recent times. Most experts agree that, provided GMOs are tested properly, the health risks to individuals should be minimal from plant products, although minor problems will occur. Health risks from animal GMOs are potentially more serious, especially when the animals are for human consumption. The potential benefits to be gained from the use of GMOs creates enormous pressure to apply the existing technology. However, there are many concerns, including the environmental and socio-economic effects, and problems of unregulated use. There is also concern about the environmental and economic costs of possible GMO accidents. GMO research is being driven by heavy investment on the part of biotechnology companies seeking new applications for GMOs. Currently a matter of great concern to consumers is the adequacy of government regulations for the labeling of food products with GMO content. This may have important trade implications for countries exporting and importing GMO produce.

### Some important points about GMOs

1. The modified DNA is in every cell of the GMO.

2. The mRNA is only expressed in specific tissues.

3. The foreign protein is only expressed in particular tissues but it may circulate in the blood or lymph or be secreted (e.g. milk).

4. In animals, the transgene is only likely to be transmitted from parent to offspring. However, viral vectors may enable accidental transfer of the transgene between unrelated animals.

5. In plants, transmission of the transgene in GMOs is possible by pollen, cuttings, and seeds (even between species).

6. If we eat the animal or plant proper, we will also be eating DNA. The DNA will remain 'intact' if raw, but "degraded" if cooked.

7. Non-transgenic food products may be processed using genetically modified bacteria or yeast, and cells containing their DNA may be in the food product.

8. A transgenic product (e.g. a protein, polypeptide or a carbohydrate) may be in the GMO, but not in the portions sold to the consumer.

### Potential effects of GMOs on the world

1. Increase in food production.

2. Decrease in use of pesticides, herbicides and animal remedies.

3. Improvement in the health of the human population and the medicines used to achieve it.

4. Possible development of transgenic products which may be harmful to some (e.g. new proteins causing allergies).

5. May have little real economic benefit to farmers (and the consumer) when increased production (as little as 10%) is weighed against cost, capital, and competition.

6. Possible (uncontrollable) spread of transgenes into other species: plants, indigenous species, animals, and humans.

7. Concerns that the release of GMOs into the environment may be irreversible.

8. Economic sanctions resulting from a consumer backlash against GMO foods and products.

9. Animal welfare and ethical issues: GM animals may suffer poor health and reduced life span.

10. GMOs may cause the emergence of pest, insect, or microbial resistance to traditional control methods.

11. May create a monopoly and dependence of developing countries on companies who are seeking to control the world's commercial seed supply.

**GMO protestors are arrested**

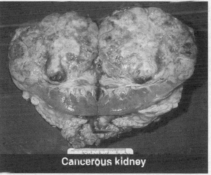

**Cancerous kidney**

**Protest against GMOs in the environment**

**Issue**: The accidental release of GMOs into the environment.

**Problem**: Recombinant DNA may be taken up by non-target organisms. Thes then may have the potential to become pests or cause disease.

**Solution**: Rigorous controls on the production and release of GMOs. GMOs could have specific genes deleted so that their growth requirements are met only in controlled environments.

**Issue**: A new gene or genes may disrupt normal gene function.

**Problem**: Gene disruption may trigger cancer. Successful expression of the desired gene is frequently very low.

**Solution**: A combination of genetic engineering, cloning, and genetic screening so that only those cells that have been successfully transformed are used to produce organisms.

**Issue**: Targeted use of transgenic organisms in the environment.

**Problem**: Once their desired function, e.g. environmental clean-up, is completed, they may be undesirable invaders in the ecosystem.

**Solution**: GMOs can be engineered to contain "suicide genes" or metabolic deficiencies so that they do not survive for long in the new environment after completion of their task.

1. Suggest why genetically modified (GM) plants are thought to pose a greater environmental threat than GM animals:

_____

_____

_____

_____

2. Describe an advantage and a problem with the use of genetically engineered herbicide resistant crop plants:

(a) Advantage: _____

_____

(b) Problem: _____

_____

3. Describe an advantage and a problem with using tropical crops genetically engineered to grow in cold regions:

(a) Advantage: _____

_____

(b) Problem: _____

_____

4. Describe an advantage and a problem with using crops that are genetically engineered to grow in marginal habitats (e.g. in very saline or poorly aerated soils):

(a) Advantage: _____

_____

(b) Problem: _____

_____

5. Describe two uses of transgenic animals within the livestock industry:

(a) _____

(b) _____

6. Recently, Britain banned the import of a genetically engineered, pest resistant corn variety containing marker genes for ampicillin antibiotic resistance. Suggest why there was concern over using such marker genes:

_____

_____

7. Many agricultural applications of DNA technology make use of transgenic bacteria which infect plants and express a foreign gene. Explain one advantage of each of the following applications of genetic engineering to crop biology:

(a) Development of nitrogen-fixing *Rhizobium* bacteria that can colonize non-legumes such as corn and wheat:

_____

(b) Addition of transgenic *Pseudomonas fluorescens* bacteria into seeds (bacterium produces a pathogen-killing toxin):

_____

8. Some of the public's fears and concerns about genetically modified food stem from moral or religious convictions, while others have a biological basis and are related to the potential biological threat posed by GMOs.

(a) Conduct a class discussion or debate to identify these fears and concerns, and list them below:

_____

_____

_____

_____

(b) Identify which of those you have listed above pose a real biological threat: _____

_____

_____

_____

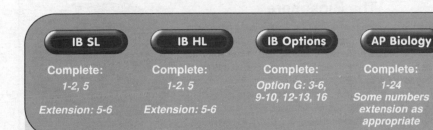

# Ecosystems

**IB SL**
Complete:
*1-2, 5*
Extension: *5-6*

**IB HL**
Complete:
*1-2, 5*
Extension: *5-6*

**IB Options**
Complete:
*Option G: 3-6,*
*9-10, 12-13, 16*

**AP Biology**
Complete:
*1-24*
*Some numbers*
*extension as*
*appropriate*

## Learning Objectives

☐ 1. Compile your own glossary from the **KEY WORDS** displayed in **bold type** in the learning objectives below.

### Biomes and Ecosystems *(pages 282-284)*

☐ 2. Define the terms: **ecology**, **ecosystem**, **community**, **population**, **species**, and **environment**. Describe the components of an ecosystem, categorizing them as **biotic** or **abiotic factors**.

☐ 3. Define the terms **biosphere** and **biome**. Recognize major **biomes** and explain how they are classified. Explain the effect of latitude, altitude, and rainfall in determining the distribution of world biomes.

☐ 4. Describe an example of a local ecosystem, including reference to the community composition and the abiotic factors that determine the ecosystem's characteristics.

### Habitats and Niches *(pages 285-296)*

☐ 5. Define the term **habitat**. Explain how **microclimates** develop and recognize the role of microclimates and **limiting factors** in species distribution and diversity.

☐ 6. Describe the biotic and abiotic factors affecting plant or animal distribution in an environment.

☐ 7. Explain how gradients in physical factors can occur over relatively short distances, e.g. on a rocky shore, or in a forest, desert, or lake. Explain the role of these **environmental gradients** in species distribution.

☐ 8. Describe the features of the two most common types of distributional variation in communities: **zonation** and **stratification**. Explain how these patterns arise and how they increase the amount of community diversity.

☐ 9. Define the term '**ecological niche**' (niche), and identify the factors that are used to describe the niche.

☐ 10. Distinguish between the **fundamental** and the **realized niche**. Explain the **competitive exclusion** principle with respect to niche overlap between species. Understand the effects of competition on niche breadth.

☐ 11. Explain the term **adaptation** and, using examples, distinguish between **physiological**, **structural**, and **behavioral adaptations**.

### Ecological Succession *(pages 297-298)*

☐ 12. Explain what is meant by **ecological succession**. Recognize succession as a community pattern in time that results from the interaction of species with their environment. Describe factors that might cause a successional change in a community.

☐ 13. Distinguish clearly between **primary** and **secondary succession**, outlining the features of each type. Include reference to the time scale over which these successions take place. Appreciate that successions do not usually follow a 'text-book' progression and that **climax** vegetation varies according to local conditions.

☐ 14. Describe how community diversity changes during a succession. Comment on the stability of pioneer and climax communities and relate this to the relative importance of abiotic and biotic factors at each stage.

☐ 15. Describe primary succession from **pioneer species** to a **climax community**, identifying the species typical of each **seral stage** (change in the biotic community).

☐ 16. Describe an example succession (either primary or secondary). Recognize **deflected successions**, where a particular community composition is maintained through human intervention (e.g. mowing or grazing).

---

See the 'Textbook Reference Grid' on pages 8-9 for textbook page references relating to material in this topic.

**Supplementary Texts**
See pages 5-6 for additional details of these texts:

■ Miller G.T. Jr., 2007. **Essentials of Ecology** (Thomson Brooks/Cole), chpt. 4.

See page 6 for details of publishers of periodicals:

### STUDENT'S REFERENCE

■ **The Lake Ecosystem** Biol. Sci. Rev., 20(3) Feb. 2008, pp. 21-25. *An excellent account of the components and functioning of lake ecosystems.*

■ **The Ecological Niche** Biol. Sci. Rev., 12(4), March 2000, pp. 31-35. *An excellent account of the niche; an often misunderstood concept that is never-the-less central to ecological theory.*

■ **Plant Succession** Biol. Sci. Rev., 14 (2) Nov. 2001, pp. 2-6. *Thorough coverage of primary and secondary succession, including the causes of different types of succession.*

■ **Don't Fear the Beaver** New Scientist, 25 Aug. 2007, pp. 42-45. *The ecology and niche of the beaver, and their positive impact on ecosystems.*

### TEACHER'S REFERENCE

■ **The Climax Concept of Succession** The Am. Biology Teacher, 58(3), March, 1996, pp.135-140. *Community, succession and a discussion of the viability of the 'climax community' concept.*

■ **Ecology and Evolution of Wall-Dwelling Organisms** The Am. Biology Teacher, 62(6), June, 2000, pp. 429-435. *How to improve understanding of habitat and niche, and community structure.*

# Components of an Ecosystem

The concept of the ecosystem was developed to describe the way groups of organisms are predictably found together in their physical environment. A community comprises all the organisms within an ecosystem. Both physical (abiotic) and biotic factors affect the organisms in a community, influencing their distribution and their survival, growth, and reproduction.

## Physical Environment

### Atmosphere
• Wind speed & direction
• Humidity
• Light intensity & quality
• Precipitation
• Air temperature

### The Biosphere

The **biosphere**, which contains all the Earth's living organisms, amounts to a narrow belt around the Earth extending from the bottom of the oceans to the upper atmosphere. Broad scale life-zones or **biomes** are evident within the biosphere, characterized according to the predominant vegetation. Within these biomes, **ecosystems** form natural units comprising the non-living, physical environment (the soil, atmosphere, and water) and the **community** (all the organisms living in a particular area).

### Community: Biotic Factors

Producers, consumers, detritivores, and decomposers interact in the community as competitors, parasites, pathogens, symbionts, predators, herbivores

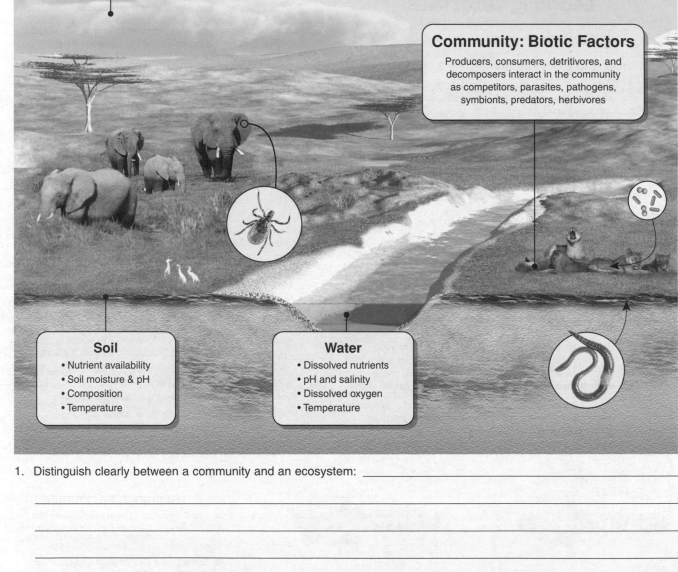

### Soil
• Nutrient availability
• Soil moisture & pH
• Composition
• Temperature

### Water
• Dissolved nutrients
• pH and salinity
• Dissolved oxygen
• Temperature

1. Distinguish clearly between a community and an ecosystem: _____

_____

_____

_____

2. Distinguish between biotic and abiotic factors: _____

_____

_____

3. Use one or more of the following terms to describe each of the features of a rainforest listed below:
   **Terms**: *population, community, ecosystem, physical factor.*

   (a) All the green tree frogs present: _____  (c) All the organisms present: _____

   (b) The entire forest: _____  (d) The humidity: _____

**A 1**

**Related Activities**: Biomes
**Web links**: racerocks.com Education Index

# Biomes

The **biosphere** encompasses all living things on Earth and comprises a number of aquatic and terrestrial **biomes**. Biomes are the largest geographically based biotic communities that can be conveniently recognized. These are large areas where the vegetation type shares a particular suite of physical requirements. Biomes have characteristic features, but the boundaries between them are not distinct. The same biome may occur in widely separated regions of the world wherever the climatic and soil conditions are similar. Terrestrial biomes are recognized for all the major climatic regions of the world and are classified on the basis of their predominant vegetation type (see diagram below and the following page).

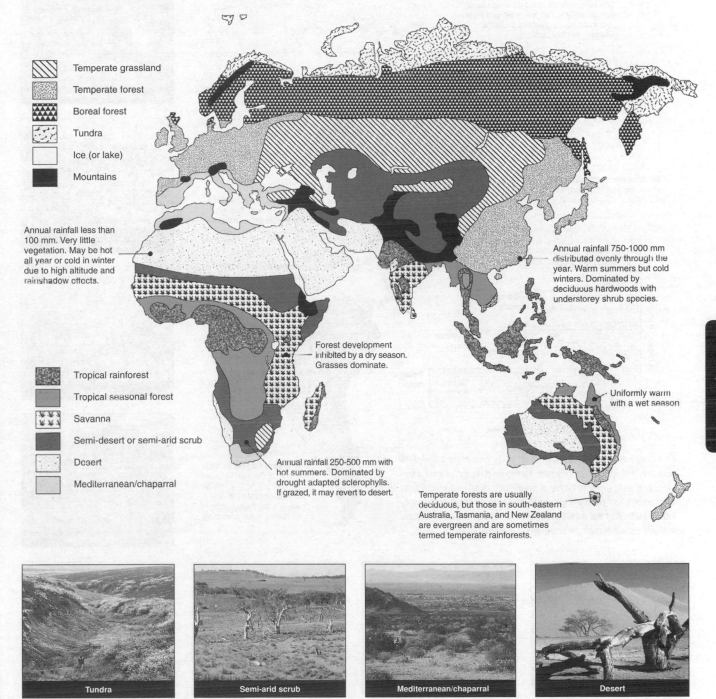

**Legend (top):**
- Temperate grassland
- Temperate forest
- Boreal forest
- Tundra
- Ice (or lake)
- Mountains

**Legend (bottom):**
- Tropical rainforest
- Tropical seasonal forest
- Savanna
- Semi-desert or semi-arid scrub
- Desert
- Mediterranean/chaparral

Annual rainfall less than 100 mm. Very little vegetation. May be hot all year or cold in winter due to high altitude and rainshadow effects.

Annual rainfall 750-1000 mm distributed evenly through the year. Warm summers but cold winters. Dominated by deciduous hardwoods with understorey shrub species.

Forest development inhibited by a dry season. Grasses dominate.

Uniformly warm with a wet season

Annual rainfall 250-500 mm with hot summers. Dominated by drought adapted sclerophylls. If grazed, it may revert to desert.

Temperate forests are usually deciduous, but those in south-eastern Australia, Tasmania, and New Zealand are evergreen and are sometimes termed temperate rainforests.

Photo captions:
- Tundra
- Semi-arid scrub
- Mediterranean/chaparral
- Desert

*Ecosystems*

1. Suggest what abiotic factor(s) limit the northern extent of boreal forest:

_____

2. Grasslands have about half the productivity of tropical rainforests, yet this is achieved with less than a tenth of the biomass; grasslands are more productive per unit of biomass. Suggest how this greater efficiency is achieved:

_____

_____

_____

**Related activities**: Physical Factors and Gradients
**Web links**: The World's Biomes

A 2

Vegetation patterns are determined largely by climate but can be modified markedly by human activity. Semi-arid areas that are overgrazed will revert to desert and have little ability to recover. Similarly, many chaparral regions no longer support their original vegetation, but are managed for vineyards and olive groves. Wherever they occur, mountainous regions are associated with their own altitude adapted vegetation. The rainshadow effect of

mountains governs the distribution of deserts in some areas too, as in Chile and the Gobi desert in Asia. The classification of biomes may vary slightly; some sources distinguish hot deserts (such as the Sahara) from cold deserts and semi-deserts (such as the Gobi). However, most classifications recognize desert, tundra, grassland and forest types and differentiate them on the basis of latitude.

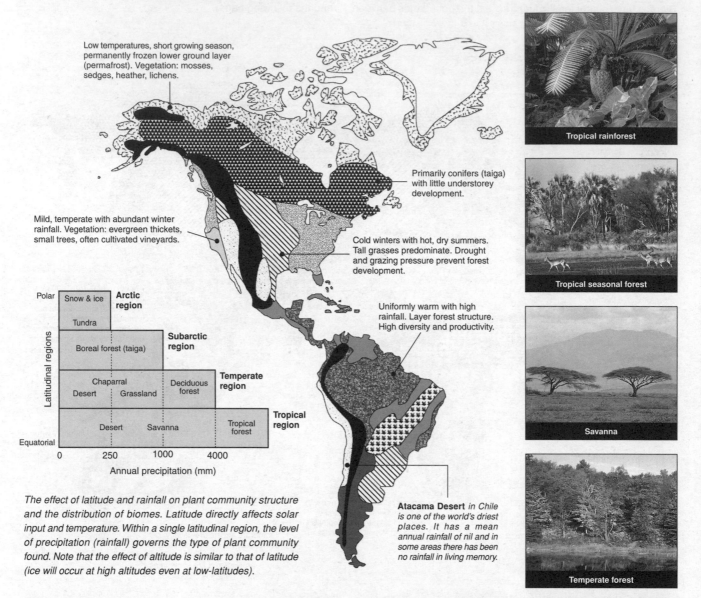

Low temperatures, short growing season, permanently frozen lower ground layer (permafrost). Vegetation: mosses, sedges, heather, lichens.

Mild, temperate with abundant winter rainfall. Vegetation: evergreen thickets, small trees, often cultivated vineyards.

Primarily conifers (taiga) with little understorey development.

Cold winters with hot, dry summers. Tall grasses predominate. Drought and grazing pressure prevent forest development.

Uniformly warm with high rainfall. Layer forest structure. High diversity and productivity.

**Atacama Desert** in Chile is one of the world's driest places. It has a mean annual rainfall of nil and in some areas there has been no rainfall in living memory.

**Tropical rainforest**

**Tropical seasonal forest**

**Savanna**

**Temperate forest**

The effect of latitude and rainfall on plant community structure and the distribution of biomes. Latitude directly affects solar input and temperature. Within a single latitudinal region, the level of precipitation (rainfall) governs the type of plant community found. Note that the effect of altitude is similar to that of latitude (ice will occur at high altitudes even at low-latitudes).

**Temperate grassland**

**Ice**

**Mountains**

**Boreal forest**

3. Suggest a reason for the distribution of deserts and semi-desert areas in northern parts of Asia and in the west of North and South America (away from equatorial regions):

_____

_____

4. Compared with its natural extent (on the map), little unaltered temperate forest now exists. Explain why this is the case:

_____

_____

_____

# Physical Factors and Gradients

Gradients in abiotic factors are found in almost every environment; they influence habitats and **microclimates**, and determine patterns of species distribution. This activity, covering the next four pages, examines the physical gradients and microclimates that might typically be found in four very different environments. Note that **dataloggers** (pictured right), are being increasingly used to gather such data. The principles of their use are covered in the topic *Practical Ecology*.

## A Desert Environment

Desert environments experience extremes in temperature and humidity, but they are not uniform with respect to these factors. This diagram illustrates hypothetical values for temperature and humidity for some of the microclimates found in a desert environment at midday.

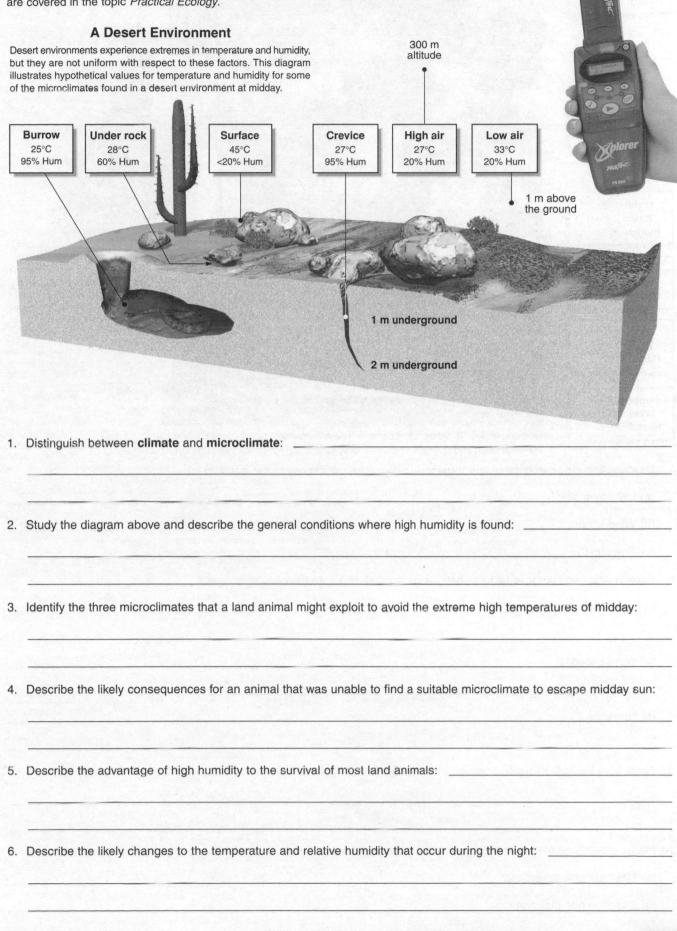

**Burrow**
25°C
95% Hum

**Under rock**
28°C
60% Hum

**Surface**
45°C
<20% Hum

**Crevice**
27°C
95% Hum

**High air**
27°C
20% Hum

**Low air**
33°C
20% Hum

300 m altitude

1 m above the ground

1 m underground

2 m underground

Ecosystems

1. Distinguish between **climate** and **microclimate**: _____

_____

2. Study the diagram above and describe the general conditions where high humidity is found: _____

_____

_____

3. Identify the three microclimates that a land animal might exploit to avoid the extreme high temperatures of midday:

_____

_____

4. Describe the likely consequences for an animal that was unable to find a suitable microclimate to escape midday sun:

_____

_____

5. Describe the advantage of high humidity to the survival of most land animals: _____

_____

_____

6. Describe the likely changes to the temperature and relative humidity that occur during the night: _____

_____

_____

**Related Activities**: Monitoring Physical Factors

RDA 2

# Physical Factors in a Tropical Rainforest

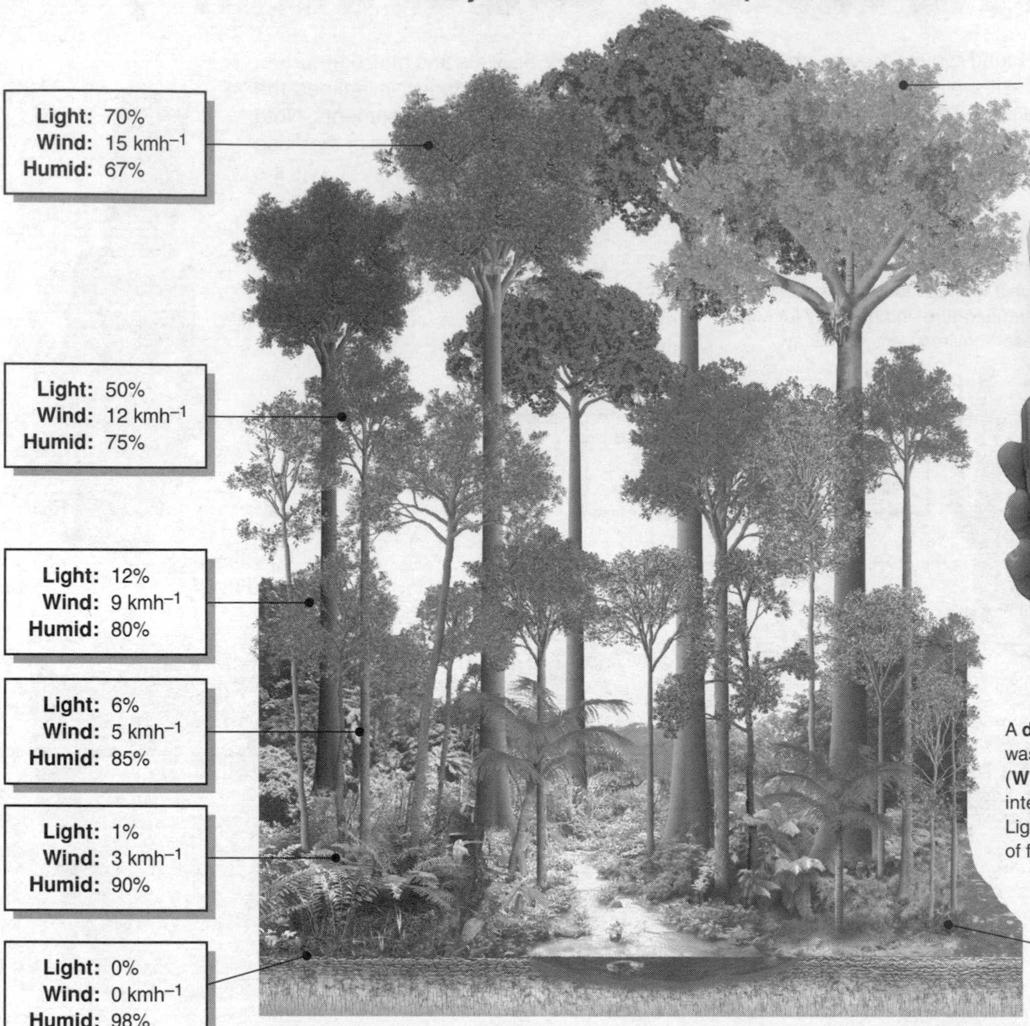

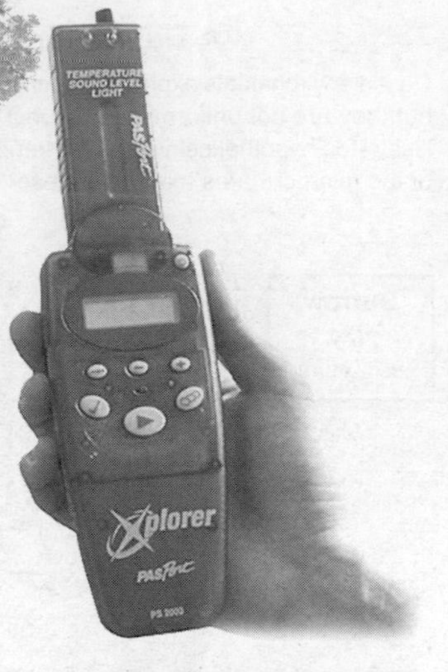

Canopy

Light: 70%
Wind: 15 kmh$^{-1}$
Humid: 67%

Light: 50%
Wind: 12 kmh$^{-1}$
Humid: 75%

Light: 12%
Wind: 9 kmh$^{-1}$
Humid: 80%

Light: 6%
Wind: 5 kmh$^{-1}$
Humid: 85%

Light: 1%
Wind: 3 kmh$^{-1}$
Humid: 90%

Light: 0%
Wind: 0 kmh$^{-1}$
Humid: 98%

A **datalogger** fitted with suitable probes was used to gather data on wind speed (**Wind**), humidity (**Humid**), and light intensity (**Light**) for each layer (left). Light intensity is given as a percentage of full sunlight.

Leaf litter

Tropical rainforests are complex communities with a vertical structure which divides the vegetation into layers. This pattern of vertical layering is called **stratification**.

7. Describe the environmental gradient (general trend) from the canopy to the leaf litter for:

(a) Light intensity: _____

(b) Wind speed: _____

(c) Humidity: _____

8. Explain why each of these factors changes as the distance from the canopy increases:

(a) Light intensity: _____

_____

(b) Wind speed: _____

_____

(c) Humidity: _____

_____

9. Apart from the light intensity, describe the other feature of light that will change with distance from the canopy:

_____

_____

10. Plants growing on the forest floor have some advantages and disadvantages with respect to the physical factors.

(a) Describe one advantage: _____

(b) Describe one disadvantage: _____

## Physical Factors at Low Tide on a Rock Platform

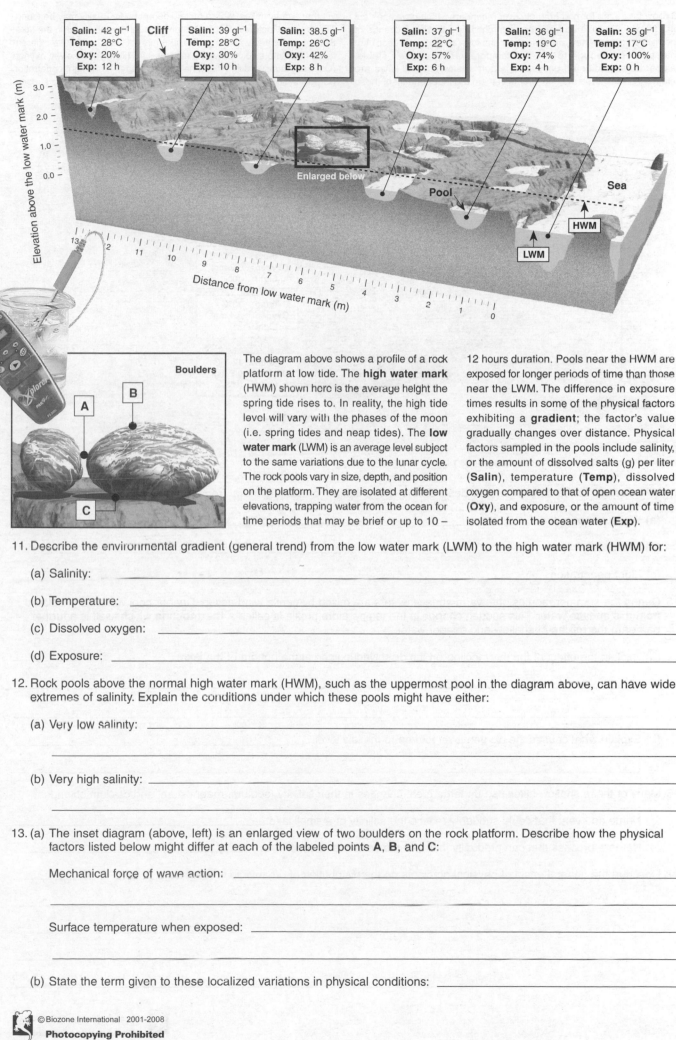

**Salin:** 42 gl⁻¹
**Temp:** 28°C
**Oxy:** 20%
**Exp:** 12 h

**Cliff**

**Salin:** 39 gl⁻¹
**Temp:** 28°C
**Oxy:** 30%
**Exp:** 10 h

**Salin:** 38.5 gl⁻¹
**Temp:** 26°C
**Oxy:** 42%
**Exp:** 8 h

**Salin:** 37 gl⁻¹
**Temp:** 22°C
**Oxy:** 57%
**Exp:** 6 h

**Salin:** 36 gl⁻¹
**Temp:** 19°C
**Oxy:** 74%
**Exp:** 4 h

**Salin:** 35 gl⁻¹
**Temp:** 17°C
**Oxy:** 100%
**Exp:** 0 h

Elevation above the low water mark (m)

Enlarged below

Pool

Sea

HWM

LWM

Distance from low water mark (m)

**Boulders**

A  B

C

The diagram above shows a profile of a rock platform at low tide. The **high water mark** (HWM) shown here is the average height the spring tide rises to. In reality, the high tide level will vary with the phases of the moon (i.e. spring tides and neap tides). The **low water mark** (LWM) is an average level subject to the same variations due to the lunar cycle. The rock pools vary in size, depth, and position on the platform. They are isolated at different elevations, trapping water from the ocean for time periods that may be brief or up to 10 –

12 hours duration. Pools near the HWM are exposed for longer periods of time than those near the LWM. The difference in exposure times results in some of the physical factors exhibiting a **gradient**; the factor's value gradually changes over distance. Physical factors sampled in the pools include salinity, or the amount of dissolved salts (g) per liter (**Salin**), temperature (**Temp**), dissolved oxygen compared to that of open ocean water (**Oxy**), and exposure, or the amount of time isolated from the ocean water (**Exp**).

11. Describe the environmental gradient (general trend) from the low water mark (LWM) to the high water mark (HWM) for:

(a) Salinity: _____

(b) Temperature: _____

(c) Dissolved oxygen: _____

(d) Exposure: _____

12. Rock pools above the normal high water mark (HWM), such as the uppermost pool in the diagram above, can have wide extremes of salinity. Explain the conditions under which these pools might have either:

(a) Very low salinity: _____

_____

(b) Very high salinity: _____

_____

13. (a) The inset diagram (above, left) is an enlarged view of two boulders on the rock platform. Describe how the physical factors listed below might differ at each of the labeled points **A**, **B**, and **C**:

Mechanical force of wave action: _____

_____

Surface temperature when exposed: _____

_____

(b) State the term given to these localized variations in physical conditions: _____

**Ecosystems**

# Physical Factors in an Oxbow Lake in Summer

**Oxbow lakes** are formed from old river meanders which have been cut off and become isolated from the main channel following a change of the river's course. They are commonly shallow (about 2-4 m deep) but may be deep enough to develop temporary, but relatively stable, temperature gradients from top to bottom (below). Small lakes are relatively closed systems and events in them are independent of those in other nearby lakes, where quite different water quality may be found. The physical factors are not constant throughout the water in the lake. Surface water and water near the lake margins can have quite different values for factors such as water temperature (**Temp**), dissolved oxygen (**Oxygen**) measured in milligrams per liter (mg l$^{-1}$), and light penetration (**Light**), indicated here as a percentage of the light striking the surface.

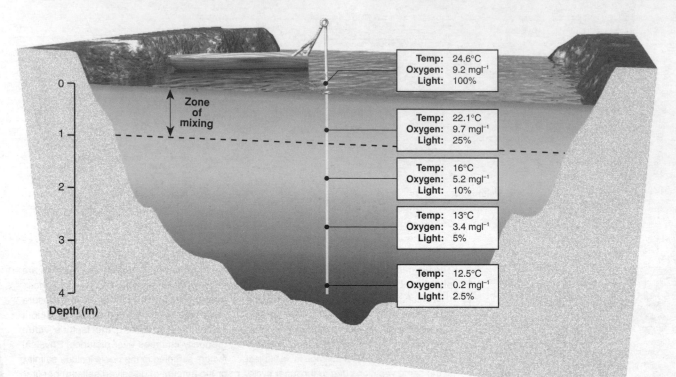

| | |
|---|---|
| **Temp:** | 24.6°C |
| **Oxygen:** | 9.2 mgl$^{-1}$ |
| **Light:** | 100% |

| | |
|---|---|
| **Temp:** | 22.1°C |
| **Oxygen:** | 9.7 mgl$^{-1}$ |
| **Light:** | 25% |

| | |
|---|---|
| **Temp:** | 16°C |
| **Oxygen:** | 5.2 mgl$^{-1}$ |
| **Light:** | 10% |

| | |
|---|---|
| **Temp:** | 13°C |
| **Oxygen:** | 3.4 mgl$^{-1}$ |
| **Light:** | 5% |

| | |
|---|---|
| **Temp:** | 12.5°C |
| **Oxygen:** | 0.2 mgl$^{-1}$ |
| **Light:** | 2.5% |

Zone of mixing

Depth (m)

14. With respect to the diagram above, describe the environmental gradient (general trend) from surface to lake bottom for:

   (a) Water temperature: _____

   (b) Dissolved oxygen: _____

   (c) Light penetration: _____

15. During the summer months, the warm surface waters are mixed by gentle wind action. Deeper cool waters are isolated from this surface water. This sudden change in the temperature profile is called a **thermocline** which itself is a further barrier to the mixing of shallow and deeper water.

   (a) Explain the effect of the thermocline on the dissolved oxygen at the bottom of the lake: _____

   _____

   _____

   (b) Explain what causes the oxygen level to drop to the low level: _____

   _____

16. Many of these shallow lakes can undergo great changes in their salinity (sodium, magnesium, and calcium chlorides):

   (a) Name an event that could suddenly reduce the salinity of a small lake: _____

   (b) Name a process that can gradually increase the salinity of a small lake: _____

17. Describe the general effect of physical gradients on the distribution of organisms in habitats: _____

   _____

   _____

   _____

# Shoreline Zonation

**Zonation** refers to the division of an ecosystem into distinct zones that experience similar abiotic conditions. In a more global sense, zonation may also refer to the broad distribution of vegetation according to latitude and altitude. Zonation is particularly clear on a rocky seashore, where assemblages of different species form a banding pattern approximately parallel to the waterline. This effect is marked in temperate regions where the prevailing weather comes from the same general direction. Exposed shores show the clearest zonation. On sheltered rocky shores there is considerable species overlap and it is only on the upper shore that distinct zones are evident. Rocky shores exist where wave action prevents the deposition of much sediment. The rock forms a stable platform for the secure attachment of organisms such as large seaweeds and barnacles. Sandy shores are less stable than rocky shores and the organisms found there are adapted to the more mobile substrate.

## Seashore Zonation Patterns

The zonation of species distribution according to an environmental gradient is well shown on rocky shorelines. In Britain, exposed rocky shores occur along much of the western coasts. Variations in low and high tide affect zonation, and in areas with little tidal variation, zonation is restricted. High on the shore, some organisms may be submerged only at spring high tide. Low on the shore, others may be exposed only at spring low tide. There is a gradation in extent of exposure and the physical conditions associated with this. Zonation patterns generally reflect the vertical movement of seawater. Sheer rocks can show marked zonation as a result of tidal changes with little or no horizontal shift in species distribution. The profiles below, show generalized zonation patterns on an exposed rocky shore (left profile) with an exposed sandy shore for comparison (right profile). **SLT** = Spring low tide mark, **MLT** = Mean low tide mark, **MHT** = Mean high tide mark, **SHT** = Spring high tide mark.

Rocky shore at Sleahead, Ireland.

### Key to species

1. Lichen: sea ivory
2. Small periwinkle *Littorina neritoides*
3. Lichen *Verrucaria maura*
4. Rough periwinkle *Littorina saxatilis*
5. Common limpet *Patella vulgaris*
6. Laver *Porphyra*
7. Spiral wrack *Fucus spiralis*
8. Australian barnacle
9. Common mussel *Mytilus edulis*
10. Common whelk *Buccinum undatum*
11. Grey topshell *Gibbula cineraria*
12. Carrageen (Irish moss) *Chondrus crispus*
13. Thongweed *Himanthalia elongata*
14. Toothed wrack *Fucus serratus*
15. Dabberlocks *Alaria esculenta*
16. Common sandhopper
17. Sandhopper *Bathyporeia pelagica*
18. Common cockle *Cerastoderma edule*
19. Lugworm *Arenicola marina*
20. Sting winkle *Ocinebra erinacea*
21. Common necklace shell *Natica alderi*
22. Rayed trough shell *Mactra corallina*
23. Sand mason worm *Lanice conchilega*
24. Sea anemone *Halcampa*
25. Pod razor shell *Ensis siliqua*
26. Sea potato *Echinocardium* (a heart urchin)

*Note: Where several species are indicated within a single zonal band, they occupy the entire zone, not just the position where their number appears.*

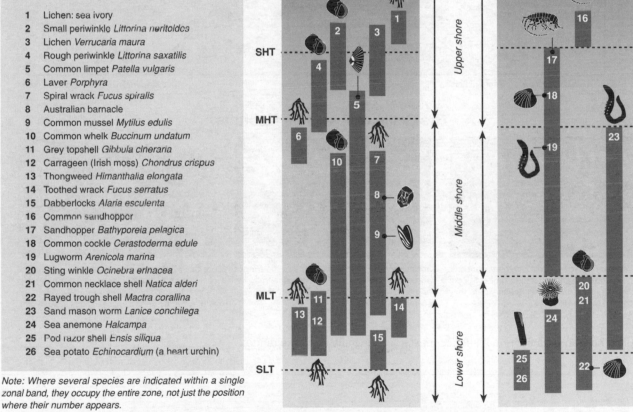

Exposed Rocky Shore — Exposed Sandy Shore

1. (a) Suggest why the time of exposure above water is a major factor controlling species distribution on a rocky shore:

_____

(b) Identify two other abiotic factors that might influence species distribution on a rocky shore: _____

_____

(c) Identify two biotic factors that might influence species distribution on a rocky shore: _____

_____

2. Describe the zonation pattern on a rocky shore: _____

_____

**Related activities**: Physical Factors and Gradients
**Web links**: Tide Pool Ecology

A 2

Ecosystems

# Habitat

The environment in which a species population (or a individual organism) lives (including all the physical and biotic factors) is termed its **habitat**. Within a prescribed habitat, each species population has a range of tolerance to variations in its physical and chemical environment. Within the population, individuals will have slightly different tolerance ranges based on small differences in genetic make-up, age, and health. The wider an organism's tolerance range for a given abiotic factor (e.g. temperature or salinity), the more likely it is that the organism will be able to survive variations in that factor. Species **dispersal** is also strongly influenced by **tolerance range**. The wider the tolerance range of a species, the more widely dispersed the organism is likely to be. As well as a tolerance range, organisms have a narrower **optimum range** within which they function best. This may vary from one stage of an organism's development to another or from one season to another. Every species has its own optimum range. Organisms will usually be most abundant where the abiotic factors are closest to the optimum range.

## Habitat Occupation and Tolerance Range

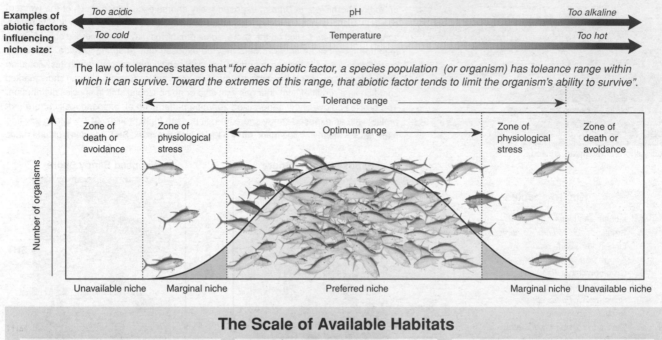

The law of tolerances states that *"for each abiotic factor, a species population (or organism) has toleance range within which it can survive. Toward the extremes of this range, that abiotic factor tends to limit the organism's ability to survive".*

## The Scale of Available Habitats

A habitat may be vast and relatively homogeneous, as is the open ocean. Barracuda (above) occur around reefs and in the open ocean where they are aggressive predators.

For non-mobile organisms, such as the fungus above, a suitable habitat may be defined by the particular environment in a relatively tiny area, such as on this decaying log.

For microbial organisms, such the bacteria and protozoans of the ruminant gut, the habitat is defined by the chemical environment within the rumen (R) of the host animal, in this case, a cow.

1. Explain how an organism's habitat occupation relates to its tolerance range: _____
   _____
   _____

2. (a) Identify the range in the diagram above in which most of the species population is found. Explain why this is the case:
   _____
   _____

   (b) Describe the greatest constraints on an organism's growth and reproduction within this range: _____
   _____

3. Describe some probable stresses on an organism forced into a marginal niche: _____
   _____
   _____

# Dingo Habitats

An organism's habitat is not always of a single type. Some animals range over a variety of habitats, partly in order to obtain different resources from different habitats, and sometimes simply because they are forced into marginal habitats by competition. Dingoes are found throughout Australia, in ecosystems as diverse as the tropical rainforests of the north to the arid deserts of the Center. Within each of these ecosystems, they may frequent several habitats or **microhabitats**. The information below shows how five dingo packs exploit a variety of habitats at one location in Australia. The table on the following page shows how dingoes are widespread in their distribution and are found living in a variety of ecosystems.

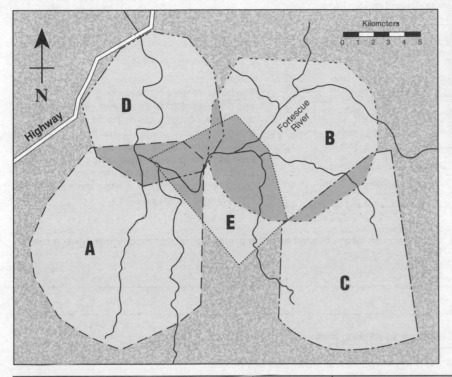

The map on the left shows the territories of five stable dingo packs (A to E) in the Fortescue River region in north-west Australia. The territories were determined by 4194 independent radio-tracking locations over 4 years. The size and nature of each territory, together with the makeup of each pack is given in the table below. The major prey of the dingoes in this region are large kangaroos (red kangaroos and euros).

Adapted from: Corbett, L. *The dingo in Australia and Asia*, 1995. University of NSW Press, after (original source) Thomson, P.C. 1992. *The behavioral ecology of dingoes in north-west Australia. IV. Social and spatial organization, and movements. Wildlife Research* 19: 543-563.

*Ecosystems* (side tab)

| Dingo pack name | Territory area (km²) | Pack size | Dingo density | Index of kangaroo abundance (%) | Habitat types (%) and habitat usage (%) in each territory | | | | | | | |
|---|---|---|---|---|---|---|---|---|---|---|---|---|
| | | | | | Riverine | | Stony | | Floodplain | | Hills | |
| Pack A | 113 | 12 | 10.6 | 15.9 | 10 | (49) | 1 | (2) | 21 | (6) | 69 | (44) |
| Pack B | 94 | 12 | | 8.5 | 14 | (43) | 9 | (10) | 38 | (25) | 39 | (23) |
| Pack C | 86 | 3 | | 3.9 | 2 | (3) | 0 | (0) | 63 | (94) | 35 | (3) |
| Pack D | 63 | 6 | | 12.3 | 12 | (35) | 5 | (8) | 46 | (20) | 37 | (37) |
| Pack E | 45 | 10 | 22.2 | 8.4 | 14 | (31) | 6 | (4) | 39 | (18) | 42 | (47) |

mean number of dingoes per 100 km² (calculated by you)

Percentage of observations of kangaroos per observations of dingoes

Portion of the territory with this kind of habitat

Percentage of time spent by the pack in this habitat

1. Calculate the density of each of the dingo packs at the Fortescue River site above (two have been done for you). Remember that to determine the density, you carry out the following calculation:

   Density = pack size ÷ territory area x 100     (to give the mean number per 100 km²)

2. Name the dominant habitat (or habitats) for each territory in the table above (e.g. riverine, stony, floodplain, hills):

   (a) Pack A: _____

   (b) Pack B: _____

   (c) Pack C: _____

   (d) Pack D: _____

   (e) Pack E: _____

**Related Activities:** Habitat     DA 2

## Dingo home range size in contrasting ecosystems

| Location (study site) | Ecosystem | Range (km²) |
|---|---|---|
| **1** Fortescue River, North-west Australia | Semi-arid, coastal plains and hills | 77 |
| **2** Simpson Desert, Central Australia | Arid, gibber (stony) and sandy desert | 67 |
| **3** Kapalga, Kakadu N.P., North Australia | Tropical, coastal wetlands and forests | 39 |
| **4** Harts Ranges, Central Australia | Semi-arid, river catchment and hills | 25 |
| **5** Kosciusko N.P., South-east Australia | Moist, cool forested mountains | 21 |
| **6** Georges Creek N.R., East Australia | Moist, cool forested tablelands | 18 |
| **7** Nadgee N.R., South-east Australia | Moist, cool coastal forests | 10 |

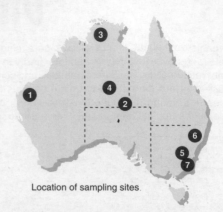

Location of sampling sites.

The **home ranges** of neighboring dingo individuals and pack **territories** sometimes overlap to some degree, but individuals or packs avoid being in these communal areas (of overlap) at the same time. This overlap occurs especially during the breeding season or in areas where resources are shared (e.g. hunting grounds, water holes). Different ecosystem types appear to affect the extent of the home ranges for dingoes living in them.

3. Study the table on the previous page and determine which (if any) was the preferred habitat for dingoes (give a reason for your answer):

_____

_____

4. The dingoes at this site were studied using radio-tracking methods.

(a) Explain how radio-tracking can be used to determine the movements of dingoes: _____

_____

_____

_____

(b) State how many independent tracking locations were recorded during this study: _____

(c) State how long a period of time the study was run for: _____

(d) Explain why so many records were needed over such a long period of time: _____

_____

_____

5. From the table on the previous page, state whether the relative kangaroo abundance (the major prey of the dingo) affects the density that a given territory can support:

_____

_____

6. Study the table at the top of this page which shows the results of an investigation into the sizes of home ranges in dingo populations from different ecosystems.

(a) Describe the feature of the ecosystems that appears to affect the size of home ranges: _____

_____

(b) Explain how this feature might affect how diverse (varied) the habitats are within the ecosystem:

_____

_____

_____

# Ecological Niche

The concept of the ecological niche has been variously described as an organism's 'job' or 'profession'. This is rather too simplistic for senior biology level. The **ecological niche** is better described as the functional position of an organism in its environment, comprising its habitat and the resources it obtains there, and the periods of time during which it is active. The diagram below illustrates the components that together define the niche of any organism. The full range of environmental conditions (biological and physical) under which an organism can exist describes its **fundamental niche**. As a result of pressure from, and interactions with, other organisms (e.g. superior competitors) species are usually forced to occupy a niche that is narrower than this and to which they are most highly adapted. This is termed the **realized niche**.

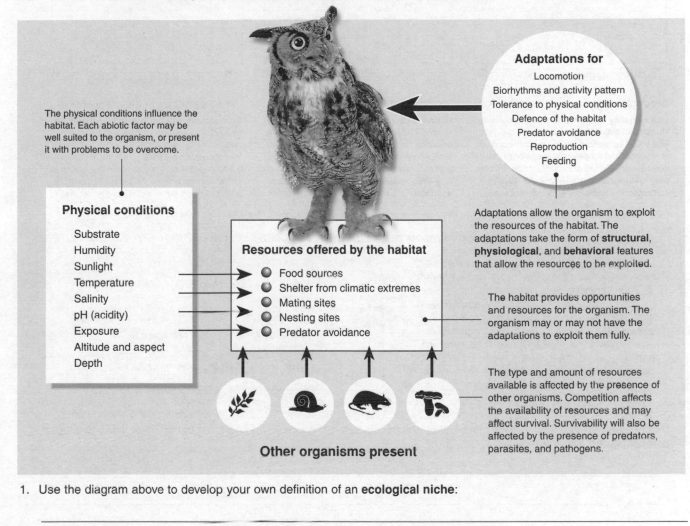

**Adaptations for**

Locomotion
Biorhythms and activity pattern
Tolerance to physical conditions
Defence of the habitat
Predator avoidance
Reproduction
Feeding

The physical conditions influence the habitat. Each abiotic factor may be well suited to the organism, or present it with problems to be overcome.

**Physical conditions**

Substrate
Humidity
Sunlight
Temperature
Salinity
pH (acidity)
Exposure
Altitude and aspect
Depth

**Resources offered by the habitat**

Food sources
Shelter from climatic extremes
Mating sites
Nesting sites
Predator avoidance

Adaptations allow the organism to exploit the resources of the habitat. The adaptations take the form of **structural**, **physiological**, and **behavioral** features that allow the resources to be exploited.

The habitat provides opportunities and resources for the organism. The organism may or may not have the adaptations to exploit them fully.

The type and amount of resources available is affected by the presence of other organisms. Competition affects the availability of resources and may affect survival. Survivability will also be affected by the presence of predators, parasites, and pathogens.

**Other organisms present**

Ecosystems

1. Use the diagram above to develop your own definition of an **ecological niche**:

_____

_____

_____

_____

_____

2. Explain why the niche actually occupied by an organism is narrower than the niche it could potentially occupy:

_____

_____

_____

3. Gause's *competitive exclusion principle* states that organisms occupying exactly the same niche cannot coexist because they will compete for the same resources. Using an example, explain how organisms with very similar habitat and feeding requirements can minimize niche overlap, i.e. how do they differentiate their niches to avoid competition:

_____

_____

_____

# Competition and Niche Size

Niche size is affected by competition. The magnitude of the effect will vary depending on whether the competition is weak, moderate, or intense, and whether it is **intraspecific** or **interspecific**. The theoretical effects of competition on niche size are outlined in the diagram below. Further coverage of this topic is provided in the chapter *Populations*.

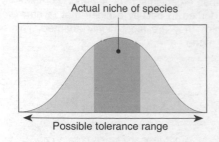

Actual niche of species

Possible tolerance range

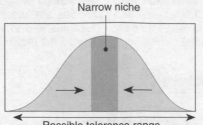

Narrow niche

Possible tolerance range

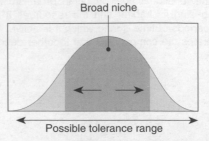

Broad niche

Possible tolerance range

**Moderate interspecific competition**

The tolerance range represents the potential (**fundamental**) niche a species could exploit. The actual or **realized** niche a species occupies is smaller than its potential niche because of competition. Niches of closely related species may overlap at the extremes, resulting in competition for resources in the zones of overlap.

**Intense interspecific competition**

When the competition from one or more closely related species becomes intense, there is selection for a more limited niche. This severe competition prevents a species from exploiting potential resources in the more extreme parts of its tolerance range. As a result, niche breadth decreases (the niche becomes narrower).

**Intense intraspecific competition**

Competition is most severe between individuals of the same species, because their resource requirements are usually identical. When intraspecific competition is intense, individuals are forced to exploit resources in the extremes of their tolerance range. This leads to expansion of the realized niche to less preferred areas.

## Overlap in resource use between competing species

From the concept of the niche arose the idea that two species with the same niche requirements could not coexist, because they would compete for the same resources, and one would exclude the other. This is known as Gause's "***competitive exclusion principle***". If two species compete for some of the same resources (e.g. food items of a particular size), their resource use curves will overlap. Within the zone of overlap competition between the two species will be intense.

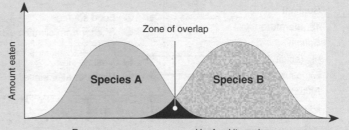

Zone of overlap

Amount eaten

**Species A**

**Species B**

Resource usage as measured by food item size

1. Distinguish between interspecific competition and intraspecific competition, and contrast the effect of these two types of competition on niche breadth:

_____

_____

_____

_____

2. Study the diagram above illustrating niche overlap between competing species and then answer the following questions:

   (a) Explain what you would expect to happen if the overlap in resource use of species A and B was to become very large (i.e. they utilized almost the same sized food item):

   _____

   (b) Describe how the degree of resource overlap might change seasonally: _____

   _____

   (c) If the zone of overlap between the resource use of the two species increased a little more from what is shown on the diagram, explain what is likely to happen to the breadth of the **realized** niche of each species:

   _____

3. Niche breadth can become broader in the presence of intense competition between members of the same species (diagram, top right). Describe one other reason why niche breadth could be very wide:

   _____

   _____

**DA 2**

**Related activities**: Niche Differentiation, Interspecific Competition, Intraspecific Competition

# Adaptations to Niche

The adaptive features that evolve in species are the result of selection pressures on them through the course of their evolution. These features enable an organism to function most effectively in its niche, enhancing its exploitation of its environment and therefore its survival. The examples below illustrate some of the adaptations of two species: a British placental mammal and a migratory Arctic bird. Note that adaptations may be associated with an animal's structure (morphology), its internal physiology, or its behavior.

## Northern or Common Mole
### (Talpa europaea)

*Head-body length: 113-159 mm, tail length: 25-40 mm, weight range: 70-130 g.*

Moles (photos above) spend most of the time underground and are rarely seen at the surface. Mole hills are the piles of soil excavated from the tunnels and pushed to the surface. The cutaway view above shows a section of tunnels and a nest chamber. Nests are used for sleeping and raising young. They are dug out within the tunnel system and lined with dry plant material.

The northern (common) mole is a widespread insectivore found throughout most of Britain and Europe, apart from Ireland. They are found in most habitats but are less common in coniferous forest, moorland, and sand dunes, where their prey (earthworms and insect larvae) are rare. They are well adapted to life underground and burrow extensively, using enlarged forefeet for digging. Their small size, tubular body shape, and heavily buttressed head and neck are typical of burrowing species.

Eyes rudimentary although they are not completely blind.

External ear openings covered by dense fur.

Short, velvety dark fur can lie in any direction, allowing easy forward or back movement.

The rotation-thrust method of digging is aided by the short, powerful limbs and the efficient lever arrangement of muscles and joints.

Clawed hindfeet give grip and move soil away.

Pink fleshy snout and keen sense of smell for locating prey.

Enlarged, spade-like forefeet form shovel-blades for digging. Claws are broad and stiff hairs widen the foot.

**Habitat and ecology**: Moles spend most of their lives in underground tunnels. Surface tunnels occur where their prey is concentrated at the surface (e.g. land under cultivation). Deeper, permanent tunnels form a complex network used repeatedly for feeding and nesting, sometimes for several generations. **Senses and behavior**: Keen sense of smell but almost blind. Both sexes are solitary and territorial except during breeding. Life span about 3 years. Moles are prey for owls, buzzards, stoats, cats, and dogs. Their activities aerate the soil and they control many soil pests. Despite this, they are regularly trapped and poisoned as pests.

## Snow Bunting
### (Plectrophenax nivalis)

The snow bunting is a small ground feeding bird that lives and breeds in the Arctic and sub-Arctic islands. Although migratory, snow buntings do not move to traditional winter homes but prefer winter habitats that resemble their Arctic breeding grounds, such as bleak shores or open fields of northern Britain and the eastern United States. Snow buntings have the unique ability to molt very rapidly after breeding. During the warmer months, the buntings are a brown color, changing to white in winter (right). They must complete this color change quickly, so that they have a new set of feathers before the onset of winter and before migration. In order to achieve this, snow buntings lose as many as four or five of their main flight wing feathers at once, as opposed to most birds, which lose only one or two.

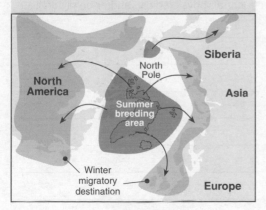

Very few small birds breed in the Arctic, because most small birds lose more heat than larger ones. In addition, birds that breed in the brief Arctic summer must migrate before the onset of winter, often traveling over large expanses of water. Large, long winged birds are better able to do this. However, the snow bunting is superbly adapted to survive in the extreme cold of the Arctic region.

Less heat is lost from white plumage compared to dark plumage.

White feathers are hollow and filled with air, which acts as an insulator. In the dark colored feathers the internal spaces are filled with pigmented cells

Snow buntings, on average, lay one or two more eggs than equivalent species further south. They are able to rear more young because the continuous daylight and the abundance of insects at high latitudes enables them to feed their chicks around the clock.

During snow storms or periods of high wind, snow buntings will burrow into snowdrifts for shelter.

**Siberia** / **North Pole** / **North America** / **Asia** / **Summer breeding area** / **Winter migratory destination** / **Europe**

**Habitat and ecology**: Widespread throughout Arctic and sub-Arctic Islands. Active throughout the day and night, resting for only 2-3 hours in any 24 hour period. Snow buntings may migrate up to 6000 km but are always found at high latitudes. **Reproduction and behavior**: The nest, which is concealed amongst stones, is made from dead grass, moss, and lichen. The male bird feeds his mate during the incubation period and helps to feed the young.

Ecosystems

RA 2

1. Describe a structural, physiological, and behavioral adaptation of the **common mole**, explaining how each adaptation assists survival:

   (a) Structural adaptation: _____

   _____

   (b) Physiological adaptation: _____

   _____

   (c) Behavioral adaptation: _____

   _____

2. Describe a structural, physiological, and behavioral adaptation of the **snow bunting**, explaining how each adaptation assists survival:

   (a) Structural adaptation: _____

   _____

   (b) Physiological adaptation: _____

   _____

   (c) Behavioral adaptation: _____

   _____

3. The rabbit is a colonial mammal which lives underground in warrens (burrow systems) and feeds on grasses, cereal crops, roots, and young trees. Rabbits are a hugely successful species worldwide and often reach plague proportions. Through discussion, or your own knowledge and research, describe **six adaptations** of rabbits, identifying them as structural (S), physiological (P), or behavioral (B). The examples below are typical:

   **Structural**: *Widely spaced eyes gives wide field of vision for surveillance and detection of danger.*

   **Physiological**: *High reproductive rate. Short gestation and high fertility aids rapid population increases when food is available.*

   **Behavioral**: *Freeze behavior when startled reduces the possibility of detection by wandering predators.*

   (a) _____

   (b) _____

   (c) _____

   (d) _____

   (e) _____

   (f) _____

4. Examples of adaptations are listed below. Identify them as predominantly structural, physiological, and/or behavioral:

   (a) Relationship of body size and shape to latitude (tropical or Arctic): _____

   (b) The production of concentrated urine in desert dwelling mammals: _____

   (c) The summer and winter migratory patterns in birds and mammals: _____

   (d) The C4 photosynthetic pathway and CAM metabolism of plants: _____

   (e) The thick leaves and sunken stomata of desert plants: _____

   (f) Hibernation or torpor in small mammals over winter: _____

   (g) Basking in lizards and snakes: _____

# Ecological Succession

Ecological succession is the process by which communities in a particular area change over time. Succession takes place as a result of complex interactions of biotic and abiotic factors. Early communities modify the physical environment causing it to change. This in turn alters the biotic community, which further alters the physical environment and so on. Each successive community makes the environment more favorable for the establishment of new species. A succession (or **sere**) proceeds in **seral stages**, until the formation of a **climax community**, which is stable until further disturbance. Early successional communities are characterized by a low species diversity, a simple structure, and broad niches. In contrast, climax communities are complex, with a large number of species interactions, narrow niches, and high species diversity.

*Composition of the community changes with time*

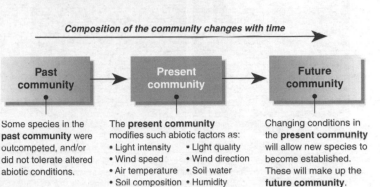

**Past community** → **Present community** → **Future community**

Some species in the **past community** were outcompeted, and/or did not tolerate altered abiotic conditions.

The **present community** modifies such abiotic factors as:
- Light intensity    • Light quality
- Wind speed    • Wind direction
- Air temperature    • Soil water
- Soil composition    • Humidity

Changing conditions in the **present community** will allow new species to become established. These will make up the **future community**.

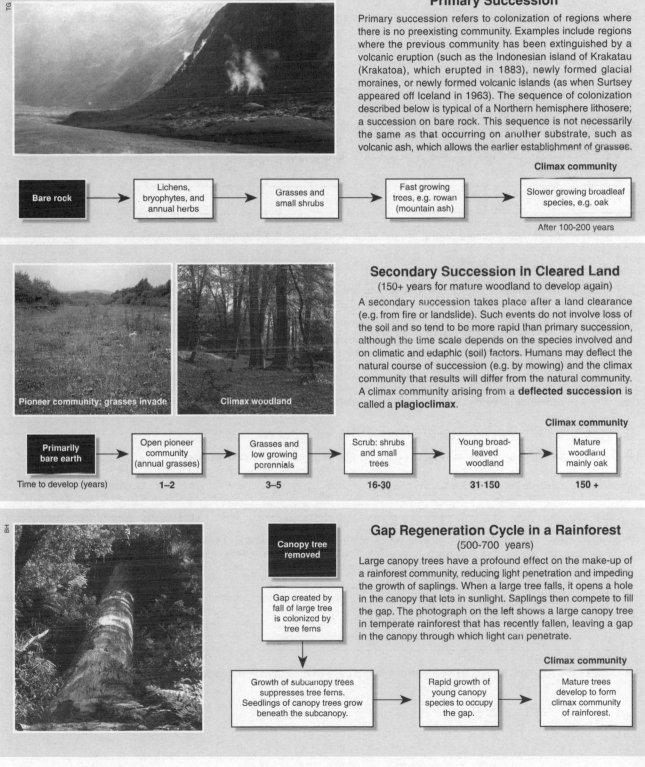

## Primary Succession

Primary succession refers to colonization of regions where there is no preexisting community. Examples include regions where the previous community has been extinguished by a volcanic eruption (such as the Indonesian island of Krakatau (Krakatoa), which erupted in 1883), newly formed glacial moraines, or newly formed volcanic islands (as when Surtsey appeared off Iceland in 1963). The sequence of colonization described below is typical of a Northern hemisphere lithosere; a succession on bare rock. This sequence is not necessarily the same as that occurring on another substrate, such as volcanic ash, which allows the earlier establishment of grasses.

**Climax community**

| Bare rock | → | Lichens, bryophytes, and annual herbs | → | Grasses and small shrubs | → | Fast growing trees, e.g. rowan (mountain ash) | → | Slower growing broadleaf species, e.g. oak |

After 100-200 years

## Secondary Succession In Cleared Land
(150+ years for mature woodland to develop again)

A secondary succession takes place after a land clearance (e.g. from fire or landslide). Such events do not involve loss of the soil and so tend to be more rapid than primary succession, although the time scale depends on the species involved and on climatic and edaphic (soil) factors. Humans may deflect the natural course of succession (e.g. by mowing) and the climax community that results will differ from the natural community. A climax community arising from a **deflected succession** is called a **plagioclimax**.

*Pioneer community: grasses invade*

*Climax woodland*

**Climax community**

| Primarily bare earth | → | Open pioneer community (annual grasses) | → | Grasses and low growing perennials | → | Scrub: shrubs and small trees | → | Young broad-leaved woodland | → | Mature woodland mainly oak |

| Time to develop (years) | 1–2 | 3–5 | 16-30 | 31-150 | 150 + |

## Gap Regeneration Cycle in a Rainforest
(500-700 years)

Large canopy trees have a profound effect on the make-up of a rainforest community, reducing light penetration and impeding the growth of saplings. When a large tree falls, it opens a hole in the canopy that lets in sunlight. Saplings then compete to fill the gap. The photograph on the left shows a large canopy tree in temperate rainforest that has recently fallen, leaving a gap in the canopy through which light can penetrate.

**Canopy tree removed**

Gap created by fall of large tree is colonized by tree ferns

↓

Growth of subcanopy trees suppresses tree ferns. Seedlings of canopy trees grow beneath the subcanopy. → Rapid growth of young canopy species to occupy the gap. → **Climax community** Mature trees develop to form climax community of rainforest.

**Related activities**: Tropical Deforestation
**Web links**: Mount St Helens

**Ecosystems**

## Secondary Succession in Cleared Land
(150+ years for mature woodland to develop again)

A secondary succession takes place after a land clearance (e.g. from fire or landslide). Such events do not involve loss of the soil and so tend to be more rapid than primary succession, although the time scale depends on the species involved and on climatic and edaphic (soil) factors. Humans may deflect the natural course of succession (e.g. by mowing) and the climax community that results will differ from the natural community. A climax community arising from a **deflected succession** is called a **plagioclimax**.

Pioneer community

Mature woodland

**Climax community**

| Primarily bare earth | → | Open pioneer community (annual grasses) | → | Grasses and low growing perennials | → | Scrub: shrubs and small trees | → | Young broad-leaved woodland | → | Mature woodland mainly oak |

Time to develop (years)    1–2    3–5    16-30    31-150    150 +

1. Distinguish between **primary** succession and **secondary** succession: _____

_____

_____

_____

2. Suggest why primary successions rarely follow the classic sequence depicted on the previous page: _____

_____

_____

_____

3. (a) Identify some early colonizers during the establishment phase of a community on bare rock: _____

_____

   (b) Describe two important roles of the species that are early colonizers of bare slopes: _____

_____

_____

_____

4. Describe a possible catastrophic event causing succession in a rainforest ecosystem: _____

_____

5. (a) Describe the effect of selective logging on the composition of a forest community: _____

_____

_____

   (b) Suggest why selective logging could be considered preferable (for forest conservation) to clear felling of trees:

_____

_____

6. (a) Explain what is meant by a **deflected succession**: _____

_____

   (b) Discuss the role that deflected successions might have in maintaining managed habitats: _____

_____

_____

_____

# Energy Flow and Nutrient Cycles

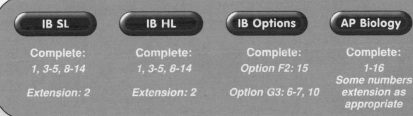

**IB SL**

Complete:
1, 3-5, 8-14

Extension: 2

**IB HL**

Complete:
1, 3-5, 8-14

Extension: 2

**IB Options**

Complete:
Option F2: 15

Option G3: 6-7, 10

**AP Biology**

Complete:
1-16
*Some numbers
extension as
appropriate*

## Learning Objectives

☐ 1. Compile your own glossary from the **KEY WORDS** displayed in **bold type** in the learning objectives below.

### Energy in Ecosystems *(pages 300, 303-304)*

☐ 2. In practical terms, explain what the energy laws mean with respect to energy conversions in ecosystems.

### Trophic relationships *(pages 301-304, 387)*

☐ 3. Describe the energy flow in ecosystems using **trophic levels**, and distinguish between **producers, primary and secondary consumers, detritivores**, and **decomposers**. Describe how energy is transferred between trophic levels in **food chains** and **food webs**.

☐ 4. Describe the **efficiency** of energy transfer between trophic levels, and explain the small biomass and low numbers of organisms at higher trophic levels. Explain what happens to the energy that is not transferred.

☐ 5. Construct **food chains** and a **food web** for a named community. Show how the organisms are interconnected through their feeding relationships and assign them to trophic levels.

☐ 6. Discuss the difficulties of classifying organisms into trophic levels.

☐ 7. With reference to the nature and function of trophic relationships, explain the term **bioaccumulation**.

☐ 8. Describe energy flow quantitatively using an **energy flow diagram**. Include reference to trophic levels, direction of energy flow, processes involved in energy transfer, energy sources, and energy sinks.

### Ecological Pyramids *(pages 305-306)*

☐ 9. Describe food chains quantitatively using **ecological pyramids**. Explain how these may be based on **numbers, biomass**, or **energy** at each trophic level.

☐ 10. Construct or interpret pyramids of energy, numbers, or biomass for different communities. Identify the relationship between each of these types of pyramids and their corresponding food chains and webs. Explain the shape of pyramid.

### Biogeochemical Cycles *(pages 307-311)*

☐ 11. Explain the terms **nutrient cycle** and **environmental reservoir**. Draw and interpret a generalized model of a nutrient cycle, identifying the roles of **primary productivity** and **decomposition** in nutrient cycling.

☐ 12. Using named examples, describe the general role of **saprotrophs** and **detritivores** in nutrient cycling.

☐ 13. Describe the stages in the **carbon cycle**. Identify the form of carbon at different stages, and use arrows to indicate nutrient flow and labels to identify processes. Describe the role of microorganisms, carbon sinks, and carbonates in the cycle.

☐ 14. Identify factors influencing the rate of carbon cycling. Recognize the role of respiration and photosynthesis in the short-term fluctuations and in the long-term global balance of oxygen and carbon dioxide.

☐ 15. Describe the stages in the **nitrogen cycle**. Identify the form of nitrogen at the different stages, and use arrows to indicate nutrient flow and labels to identify processes. Identify and explain the role of microorganisms in the cycle: **nitrifying bacteria** (*Nitrosomonas, Nitrobacter*), **nitrogen-fixing bacteria** (*Rhizobium, Azotobacter*), and **denitrifying bacteria** (*Pseudomonas*).

☐ 16. Describe the features of the **water cycle**. Understand the ways in which water is cycled between various reservoirs and describe the major processes, including: **evaporation, condensation, precipitation, runoff**. Appreciate how humans intervene in the water cycle.

---

 **Textbooks**

 See the 'Textbook Reference Grid' on pages 8-9 for textbook page references relating to material in this topic.

**Supplementary Texts**
See pages 5-6 for additional details of these texts:

■ Adds, J. *et al.*, 2004. **Exchange & Transport, Energy & Ecosystems** (NelsonThornes), chpt. 6 & 7

 **Presentation MEDIA** to support this topic:
**ECOLOGY:**
• **Communities**

 **Periodicals**

See page 6 for details of publishers of periodicals:

### STUDENT'S REFERENCE

■ **The Lake Ecosystem** Biol. Sci. Rev., 20(3) Feb. 2008, pp. 21-25. *An excellent account of the components and functioning of lake ecosystems.*

■ **Microbes and Nutrient Cycling** Biol. Sci. Rev., 19(1) Sept. 2006, pp. 16-20. *The roles of microorganisms in nutrient cycling.*

■ **Ultimate interface** New Scientist, 14 Nov. 1998 (Inside Science). *Biogeochemical cycling in the biosphere, with emphasis on the role of the soil.*

■ **The Nitrogen Cycle** Biol. Sci. Rev., 13(2) Nov. 2000, pp. 25-27. *The nitrogen cycle: conversions, role in ecosystems, and the influence of humans.*

■ **One Rate to Rule Them All** New Scientist, 1 May 2004, pp. 38-41. *A universal law governing metabolic rates helps to explain energy flow through ecosystems now and in the future.*

 **Internet**

See pages 10-11 for details of how to access **Bio Links** from our web site: **www.thebiozone.com** From Bio Links, access sites under the topics:

**ECOLOGY > Energy Flows and Nutrient Cycles:** • A marine food web • Bioaccumulation • Human alteration of the global nitrogen cycle • Nitrogen: The essential element • The carbon cycle • The nitrogen cycle • The water cycle • Trophic pyramids and food webs

# Energy Inputs and Outputs

Within ecosystems, organisms are assigned to **trophic levels** based on the way in which they obtain their energy (**producers**, or autotrophs, and **consumers**, or heterotrophs). Light is the initial energy source for almost all ecosystems and photosynthesis is the main route by which energy enters most food chains. Energy flows through ecosystems in the high energy chemical bonds within **organic matter** and, in accordance with the second law of thermodynamics, is dissipated as it is transferred through trophic levels. In contrast, nutrients move within and between ecosystems in **biogeochemical cycles** involving exchanges between the atmosphere, the Earth's crust, water, and living organisms. Energy flows through trophic levels rather inefficiently, with only 5-20% of usable energy being transferred to the subsequent level. Energy not used for metabolic processes is lost as heat.

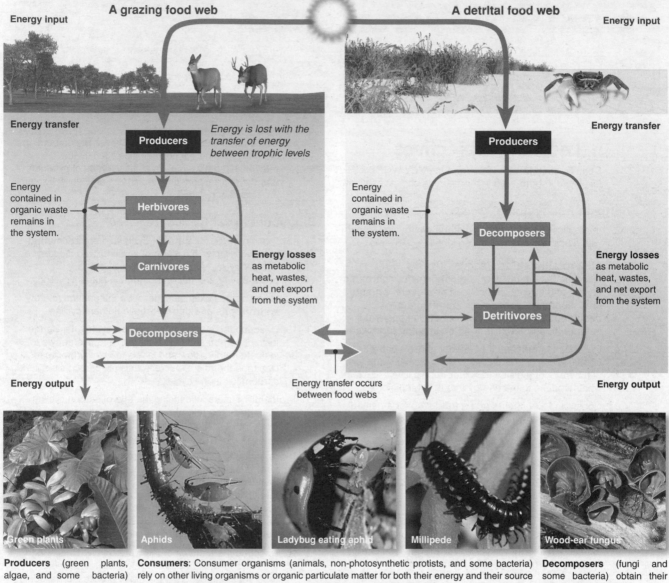

**A grazing food web**

Energy input

Energy transfer

Producers

*Energy is lost with the transfer of energy between trophic levels*

Energy contained in organic waste remains in the system.

Herbivores

Carnivores

Decomposers

**Energy losses** as metabolic heat, wastes, and net export from the system

Energy output

**A detrital food web**

Energy input

Energy transfer

Producers

Energy contained in organic waste remains in the system.

Decomposers

Detritivores

**Energy losses** as metabolic heat, wastes, and net export from the system

Energy output

Energy transfer occurs between food webs

Green plants

Aphids

Ladybug eating aphid

Millipede

Wood-ear fungus

**Producers** (green plants, algae, and some bacteria) make their own food from simple inorganic carbon sources (e.g. $CO_2$). Sunlight is the most common energy source for this process.

**Consumers**: Consumer organisms (animals, non-photosynthetic protists, and some bacteria) rely on other living organisms or organic particulate matter for both their energy and their source of carbon. **First order consumers**, such as aphids (left), feed directly on producers. **Second** (and higher) **order consumers**, such as ladybugs (centre) feed on other consumers. **Detritivores** consume (ingest and digest) detritus (decomposing organic material) from every trophic level. In doing so, they contribute to decomposition and the recycling of nutrients. Common detritivores includes millipedes (right), woodlice, and many terrestrial worms.

**Decomposers** (fungi and some bacteria) obtain their energy and carbon from the extracellular breakdown of (usually dead) organic matter (DOM). Decomposers play a central role in nutrient cycling.

1. Describe the differences between **producers** and **consumers** with respect to their role in energy transfers:

_____

_____

2. With respect to energy flow, describe a major difference between a detrital and a grazing food web: _____

_____

_____

3. Distinguish between detritivores and decomposers with respect to how their contributions to nutrient cycling:

_____

_____

_____

**Related activities**: Energy Flow in an Ecosystem, Food Chains and Webs, Ecological Pyramids

# Food Chains and Webs

Every ecosystem has a **trophic structure**: a hierarchy of feeding relationships which determines the pathways for energy flow and nutrient cycling. Species are assigned to trophic levels on the basis of their sources of nutrition, with the first trophic level (the **producers**), ultimately supporting all other (consumer) levels. Consumers are ranked according to the trophic level they occupy, although some consumers may feed at several different trophic levels. The sequence of organisms, each of which is a source of food for the next, is called a **food chain**. The different food chains in an ecosystem are interconnected to form a complex web of feeding interactions called a **food web**. In the example of a lake ecosystem below, your task is assemble the organisms into a food web in a way that illustrates their trophic status and their relative trophic position(s).

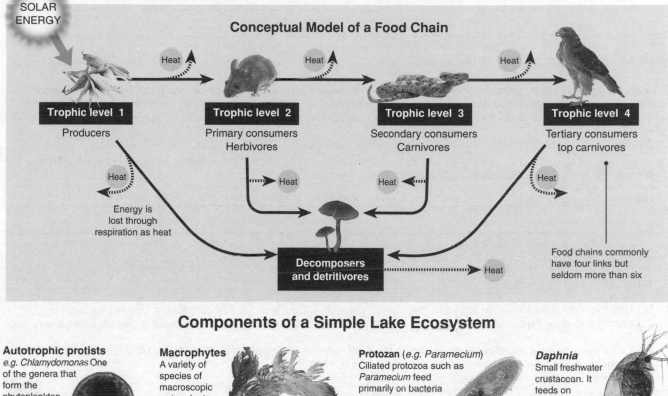

## Conceptual Model of a Food Chain

SOLAR ENERGY

Heat | Heat | Heat

**Trophic level 1**
Producers

**Trophic level 2**
Primary consumers
Herbivores

**Trophic level 3**
Secondary consumers
Carnivores

**Trophic level 4**
Tertiary consumers
top carnivores

Heat | Heat | Heat | Heat

Energy is lost through respiration as heat

**Decomposers and detritivores**
Heat

Food chains commonly have four links but seldom more than six

## Components of a Simple Lake Ecosystem

**Autotrophic protists**
*e.g. Chlamydomonas* One of the genera that form the phytoplankton (or algae).

**Macrophytes**
A variety of species of macroscopic water plants adapted for being submerged, free-floating, or growing at the lake margin.

**Protozan** (*e.g. Paramecium*)
Ciliated protozoa such as *Paramecium* feed primarily on bacteria and microscopic algae such as *Chlamydomonas*.

**Daphnia**
Small freshwater crustacean. It feeds on planktonic algae by filtering them from the water with its limbs.

**Great pond snail** (*Limnaea*)
Omnivorous pond snail, eating both plant and animal material, living or dead, although the main diet is aquatic macrophytes.

**Diving beetle** (*Dytiscus*)
Predators of aquatic insect larvae and adult insects blown into the lake. The will also eat organic detritus collected from the bottom mud.

**Asplanchna**
A large, carnivorous **rotifer** that feeds on protozoa and young zooplankton (e.g. *Daphnia*). Note that most rotifers are small herbivores.

**Herbivorous water beetles** (*e.g. Hydrophilus*)
Feed on water plants, although the young beetle larvae are carnivorous, feeding primarily on small pond snails.

**Leech** (*Glossiphonia*)
Fluid feeding predator of smaller invertebrates, including rotifers, small pond snails, and worms.

**Mosquito larva**
The larvae of most mosquito species, e.g. *Culex*, feed on planktonic algae before passing through a pupal stage and undergoing metamorphosis into adult mosquitoes.

**Hydra**
A small carnivorous cnidarian that captures small prey items such as small *Daphnia* and insect arvae using its stinging cells on the tentacles.

**Dragonfly larva**
Large aquatic insect larvae that are feed on small invertebrates including *Hydra*, *Daphnia*, other insect larvae, and leeches.

**Carp** (*Cyprinus*)
A heavy bodied freshwater fish that feeds mainly on bottom living insect larvae and snails, but will also take some plant material (not algae).

**Three-spined stickleback** (*Gasterosteus*)
A common fish of freshwater ponds and lakes. It feeds mainly on small invertebrates such as *Daphnia* and insect larvae.

NYSDEC

**Pike** (*Esox lucius*)
A top ambush predator of all smaller fish and amphibians, although they are also opportunistic predators of rodents and small birds.

**Detritus**
Decaying organic matter from within the lake itself or it may be washed in from the lake margins.

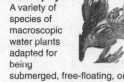

**Energy Flow and Nutrient Cycles**

**Related activities**: Energy Inputs and Outputs, Energy Flow in an Ecosystem
**Web links**: Fitting Algae into the Food Web, Marine Food Webs

A 2

1.  (a) Describe what happens to the **amount** of energy available to each successive trophic level in a food chain:

    _____

    (b) Explain why this is the case: _____

    _____

2.  Describe the trophic structure of ecosystems, including reference to **food chains** and **trophic** levels:

    _____

    _____

    _____

3.  From the information provided for the lake food web components on the previous page, construct **five** different **food chains** to show the feeding relationships between the organisms. Some food chains may be shorter than others and some species will appear in more than one food chain. An example has been completed for you.

    Example 1:     Macrophyte  ⟶  Herbivorous water beetle  ⟶  Carp  ⟶  Pike

    (a) _____

    (b) _____

    (c) _____

    (d) _____

    (e) _____

4.  (a) Use the food chains created above to help you to draw up a **food web** for this community. Use the information supplied to draw arrows showing the flow of **energy** between species (only energy **from** the detritus is required).

    (b) Label each species to indicate its position in the food web, i.e. its trophic level (**T1, T2, T3, T4, T5**). Where a species occupies more than one trophic level, indicate this, e.g. **T2/3**:

| **Tertiary and higher level consumers (carnivores)** | | | |
|---|---|---|---|
| Pike | | Carp | |

| **Tertiary consumers (carnivores)** | | | |
|---|---|---|---|
| | | Dragonfly larva | Three-spined stickleback |
| Hydra | Diving beetle (*Dytiscus*) | Leech | |

| **Secondary consumers (carnivores)** | | | |
|---|---|---|---|
| Mosquito larva | *Asplanchna* | | |

| **Primary consumers (herbivores)** | | | |
|---|---|---|---|
| *Daphnia* | *Paramecium* | Herbivorous water beetle (adult) | Great pond snail |

| **Producers** | | | |
|---|---|---|---|
| Planktonic algae | | | Macrophytes |

**Detritus and bacteria**

# Energy Flow in an Ecosystem

The flow of energy through an ecosystem can be measured and analyzed. It provides some idea as to the energy trapped and passed on at each trophic level. Each trophic level in a food chain or web contains a certain amount of biomass: the dry weight of all organic matter contained in its organisms. Energy stored in biomass is transferred from one trophic level to another (by eating, defecation etc.), with some being lost as low-grade heat energy to the environment in each transfer. Three definitions are useful:

- **Gross primary production**: The total of organic material produced by plants (including that lost to respiration).
- **Net primary production**: The amount of biomass that is available to consumers at subsequent trophic levels.

- **Secondary production**: The amount of biomass at higher trophic levels (consumer production). Production figures are sometimes expressed as rates (**productivity**).

The percentage of energy transferred from one trophic level to the next varies between 5% and 20% and is called the **ecological efficiency** (efficiency of energy transfer). An average figure of 10% is often used. The path of energy flow in an ecosystem depends on its characteristics. In a tropical forest ecosystem, most of the primary production enters the detrital and decomposer food chains. However, in an ocean ecosystem or an intensively grazed pasture more than half the primary production may enter the grazing food chain.

## Energy Flow Through an Ecosystem

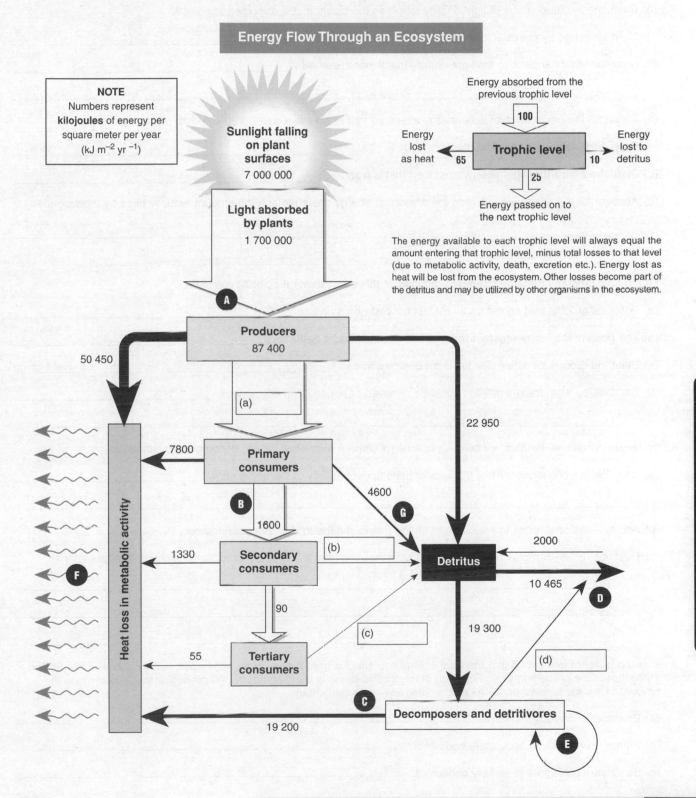

**NOTE**
Numbers represent **kilojoules** of energy per square meter per year
(kJ m$^{-2}$ yr$^{-1}$)

Sunlight falling on plant surfaces
7 000 000

Light absorbed by plants
1 700 000

Energy absorbed from the previous trophic level
100

Energy lost as heat 65 — **Trophic level** — 10 Energy lost to detritus

25

Energy passed on to the next trophic level

The energy available to each trophic level will always equal the amount entering that trophic level, minus total losses to that level (due to metabolic activity, death, excretion etc.). Energy lost as heat will be lost from the ecosystem. Other losses become part of the detritus and may be utilized by other organisms in the ecosystem.

**Producers** 87 400

50 450

A

(a)

Heat loss in metabolic activity

**Primary consumers**
7800

B
1600

22 950

4600

G

**Secondary consumers**
1330

(b)

**Detritus**

2000

10 465

D

90

(c)

19 300

**Tertiary consumers**
55

(d)

C

19 200

**Decomposers and detritivores**

E

F

Energy Flow and Nutrient Cycles

**Related activities**: The Carbon Cycle

DA 3

1. Study the diagram on the previous page illustrating energy flow through a hypothetical ecosystem. Use the example at the top of the page as a guide to calculate the missing values (a)–(d) in the diagram. Note that the sum of the energy inputs always equals the sum of the energy outputs. Place your answers in the spaces provided on the diagram.

2. Describe the original source of energy that powers this ecosystem: _____

3. Identify the processes that are occurring at the points labeled **A – G** on the diagram:

   A. _____     E. _____

   B. _____     F. _____

   C. _____     G. _____

   D. _____

4. (a) Calculate the percentage of light energy falling on the plants that is absorbed at point A:

   Light absorbed by plants ÷ sunlight falling on plant surfaces x 100  =  _____

   (b) Describe what happens to the light energy that is not absorbed: _____

   _____

5. (a) Calculate the percentage of light energy absorbed that is actually converted (fixed) into producer energy:

   Producers ÷ light absorbed by plants  x 100  =  _____

   (b) State the **amount** of light energy absorbed that is **not** fixed: _____

   (c) Account for the difference between the amount of energy absorbed and the amount actually fixed by producers:

   _____

   _____

6. Of the total amount of energy **fixed** by producers in this ecosystem (at point **A**) calculate:

   (a) The total amount that ended up as metabolic waste heat (in kJ): _____

   (b) The percentage of the energy fixed that ended up as waste heat: _____

7. (a) State the groups for which detritus is an energy source: _____

   (b) Describe by what means detritus could be removed or added to an ecosystem: _____

   _____

8. In certain conditions, detritus will build up in an environment where few (or no) decomposers can exist.

   (a) Describe the consequences of this lack of decomposer activity to the energy flow: _____

   _____

   (b) Add an additional arrow to the diagram on the previous page to illustrate your answer.

   (c) Describe three examples of materials that have resulted from a lack of decomposer activity on detrital material:

   _____

   _____

   _____

9. The **ten percent law** states that the total energy content of a trophic level in an ecosystem is only about one-tenth (or 10%) that of the preceding level. For each of the trophic levels in the diagram on the preceding page, determine the amount of energy passed on to the next trophic level as a percentage:

   (a) Producer to primary consumer: _____

   (b) Primary consumer to secondary consumer: _____

   (c) Secondary consumer to tertiary consumer: _____

# Ecological Pyramids

The trophic levels of any ecosystem can be arranged in a pyramid shape. The first trophic level is placed at the bottom and subsequent trophic levels are stacked on top in their 'feeding sequence'. Ecological pyramids can illustrate changes in the **numbers**, **biomass** (weight), or **energy** content of organisms at each level. Each of these three kinds of pyramids tell us something different about the flow of energy and materials between one trophic level and the next. The type of pyramid you choose in order to express information about the ecosystem will depend on what particular features of the ecosystem you are interested in and, of course, the type of data you have collected.

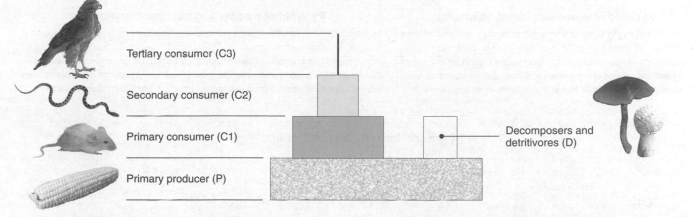

Tertiary consumer (C3)

Secondary consumer (C2)

Primary consumer (C1)

Primary producer (P)

Decomposers and detritivores (D)

The generalized ecological pyramid pictured above shows a conventional pyramid shape, with a large number (or biomass) of producers forming the base for an increasingly small number (or biomass) of consumers. Decomposers are placed at the level of the primary consumers and off to the side. They may obtain energy from many different trophic levels and so do not fit into the conventional pyramid structure. For any particular ecosystem at any one time (e.g. the forest ecosystem below), the shape of this typical pyramid can vary greatly depending on whether the trophic relationships are expressed as numbers, biomass or energy.

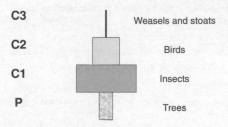

C3  Weasels and stoats
C2  Birds
C1  Insects
P   Trees

**Numbers in a forest community**

Pyramids of numbers display the number of individual organisms at each trophic level. The pyramid above has few producers, but they may be of a very large size (e.g. trees). This gives an 'inverted pyramid' although not all pyramids of numbers are like this.

**Biomass in a forest community**

Biomass pyramids measure the 'weight' of biological material at each trophic level. Water content of organisms varies, so 'dry weight' is often used. Organism size is taken into account, so meaningful comparisons of different trophic levels are possible.

**Energy in a forest community**

Pyramids of energy are often very similar to biomass pyramids. The energy content at each trophic level is generally comparable to the biomass (i.e. similar amounts of dry biomass tend to have about the same energy content).

1. Describe what the three types of ecological pyramids measure:

   (a) Number pyramid: _____

   (b) Biomass pyramid: _____

   (c) Energy pyramid: _____

2. Explain the advantage of using a biomass or energy pyramid rather than a pyramid of numbers to express the relationship between different trophic levels:

   _____
   _____

3. Explain why it is possible for the forest ecosystem (on the next page) to have very few producers supporting a large number of consumers:

   _____
   _____

**Related activities**: Energy Flow in an Ecosystem

DA 2

Energy Flow and Nutrient Cycles

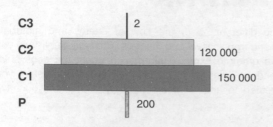

### Pyramid of numbers: forest community

In a forest community a few producers may support a large number of consumers. This is due to the large size of the producers; large trees can support many individual consumer organisms. The example above shows the numbers at each trophic level for an oak forest in England, in an area of 10 m².

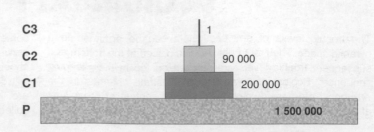

### Pyramid of numbers: grassland community

In a grassland community a large number of producers are required to support a much smaller number of consumers. This is due to the small size of the producers. Grass plants can support only a few individual consumer organisms and take time to recover from grazing pressure. The example above shows the numbers at each trophic level for a derelict grassland area (10 m²) in Michigan, United States.

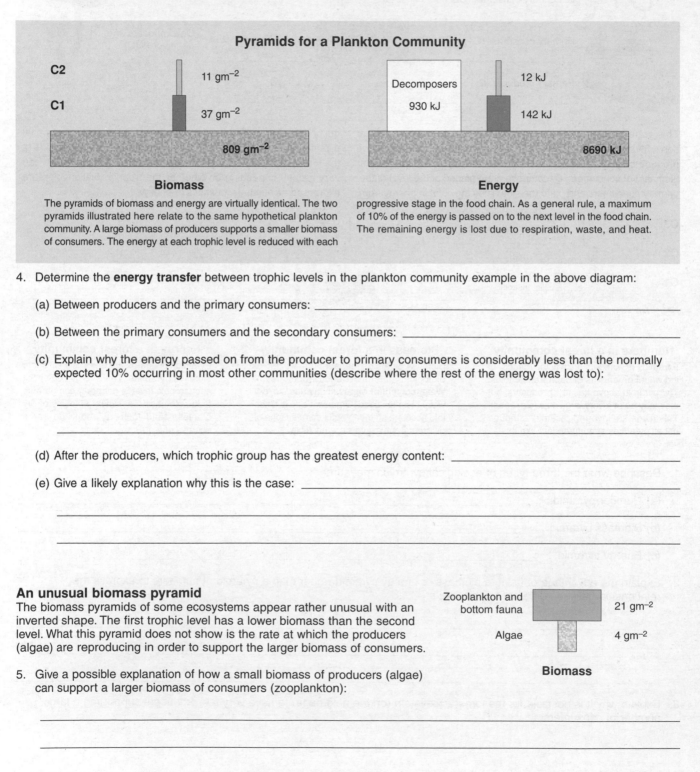

## Pyramids for a Plankton Community

**Biomass**

**Energy**

The pyramids of biomass and energy are virtually identical. The two pyramids illustrated here relate to the same hypothetical plankton community. A large biomass of producers supports a smaller biomass of consumers. The energy at each trophic level is reduced with each progressive stage in the food chain. As a general rule, a maximum of 10% of the energy is passed on to the next level in the food chain. The remaining energy is lost due to respiration, waste, and heat.

4. Determine the **energy transfer** between trophic levels in the plankton community example in the above diagram:

(a) Between producers and the primary consumers: _____

(b) Between the primary consumers and the secondary consumers: _____

(c) Explain why the energy passed on from the producer to primary consumers is considerably less than the normally expected 10% occurring in most other communities (describe where the rest of the energy was lost to):

_____

_____

(d) After the producers, which trophic group has the greatest energy content: _____

(e) Give a likely explanation why this is the case: _____

_____

_____

## An unusual biomass pyramid

The biomass pyramids of some ecosystems appear rather unusual with an inverted shape. The first trophic level has a lower biomass than the second level. What this pyramid does not show is the rate at which the producers (algae) are reproducing in order to support the larger biomass of consumers.

Zooplankton and bottom fauna    21 gm⁻²

Algae    4 gm⁻²

**Biomass**

5. Give a possible explanation of how a small biomass of producers (algae) can support a larger biomass of consumers (zooplankton):

_____

_____

_____

# The Nitrogen Cycle

Nitrogen is a crucial element for all living things, forming an essential part of the structure of proteins and nucleic acids. The Earth's atmosphere is about 80% nitrogen gas ($N_2$), but molecular nitrogen is so stable that it is only rarely available directly to organisms and is often in short supply in biological systems. Bacteria play an important role in transferring nitrogen between the biotic and abiotic environments. Some bacteria are able to fix atmospheric nitrogen, while others convert ammonia to nitrate and thus make it available for incorporation into plant and animal tissues. Nitrogen-fixing bacteria are found living freely in the soil (Azotobacter) and living symbiotically with some plants in root nodules (Rhizobium). Lightning discharges also cause the oxidation of nitrogen gas to nitrate which ends up in the soil. Denitrifying bacteria reverse this activity and return fixed nitrogen to the atmosphere. Humans intervene in the nitrogen cycle by producing, and applying to the land, large amounts of nitrogen fertilizer. Some applied fertilizer is from organic sources (e.g. green crops and manures) but much is inorganic, produced from atmospheric nitrogen using an energy-expensive industrial process. Overuse of nitrogen fertilizers may lead to pollution of water supplies, particularly where land clearance increases the amount of leaching and runoff into ground and surface waters.

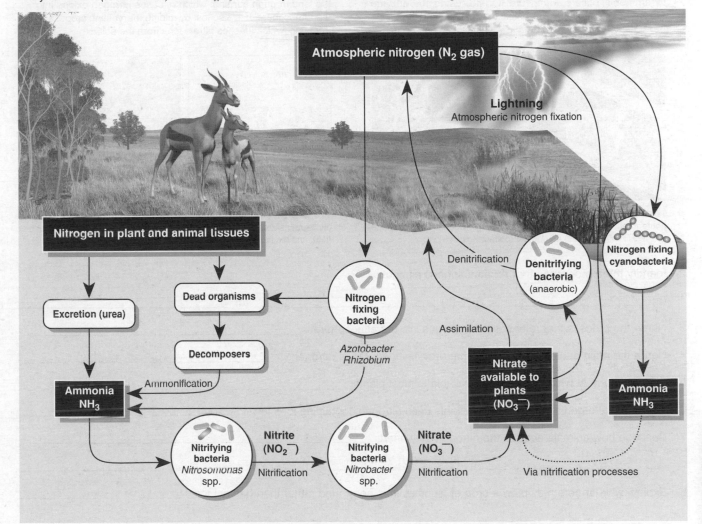

1. Describe five instances in the nitrogen cycle where **bacterial** action is important. Include the name of each of the processes and the changes to the form of nitrogen involved:

(a) _____

_____

(b) _____

_____

(c) _____

_____

(d) _____

_____

(e) _____

Energy Flow and Nutrient Cycles

**Related activities**: Pollution
**Web links**: Nitrogen Cycle Animation

A 2

## Nitrogen Fixation in Root Nodules

**Root nodules** are a root **symbiosis** between a higher plant and a bacterium. The bacteria fix atmospheric nitrogen and are extremely important to the nutrition of many plants, including the economically important legume family. Root nodules are extensions of the root tissue caused by entry of a bacterium. In legumes, this bacterium is *Rhizobium*. Other bacterial genera are involved in the root nodule symbioses in non-legume species.

The bacteria in these symbioses live in the nodule where they fix atmospheric nitrogen and provide the plant with most, or all, of its nitrogen requirements. In return, they have access to a rich supply of carbohydrate. The fixation of atmospheric nitrogen to ammonia occurs within the nodule, using the enzyme **nitrogenase**. Nitrogenase is inhibited by oxygen and the nodule provides a low $O_2$ environment in which fixation can occur.

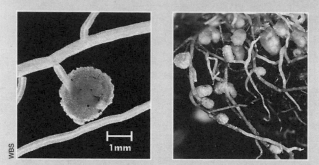

Two examples of legume nodules caused by *Rhizobium*. The photographs above show the size of a single nodule (left), and the nodules forming clusters around the roots of *Acacia* (right).

## Human Intervention in the Nitrogen Cycle

Until about sixty years ago, microbial nitrogen fixation (left) was the only mechanism by which nitrogen could be made available to plants. However, during WW II, Fritz Haber developed the **Haber process** whereby nitrogen and hydrogen gas are combined to form gaseous ammonia. The ammonia is converted into ammonium salts and sold as inorganic fertilizer. Its application has revolutionized agriculture by increasing crop yields.

As well as adding nitrogen fertilizers to the land, humans use anaerobic bacteria to break down livestock wastes and release $NH_3$ into the soil. They also intervene in the nitrogen cycle by discharging **effluent** into waterways. Nitrogen is removed from the land through burning, which releases nitrogen oxides into the atmosphere. It is also lost by mining, harvesting crops, and irrigation, which leaches nitrate ions from the soil.

Two examples of human intervention in the nitrogen cycle. The photographs above show the aerial application of a commercial fertilizer (left), and the harvesting of an agricultural crop (right).

2. Identify three processes that **fix** atmospheric nitrogen:

   (a) _____ (b) _____ (c) _____

3. Name the process that releases nitrogen gas into the atmosphere: _____

4. Name the main geological reservoir that provides a source of nitrogen: _____

5. State the form in which nitrogen is available to most plants: _____

6. Name a vital organic compound that plants need nitrogen containing ions for: _____

7. Describe how animals acquire the nitrogen they need: _____

   _____

8. Explain why farmers may plow a crop of legumes into the ground rather than harvest it: _____

   _____

9. Describe five ways in which humans may intervene in the nitrogen cycle and the effects of these interventions:

   (a) _____

   _____

   (b) _____

   _____

   (c) _____

   _____

   (d) _____

   _____

   (e) _____

   _____

# The Carbon Cycle

Carbon is an essential element in living systems, providing the chemical framework to form the molecules that make up living organisms (e.g. proteins, carbohydrates, fats, and nucleic acids). Carbon also makes up approximately 0.03% of the atmosphere as the gas carbon dioxide ($CO_2$), and it is present in the ocean as carbonate and bicarbonate, and in rocks such as limestone. Carbon cycles between the living (biotic) and non-living (abiotic)

environment: it is fixed in the process of photosynthesis and returned to the atmosphere in respiration. Carbon may remain locked up in biotic or abiotic systems for long periods of time as, for example, in the wood of trees or in fossil fuels such as coal or oil. Human activity has disturbed the balance of the carbon cycle (the global carbon budget) through activities such as combustion (e.g. the burning of wood and **fossil fuels**) and deforestation.

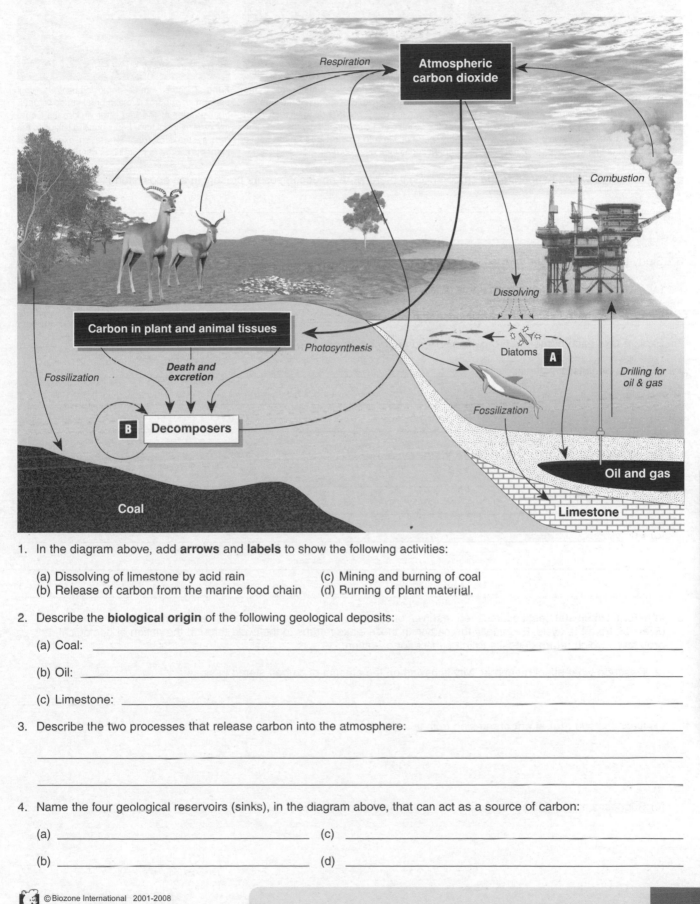

1. In the diagram above, add **arrows** and **labels** to show the following activities:

   (a) Dissolving of limestone by acid rain
   (b) Release of carbon from the marine food chain

   (c) Mining and burning of coal
   (d) Burning of plant material.

2. Describe the **biological origin** of the following geological deposits:

   (a) Coal: _____

   (b) Oil: _____

   (c) Limestone: _____

3. Describe the two processes that release carbon into the atmosphere: _____

   _____

   _____

4. Name the four geological reservoirs (sinks), in the diagram above, that can act as a source of carbon:

   (a) _____    (c) _____

   (b) _____    (d) _____

**Related activities**: Organic Molecules, Global Warming

A 2

Energy Flow and Nutrient Cycles

**Termite mound in rainforest**

**Dung beetle on cow pat**

**Bracket fungus on tree trunk**

**Termites**: These insects play an important role in nutrient recycling. With the aid of symbiotic protozoans and bacteria in their guts, they can digest the tough cellulose of woody tissues in trees. Termites fulfill a vital function in breaking down the endless rain of debris in tropical rainforests.

**Dung beetles**: Beetles play a major role in the decomposition of animal dung. Some beetles merely eat the dung, but true dung beetles, such as the scarabs and *Geotrupes*, bury the dung and lay their eggs in it to provide food for the beetle grubs during their development.

**Fungi**: Together with decomposing bacteria, fungi perform an important role in breaking down dead plant matter in the leaf litter of forests. Some mycorrhizal fungi have been found to link up to the root systems of trees where an exchange of nutrients occurs (a mutualistic relationship).

5. Explain what would happen to the carbon cycle if there were no decomposers present in an ecosystem:

_____

_____

6. Study the diagram on the previous page and identify the processes represented at the points labeled [**A**] and [**B**]:

(a) Process carried out by the diatoms at label **A**: _____

(b) Process carried out by the decomposers at label **B**: _____

7. Explain how each of the three organisms listed below has a role to play in the carbon cycle:

(a) Dung beetles: _____

_____

_____

(b) Termites: _____

_____

_____

(c) Fungi: _____

_____

_____

8. In natural circumstances, accumulated reserves of carbon such as peat, coal and oil represent a **sink** or natural diversion from the cycle. Eventually the carbon in these sinks returns to the cycle through the action of geological processes which return deposits to the surface for oxidation.

(a) Describe what effect human activity is having on the amount of carbon stored in sinks: _____

_____

(b) Describe two **global effects** arising from this activity: _____

_____

_____

(c) Suggest what could be done to prevent or alleviate these effects: _____

_____

_____

# The Water Cycle

The hydrologic cycle (water cycle), collects, purifies, and distributes the earth's fixed supply of water. The main processes in this water recycling are described below. Besides replenishing inland water supplies, rainwater causes erosion and is a major medium for transporting dissolved nutrients within and among ecosystems. On a global scale, evaporation (conversion of water to gaseous water vapor) exceeds precipitation (rain, snow etc.) over the oceans. This results in a net movement of water vapor (carried by winds) over the land. On land, precipitation exceeds evaporation. Some of this precipitation becomes locked up in snow and ice, for varying lengths of time. Most forms surface and groundwater systems that flow back to the sea, completing the major part of the cycle. Living organisms, particularly plants, participate to varying degrees in the water cycle. Over the sea, most of the water vapor is due to evaporation alone. However on land, about 90% of the vapor results from plant transpiration. Animals (particularly humans) intervene in the cycle by utilizing the resource for their own needs.

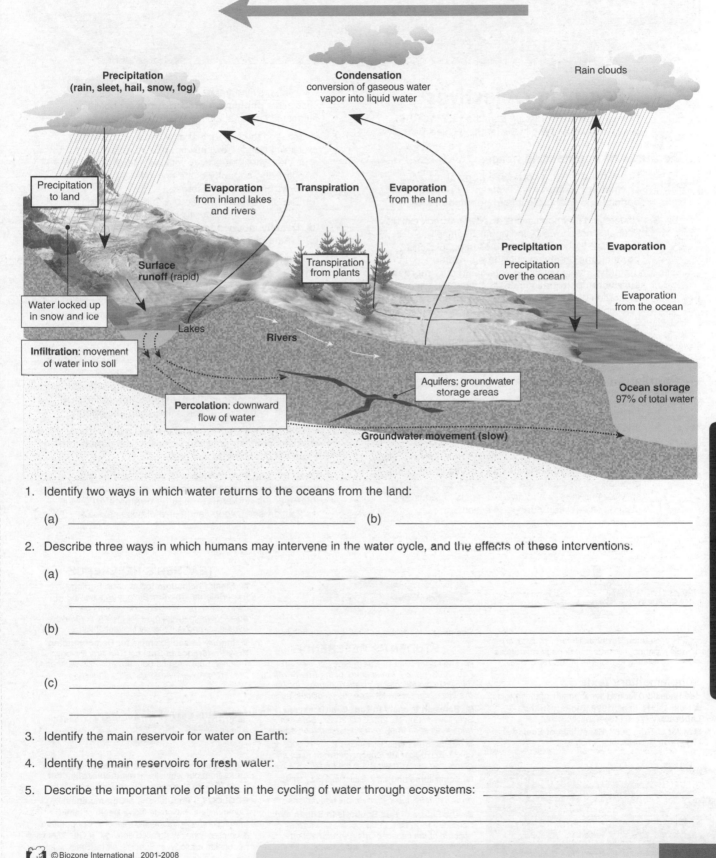

1. Identify two ways in which water returns to the oceans from the land:

(a) _____     (b) _____

2. Describe three ways in which humans may intervene in the water cycle, and the effects of these interventions.

(a) _____

_____

(b) _____

_____

(c) _____

_____

3. Identify the main reservoir for water on Earth: _____

4. Identify the main reservoirs for fresh water: _____

5. Describe the important role of plants in the cycling of water through ecosystems: _____

_____

**Related activities:** Pollution

A 2

**Energy Flow and Nutrient Cycles**

# Populations

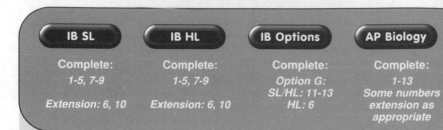

| IB SL | IB HL | IB Options | AP Biology |
|---|---|---|---|
| Complete: 1-5, 7-9 | Complete: 1-5, 7-9 | Complete: Option G: SL/HL: 11-13 HL: 6 | Complete: 1-13 Some numbers extension as appropriate |
| Extension: 6, 10 | Extension: 6, 10 | | |

## Learning Objectives

☐ 1. Compile your own glossary from the **KEY WORDS** displayed in **bold type** in the learning objectives below.

### Features of Populations *(pages 313-314, 321-322)*

☐ 2. Recall the difference between a **population** and a **community**. Explain what is meant by **population density** and distinguish it from **population size**.

☐ 3. Understand that populations are dynamic and exhibit attributes not shown by individuals themselves. Recognize the following attributes of populations: **population density**, population **distribution**, birth rate **(natality)**, mean (average) age, death rate **(mortality)**, **survivorship**, migration rate, average brood size, proportion of females breeding, **age structure**. Recognize that these attributes are population specific.

☐ 4. Describe the distribution patterns of organisms within their range: **uniform**, **random**, and **clumped**. Describe factors governing each type of distribution.

### Population Growth and Size *(pages 315-320)*

☐ 5. Describe how population size can be affected by **births**, **deaths**, and **migration** and express the relationship in an equation.

☐ 6. Recognize the value of **life tables** in providing information of patterns of population birth and mortality. Explain the role of **survivorship curves** in analyzing populations. Describe the features of type I, II, and III survivorship curves and give examples. If required, distinguish between *r* and K selection.

☐ 7. Describe how the trends in population change can be shown in a **population growth curve** of population numbers (Y axis) against time (X axis).

☐ 8. Understand the factors that affect final population size, explaining clearly how they operate and providing examples where necessary. Include reference to:
   (a) **Carrying capacity** of the environment.
   (b) **Environmental resistance**.
   (c) **Density dependent factors**, e.g. intraspecific competition, interspecific competition, predation.
   (d) **Density independent factors**, e.g. climatic events.
   (e) **Limiting factors**, e.g. soil nutrient.

☐ 9. Distinguish between **exponential** and **sigmoidal growth curves**. Create labeled diagrams of these curves, indicating the different phases of growth and the factors regulating population growth at each stage.

☐ 10. Recognize patterns of population growth in colonizing, stable, declining, and oscillating populations.

### Species Interactions *(pages 323-331 and the TRC)*

☐ 11. Explain the nature of the **interspecific interactions** occurring in communities. Recognize: **competition**, **mutualism**, **commensalism**, **exploitation** (parasitism, predation, herbivory), **amensalism**, and **allelopathy**.

☐ 12. Describing at least one example, explain the possible effects of predator-prey interactions on the **population sizes** of both predator and prey.

☐ 13. Describe, and give examples of, **interspecific** and **intraspecific competition**. Explain the effects of **interspecific** and/or **intraspecific competition** on the distribution and/or population size of two species.

---

See the 'Textbook Reference Grid' on pages 8-9 for textbook page references relating to material in this topic.

**Supplementary Texts**

See pages 5-6 for additional details of these texts:
■ Helms, D.R. *et al.*, 1998. **Biology in the Laboratory** (W.H. Freeman), #43, #44.
■ Miller G.T. Jr., 2007. **Essentials of Ecology** (Thomson Brooks/Cole), chpt. 9.

**Presentation MEDIA** to support this topic:
**ECOLOGY:**
• Populations
• Communities

See page 6 for details of publishers of periodicals:
**STUDENT'S REFERENCE**
■ **The Other Side of Eden** Biol. Sci. Rev., 15(3) Feb. 2003, pp. 2-7. *An account of the Eden Project; its role in modeling ecosystem dynamics, including the interactions between species, is discussed.*

■ **Batesian Mimicry in Your Own Backyard** Biol. Sci. Rev., 17(3) Feb. 2005, pp. 25-27. *Batesian mimicry is seen in even the most common species.*

■ **Inside Story** New Scientist, 29 April 2000, pp. 36-39. *Ecological interactions between fungi and plants and animals: what are the benefits?*

■ **Logarithms and Life** Biol. Sci. Rev., 13(4) March 2001, pp. 13-15. *The basics of logarithmic growth and its application to real populations.*

■ **The Future of Red Squirrels in Britain** Biol. Sci. Rev., 16(2) Nov. 2003, pp. 8-11. *A further account of the impact of the grey squirrel on Britain's native red squirrel populations.*

**TEACHER'S REFERENCE**
■ **Small Enclosures for Aquatic Ecology Experiments** The Am. Biology Teacher, 62 (6), June, 2000, pp. 424-428. *Using small aquatic populations to investigate life cycles, population dynamics, and community interactions.*

■ **Inquiry-Based Exercise for Demonstrating Prey Preference in Snakes** The Am. Biology Teacher, 68(4), April, 2006, pp. 213-220. *Illustrating predator-prey relationships using snakes.*

See pages 10-11 for details of how to access **Bio Links** from our web site: **www.thebiozone.com** From Bio Links, access sites under the topics:

**ECOLOGY > Populations & Communities:** • Communities • Competition • Death squared • Interactions • Intraspecific relations: Cooperation & competition • Population ecology • Quantitative population ecology • Species interactions

# Features of Populations

Populations have a number of attributes that may be of interest. Usually, biologists wish to determine **population size** (the total number of organisms in the population). It is also useful to know the **population density** (the number of organisms per unit area). The density of a population is often a reflection of the **carrying capacity** of the environment, i.e. how many organisms a particular environment can support. Populations also have structure; particular ratios of different ages and sexes. These data enable us to determine whether the population is declining or increasing in size. We can also look at the **distribution** of organisms within their environment and so determine what particular aspects of the habitat are favored over others. One way to retrieve information from populations is to **sample** them. Sampling involves collecting data about features of the population from samples of that population (since populations are usually too large to examine in total). Sampling can be done directly through a number of sampling methods or indirectly (e.g. monitoring calls, looking for droppings or other signs). Some of the population attributes that we can measure or calculate are illustrated on the diagram below.

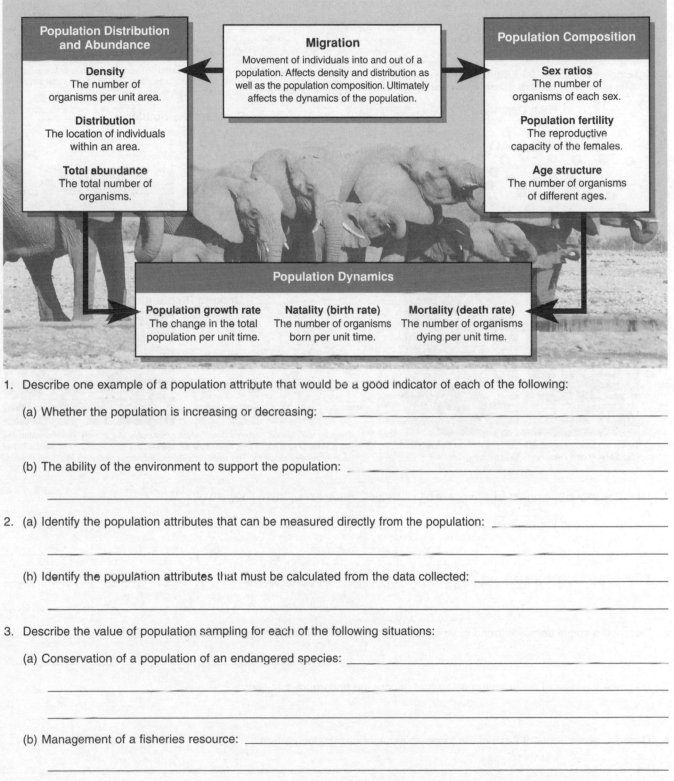

**Population Distribution and Abundance**

**Density**
The number of organisms per unit area.

**Distribution**
The location of individuals within an area.

**Total abundance**
The total number of organisms.

**Migration**
Movement of individuals into and out of a population. Affects density and distribution as well as the population composition. Ultimately affects the dynamics of the population.

**Population Composition**

**Sex ratios**
The number of organisms of each sex.

**Population fertility**
The reproductive capacity of the females.

**Age structure**
The number of organisms of different ages.

**Population Dynamics**

**Population growth rate**
The change in the total population per unit time.

**Natality (birth rate)**
The number of organisms born per unit time.

**Mortality (death rate)**
The number of organisms dying per unit time.

1. Describe one example of a population attribute that would be a good indicator of each of the following:

   (a) Whether the population is increasing or decreasing: _____

   _____

   (b) The ability of the environment to support the population: _____

   _____

2. (a) Identify the population attributes that can be measured directly from the population: _____

   _____

   (b) Identify the population attributes that must be calculated from the data collected: _____

   _____

3. Describe the value of population sampling for each of the following situations:

   (a) Conservation of a population of an endangered species: _____

   _____

   _____

   (b) Management of a fisheries resource: _____

   _____

   _____

   _____

Related activities: Density and Distribution, Population Age Structure, Endangered Species, Fisheries Management

A 2

# Density and Distribution

Distribution and density are two interrelated properties of populations. Population density is the number of individuals per unit area (for land organisms) or volume (for aquatic organisms). Careful observation and precise mapping can determine the distribution patterns for a species. The three basic distribution patterns are: random, clumped and uniform. In the diagram below, the circles represent individuals of the same species. It can also represent populations of different species.

### Low Density

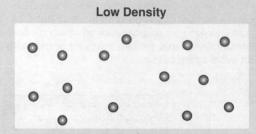

In low density populations, individuals are spaced well apart. There are only a few individuals per unit area or volume (e.g. highly territorial, solitary mammal species).

### High Density

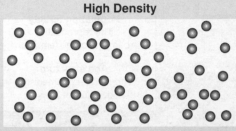

In high density populations, individuals are crowded together. There are many individuals per unit area or volume (e.g. colonial organisms, such as many corals).

Tigers are solitary animals, found at low densities.

Termites form well organized, high density colonies.

### Random Distribution

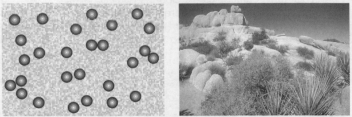

Random distributions occur when the spacing between individuals is irregular. The presence of one individual does not directly affect the location of any other individual. Random distributions are uncommon in animals but are often seen in plants.

### Clumped Distribution

Clumped distributions occur when individuals are grouped in patches (sometimes around a resource). The presence of one individual increases the probability of finding another close by. Such distributions occur in herding and highly social species.

### Uniform Distribution

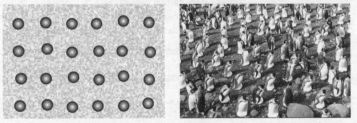

Regular distribution patterns occur when individuals are evenly spaced within the area. The presence of one individual decreases the probability of finding another individual very close by. The penguins illustrated above are also at a high density.

1. Describe why some organisms may exhibit a clumped distribution pattern because of:

   (a) Resources in the environment: _____

   _____

   (b) A group social behavior: _____

   _____

2. Describe a social behavior found in some animals that may encourage a uniform distribution: _____

   _____

3. Describe the type of environment that would encourage uniform distribution: _____

   _____

4. Describe an example of each of the following types of distribution pattern:

   (a) Clumped: _____

   (b) Random (more or less): _____

   (c) Uniform (more or less): _____

**Related activities**: Features of Populations

# Population Regulation

Very few species show continued exponential growth. Population size is regulated by factors that limit population growth. The diagram below illustrates how population size can be regulated by environmental factors. **Density independent factors** may affect all individuals in a population equally. Some, however, may be better able to adjust to them. **Density dependent factors** have a greater affect when the population density is higher. They become less important when the population density is low.

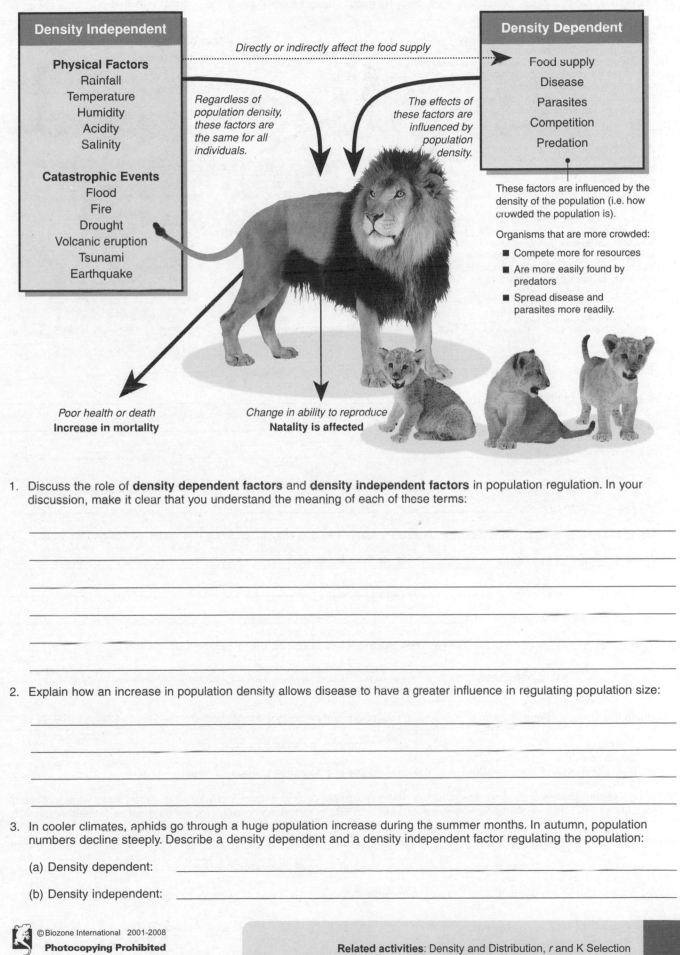

**Density Independent**

**Physical Factors**
Rainfall
Temperature
Humidity
Acidity
Salinity

**Catastrophic Events**
Flood
Fire
Drought
Volcanic eruption
Tsunami
Earthquake

*Directly or indirectly affect the food supply*

*Regardless of population density, these factors are the same for all individuals.*

*The effects of these factors are influenced by population density.*

**Density Dependent**

Food supply
Disease
Parasites
Competition
Predation

These factors are influenced by the density of the population (i.e. how crowded the population is).

Organisms that are more crowded:

■ Compete more for resources
■ Are more easily found by predators
■ Spread disease and parasites more readily.

*Poor health or death*
**Increase in mortality**

*Change in ability to reproduce*
**Natality is affected**

1. Discuss the role of **density dependent factors** and **density independent factors** in population regulation. In your discussion, make it clear that you understand the meaning of each of these terms:

_____

_____

_____

_____

_____

_____

2. Explain how an increase in population density allows disease to have a greater influence in regulating population size:

_____

_____

_____

_____

3. In cooler climates, aphids go through a huge population increase during the summer months. In autumn, population numbers decline steeply. Describe a density dependent and a density independent factor regulating the population:

(a) Density dependent: _____

(b) Density independent: _____

**Related activities**: Density and Distribution, *r* and K Selection

A 1

# Population Growth

Organisms do not generally live alone. A **population** is a group of organisms of the same species living together in one geographical area. This area may be difficult to define as populations may comprise widely dispersed individuals that come together only infrequently (e.g. for mating). The number of individuals comprising a population may also fluctuate considerably over time. These changes make populations dynamic: populations gain individuals through births or immigration, and lose individuals through deaths and emigration. For a population in **equilibrium**, these factors balance out and there is no net change in the population abundance. When losses exceed gains, the population declines.

*Births*, *deaths*, *immigrations* (movements into the population) and *emigrations* (movements out of the population) are events that determine the numbers of individuals in a population. Population growth depends on the number of individuals added to the population from births and immigration, minus the number lost through deaths and emigration. This is expressed as:

> **Population growth =**
>
> **Births – Deaths + Immigration – Emigration**
> **(B)        (D)           (I)                (E)**

The difference between immigration and emigration gives *net migration*. Ecologists usually measure the **rate** of these events. These rates are influenced by environmental factors and by the characteristics of the organisms themselves. Rates in population studies are commonly expressed in one of two ways:

• Numbers per unit time, e.g. 20 150 live births per year.

• Per capita rate (number per head of population), e.g. 122 live births per 1000 individuals per year (12.2%).

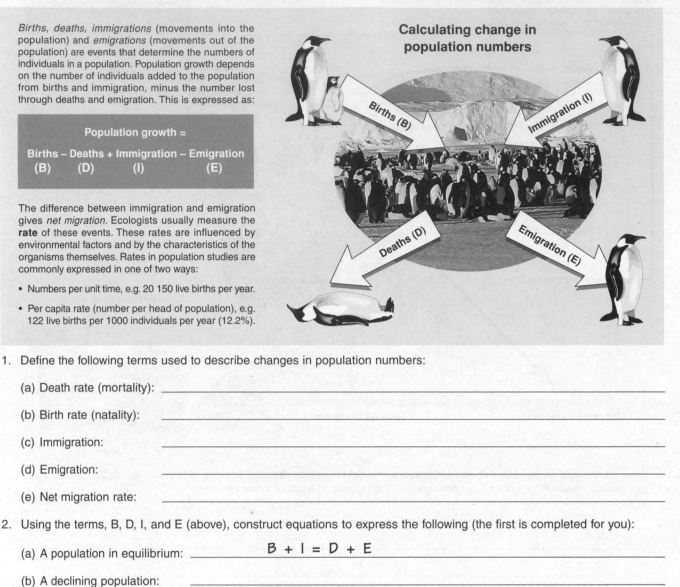

**Calculating change in population numbers**

Births (B)   Immigration (I)

Deaths (D)   Emigration (E)

1. Define the following terms used to describe changes in population numbers:

   (a) Death rate (mortality): _____

   (b) Birth rate (natality): _____

   (c) Immigration: _____

   (d) Emigration: _____

   (e) Net migration rate: _____

2. Using the terms, B, D, I, and E (above), construct equations to express the following (the first is completed for you):

   (a) A population in equilibrium: $B + I = D + E$

   (b) A declining population: _____

   (c) An increasing population: _____

3. The rate of population change can be expressed as the interaction of all these factors:

   > Rate of population change = Birth rate − Death rate + Net migration rate (positive or negative)

   Using the formula above, determine the annual rate of population change for Mexico and the United States in 1972:

   |  | USA | Mexico |  |  |
   |---|---|---|---|---|
   | Birth rate | 1.73% | 4.3% | Rate of population change for USA | = _____ |
   | Death rate | 0.93% | 1.0% |  |  |
   | Net migration rate | +0.20% | 0.0% | Rate of population change for Mexico | = _____ |

4. A population started with a total number of 100 individuals. Over the following year, population data were collected. Calculate birth rates, death rates, net migration rate, and rate of population change for the data below (as percentages):

   (a) Births = 14: Birth rate = _____   (b) Net migration = +2: Net migration rate = _____

   (c) Deaths = 20: Death rate = _____   (d) Rate of population change = _____

   (e) State whether the population is increasing or declining: _____

**DA 1**

**Related activities**: Features of Populations
**Web links**: Modeling Population Growth 1, Modeling Population Growth 2

 © Biozone International 2001-2008
**Photocopying Prohibited**

# Life Tables and Survivorship

The numerical data collected during a population study can be presented as a table of figures called a **life table** or graphically as a **survivorship curve**. These alternative presentations are shown below. Survivorship curves start at 1000 and, as the population ages, the number of survivors progressively declines. The shape of a survivorship curve shows graphically at which life stages the highest mortality occurs. Wherever the curve becomes steep, there is an increase in mortality. Some organisms suffer high losses of early life stages and compensate by producing vast numbers of offspring. Populations with higher survival rates for juveniles usually produce fewer young and have some degree of parental care. Note that many species exhibit a mix of two of the three basic types. Some birds have a high chick mortality (Type III) but adult mortality is fairly constant (Type II). Some invertebrates have high mortality only when moulting (e.g. crabs) and show a stepped curve.

### Life table for a population of the barnacle *Balanus*

| Age (yr) | No. alive at the start of the age interval | Proportion of original no. surviving at the start of the age interval | No. dying during the age interval | Mortality (d) |
|---|---|---|---|---|
| 0 | 142 | 1.000 | 80 | 0.563 |
| 1 | 62 | 0.437 | 28 | 0.452 |
| 2 | 34 | 0.239 | 14 | 0.412 |
| 3 | 20 | 0.141 | 5 | 0.250 |
| 4 | 15 | 0.106 | 4 | 0.267 |
| 5 | 11 | 0.078 | 5 | 0.454 |
| 6 | 6 | 0.042 | 4 | 0.667 |
| 7 | 2 | 0.014 | 0 | 0.000 |
| 8 | 2 | 0.014 | 2 | 1.000 |
| 9 | 0 | 0.0 | — | — |

Life tables, such as that shown left, provide a summary of mortality for a population (usually for a group of individuals of the same age). The basic data are just the number of individuals remaining alive at successive sampling times. Life table data can tell us the ages at which most mortality occurs in a population. They can also provide information about life span and population age structure.

Life table data can be presented graphically as a **survivorship curve** (see below). Survivorship curves use a semi-log plot of the number of individuals surviving per thousand in the population against age. They are standardized as the number of survivors per 1000 individuals so that populations of different types can be easily compared.

**Large mammals: Type I**

**Rodents: Type II**

***Hydra*: Type II**

**Barnacles: Type III**

**Type I (or late loss) survivorship curve**
Mortality (death rate) is very low in the infant and juvenile years, and throughout most of adult life. Mortality increases rapidly in old age. **Examples**: Humans (in developed countries) and many other large mammals (e.g. big cats, elephants).

**Type II (or constant loss) survivorship curve**
Mortality is relatively constant through all life stages (no one age is more susceptible than another). **Examples**: Some invertebrates such as *Hydra*, some birds, some annual plants, some lizards, and many rodents.

**Type III (or early loss) survivorship curve**
Mortality is very high during early life stages, followed by a very low death rate for the few individuals reaching adulthood. **Examples**: Many fish (not mouth brooders) and most marine invertebrates (e.g. oysters, barnacles).

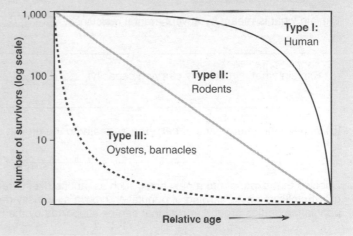

1. Explain why human populations might not necessarily show a Type I curve: _____

_____

2. Explain how populations with a Type III survivorship compensate for the high mortality during early life stages: _____

_____

3. Describe the features of a species with a Type I survivorship that aid in high juvenile survival: _____

_____

4. In the *Balanus* example above, state when most of the group die: _____

**Related activities**: Population Age Structure, *r* and *K* Selection

**DA 2**

# Population Growth Curves

Populations becoming established in a new area for the first time are often termed **colonizing populations** (below, left). They may undergo a rapid **exponential** (logarithmic) increase in numbers as there are plenty of resources to allow a high birth rate, while the death rate is often low. Exponential growth produces a J-shaped growth curve that rises steeply as more and more individuals contribute to the population increase. If the resources of the new habitat were endless (inexhaustible) then the population would continue to increase at an **exponential** rate. However, this rarely happens in natural populations. Initially, growth may be exponential (or nearly so), but as the population grows, its increase will slow and it will stabilize at a level that can be supported by the environment (called the carrying capacity or K). This type of growth is called sigmoidal and produces the **logistic growth curve** (below, right). **Established populations** will fluctuate about K, often in a regular way (gray area on the graph below, right). Some species will have populations that vary little from this stable condition, while others may oscillate wildly.

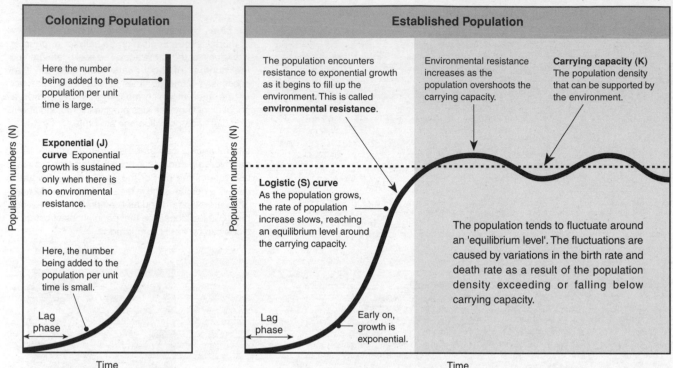

**Colonizing Population**

Here the number being added to the population per unit time is large.

**Exponential (J) curve** Exponential growth is sustained only when there is no environmental resistance.

Here, the number being added to the population per unit time is small.

Lag phase

Population numbers (N)

Time

**Established Population**

The population encounters resistance to exponential growth as it begins to fill up the environment. This is called **environmental resistance**.

Environmental resistance increases as the population overshoots the carrying capacity.

**Carrying capacity (K)** The population density that can be supported by the environment.

**Logistic (S) curve** As the population grows, the rate of population increase slows, reaching an equilibrium level around the carrying capacity.

The population tends to fluctuate around an 'equilibrium level'. The fluctuations are caused by variations in the birth rate and death rate as a result of the population density exceeding or falling below carrying capacity.

Lag phase

Early on, growth is exponential.

Population numbers (N)

Time

1. Explain why populations tend not to continue to increase exponentially in an environment: _____

_____

2. Explain what is meant by environmental resistance: _____

_____

3. (a) Explain what is meant by carrying capacity: _____

_____

   (b) Explain the importance of **carrying capacity** to the growth and maintenance of population numbers: _____

_____

4. Species that expand into a new area, such as rabbits did in areas of Australia, typically show a period of rapid population growth followed by a slowing of population growth as density dependent factors become more important and the population settles around a level that can be supported by the carrying capacity of the environment.

   (a) Explain why a newly introduced consumer (e.g. rabbit) would initially exhibit a period of exponential population growth:

_____

_____

   (b) Describe a likely outcome for a rabbit population after the initial rapid increase had slowed: _____

_____

5. Describe the effect that introduced grazing species might have on the carrying capacity of the environment:

_____

_____

**DA 2**    **Related activities**: *r* and K Selection

# Growth in a Bacterial Population

Bacteria normally reproduce by a process called **binary fission**; a simple mitotic cell division that is preceded by cell elongation and involves one cell dividing in two. The time required for a cell to divide is the **generation time** and it varies between organisms and with environmental conditions such as temperature. When a few bacteria are inoculated into a liquid growth medium, and the population is counted at intervals, it is possible to plot a

**bacterial growth curve** that shows the growth of cells over time. In this activity, you will simulate this for a hypothetical bacterial population with a generation time of 20 minutes. In a bacterial culture with a limited nutrient supply, four growth phases are evident: the early **lag phase**, the **log phase** of exponential growth, the **stationary phase** when growth rate slows, and the **death** phase, when the population goes into logarithmic decline.

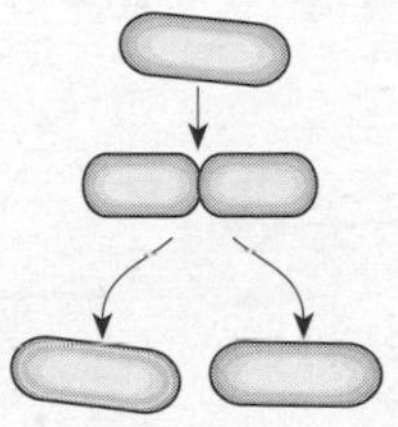

One bacterial cell

Binary fission

Two bacterial cells

| Time (mins) | Population size |
|---|---|
| 0 | 1 |
| 20 | 2 |
| 40 | 4 |
| 60 | 8 |
| 80 | |
| 100 | |
| 120 | |
| 140 | |
| 160 | |
| 180 | |
| 200 | |
| 220 | |
| 240 | |
| 260 | |
| 280 | |
| 300 | |
| 320 | |
| 340 | |
| 360 | |

1. Complete the table (above) by doubling the number of bacteria for every 20 minute interval.

2. Graph the results on the grid above. Make sure that you choose suitable scales for each axis. Label the axes and mark out (number) the scale for each axis. Identify the lag and log phases of growth and mark them on the graph.

3. State how many bacteria were present after:  1 hour: _____  3 hours: _____  6 hours: _____

4. Describe the shape of the curve you have plotted: _____

5. Predict what would happen to the shape of the growth curve of this population assuming no further input of nutrients:

_____

_____

**Related activities**: Population Growth Curves

DA 2

# r and K Selection

Two parameters govern the logistic growth of populations: the intrinsic rate of natural increase or biotic potential (this is the maximum reproductive potential of an organism, symbolized by an italicized *r*), and the carrying capacity (saturation density) of the environment (represented by the letter **K**). Species can be characterized by the relative importance of *r* and K in their life cycles. Species with a high intrinsic capacity for population increase are called ***r*-selected species**, and include algae, bacteria, rodents, many insects, and most annual plants. These species show life history features associated with rapid growth in disturbed environments. To survive, they must continually invade new areas to compensate for being replaced by more competitive species. In contrast, **K-selected** species, which include most large mammals, birds of prey, and large, long-lived plants, exist near the carrying capacity of their environments and are pushed in competitive environments to use resources more efficiently. These species have fewer offspring and longer lives, and put their energy into nuturing their young to reproductive age. Most organisms have reproductive patterns between these two extremes. Both *r*-selected species (crops) and K-selected species (livestock) are found in agriculture.

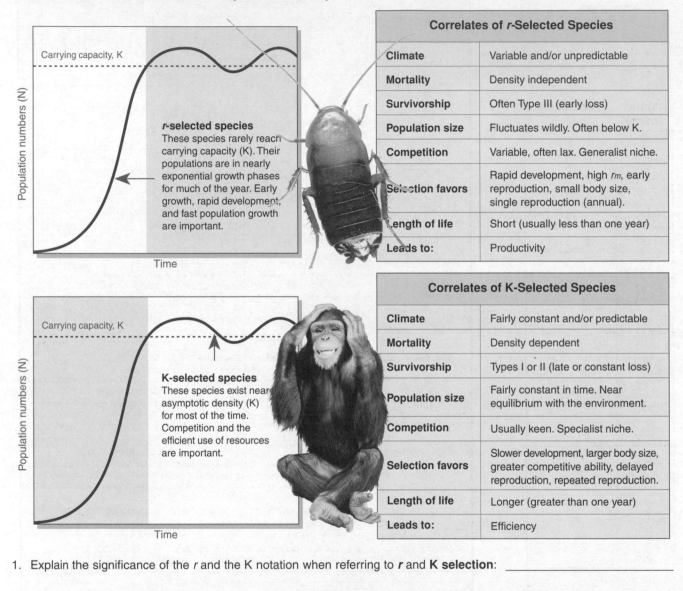

**r-selected species**
These species rarely reach carrying capacity (K). Their populations are in nearly exponential growth phases for much of the year. Early growth, rapid development, and fast population growth are important.

**K-selected species**
These species exist near asymptotic density (K) for most of the time. Competition and the efficient use of resources are important.

### Correlates of *r*-Selected Species

| | |
|---|---|
| **Climate** | Variable and/or unpredictable |
| **Mortality** | Density independent |
| **Survivorship** | Often Type III (early loss) |
| **Population size** | Fluctuates wildly. Often below K. |
| **Competition** | Variable, often lax. Generalist niche. |
| **Selection favors** | Rapid development, high $r_m$, early reproduction, small body size, single reproduction (annual). |
| **Length of life** | Short (usually less than one year) |
| **Leads to:** | Productivity |

### Correlates of K-Selected Species

| | |
|---|---|
| **Climate** | Fairly constant and/or predictable |
| **Mortality** | Density dependent |
| **Survivorship** | Types I or II (late or constant loss) |
| **Population size** | Fairly constant in time. Near equilibrium with the environment. |
| **Competition** | Usually keen. Specialist niche. |
| **Selection favors** | Slower development, larger body size, greater competitive ability, delayed reproduction, repeated reproduction. |
| **Length of life** | Longer (greater than one year) |
| **Leads to:** | Efficiency |

1. Explain the significance of the *r* and the K notation when referring to *r* and **K selection**: _____

_____

2. Giving an example, explain why *r*-selected species tend to be **opportunists**: _____

_____

_____

3. Explain why K-selected species are also called **competitor species**: _____

_____

_____

4. Suggest why many K-selected species are often vulnerable to extinction: _____

_____

**Related activities**: Life Tables and Survivorship, Population Growth Curves

# Population Age Structure

The **age structure** of a population refers to the relative proportion of individuals in each age group in the population. The age structure of populations can be categorized according to specific age categories (such as years or months), but also by other measures such as life stage (egg, larvae, pupae, instars), of size class (height or diameter in plants). Population growth is strongly influenced by age structure; a population with a high proportion of reproductive and prereproductive aged individuals has a much greater potential for population growth than one that is dominated by older individuals. The ratio of young to adults in a relatively stable population of most mammals and birds is approximately 2:1 (below, left). Growing populations in general are characterized by a large and increasing number of young, whereas a population in decline typically has a decreasing number of young. Population age structures are commonly represented as pyramids, in which the proportions of individuals in each age/size class are plotted with the youngest individuals at the pyramid's base. The number of individuals moving from one age class to the next influences the age structure of the population from year to year. The loss of an age class (e.g. through overharvesting) can profoundly influence a population's viability and can even lead to population collapse.

## Age Structures in Animal Populations

These theoretical age pyramids, which are especially applicable to birds and mammals, show how growing populations are characterized by a high ratio of young (white bar) to adult age classes (gray bars). Aging populations with poor production are typically dominated by older individuals.

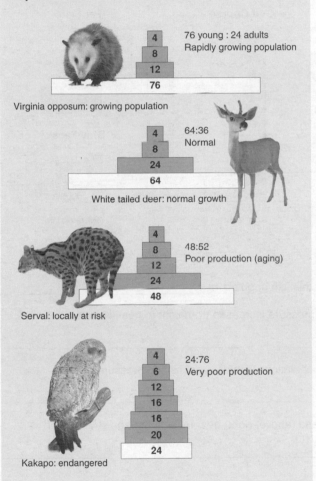

Virginia opposum: growing population
4 / 8 / 12 / 76
76 young : 24 adults
Rapidly growing population

White tailed deer: normal growth
4 / 8 / 24 / 64
64:36
Normal

Serval: locally at risk
4 / 8 / 12 / 24 / 48
48:52
Poor production (aging)

Kakapo: endangered
4 / 6 / 12 / 16 / 16 / 20 / 24
24:76
Very poor production

## Age Structures in Human Populations

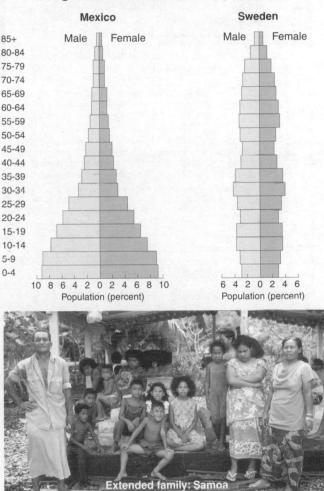

**Mexico**

85+ 80-84 75-79 70-74 65-69 60-64 55-59 50-54 45-49 40-44 35-39 30-34 25-29 20-24 15-19 10-14 5-9 0-4

Male / Female

10 8 6 4 2 0 2 4 6 8 10
Population (percent)

**Sweden**

Male / Female

6 4 2 0 2 4 6
Population (percent)

Extended family: Samoa

Most of the growth in human populations in recent years has occurred in the developing countries in Africa, Asia, and Central and South America. This is reflected in their age structure; a large proportion of the population comprises individuals younger than 15 years (age pyramid above, left). Even if each has fewer children, the population will continue to increase for many years. The stable age structure of Sweden is shown for comparison.

1. For the theoretical age pyramids above left:

(a) State the approximate ratio of young to adults in a rapidly increasing population: _____

(b) Suggest why changes in population age structure alone are not necessarily a reliable predictor of population trends:

_____

_____

2. Explain why the population of Mexico is likely to continue to increase rapidly even if the rate of population growth slows:

_____

_____

Related activities: Features of Populations, Fisheries Management

RDA 2

Analyzes of the age structure of populations can assist in their management because it can indicate where most population mortality occurs and whether or not reproductive individuals are being replaced. The age structure of plant and animal populations can be examined; a common method is through an analysis of size which is often related to age in a predictable way.

### Managed Fisheries

The graphs below illustrate the age structure of a hypothetical fish population under different fishing pressures. The age structure of the population is determined by analyzing the fish catch to determine the frequency of fish in each size (age) class.

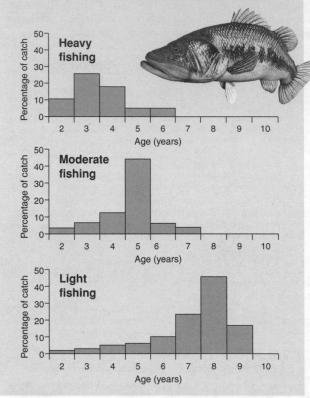

### Thatch Palm Populations on Lord Howe Island

Lord Howe Island is a narrow sliver of land approximately 770 km northeast of Sydney. The age structure of populations of the thatch palm *Howea forsteriana* was determined at three locations on the island: the golf course, Gray Face and Far Flats. The height of the stem was used as an indication of age. The differences in age structure between the three sites are mainly due to the extent of grazing at each site.

3. For the managed fish population above left:

   (a) Name the general factor that changes the age structure of this fish population: _____

   (b) Describe how the age structure changes when the fishing pressure increases from light to heavy levels:

   _____

4. State the most common age class for each of the above fish populations with different fishing pressures:

   (a) Heavy: _____   (b) Moderate: _____   (c) Light: _____

5. Determine which of the three sites sampled on Lord Howe Island (above, right) best reflects the age structure of:

   (a) An ungrazed population: _____

   Reason for your answer: _____

   (b) A heavily grazed and mown population: _____

   Reason for your answer: _____

6. Describe the likely long term prospects for the population at the golf course: _____

   _____

7. Describe a potential problem with using size to estimate age: _____

   _____

8. Explain why a knowledge of age structure could be important in managing a resource: _____

   _____

# Species Interactions

No organism exists in isolation. Each takes part in many interactions, both with other organisms and with the non-living components of the environment. Species interactions may involve only occasional or indirect contact (predation or competition) or they may involve close association or **symbiosis**. Symbiosis is a term that encompasses a variety of interactions involving close species contact. There are three types of symbiosis: **parasitism** (a form of exploitation), **mutualism**, and **commensalism**. Species interactions affect population densities and are important in determining community structure and composition. Some interactions, such as **allelopathy**, may even determine species presence or absence in an area.

## Examples of Species Interactions

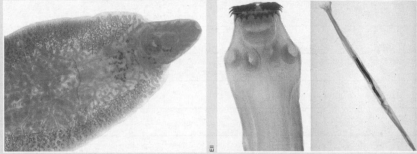

**Parasitism** is a common exploitative relationship in plants and animals. A parasite exploits the resources of its host (e.g. for food, shelter, warmth) to its own benefit. The host is harmed, but usually not killed. **Endoparasites**, such as liver flukes (left), tapeworms (center) and nematodes (right), are highly specialized to live inside their hosts, attached by hooks or suckers to the host's tissues.

**Ectoparasites**, such as ticks (above), mites, and fleas, live attached to the outside of the host, where they suck body fluids, cause irritation, and may act as vectors for disease causing microorganisms.

**Mutualism** involves an intimate association between two species that offers advantage to both. **Lichens** (above) are the result of a mutualism between a fungus and an alga (or cyanobacterium).

Termites have a mutualistic relationship with the cellulose digesting bacteria in their guts. A similar mutualistic relationship exists between ruminants and their gut microflora of bacteria and ciliates.

In **commensal** relationships, such as between this large grouper and a remora, two species form an association where one organism, the commensal, benefits and the other is neither harmed or helped.

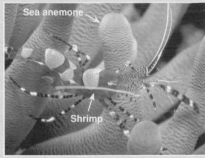

Many species of decapod crustaceans, such as this anemone shrimp, are commensal with sea anemones. The shrimp gains by being protected from predators by the anemone's tentacles.

Interactions involving **competition** for the same food resources are dominated by the largest, most aggressive species. Here, hyaenas compete for a carcass with vultures and maribou storks.

**Predation** is an easily identified relationship, as one species kills and eats another (above). Herbivory is similar type of exploitation, except that the plant is usually not killed by the herbivore.

1. Discuss each of the following interspecific relationships, including reference to the species involved, their role in the interaction, and the specific characteristics of the relationship:

(a) **Mutualism** between ruminant herbivores and their gut microflora: _____

_____

_____

_____

_____

**Related activities**: Interspecific Competition
**Web links**: Nearctica Ecology: Mutualism

RA 2

(b) **Commensalism** between a shark and a remora: _____

_____

_____

_____

(c) **Parasitism** between a tapeworm and its human host: _____

_____

_____

(d) **Parasitism** between a cat flea and its host: _____

_____

_____

_____

2. Summarize your knowledge of species interactions by completing the following, entering a (+), (−), or (0) for species B, and writing a brief description of each term. Codes: (+): species benefits, (−): species is harmed, (0): species is unaffected.

| Interaction | Species A | Species B | Description of relationship |
|---|---|---|---|
| (a) Mutualism | + | | |
| (b) Commensalism | + | | |
| (c) Parasitism | − | | |
| (d) Amensalism | 0 | | |
| (e) Predation | − | | |
| (f) Competition | − | | |
| (g) Herbivory | + | | |
| (h) Antibiosis | + / 0 | | |

3. For each of the interactions between two species described below, choose the correct term to describe the interaction and assign a +, − or 0 for each species involved in the space supplied. Use the completed table above to help you:

| Description | Term | Species A | Species B |
|---|---|---|---|
| (a) A tiny cleaner fish picking decaying food from the teeth of a much larger fish (e.g. grouper). | Mutualism | Cleaner fish + | Grouper + |
| (b) Ringworm fungus growing on the skin of a young child. | | Ringworm | Child |
| (c) Human effluent containing poisonous substances killing fish in a river downstream of discharge. | | Humans | Fish |
| (d) Humans planting cabbages to eat only to find that the cabbages are being eaten by slugs. | | Humans | Slugs |
| (e) A shrimp that gets food scraps and protection from sea anemones, which appear to be unaffected. | | Shrimp | Anemone |
| (f) Birds follow a herd of antelopes to feed off disturbed insects, antelopes alerted to danger by the birds. | | Birds | Antelope |

# Predator-Prey Strategies

A predator with prey is one of the most conspicuous species interactions and in most, but not all, cases the predator and prey are different species. Predators have numerous adaptations for locating, identifying, and subduing prey. Prey can avoid being eaten by using passive defenses, such as hiding, or active ones, such as escaping or defending themselves against predators.

## Predator Avoidance Strategies

**Mimicry**
Harmless prey gain immunity from attack by mimicking harmful animals. This is called **Batesian mimicry**.

**Poisonous**
Poisonous animals often advertise the fact that they are unpalatable by using brightly colored and gaudy markings.

**Visual deception**
Deceptive markings such as large, fake eyes can apparently deceive predators, allowing the prey to escape.

**Chemical defense**
Some animals can produce offensive smelling chemicals. American skunks squirt a nauseous fluid at attackers.

**Offensive weapons**
Offensive weapons are essential if prey are to actively fend off an attack by a predator.

**Camouflage**
Cryptic shape and coloration allows some animals to blend into their background, like this insect above.

## Prey Capturing Strategies

**Concealment**
Some animals camouflage themselves in their surroundings, striking when the prey comes within reach.

**Filter feeding**
Many marine animals (e.g. barnacles, baleen whales, sponges, manta rays) filter the water to extract tiny plankton.

**Tool use**
Some animals are gifted tool users. Chimpanzees use carefully prepared twigs to extract termites from mounds.

**Stealth**
The night hunting ability of some poisonous snakes is greatly helped by the presence of infrared senses.

**Lures**
This angler fish, glow worms, and a type of spider all use lures to attract prey within striking range.

**Traps**
Spiders have developed a unique method of trapping their prey. Strong, sticky silk threads trap flying insects.

1. Describe a behavior of prey that is actively defensive: _____

2. Describe the behavior of a named predator that facilitates prey capture: _____

3. Explain why poisonous (unpalatable) animals are often brightly colored so that they are easily seen: _____

4. Describe the purpose of large, fake eyes on some butterflies and fish: _____

5. Explain how Batesian mimicry **benefits** the mimic (the one that is actually edible): _____

6. Describe a **behavior** typical of a (named) prey species that makes them difficult to detect by a predator: _____

# Predator-Prey Interactions

Some mammals, particularly in highly seasonal environments, exhibit regular cycles in their population numbers. Snowshoe hares in Canada exhibit such a cycle of population fluctuation that has a periodicity of 9–11 years. Populations of lynx in the area show a similar periodicity. Contrary to early suggestions that the lynx controlled the size of the hare population, it is now known that the fluctuations in the hare population are governed by other factors, probably the availability of palatable grasses. The fluctuations in the lynx numbers however, do appear to be the result of fluctuations in the numbers of hares (their principal food item). This is true of most **vertebrate** predator-prey systems: predators do not usually control prey populations, which tend to be regulated by other factors such as food availability and climatic factors. Most predators have more than one prey species, although one species may be preferred. Characteristically, when one prey species becomes scarce, a predator will "switch" to another available prey item. Where one prey species is the principal food item and there is limited opportunity for prey switching, fluctuations in the prey population may closely govern predator cycles.

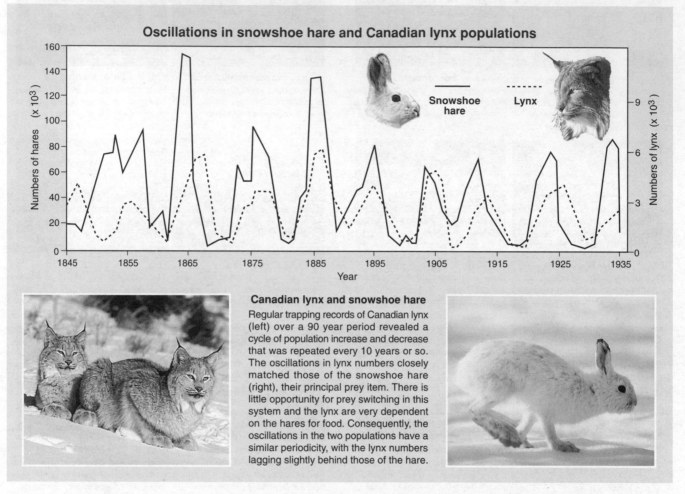

**Oscillations in snowshoe hare and Canadian lynx populations**

Snowshoe hare — Lynx

**Canadian lynx and snowshoe hare**

Regular trapping records of Canadian lynx (left) over a 90 year period revealed a cycle of population increase and decrease that was repeated every 10 years or so. The oscillations in lynx numbers closely matched those of the snowshoe hare (right), their principal prey item. There is little opportunity for prey switching in this system and the lynx are very dependent on the hares for food. Consequently, the oscillations in the two populations have a similar periodicity, with the lynx numbers lagging slightly behind those of the hare.

1. (a) From the graph above, determine the lag time between the population peaks of the hares and the lynx:

_____

(b) Explain why there is this time lag between the increase in the hare population and the response of the lynx:

_____

2. Suggest why the lynx populations appear to be so dependent on the fluctuations on the hare: _____

_____

_____

3. (a) In terms of birth and death rates, explain how the availability of palatable food might regulate the numbers of hares:

_____

_____

(b) Explain how a decline in available palatable food might affect their ability to withstand predation pressure:

_____

_____

**Related activities**: Predator-Prey Strategies, Population Growth

# Intraspecific Competition

Some of the most intense competition occurs between individuals of the same species (**intraspecific competition**). Most populations have the capacity to grow rapidly, but their numbers cannot increase indefinitely because environmental resources are finite. Every ecosystem has a **carrying capacity** (K), defined as the number of individuals in a population that the environment can support. Intraspecific competition for resources increases with increasing population size and, at carrying capacity, it reduces the per capita growth rate to zero. When the demand for a particular resource (e.g. food, water, nesting sites, nutrients, or light) exceeds supply, that resource becomes a **limiting factor**. Populations respond to resource limitation by reducing their population growth rate (e.g. through lower birth rates or higher mortality). The response of individuals to limited resources varies depending on the organism. In many invertebrates and some vertebrates such as frogs, individuals reduce their growth rate and mature at a smaller size. In some vertebrates, territoriality spaces individuals apart so that only those with adequate resources can breed. When resources are very limited, the number of available territories will decline.

## Intraspecific Competition

**Scramble competition in caterpillars**

Direct competition for available food between members of the same species is called **scramble competition**. In some situations where scramble competition is intense, none of the competitors gets enough food to survive.

**Contest competition in wolves**

In some cases, competition is limited by hierarchies existing within a social group. Dominant individuals receive adequate food, but individuals low in the hierarchy must **contest** the remaining resources and may miss out.

**Display of a male anole**

Intraspecific competition may be for mates or breeding sites, as well as for food. In anole lizards (above), males have a bright red throat pouch and use much of their energy displaying to compete with other males for available mates.

## Competition Between Tadpoles of *Rana tigrina*

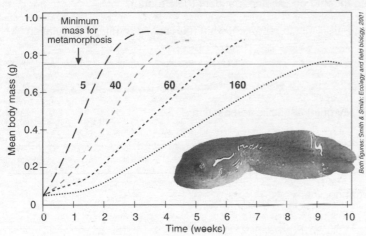

Both figures: Smith & Smith: Ecology and field biology, 2001

Food shortage reduces both individual growth rate and survival, and population growth. In some organisms, where there is a metamorphosis or a series of moults before adulthood (e.g. frogs, crustacean zooplankton, and butterflies), individuals may die before they mature.

The graph (left) shows how the growth rate of tadpoles (*Rana tigrina*) declines as the density increases from 5 to 160 individuals (in the same sized space).

- At high densities, tadpoles grow more slowly, taking longer to reach the minimum size for metamorphosis (0.75 g), and decreasing their chances of successfully metamorphosing from tadpoles into frogs.
- Tadpoles held at lower densities grow faster, to a larger size, metamorphosing at an average size of 0.889 g.
- In some species, such as frogs and butterflies, the adults and juveniles reduce the intensity of intraspecific competition by exploiting different food resources.

1. Using an example, predict the likely effects of **intraspecific competition** on each of the following:

(a) Individual growth rate: _____

_____

_____

(b) Population growth rate: _____

_____

_____

(c) Final population size: _____

_____

_____

**Related activities**: Population Growth Curves

RA 2

## Golden eagle breeding territories in Northern Scotland, 1967

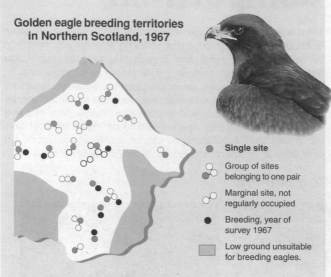

- ● Single site
- ⟨⟩ Group of sites belonging to one pair
- ○ Marginal site, not regularly occupied
- ● Breeding, year of survey 1967
- ▨ Low ground unsuitable for breeding eagles.

Territoriality in birds and other animals is usually a result of intraspecific competition. It frequently produces a pattern of uniform distribution over an area of suitable habitat, although this depends somewhat on the distribution of resources. The diagram above shows the territories of golden eagles (*Aquila chrysaetos*) in Scotland. Note the relatively uniform distribution of the breeding sites.

### Territoriality in Great Tits (*Parus major*)

Six breeding pairs of great tits were removed from an oak woodland (below). Within three days, four new pairs had moved into the unoccupied areas (below, right) and some residents had expanded their territories. The new birds moved in from territories in hedgerows, considered to be suboptimal habitat. This type of territorial behavior limits the density of breeding animals in areas of optimal habitat.

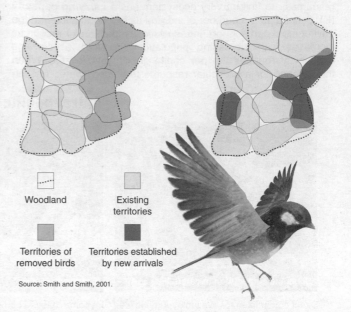

- ⬚ Woodland
- ▢ Existing territories
- ▨ Territories of removed birds
- ■ Territories established by new arrivals

Source: Smith and Smith, 2001.

2. In the tank experiment with *Rana* (see previous page), the tadpoles were contained in a fixed volume with a set amount of food:

(a) Describe how *Rana* tadpoles respond to resource limitation: _____

_____

(b) Categorize the effect on the tadpoles as density-dependent / density-independent (delete one).

(c) Comment on how much the results of this experiment are likely to represent what happens in a natural population:

_____

_____

3. Identify two ways in which animals can reduce the intensity of intraspecific competition:

(a) _____

(b) _____

4. (a) Suggest why carrying capacity of an ecosystem might decline: _____

_____

(b) Predict how a decline in carrying capacity might affect final population size: _____

_____

_____

5. Using appropriate examples, discuss the role of territoriality in reducing intraspecific competition:

_____

_____

_____

_____

_____

_____

_____

# Interspecific Competition

In naturally occurring populations, direct competition between different species (**interspecific competition**) is usually less intense than intraspecific competition because coexisting species have evolved slight differences in their realized niches, even though their fundamental niches may overlap (a phenomenon termed **niche differentiation**). However, when two species with very similar niche requirements are brought into direct competition through the introduction of a foreign species, one usually benefits at the expense of the other. The inability of two species with the same described niche to coexist is referred to as the **competitive exclusion principle**. In Britain, introduction of the larger, more aggressive, gray squirrel in 1876 has contributed to a contraction in range of the native red squirrel (below), and on the Scottish coast, this phenomenon has been well documented in barnacle species (see next page). The introduction of ecologically aggressive species is often implicated in the displacement or decline of native species, although there may be more than one contributing factor. Displacement of native species by introduced ones is more likely if the introduced competitor is also adaptable and hardy. It can be difficult to provide evidence of decline in a species as a direct result of competition, but it is often inferred if the range of the native species contracts and that of the introduced competitor shows a corresponding increase.

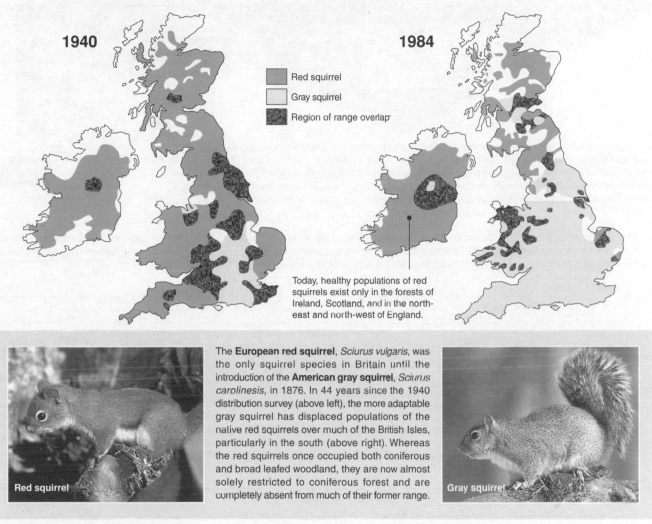

**1940**

**1984**

Red squirrel
Gray squirrel
Region of range overlap

Today, healthy populations of red squirrels exist only in the forests of Ireland, Scotland, and in the north-east and north-west of England.

The **European red squirrel**, *Sciurus vulgaris*, was the only squirrel species in Britain until the introduction of the **American gray squirrel**, *Sciurus carolinesis*, in 1876. In 44 years since the 1940 distribution survey (above left), the more adaptable gray squirrel has displaced populations of the native red squirrels over much of the British Isles, particularly in the south (above right). Whereas the red squirrels once occupied both coniferous and broad leafed woodland, they are now almost solely restricted to coniferous forest and are completely absent from much of their former range.

Red squirrel

Gray squirrel

1. Outline the evidence to support the view that the red-gray squirrel distributions in Britain are an example of the competitive exclusion principle:

_____

_____

_____

2. Some biologists believe that competition with grey squirrels is only one of the factors contributing to the decline in the red squirrels in Britain. Explain the evidence from the 1984 distribution map that might support this view:

_____

_____

_____

_____

**Related activities**: Niche Differentiation, Competition and Niche Size, The Impact of Alien Species

RA 2

# Competitive Exclusion in Barnacles

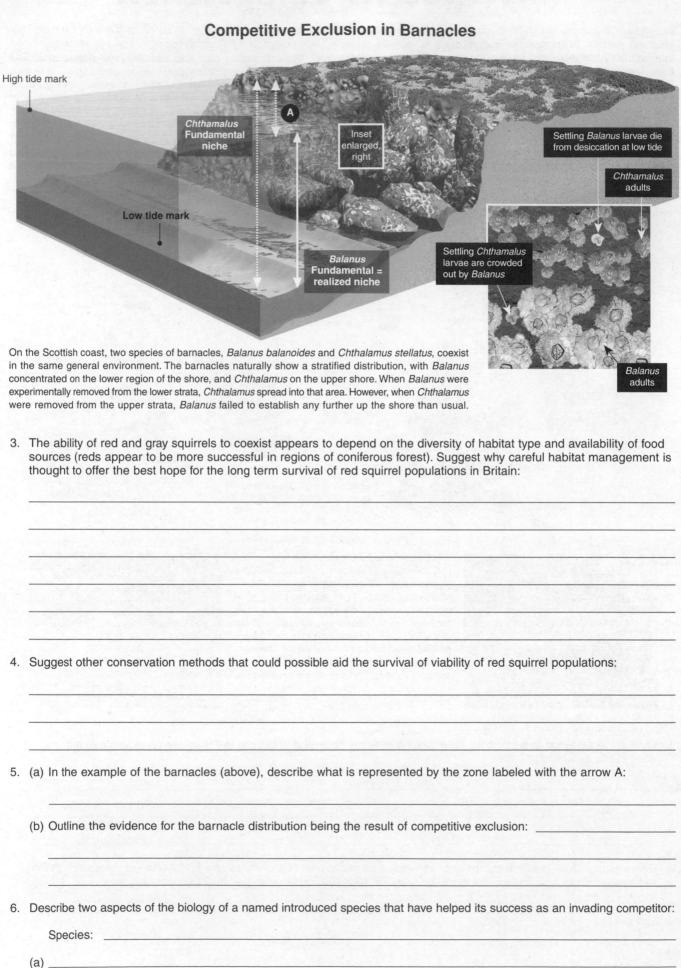

**High tide mark**

*Chthamalus* **Fundamental niche**

**A**

**Inset enlarged, right**

**Low tide mark**

*Balanus* **Fundamental = realized niche**

Settling *Balanus* larvae die from desiccation at low tide

*Chthamalus* adults

Settling *Chthamalus* larvae are crowded out by *Balanus*

*Balanus* adults

On the Scottish coast, two species of barnacles, *Balanus balanoides* and *Chthalamus stellatus*, coexist in the same general environment. The barnacles naturally show a stratified distribution, with *Balanus* concentrated on the lower region of the shore, and *Chthalamus* on the upper shore. When *Balanus* were experimentally removed from the lower strata, *Chthalamus* spread into that area. However, when *Chthalamus* were removed from the upper strata, *Balanus* failed to establish any further up the shore than usual.

3. The ability of red and gray squirrels to coexist appears to depend on the diversity of habitat type and availability of food sources (reds appear to be more successful in regions of coniferous forest). Suggest why careful habitat management is thought to offer the best hope for the long term survival of red squirrel populations in Britain:

_____

_____

_____

_____

_____

_____

4. Suggest other conservation methods that could possible aid the survival of viability of red squirrel populations:

_____

_____

_____

5. (a) In the example of the barnacles (above), describe what is represented by the zone labeled with the arrow A:

_____

(b) Outline the evidence for the barnacle distribution being the result of competitive exclusion: _____

_____

_____

6. Describe two aspects of the biology of a named introduced species that have helped its success as an invading competitor:

Species: _____

(a) _____

(b) _____

# Niche Differentiation

Competition is most intense between members of the same species because their habitat and resource requirements are identical. In naturally occurring populations, **interspecific competition** (between different species) is usually less intense than intraspecific competition because coexisting species have developed (through evolution) slight differences in their realized niches. In fact, when the niches of naturally coexisting species are described, there is seldom much overlap. Species with similar ecological requirements may reduce competition by exploiting microhabitats within the ecosystem. In the eucalypt forest below, different bird species exploit tree trunks, leaf litter, different levels within the canopy, and air space. Competition may also be reduced by exploiting the same resources at a different time of the day or year.

## Reducing competition in a eucalypt forest

The diagram on the left shows the foraging heights of birds in an eastern Australian eucalypt forest. A wide variety of food resources are offered by the structure of the forest. Different layers of the forest allow birds to specialize in foraging at different heights. The ground-dwelling yellow-throated scrubwren and ground thrush have robust legs and feet, while the white-throated treecreeper has long toes and large curved claws and the swifts are extremely agile fliers capable of catching insects on the wing.

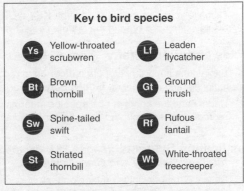

### Key to bird species

| | | | |
|---|---|---|---|
| **Ys** | Yellow-throated scrubwren | **Lf** | Leaden flycatcher |
| **Bt** | Brown thornbill | **Gt** | Ground thrush |
| **Sw** | Spine-tailed swift | **Rf** | Rufous fantail |
| **St** | Striated thornbill | **Wt** | White-throated treecreeper |

Adapted from: Recher, Lunney & Dunn (1986): *A Natural Legacy. Ecology in Australia.* Maxwell Macmillan Publishing Australia.

## Distribution of ecologically similar fish

The diagram below shows the distribution of ecologically similar damsel fish over a coral reef at Heron Island, Queensland, Australia. The habitat and resource requirements of these species overlap considerably.

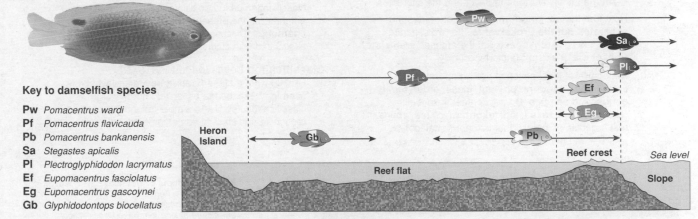

### Key to damselfish species

**Pw** *Pomacentrus wardi*
**Pf** *Pomacentrus flavicauda*
**Pb** *Pomacentrus bankanensis*
**Sa** *Stegastes apicalis*
**Pl** *Plectroglyphidodon lacrymatus*
**Ef** *Eupomacentrus fasciolatus*
**Eg** *Eupomacentrus gascoynei*
**Gb** *Glyphidodontops biocellatus*

1. Describe two ways in which species can avoid directly competing for the same resources in their habitat:

(a) _____

(b) _____

2. Explain why **intraspecific** competition is more intense than **interspecific** competition: _____

_____

3. Suggest how the damsel fish on the reef at Heron Island (above) might reduce competition: _____

_____

_____

Related activities: Competition and Niche Size, Interspecific Competition, Intraspecific Competition

A 2

# Classification

**IB SL** — Complete: *1, 4-12*

**IB HL** — Complete: *1, 4-12*

**IB Options** — Complete: Option D: SL/HL: *3* HL: *2, 11* Option F: *10*

**AP Biology** — Complete: *1-12*

## Learning Objectives

☐ 1. Compile your own glossary from the **KEY WORDS** displayed in **bold type** in the learning objectives below.

### Species and Biodiversity *(page 381)*

☐ 2. Explain the importance of **classification** in recognizing, appreciating, and conserving **biodiversity** on Earth.

☐ 3. Understand the concept of a **species** in terms of their reproductive isolation and potential for breeding.

### Classification Systems *(pages 333, 335-346, and the TRC: Ecology and Classification)*

☐ 4. Describe the principles and importance of scientific classification. Recognize **taxonomy** as the study of the theory and practice of classification.

☐ 5. Describe the **distinguishing features** of each of the kingdoms in the **five kingdom classification system**:
- **Prokaryotae**: bacteria and cyanobacteria.
- **Protista**: includes the algae and protozoans.
- **Fungi**: includes yeasts, moulds, and mushrooms.
- **Plantae**: includes mosses, liverworts, tracheophytes.
- **Animalia**: all invertebrate phyla and the chordates.

Note that the **six kingdom classification system separates out the Prokaryotae** into two separate kingdoms, i.e. **Archaebacteria**: the archaebacteria and **Eubacteria**: the "true" bacteria.

☐ 6. Recognize at least seven major **taxonomic categories**: **kingdom, phylum, class, order, family, genus**, and **species**. Do not confuse taxonomic categories with **taxa** (sing. **taxon**), which are groups of real organisms: "genus" is a taxonomic category, whereas the genus *Drosophila* is a taxon.

☐ 7. Understand the basis for assigning organisms into different taxonomic categories. Recall what is meant by a **distinguishing feature**. Explain that species are usually classified on the basis of **shared derived characters** rather than primitive (ancestral) characters. *For example, within the subphylum Vertebrata, the presence of a backbone is a derived, therefore a distinguishing, feature. However, within the class Mammalia, the backbone is an ancestral feature and is not distinguishing, whereas mammary glands (a distinguishing feature) are derived.*

☐ 8. Explain how **binomial nomenclature** is used to classify organisms. Explain the limitations of using **common names** to identify organisms.

☐ 9. Recognize the relationship between classification and **phylogeny**. Appreciate that newer schemes attempt to better reflect the true phylogeny of organisms.

### New classification schemes *(pages 333-334)*

☐ 10. Recognise the recent reclassification of organisms into three **domains**: **Archaea, Eubacteria**, and **Eukarya**. Explain the basis and rationale for this classification.

☐ 11. Appreciate that **cladistics** provides a method of classification based on relatedness, and that it emphasizes the presence of **shared derived characters**. Discuss the benefits and disadvantages associated with cladistic schemes.

### Classification keys *(pages 347-349)*

☐ 12. Explain what a **classification key** is and what it is used for. Describe the essential features of a classification key. Use a simple taxonomic key to recognise and classify some common organisms.

---

■ **Is it Kingdoms or Domains?** The Am. Biology Teacher, 66(4), April 2004, pp. 268-276. *How do potentially larger groupings such as domains fit into our picture of kingdom-based classification?*

See the 'Textbook Reference Grid' on pages 8-9 for textbook page references relating to material in this topic.

**Supplementary Texts**
See page 5 for additional details of this text:
■ Helms, D.R. *et al.*, 1998. **Biology in the Laboratory** (W.H. Freeman), #321-27.

See page 6 for details of publishers of periodicals:
■ **Biological Keys** The Am. Biology Teacher, 66(3), March 2004, pp. 202-207. *Taxonomic categorization and learning to use biological keys.*

■ **Seeing the Forest Through the Trees** The Am. Biology Teacher, 68(3), March 2006, pp. 149-151. *Helping students appreciate life's diversity by building the tree of life using photographs.*

■ **A Universal Phylogenetic Tree** The Am. Biology Teacher, 63(3), March 2001, pp. 164-170. *Three domains versus five kingdoms systems.*

■ **The Species Problem and the Value of Teaching the Complexities of Species** The Am. Biology Teacher, 66(6), Aug. 2004, pp. 413-417. *Problems with the complexities of species.*

■ **A Passion for Order** National Geographic, 211(6) June 2007, pp. 73-87. *The history of Carl Linnaeus and the classification of plant species.*

**Presentation MEDIA** to support this topic:
**ECOLOGY:**
• Biodiversity & Conservation

See pages 10-11 for details of how to access **Bio Links** from our web site: **www.thebiozone.com** From Bio Links, access sites under the topics:

**BIODIVERSITY > Taxonomy and Classification:**
• Birds and DNA • Taxonomy: Classifying life • The phylogeny of life... *and others*

**MICROBIOLOGY > General Microbiology:**
• British Mycological Society • Major groups of prokaryotes • The microbial world ... *and others*

**PLANT BIOLOGY > Classification and Diversity:**
• Flowering plant diversity ... *and others*

# The New Tree of Life

With the advent of more efficient genetic (DNA) sequencing technology, the genomes of many bacteria began to be sequenced. In 1996, the results of a scientific collaboration examining DNA evidence confirmed the proposal that life comprises three major evolutionary lineages (domains) and not two as was the convention. The recognized lineages were the **Eubacteria**, the **Eukarya** and the **Archaea** (formerly the Archaebacteria). The new classification reflects the fact that there are very large differences between the archaea and the eubacteria. All three domains probably had a distant common ancestor.

### A Five (or Six) Kingdom World (right)

The diagram (right) represents the **five kingdom system** of classification commonly represented in many biology texts. It recognizes two basic cell types: prokaryote and eukaryote. The domain Prokaryota includes all bacteria and cyanobacteria. Domain Eukaryota includes protists, fungi, plants, and animals. More recently, based on 16S ribosomal RNA sequence comparisons, Carl Woese divided the prokaryotes into two kingdoms, the Eubacteria and Archaebacteria. Such **six-kingdom systems** are also commonly recognized in texts.

### A New View of the World (below)

In 1996, scientists deciphered the full DNA sequence of an unusual bacterium called *Methanococcus jannaschii*. An **extremophile**, this methane-producing archaebacterium lives at 85°C; a temperature lethal for most bacteria as well as eukaryotes. The DNA sequence confirmed that life consists of three major evolutionary lineages, not the two that have been routinely described. Only 44% of this archaebacterium's genes resemble those in bacteria or eukaryotes, or both.

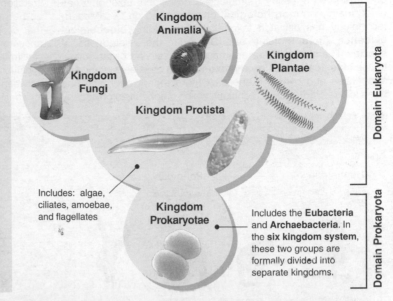

Includes: algae, ciliates, amoebae, and flagellates

Includes the **Eubacteria** and **Archaebacteria**. In the **six kingdom system**, these two groups are formally divided into separate kingdoms.

### Domain Eubacteria

Lack a distinct nucleus and cell organelles. Generally prefer less extreme environments than Archaea. Includes well-known pathogens, many harmless and beneficial species, and the cyanobacteria (photosynthetic bacteria containing the pigments chlorophyll *a* and phycocyanin).

### Domain Archaea

Closely resemble eubacteria in many ways but cell wall composition and aspects of metabolism are very different. Live in extreme environments similar to those on primeval Earth. They may utilize sulfur, methane, or halogens (chlorine, fluorine), and many tolerate extremes of temperature, salinity, or pH.

### Domain Eukarya

Complex cell structure with organelles and nucleus. This group contains four of the kingdoms classified under the more traditional system. Note that Kingdom Protista is separated into distinct groups: e.g. amoebae, ciliates, flagellates.

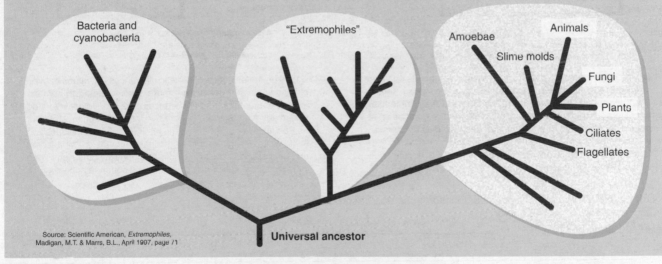

Source: Scientific American, *Extremophiles*, Madigan, M.T. & Marrs, B.L., April 1997, page 71

**Universal ancestor**

1. Explain why some scientists have recommended that the conventional classification of life be revised so that the Archaea, Eubacteria and Eukarya are three separate domains:

_____

_____

2. Describe one feature of the three domain system that is very different from the five kingdom classification:

_____

_____

3. Describe one way in which the three domain system and the six kingdom classification are alike:

_____

**Related activities**: Features of Taxonomic Groups, Features of the Five Kingdoms   **Web links**: Types of Microbes, Introduction to the Archaea

A 2

# New Classification Schemes

**Taxonomy** is the study of classification. Ever since Darwin, the aim of classification has been to organize species, and to reflect their evolutionary history (**phylogeny**). Each successive group in the taxonomic hierarchy should represent finer and finer branching from a common ancestor. In order to reconstruct evolutionary history, phylogenetic trees must be based on features that are due to shared ancestry (homologies). Traditional taxonomy has relied mainly on **morphological characters** to do this. Modern technology has assisted taxonomy by providing **biochemical evidence** (from proteins and DNA) for the relatedness of species. The most familiar approach to classifying organisms is to use **classical evolutionary taxonomy**. It considers branching sequences and overall likeness. A more recent approach has been to use **cladistics**: a technique which emphasizes phylogeny

or relatedness, usually based on biochemical evidence (and largely ignoring morphology or appearance). Each branch on the tree marks the point where a new species has arisen by evolution. Traditional and cladistic schemes do not necessarily conflict, but there have been reclassifications of some taxa (notably the primates, but also the reptiles, dinosaurs, and birds). Traditional taxonomists criticise cladistic schemes because they do not recognise the amount of visible change in morphology that occurs in species after their divergence from a common ancestor. Popular classifications will probably continue to reflect similarities and differences in appearance, rather than a strict evolutionary history. In this respect, they are a compromise between phylogeny and the need for a convenient filing system for species diversity.

## A Classical Taxonomic View

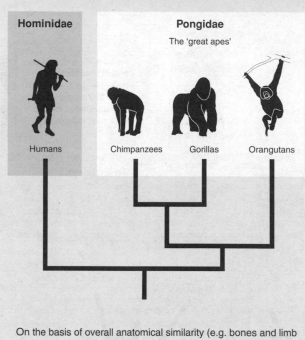

On the basis of overall anatomical similarity (e.g. bones and limb length, teeth, musculature), apes are grouped into a family (Pongidae) that is separate from humans and their immediate ancestors (Hominidae). The family Pongidae (the great apes) is not monophyletic (of one phylogeny), because it stems from an ancestor that also gave rise to a species in another family (i.e. humans). This traditional classification scheme is now at odds with schemes derived after considering genetic evidence.

## A Cladistic View

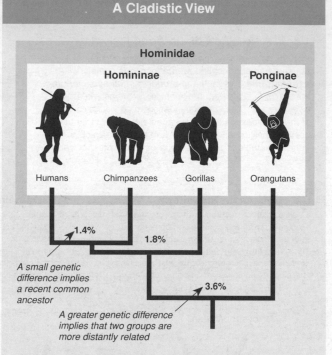

Based on the evidence of genetic differences (% values above), chimpanzees and gorillas are more closely related to humans than to orangutans, and chimpanzees are more closely related to humans than they are to gorillas. Under this scheme there is no true family of great apes. The family Hominidae includes two subfamilies: Ponginae and Homininae (humans, chimpanzees, and gorillas). This classification is monophyletic: the Hominidae includes all the species that arise from a common ancestor.

1. Briefly explain the benefits of classification schemes based on:

   (a) Morphological characters: _____

   _____

   _____

   (b) Relatedness in time (from biochemical evidence): _____

   _____

   _____

2. Describe the contribution of biochemical evidence to taxonomy: _____

   _____

3. Based on the diagram above, state the family to which the chimpanzees belong under:

   (a) A traditional scheme: _____  (b) A cladistic scheme: _____

**A 2**     **Related activities**: Classification System

# Features of Taxonomic Groups

In order to distinguish organisms, it is desirable to classify and name them (a science known as **taxonomy**). An effective classification system requires features that are distinctive to a particular group of organisms. Revised classification systems, recognizing three domains (rather than five or six kingdoms) are now recognized as better representations of the true diversity of life. However, for the purposes of describing the groups with which we are most familiar, the five kingdom system (used here) is still appropriate. The distinguishing features of some major **taxa** are provided in the following pages by means of diagrams and brief summaries. Note that most animals show **bilateral symmetry** (body divisible into two halves that are mirror images). **Radial symmetry** (body divisible into equal halves through various planes) is a characteristic of cnidarians and ctenophores.

Classification

## Kingdom: PROKARYOTAE (Bacteria)

- Also known as monerans or prokaryotes.
- Two major bacterial lineages are recognized: the primitive **Archaebacteria** and the more advanced **Eubacteria**.
- All have a prokaryotic cell structure: they lack the nuclei and chromosomes of eukaryotic cells, and have smaller (70S) ribosomes.
- Have a tendency to spread genetic elements across species barriers by sexual conjugation, viral transduction and other processes.
- Can reproduce rapidly by binary fission in the absence of sex.

- Have evolved a wider variety of metabolism types than eukaryotes.
- Bacteria grow and divide or aggregate into filaments or colonies of various shapes.
- They are taxonomically identified by their appearance (form) and through biochemical differences.

**Species diversity**: 10 000 + Bacteria are rather difficult to classify to the species level because of their relatively rampant genetic exchange, and because their reproduction is usually asexual.

### Eubacteria

- Also known as 'true bacteria', they probably evolved from the more ancient Archaebacteria.
- Distinguished from Archaebacteria by differences in cell wall composition, nucleotide structure, and ribosome shape.
- Very diverse group comprises most bacteria.
- The **gram stain** provides the basis for distinguishing two broad groups of bacteria. It relies on the presence of peptidoglycan (unique to bacteria) in the cell wall. The stain is easily washed from the thin peptidoglycan layer of gram negative walls but is retained by the thick peptidoglycan layer of gram positive cells, staining them a dark violet color.

### Gram-Positive Bacteria

The walls of gram positive bacteria consist of many layers of peptidoglycan forming a thick, single-layered structure that holds the gram stain.

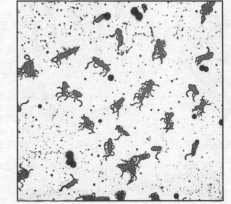

*Bacillus alvei*: a gram positive, flagellated bacterium. Note how the cells appear dark.

### Gram-Negative Bacteria

The cell walls of gram negative bacteria contain only a small proportion of peptidoglycan, so the dark violet stain is not retained by the organisms.

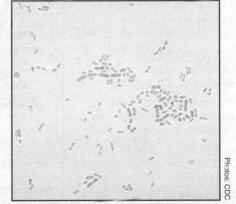

Photos: CDC

*Alcaligenes odorans*: a gram negative bacterium. Note how the cells appear pale.

## Kingdom: FUNGI

- Heterotrophic.
- Rigid cell wall made of chitin.
- Vary from single celled to large multicellular organisms.
- Mostly saprotrophic (i.e. feeding on dead or decaying material).
- Terrestrial and immobile.

**Examples:**
Mushrooms/toadstools, yeasts, truffles, morels, molds, and lichens.

**Species diversity**: 80 000 +

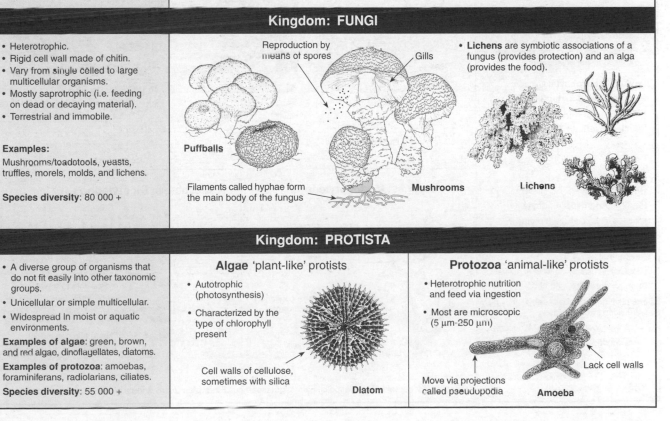

Reproduction by means of spores

Gills

Puffballs

Filaments called hyphae form the main body of the fungus

**Mushrooms**

- **Lichens** are symbiotic associations of a fungus (provides protection) and an alga (provides the food).

**Lichens**

## Kingdom: PROTISTA

- A diverse group of organisms that do not fit easily into other taxonomic groups.
- Unicellular or simple multicellular.
- Widespread in moist or aquatic environments.

**Examples of algae**: green, brown, and red algae, dinoflagellates, diatoms.

**Examples of protozoa**: amoebas, foraminiferans, radiolarians, ciliates.

**Species diversity**: 55 000 +

### Algae 'plant-like' protists

- Autotrophic (photosynthesis)
- Characterized by the type of chlorophyll present

Cell walls of cellulose, sometimes with silica

**Diatom**

### Protozoa 'animal-like' protists

- Heterotrophic nutrition and feed via ingestion
- Most are microscopic (5 µm-250 µm)

Move via projections called pseudopodia

Lack cell walls

**Amoeba**

# Kingdom: PLANTAE

- Multicellular organisms (the majority are photosynthetic and contain chlorophyll).
- Cell walls made of cellulose; Food is stored as starch.
- Subdivided into two major divisions based on tissue structure: **Bryophytes** (non-vascular) and **Tracheophytes** (vascular) plants.

## Non-Vascular Plants:

- Non vascular, lacking transport tissues (no xylem or phloem).
- They are small and restricted to moist, terrestrial environments.
- Do not possess 'true' roots, stems or leaves

**Phylum Bryophyta:** Mosses, liverworts, and hornworts.

**Species diversity:** 18 600 +

## Vascular Plants:

- Vascular: possess transport tissues.
- Possess true roots, stems, and leaves, as well as stomata.
- Reproduce via spores, not seeds.
- Clearly defined *alternation of sporophyte and gametophyte generations.*

## Seedless Plants:

Spore producing plants, includes:

**Phylum Filicinophyta:** Ferns
**Phylum Sphenophyta:** Horsetails
**Phylum Lycophyta:** Club mosses

**Species diversity:** 13 000 +

## Seed Plants:

Also called Spermatophyta. Produce seeds housing an embryo. Includes:

*Gymnosperms*

- Lack enclosed chambers in which seeds develop.
- Produce seeds in cones which are exposed to the environment.

**Phylum Cycadophyta:** Cycads
**Phylum Ginkgophyta:** Ginkgoes
**Phylum Coniferophyta:** Conifers

**Species diversity:** 730 +

*Angiosperms*

**Phylum: Angiospermophyta**

- Seeds in specialized reproductive structures called flowers.
- Female reproductive ovary develops into a fruit.
- Pollination usually via wind or animals.

**Species diversity:** 260 000 +

The phylum Angiospermophyta may be subdivided into two classes:

Class *Monocotyledoneae* (Monocots)
Class *Dicotyledoneae* (Dicots)

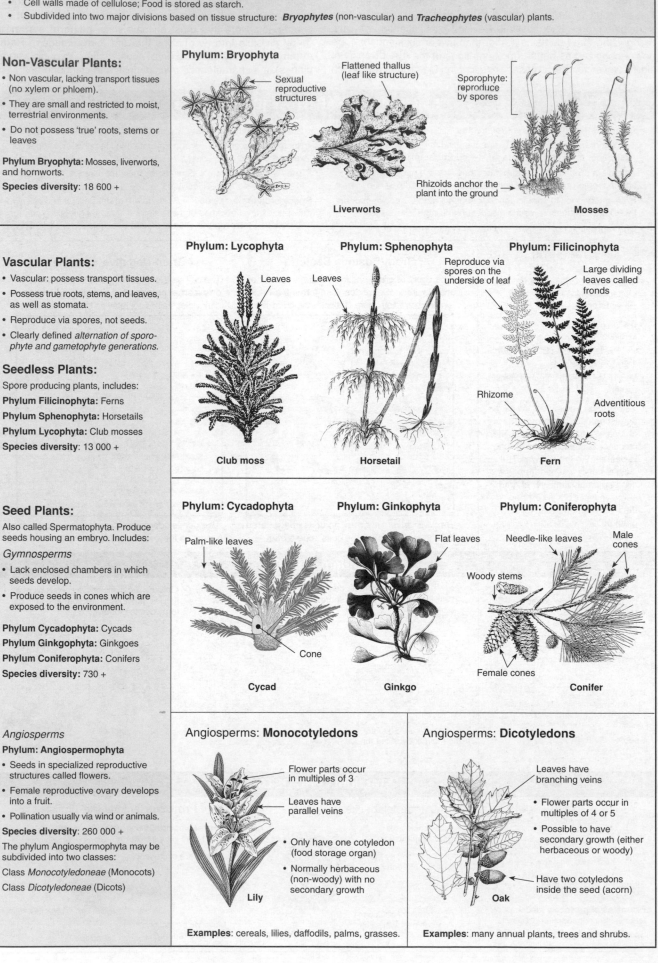

**Phylum: Bryophyta**

Sexual reproductive structures — Flattened thallus (leaf like structure)

Sporophyte: reproduce by spores

Rhizoids anchor the plant into the ground

**Liverworts**

**Mosses**

**Phylum: Lycophyta** — Leaves — **Club moss**

**Phylum: Sphenophyta** — Leaves — **Horsetail**

**Phylum: Filicinophyta** — Reproduce via spores on the underside of leaf — Large dividing leaves called fronds — Rhizome — Adventitious roots — **Fern**

**Phylum: Cycadophyta** — Palm-like leaves — Cone — **Cycad**

**Phylum: Ginkophyta** — Flat leaves — **Ginkgo**

**Phylum: Coniferophyta** — Needle-like leaves — Male cones — Woody stems — Female cones — **Conifer**

**Angiosperms: Monocotyledons**

- Flower parts occur in multiples of 3
- Leaves have parallel veins
- Only have one cotyledon (food storage organ)
- Normally herbaceous (non-woody) with no secondary growth

**Lily**

**Examples:** cereals, lilies, daffodils, palms, grasses.

**Angiosperms: Dicotyledons**

- Leaves have branching veins
- Flower parts occur in multiples of 4 or 5
- Possible to have secondary growth (either herbaceous or woody)
- Have two cotyledons inside the seed (acorn)

**Oak**

**Examples:** many annual plants, trees and shrubs.

# Kingdom: ANIMALIA

- Over 800 000 species described in 33 existing phyla.
- Multicellular, heterotrophic organisms.
- Animal cells lack cell walls.

- Further subdivided into various major phyla on the basis of body symmetry, type of body cavity, and external and internal structures.

## Phylum: Rotifera

- A diverse group of small organisms with sessile, colonial, and planktonic forms.
- Most freshwater, a few marine.
- Typically reproduce via cyclic parthenogenesis.
- Characterized by a wheel of cilia on the head used for feeding and locomotion, a large muscular pharynx (mastax) with jaw like trophi, and a foot with sticky toes.

**Species diversity:** 1500 +

Cilia
Head
Mastax
Foot
Toes

**Bdelloid:** non planktonic, creeping rotifer

Spines for protection against predators
Lorica
Ovary
Eggs

Planktonic forms swim using their crown of cilia

## Phylum: Porifera

- Lack organs.
- All are aquatic (mostly marine).
- Asexual reproduction by budding.
- Lack a nervous system.

**Examples:** sponges.

**Species diversity:** 8000 +

Body wall perforated by pores through which water enters
Water leaves by a larger opening - the osculum
**Sponge**

- Capable of regeneration (the replacement of lost parts)
- Possess spicules (needle-like internal structures) for support and protection

**Tube sponge**
Sessile (attach to ocean floor)

## Phylum: Cnidaria

- Two basic body forms.

  Medusa: umbrella shaped and free swimming by pulsating bell.

  Polyp: cylindrical, some are sedentary, others can glide, or somersault or use tentacles as legs.

- Some species have a life cycle that alternates between a polyp stage and a medusa stage.
- All are aquatic (most are marine).

**Examples:** Jellyfish, sea anemones, hydras, and corals.

**Species diversity:** 11 000 +

Some have air-filled floats
Single opening acts as mouth and anus
Polyps may aggregate in colonies
Nematocysts (stinging cells)
**Brain coral**
**Jellyfish (Portuguese man-o-war)**
Polyps stick to seabed
**Sea anemone**
**Colonial polyps**
Contraction of the bell propels the free swimming medusa

## Phylum: Platyhelminthes

- Unsegmented body.
- Flattened body shape.
- Mouth, but no anus.
- Many are parasitic.

**Examples:** Tapeworms, planarians, flukes.

**Species diversity:** 20 000 +

Hooks
Detail of head (scolex)
**Liver fluke**
**Tapeworm**
**Planarian**

## Phylum: Nematoda

- Tiny, unsegmented roundworms.
- Many are plant/animal parasites

**Examples:** Hookworms, stomach worms, lung worms, filarial worms

**Species diversity:** 80 000 - 1 million

Muscular pharynx
Ovary
Anus
Mouth
Intestine
A general nematode body plan
A roundworm parasite

## Phylum: Annelida

- Cylindrical, segmented body with chaetae (bristles).
- Move using hydrostatic skeleton and/or parapodia (appendages).

**Examples:** Earthworms, leeches, polychaetes (including tubeworms).

**Species diversity:** 15 000 +

Mouth
Clitellum
Segments with parapodia (fleshy projections)
Anterior sucker
Posterior sucker
Anus
**Earthworm**
**Polychaete**
**Leech**

# Kingdom: ANIMALIA (continued)

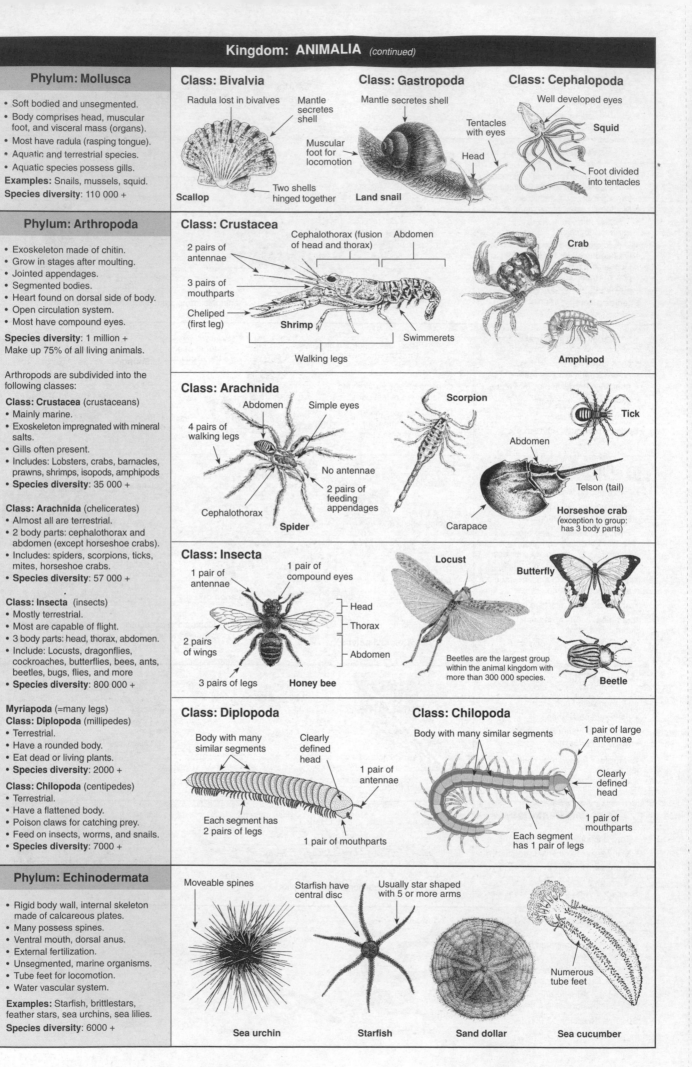

## Phylum: Mollusca

- Soft bodied and unsegmented.
- Body comprises head, muscular foot, and visceral mass (organs).
- Most have radula (rasping tongue).
- Aquatic and terrestrial species.
- Aquatic species possess gills.

**Examples:** Snails, mussels, squid.
**Species diversity:** 110 000 +

### Class: Bivalvia

Radula lost in bivalves

Mantle secretes shell

Two shells hinged together

**Scallop**

### Class: Gastropoda

Mantle secretes shell

Muscular foot for locomotion

**Land snail**

### Class: Cephalopoda

Well developed eyes

Tentacles with eyes

Head

**Squid**

Foot divided into tentacles

## Phylum: Arthropoda

- Exoskeleton made of chitin.
- Grow in stages after moulting.
- Jointed appendages.
- Segmented bodies.
- Heart found on dorsal side of body.
- Open circulation system.
- Most have compound eyes.

**Species diversity:** 1 million +
Make up 75% of all living animals.

Arthropods are subdivided into the following classes:

**Class: Crustacea** (crustaceans)
- Mainly marine.
- Exoskeleton impregnated with mineral salts.
- Gills often present.
- Includes: Lobsters, crabs, barnacles, prawns, shrimps, isopods, amphipods
- **Species diversity:** 35 000 +

**Class: Arachnida** (chelicerates)
- Almost all are terrestrial.
- 2 body parts: cephalothorax and abdomen (except horseshoe crabs).
- Includes: spiders, scorpions, ticks, mites, horseshoe crabs.
- **Species diversity:** 57 000 +

**Class: Insecta** (insects)
- Mostly terrestrial.
- Most are capable of flight.
- 3 body parts: head, thorax, abdomen.
- Include: Locusts, dragonflies, cockroaches, butterflies, bees, ants, beetles, bugs, flies, and more
- **Species diversity:** 800 000 +

**Myriapoda** (=many legs)
**Class: Diplopoda** (millipedes)
- Terrestrial.
- Have a rounded body.
- Eat dead or living plants.
- **Species diversity:** 2000 +

**Class: Chilopoda** (centipedes)
- Terrestrial.
- Have a flattened body.
- Poison claws for catching prey.
- Feed on insects, worms, and snails.
- **Species diversity:** 7000 +

### Class: Crustacea

2 pairs of antennae

Cephalothorax (fusion of head and thorax)

Abdomen

3 pairs of mouthparts

Cheliped (first leg)

**Shrimp**

Swimmerets

Walking legs

**Crab**

**Amphipod**

### Class: Arachnida

4 pairs of walking legs

Abdomen

Simple eyes

No antennae

2 pairs of feeding appendages

Cephalothorax

**Spider**

**Scorpion**

Carapace

Abdomen

**Tick**

Telson (tail)

**Horseshoe crab**
(exception to group: has 3 body parts)

### Class: Insecta

1 pair of antennae

1 pair of compound eyes

Head

Thorax

Abdomen

2 pairs of wings

3 pairs of legs

**Honey bee**

**Locust**

**Butterfly**

Beetles are the largest group within the animal kingdom with more than 300 000 species.

**Beetle**

### Class: Diplopoda

Body with many similar segments

Clearly defined head

1 pair of antennae

Each segment has 2 pairs of legs

1 pair of mouthparts

### Class: Chilopoda

Body with many similar segments

1 pair of large antennae

Clearly defined head

1 pair of mouthparts

Each segment has 1 pair of legs

## Phylum: Echinodermata

- Rigid body wall, internal skeleton made of calcareous plates.
- Many possess spines.
- Ventral mouth, dorsal anus.
- External fertilization.
- Unsegmented, marine organisms.
- Tube feet for locomotion.
- Water vascular system.

**Examples:** Starfish, brittlestars, feather stars, sea urchins, sea lilies.
**Species diversity:** 6000 +

Moveable spines

Starfish have central disc

Usually star shaped with 5 or more arms

Numerous tube feet

**Sea urchin**

**Starfish**

**Sand dollar**

**Sea cucumber**

# Kingdom: ANIMALIA (continued)

## Phylum: Chordata

- Dorsal notochord (flexible, supporting rod) present at some stage in the life history.
- Post-anal tail present at some stage in their development.
- Dorsal, tubular nerve cord.
- Pharyngeal slits present.
- Circulation system closed in most.
- Heart positioned on ventral side.

**Species diversity: 48 000 +**

- A very diverse group with several sub-phyla:
  - Urochordata (sea squirts, salps)
  - Cephalochordata (lancelet)
  - Craniata (vertebrates)

**Sub-Phylum Craniata** (vertebrates)
- Internal skeleton of cartilage or bone.
- Well developed nervous system.
- Vertebral column replaces notochord.
- Two pairs of appendages (fins or limbs) attached to girdles.

Further subdivided into:

**Class: Chondrichthyes** (cartilaginous fish)
- Skeleton of cartilage (not bone).
- No swim bladder.
- All aquatic (mostly marine).
- Include: Sharks, rays, and skates.

**Species diversity: 850 +**

**Class: Osteichthyes** (bony fish)
- Swim bladder present.
- All aquatic (marine and fresh water).

**Species diversity: 21 000 +**

**Class: Amphibia** (amphibians)
- Lungs in adult, juveniles may have gills (retained in some adults).
- Gas exchange also through skin.
- Aquatic and terrestrial (limited to damp environments).
- Include: Frogs, toads, salamanders, and newts.

**Species diversity: 3900 +**

**Class Reptilia** (reptiles)
- Ectotherms with no larval stages.
- Teeth are all the same type.
- Eggs with soft leathery shell.
- Mostly terrestrial.
- Include: Snakes, lizards, crocodiles, turtles, and tortoises.

**Species diversity: 7000 +**

**Class: Aves** (birds)
- Terrestrial endotherms.
- Eggs with hard, calcareous shell.
- Strong, light skeleton.
- High metabolic rate.
- Gas exchange assisted by air sacs.

**Species diversity: 8600 +**

**Class: Mammalia** (mammals)
- Endotherms with hair or fur.
- Mammary glands produce milk.
- Glandular skin with hair or fur.
- External ear present.
- Teeth are of different types.
- Diaphragm between thorax/abdomen.

**Species diversity: 4500 +**
Subdivided into three subclasses:
*Monotremes, marsupials, placentals.*

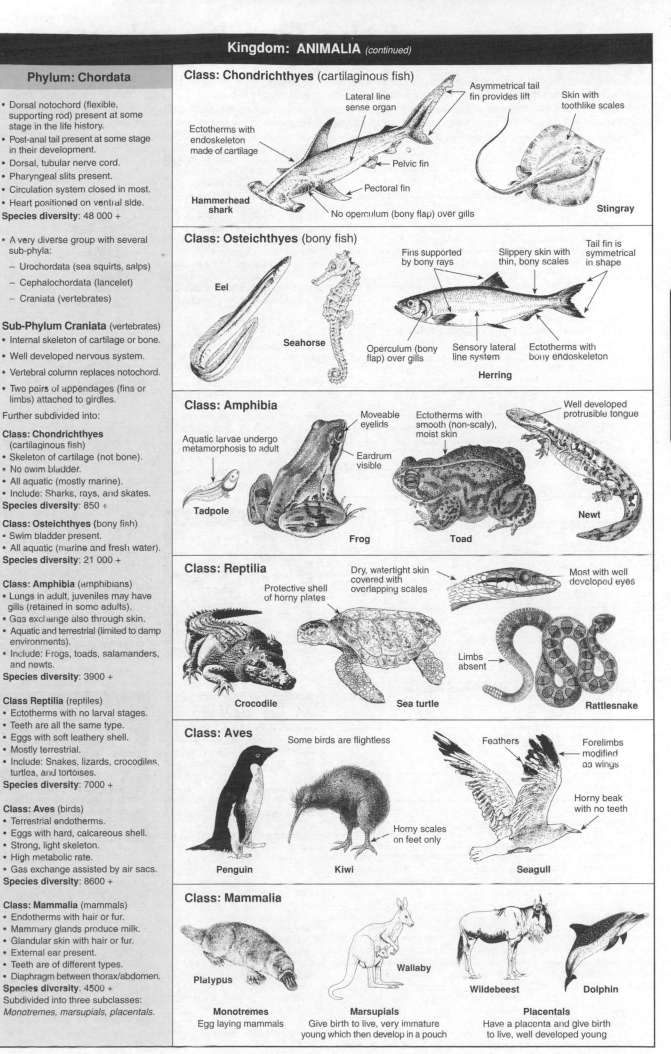

### Class: Chondrichthyes (cartilaginous fish)

Lateral line sense organ
Asymmetrical tail fin provides lift
Skin with toothlike scales
Ectotherms with endoskeleton made of cartilage
Pelvic fin
Pectoral fin
No operculum (bony flap) over gills
**Hammerhead shark**
**Stingray**

### Class: Osteichthyes (bony fish)

Fins supported by bony rays
Slippery skin with thin, bony scales
Tail fin is symmetrical in shape
**Eel**
**Seahorse**
Operculum (bony flap) over gills
Sensory lateral line system
Ectotherms with bony endoskeleton
**Herring**

### Class: Amphibia

Aquatic larvae undergo metamorphosis to adult
Moveable eyelids
Ectotherms with smooth (non-scaly), moist skin
Well developed protrusible tongue
Eardrum visible
**Tadpole**
**Frog**
**Toad**
**Newt**

### Class: Reptilia

Dry, watertight skin covered with overlapping scales
Most with well developed eyes
Protective shell of horny plates
Limbs absent
**Crocodile**
**Sea turtle**
**Rattlesnake**

### Class: Aves

Some birds are flightless
Feathers
Forelimbs modified as wings
Horny beak with no teeth
Horny scales on feet only
**Penguin**
**Kiwi**
**Seagull**

### Class: Mammalia

**Platypus**
**Wallaby**
**Wildebeest**
**Dolphin**
**Monotremes**
Egg laying mammals
**Marsupials**
Give birth to live, very immature young which then develop in a pouch
**Placentals**
Have a placenta and give birth to live, well developed young

# Features of the Five Kingdoms

The classification of organisms into taxonomic groups is based on how biologists believe they are related in an evolutionary sense. Organisms in a taxonomic group share features which set them apart from other groups. By identifying these **distinguishing** **features**, it is possible to develop an understanding of the evolutionary history of the group. The focus of this activity is to summarize the distinguishing features of each of the five kingdoms in the five kingdom classification system.

1. Distinguishing features of Kingdom **Prokaryotae**:

_____

_____

_____

_____

_____

_____

2. Distinguishing features of Kingdom **Protista**:

_____

_____

_____

_____

_____

_____

_____

3. Distinguishing features of Kingdom **Fungi**:

_____

_____

_____

_____

_____

_____

4. Distinguishing features of Kingdom **Plantae**:

_____

_____

_____

_____

_____

_____

_____

5. Distinguishing features of Kingdom **Animalia**:

_____

_____

_____

_____

_____

_____

_____

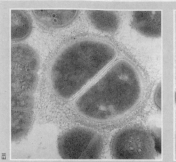
*Staphylococcus* dividing

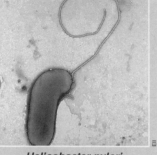
*Helicobacter pylori*

Red blood cell
*Trypanosoma* parasite

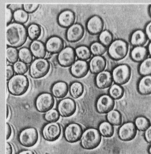
*Amoeba*

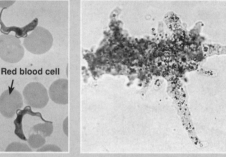
Mushrooms

Yeast cells in solution

Maple seeds

Pea plants

Cicada moulting

Gibbon

# Features of Microbial Groups

A microorganism (or microbe) is literally a microscopic organism. The term is usually reserved for the organisms studied in microbiology: bacteria, fungi, microscopic protistans, and viruses. Most of these taxa also have macroscopic representatives. This is especially the case within the fungi. The distinction between a macrofungus and a microfungus is an artificial but convenient one. Unlike **microfungi**, which are made conspicuous by the diseases or decay they cause, **macrofungi** are the ones most likely to be observed with the naked eye. Examples of microfungi, which include yeasts and pathogenic species, are illustrated in this activity. Macrofungi, which include mushrooms, toadstools, and lichens, are illustrated in *Features of Macrofungi and Plants*.

1. Distinguishing features of Kingdom **Prokaryotae**:

_____

_____

_____

_____

_____

_____

_____

2. Distinguishing features of Kingdom **Protista**:

_____

_____

_____

_____

_____

_____

_____

_____

3. Distinguishing features of Kingdom **Fungi** (microfungi):

_____

_____

_____

_____

_____

_____

_____

_____

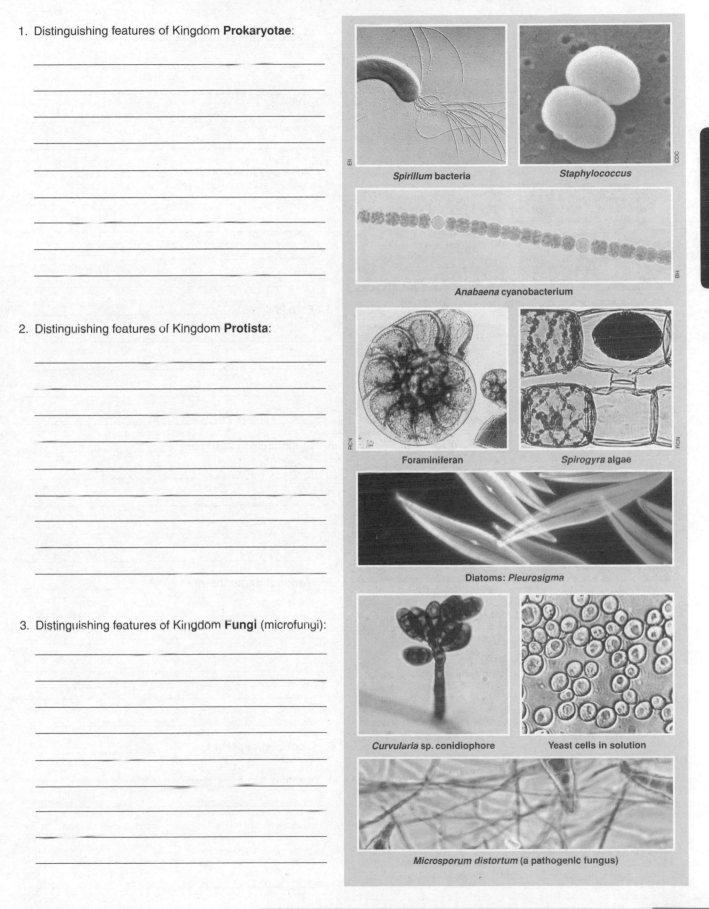

*Spirillum* bacteria

*Staphylococcus*

*Anabaena* cyanobacterium

Foraminiferan

*Spirogyra* algae

Diatoms: *Pleurosigma*

*Curvularia* sp. conidiophore

Yeast cells in solution

*Microsporum distortum* (a pathogenic fungus)

Classification

Related activities: The New Tree of Life, Features of Taxonomic Groups, Features of Macrofungi and Plants

RA 1

# Features of Macrofungi and Plants

Although plants and fungi are some of the most familiar organisms in our environment, their classification has not always been straightforward. We know now that the plant kingdom is monophyletic, meaning that it is derived from a common ancestor. The variety we see in plant taxa today is a result of their enormous diversification from the first plants. Although the fungi were once grouped together with the plants, they are unique organisms that differ from other eukaryotes in their mode of nutrition, structural organization, growth, and reproduction. The focus of this activity is to summarize the features of the fungal kingdom (**macrofungi**), the major divisions of the plant kingdom, and the two classes of flowering plants (angiosperms).

Lichen

Bracket fungus

Liverwort

Moss

Fern frond

Ground fern

Pine tree cone

Cycad

Coconut palms

Wheat plants

Deciduous tree

Flowering plant

1. **Macrofungi** features: _____

_____

_____

_____

_____

2. **Moss** and **liverwort** features: _____

_____

_____

_____

_____

3. **Fern** features: _____

_____

_____

_____

_____

4. **Gymnosperm** features: _____

_____

_____

_____

_____

5. **Monocot angiosperm** features: _____

_____

_____

_____

_____

_____

6. **Dicot angiosperm** features: _____

_____

_____

_____

_____

**R 1**

**Related activities:** The New Tree of Life, Features of Taxonomic Groups

# Features of Animal Taxa

The animal kingdom is classified into about 35 major **phyla**. Representatives of the more familiar taxa are illustrated below: **cnidarians** (includes jellyfish, sea anemones, and corals), **annelids** (segmented worms), **arthropods** (insects, crustaceans, spiders, scorpions, centipedes and millipedes), **molluscs** (snails, bivalve shellfish, squid and octopus), **echinoderms** (starfish and sea urchins), **vertebrates** from the phylum **chordates** (fish, amphibians, reptiles, birds, and mammals). The **arthropods** and the **vertebrates** have been represented in more detail, giving the **classes** for each of these **phyla**. This activity asks you to describe the **distinguishing features** of each of the taxa represented below.

Sea anemones

Jellyfish

Tubeworms

Earthworm

Long-horned beetle

Butterfly

Crab

Woodlouse

Scorpion

Spider

Centipede

Millipede

1. **Cnidarian** features: _____

_____

_____

_____

_____

2. **Annelid** features: _____

_____

_____

_____

_____

3. **Insect** features: _____

_____

_____

_____

_____

4. **Crustacean** features: _____

_____

_____

_____

_____

5. **Arachnid** features: _____

_____

_____

_____

_____

6. **Myriapod** (class Chilopoda and Diplopoda) features:

_____

_____

_____

_____

Related activities: The New Tree of Life, Features of Taxonomic Groups

R 1

Classification

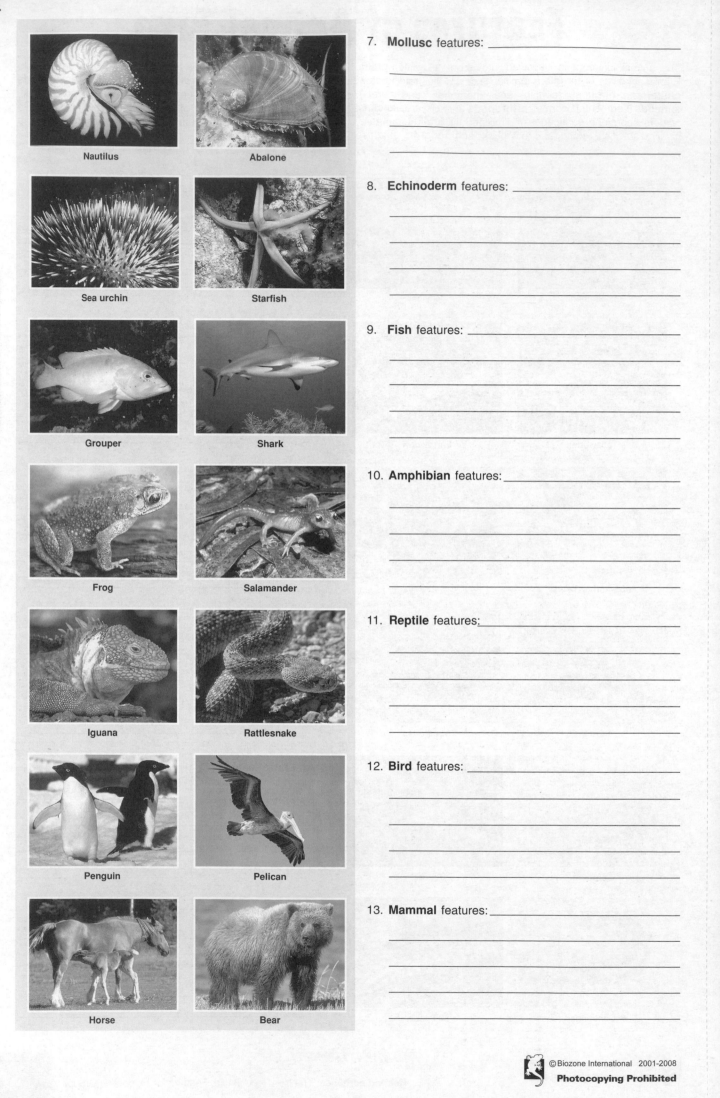

Nautilus

Abalone

Sea urchin

Starfish

Grouper

Shark

Frog

Salamander

Iguana

Rattlesnake

Penguin

Pelican

Horse

Bear

7. **Mollusc** features: _____

_____

_____

_____

_____

8. **Echinoderm** features: _____

_____

_____

_____

_____

9. **Fish** features: _____

_____

_____

_____

_____

10. **Amphibian** features: _____

_____

_____

_____

_____

11. **Reptile** features: _____

_____

_____

_____

_____

12. **Bird** features: _____

_____

_____

_____

_____

13. **Mammal** features: _____

_____

_____

_____

_____

# Classification System

The classification of organisms is designed to reflect how they are related to each other. The fundamental unit of classification of living things is the **species** (see the *TRC: The Species Concept* for a definition of a species). Its members are so alike genetically that they can interbreed. This genetic similarity also means that they are almost identical in their physical and other characteristics. Species are classified further into larger, more comprehensive categories (higher taxa). It must be emphasized that all such higher classifications are human inventions to suit a particular purpose.

1. The table below shows part of the classification for humans using the seven major levels of classification. For this question, use the example of the classification of the Ethiopian hedgehog, on the next page, as a guide.

   (a) Complete the list of the classification levels on the left hand side of the table below:

   | Classification level | Human classification |
   |---|---|
   | 1. _____ | _____ |
   | 2. _____ | _____ |
   | 3. _____ | _____ |
   | 4. _____ | _____ |
   | 5. Family | Hominidae |
   | 6. _____ | _____ |
   | 7. _____ | _____ |

   (b) The name of the Family that humans belong to has already been entered into the space provided. Complete the classification for humans (*Homo sapiens*) on the table above.

2. Describe the two-part scientific naming system (called the **binomial system**) which is used to name organisms:

   _____

   _____

3. Give two reasons why the classification of organisms is important:

   (a) _____

   _____

   (b) _____

   _____

4. Traditionally, the classification of organisms has been based largely on similarities in physical appearance. More recently, new methods involving biochemical comparisons have been used to provide new insights into how species are related. Describe an example of a biochemical method for comparing how species are related:

   _____

   _____

   _____

5. As an example of physical features being used to classify organisms, mammals have been divided into three major sub-classes: monotremes, marsupials, and placentals. Describe the main physical feature distinguishing each of these taxa:

   (a) Monotreme: _____

   _____

   (b) Marsupial: _____

   _____

   (c) Placental: _____

   _____

**Related activities**: New Classification Schemes, Classification Keys, Features of Taxonomic Groups

RA 2

Classification

# Classification of the Ethiopian Hedgehog

Below is the classification for the **Ethiopian hedgehog**. Only one of each group is subdivided in this chart showing the levels that can be used in classifying an organism. Not all possible subdivisions have been shown here. For example, it is possible to indicate such categories as **super-class** and **sub-family**. The only natural category is the **species**, often separated into geographical **races**, or **sub-species**, which generally differ in appearance.

**Kingdom:**

**Animalia**
Animals; one of five kingdoms

**Phylum:**

**Chordata**
Animals with a notochord (supporting rod of cells along the upper surface)
*tunicates, salps, lancelets, and vertebrates*

23 other phyla

**Sub-phylum:**

**Vertebrata**
Animals with backbones
*fish, amphibians, reptiles, birds, mammals*

**Class:**

**Mammalia**
Animals that suckle their young on milk from mammary glands
*placentals, marsupials, monotremes*

**Sub-class:**

**Eutheria or Placentals**
Mammals whose young develop for some time in the female's reproductive tract gaining nourishment from a placenta
*placental mammals*

**Order:**

**Insectivora**
Insect eating mammals
*An order of over 300 species of primitive, small mammals that feed mainly on insects and other small invertebrates.*

17 other orders

**Sub-order:**

**Erinaceomorpha**
The hedgehog-type insectivores. One of the three suborders of insectivores. The other suborders include the tenrec-like insectivores (*tenrecs and golden moles*) and the shrew-like insectivores (*shrews, moles, desmans, and solenodons*).

**Family:**

**Erinaceidae**
The only family within this suborder. Comprises two subfamilies: the true or spiny hedgehogs and the moonrats (gymnures). Representatives in the family include the common European hedgehog, desert hedgehog, and the moonrats.

**Genus:**

***Paraechinus***
One of eight genera in this family. The genus *Paraechinus* includes three species which are distinguishable by a wide and prominent naked area on the scalp.

7 other genera

**Species:**

***aethiopicus***
The Ethiopian hedgehog inhabits arid coastal areas. Their diet consists mainly of insects, but includes small vertebrates and the eggs of ground nesting birds.

3 other species

The order *Insectivora* was first introduced to group together shrews, moles, and hedgehogs. It was later extended to include tenrecs, golden moles, desmans, tree shrews, and elephant shrews and the taxonomy of the group became very confused. Recent reclassification of the elephant shrews and tree shrews into their own separate orders has made the Insectivora a more cohesive group taxonomically.

**Ethiopian hedgehog**
*Paraechinus aethiopicus*

# Classification Keys

Classification systems provide biologists with a way in which to identify species. They also indicate how closely related, in an evolutionary sense, each species is to others. An organism's classification should include a clear, unambiguous **description**, an accurate **diagram**, and its unique name, denoted by the **genus** and **species**. Classification keys are used to identify an organism and assign it to the correct species (assuming that the organism has already been formally classified and is included in the key). Typically, keys are **dichotomous** and involve a series of linked steps. At each step, a choice is made between two features; each alternative leads to another question until an identification is made. If the organism cannot be identified, it may be a new species or the key may need revision. Two examples of **dichotomous keys** are provided here. The first (below) describes features for identifying the larvae of various genera within the order Trichoptera (caddisflies). From this key you should be able to assign a generic name to each of the caddisfly larvae pictured. The key on the next page identifies aquatic insect orders.

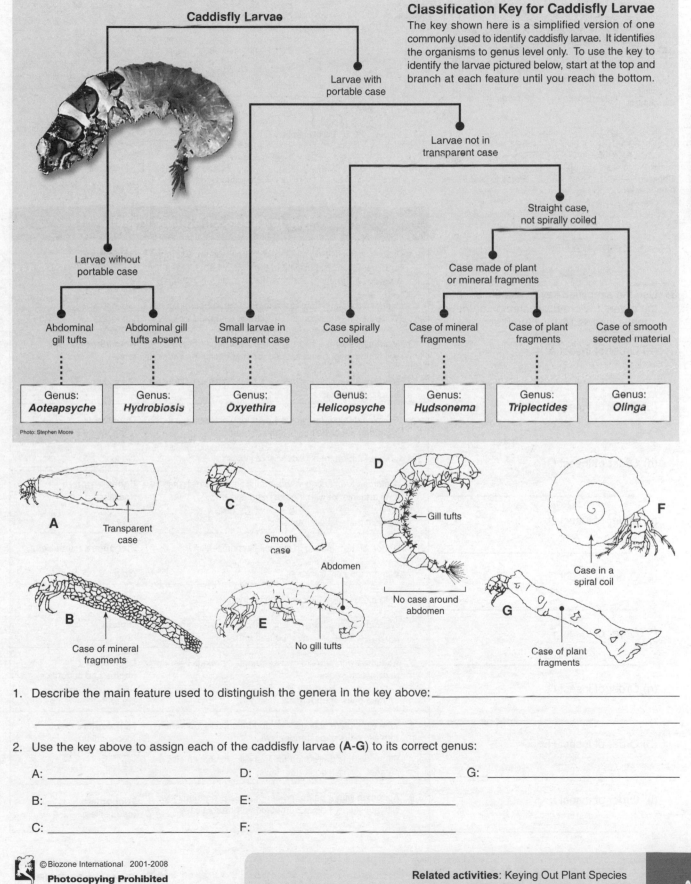

## Classification Key for Caddisfly Larvae

The key shown here is a simplified version of one commonly used to identify caddisfly larvae. It identifies the organisms to genus level only. To use the key to identify the larvae pictured below, start at the top and branch at each feature until you reach the bottom.

**Caddisfly Larvae**

Larvae with portable case

Larvae not in transparent case

Straight case, not spirally coiled

Larvae without portable case

Case made of plant or mineral fragments

| Abdominal gill tufts | Abdominal gill tufts absent | Small larvae in transparent case | Case spirally coiled | Case of mineral fragments | Case of plant fragments | Case of smooth secreted material |
| --- | --- | --- | --- | --- | --- | --- |
| Genus: **Aoteapsyche** | Genus: **Hydrobiosis** | Genus: **Oxyethira** | Genus: **Helicopsyche** | Genus: **Hudsonema** | Genus: **Triplectides** | Genus: **Olinga** |

Photo: Stephen Moore

**A** — Transparent case

**B** — Case of mineral fragments

**C** — Smooth case

**D** — Gill tufts, No case around abdomen

**E** — Abdomen, No gill tufts

**F** — Case in a spiral coil

**G** — Case of plant fragments

1. Describe the main feature used to distinguish the genera in the key above: _____

_____

2. Use the key above to assign each of the caddisfly larvae (**A-G**) to its correct genus:

A: _____   D: _____   G: _____

B: _____   E: _____

C: _____   F: _____

**Related activities**: Keying Out Plant Species
**Web links**: What is the Key to Classification?

A 2

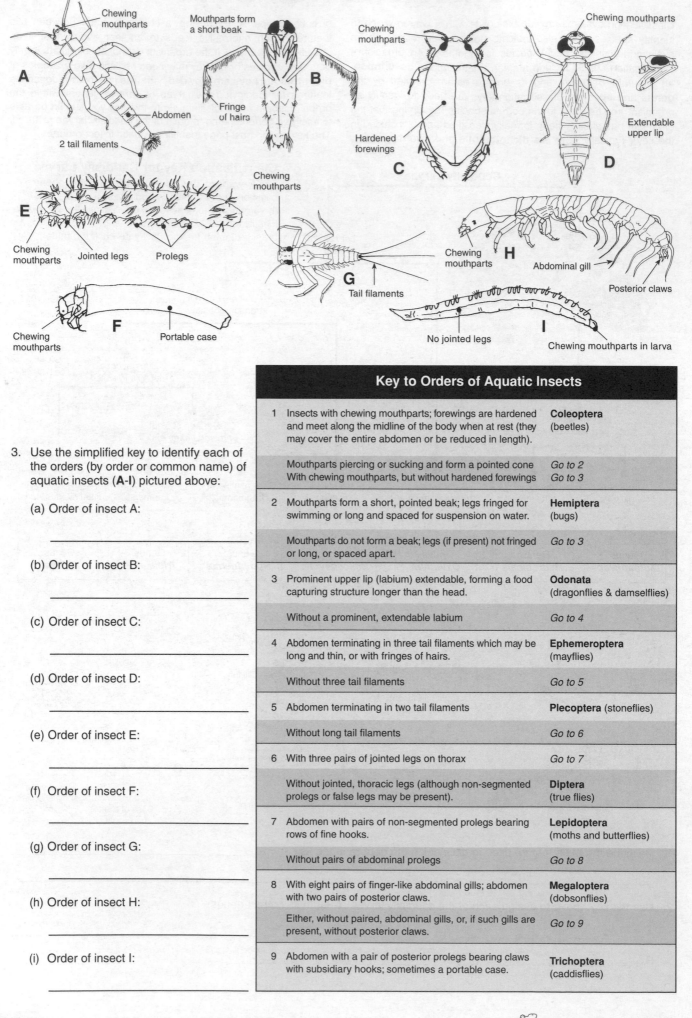

**A** — Chewing mouthparts; Abdomen; 2 tail filaments

**B** — Mouthparts form a short beak; Fringe of hairs

**C** — Chewing mouthparts; Hardened forewings

**D** — Chewing mouthparts; Extendable upper lip

**E** — Chewing mouthparts; Jointed legs; Prolegs

**F** — Chewing mouthparts; Portable case

**G** — Chewing mouthparts; Tail filaments

**H** — Chewing mouthparts; Abdominal gill; Posterior claws

**I** — No jointed legs; Chewing mouthparts in larva

3. Use the simplified key to identify each of the orders (by order or common name) of aquatic insects (**A-I**) pictured above:

(a) Order of insect A:

_____

(b) Order of insect B:

_____

(c) Order of insect C:

_____

(d) Order of insect D:

_____

(e) Order of insect E:

_____

(f) Order of insect F:

_____

(g) Order of insect G:

_____

(h) Order of insect H:

_____

(i) Order of insect I:

_____

## Key to Orders of Aquatic Insects

| | | |
|---|---|---|
| 1 | Insects with chewing mouthparts; forewings are hardened and meet along the midline of the body when at rest (they may cover the entire abdomen or be reduced in length). | **Coleoptera** (beetles) |
| | Mouthparts piercing or sucking and form a pointed cone<br>With chewing mouthparts, but without hardened forewings | *Go to 2*<br>*Go to 3* |
| 2 | Mouthparts form a short, pointed beak; legs fringed for swimming or long and spaced for suspension on water. | **Hemiptera** (bugs) |
| | Mouthparts do not form a beak; legs (if present) not fringed or long, or spaced apart. | *Go to 3* |
| 3 | Prominent upper lip (labium) extendable, forming a food capturing structure longer than the head. | **Odonata** (dragonflies & damselflies) |
| | Without a prominent, extendable labium | *Go to 4* |
| 4 | Abdomen terminating in three tail filaments which may be long and thin, or with fringes of hairs. | **Ephemeroptera** (mayflies) |
| | Without three tail filaments | *Go to 5* |
| 5 | Abdomen terminating in two tail filaments | **Plecoptera** (stoneflies) |
| | Without long tail filaments | *Go to 6* |
| 6 | With three pairs of jointed legs on thorax | *Go to 7* |
| | Without jointed, thoracic legs (although non-segmented prolegs or false legs may be present). | **Diptera** (true flies) |
| 7 | Abdomen with pairs of non-segmented prolegs bearing rows of fine hooks. | **Lepidoptera** (moths and butterflies) |
| | Without pairs of abdominal prolegs | *Go to 8* |
| 8 | With eight pairs of finger-like abdominal gills; abdomen with two pairs of posterior claws. | **Megaloptera** (dobsonflies) |
| | Either, without paired, abdominal gills, or, if such gills are present, without posterior claws. | *Go to 9* |
| 9 | Abdomen with a pair of posterior prolegs bearing claws with subsidiary hooks; sometimes a portable case. | **Trichoptera** (caddisflies) |

# Keying Out Plant Species

Dichotomous keys are a useful tool in biology and can enable identification to the species level provided the characteristics chosen are appropriate for separating species. Keys are extensively used by botanists as they are quick and easy to use in the field, although they sometimes rely on the presence of particular plant parts such as fruits or flowers. Some also require some specialist knowledge of plant biology. The following simple activity requires you to identify five species of the genus *Acer* from illustrations of the leaves. It provides valuable practice in using characteristic features to identify plants to species level.

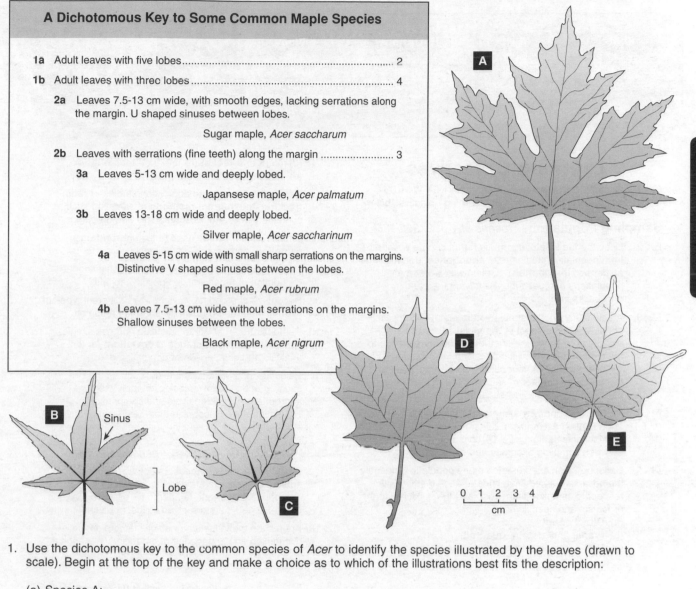

### A Dichotomous Key to Some Common Maple Species

**1a** Adult leaves with five lobes.........................................................................2

**1b** Adult leaves with three lobes ...............................................................4

    **2a** Leaves 7.5-13 cm wide, with smooth edges, lacking serrations along the margin. U shaped sinuses between lobes.

                  Sugar maple, *Acer saccharum*

    **2b** Leaves with serrations (fine teeth) along the margin ........................ 3

        **3a** Leaves 5-13 cm wide and deeply lobed.

                  Japansese maple, *Acer palmatum*

        **3b** Leaves 13-18 cm wide and deeply lobed.

                  Silver maple, *Acer saccharinum*

        **4a** Leaves 5-15 cm wide with small sharp serrations on the margins. Distinctive V shaped sinuses between the lobes.

                  Red maple, *Acer rubrum*

        **4b** Leaves 7.5-13 cm wide without serrations on the margins. Shallow sinuses between the lobes.

                  Black maple, *Acer nigrum*

1. Use the dichotomous key to the common species of *Acer* to identify the species illustrated by the leaves (drawn to scale). Begin at the top of the key and make a choice as to which of the illustrations best fits the description:

    (a) Species A: _____

    (b) Species B: _____

    (c) Species C: _____

    (d) Species D: _____

    (e) Species E: _____

2. Identify a feature that could be used to identify maple species when leaves are absent: _____

3. Suggest why it is usually necessary to consider a number of different features in order to classify plants to species level:

    _____

    _____

4. When identifying a plant, suggest what you should be sure of before using a key to classify it to species level:

    _____

    _____

# Practical Ecology

**IB SL**
Complete:
*1, 10-11*

**IB HL**
Complete:
*1, 10-11*

**IB Options**
Complete:
*Option G:*
*SL/HL: 5(b)-(c),*
*7, 13*
*HL: 5(d)*

**AP Biology**
Complete:
*1-13*
*Some numbers*
*extension as*
*appropriate*

## Learning Objectives

☐ 1. Compile your own glossary from the **KEY WORDS** displayed in **bold type** in the learning objectives below.

### Sampling Populations *(pages 351-352, 355-366)*

☐ 2. Describe the type of information that can be obtained from population studies (e.g. **abundance**, **density**, **age structure**, **distribution**). Explain why we **sample** populations and describe the advantages and drawbacks involved.

☐ 3. A field study should enable you to test a hypothesis about a certain aspect of a population. You should provide an outline of your study including reference to the type of data you will collect and the methods you will use, the size of your sampling unit (e.g. quadrat size) and the number of samples you will take, the assumptions of your investigation, and controls.

☐ 4. Explain how and why sample size affects the accuracy of population estimates. Explain how you would decide on a suitable sample size. Discuss the compromise between sampling accuracy and sampling effort.

☐ 5. Describe techniques used to study populations. Identify the advantages and limitations of each method with respect to sampling time, cost, and the suitability to the organism and specific habitat type:
(a) **Direct counts**
(b) **Frame** and/or **point quadrats**
(c) **Belt** and/or **line transects**

(d) **Mark and recapture** and the **Lincoln index**
(e) **Netting** and **trapping**

☐ 6. Recognise the value to population studies of **radio-tracking** and **indirect methods** of sampling such as counting nests, and recording calls and droppings.

☐ 7. Describe the methods used to ensure **random sampling**, and appreciate why this is important.

☐ 8. Describe **qualitative methods** for investigating the distribution of organisms in specific habitats.

☐ 9. Recognize appropriate ways in which different types of data may be recorded, analyzed, and presented.

☐ 10. Demonstrate an ability to calculate and use simple statistics (**mean** and **standard deviation**) for the analysis and comparison of population data.

☐ 11. Calculate simple statistical tests, such as the chi-squared and student's *t* test, and apply them appropriately to the analysis and comparison of population data. Recognize that the design of any field study will determine how the data can be analyzed.

### Measuring Abiotic Factors *(pages 353-354)*

☐ 12. Describe methods to measure abiotic factors in a habitat. Include reference to the following (as appropriate): pH, light, temperature, dissolved oxygen, current speed, total dissolved solids, and conductivity.

☐ 13. Appreciate the influence of abiotic factors on the distribution and abundance of organisms in a habitat.

---

See the 'Textbook Reference Grid' on pages 8-9 for textbook page references relating to material in this topic.

**Supplementary Texts**
See pages 5-6 for additional details of these texts:
■ Adds, J., *et al.,* 2004. **Genetics, Evolution and Biodiversity,** (NelsonThornes), chpt. 3 as required.

■ Cadogan, A. and Sutton, R., 2002. **Maths for Advanced Biology** (NelsonThornes), as required.

■ Helms, D.R. *et al.*, 1998. **Biology in the Laboratory** (W.H. Freeman), #45.

■ Jones, A., *et al.*, 2003. **Practical Skills in Biology** (Addison-Wesley).

**Presentation MEDIA** to support this topic:
**ECOLOGY:**
• **Ecosystems**
• **Practical Ecology**

**Periodicals**

See page 6 for details of publishers of periodicals:

#### STUDENT'S REFERENCE
■ **British Butterflies in Decline** Biol. Sci. Rev., 14(4) April 2002, pp. 10-13. *Documented changes in the distribution of British butterfly species. This account includes a description of the techniques used to monitor changes in population numbers.*

■ **Bird Ringing** Biol. Sci. Rev., 14(3) Feb. 2002, pp. 14-19. *The practical investigation of populations of highly mobile organisms. Includes discussion of mark and recapture, and ringing methods.*

#### TEACHER'S REFERENCE
■ **Ecology Fieldwork in 16 to 19 Biology** SSR, 84(307) Dec. 2002, pp. 87. *Examining the fieldwork opportunities provided to 16-19 students.*

■ **Trash Ecology** The Am. Biology Teacher, 66(9), Nov. 2004, pp. 613-619. *Transects through trash to investigate density, frequency, and biomass.*

■ **Using Artificial Nests to Study Nest Predation in Birds** The Am. Biology Teacher, 67(2), Feb. 2005, pp. 105-110. *Field activities to demonstrate factors affecting predation on nests.*

■ **Enhancing Student Understanding of Environmental Sciences Research** The Am. Biology Teacher, 63(4), April, 2001, pp. 236-241. *Ideas for improving understanding in practical ecology: sampling, field study design, and data analysis and interpretation.*

■ **Long-Term Plant Biodiversity Study** The Am. Biology Teacher, 68(4), April 2006, pp. 213-220. *A long-term study and assessment of biodiversity in an urban green space.*

See pages 10-11 for details of how to access **Bio Links** from our web site: **www.thebiozone.com** From Bio Links, access sites under the topics:

**ECOLOGY > Environmental Monitoring:** • Amphibian monitoring program • Environmental Protection Agency • Remote sensing and monitoring > **Populations and Communities:** • Quantitative population ecology • Sirtracking for wildlife research

**STUDENT PROJECTS:** • A scientific report • Chi-square lesson • Scientific investigation • Study skills: biology • The scientific method • Tree lupins • Woodlice online *...and others*

# Designing Your Field Study

The figure below provides an example and some ideas for designing a field study. It provides a framework which can be modified for most simple comparative field investigations. For reasons of space, the full methodology is not included.

**Pill millipede**
*Glomeris marginata*

**Oak woodland**

**Coniferous woodland**

## Observation

A student read that a particular species of pill millipede (left) is extremely abundant in forest leaf litter, but a search in the litter of a conifer-dominated woodland near his home revealed only very low numbers of this millipede species.

## Hypothesis

This millipede species is adapted to a niche in the leaf litter of oak woodlands and is abundant there. However, it is rare in the litter of coniferous woodland. The **null hypothesis** is that there is no difference between the abundance of this millipede species in oak and coniferous woodland litter.

## Oak or coniferous woodland

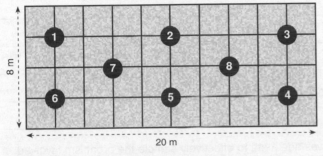

**8 m**

**20 m**

**1** Sampling sites numbered 1-8 at evenly spaced intervals on a 2 x 2 m grid within an area of 20 m x 8 m.

## Sampling equipment: leaf litter light trap

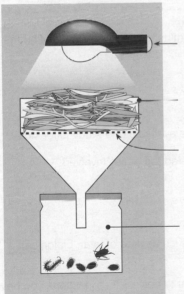

Light from a battery operated lamp drives the invertebrates down through the leaf litter.

Large (diameter 300 mm) funnel containing leaf litter resting on a gauze platform.

Gauze allows invertebrates of a certain size to move down the funnel.

Collecting jar placed in the litter on the forest floor traps the invertebrates that fall through the gauze and prevents their escape.

## Sampling Program

A sampling program was designed to test the **prediction** that the millipedes would be more abundant in the leaf litter of oak woodlands than in coniferous woodlands.

## Equipment and Procedure

**Sites:** For each of the two woodland types, an area 20 x 8 m was chosen and marked out in 2 x 2 m grids. Eight sampling sites were selected, evenly spaced along the grid as shown.

- The general area for the study chosen was selected on the basis of the large amounts of leaf litter present.
- Eight sites were chosen as the largest number feasible to collect and analyze in the time available.
- The two woodlands were sampled on sequential days.

**Capture of millipedes:** At each site, a 0.4 x 0.4 m quadrat was placed on the forest floor and the leaf litter within the quadrat was collected. Millipedes and other leaf litter invertebrates were captured using a simple gauze lined funnel containing the leaf litter from within the quadrat. A lamp was positioned over each funnel for two hours and the invertebrates in the litter moved down and were trapped in the collecting jar.

- After two hours each jar was labeled with the site number and returned to the lab for analysis.
- The litter in each funnel was bagged, labeled with the site number and returned to the lab for weighing.
- The number of millipedes at each site was recorded.
- The numbers of other invertebrates (classified into major taxa) were also noted for reference.

## Assumptions

- The areas chosen in each woodland were representative of the woodland types in terms of millipede abundance.
- Eight sites were sufficient to adequately sample the millipede populations in each forest.
- A quadrat size of 0.4 x 0.4 m contained enough leaf litter to adequately sample the millipedes at each site.
- The millipedes were not preyed on by any of the other invertebrates captured in the collecting jar.
- All the invertebrates within the quadrat were captured.
- Millipedes moving away from the light are effectively captured by the funnel apparatus and cannot escape.
- Two hours was long enough for the millipedes to move down through the litter and fall into the trap.

Note that these last two assumptions could be tested by examining the bagged leaf litter for millipedes after returning to the lab.

### Notes on collection and analysis

- Mean millipede abundance was calculated from the counts from the eight sites. The difference in abundance at the sites was tested using a Student's *t* test.
- After counting and analysis of the samples, all the collected invertebrates were returned to the sites.

**Practical Ecology**

**Related activities**: Quadrat-Based Estimates

**A 3**

## A Note About Sample Size

When designing a field study, the size of your sampling unit (e.g. quadrat size) and the sample size (the number of samples you will take) should be major considerations. There are various ways to determine the best quadrat size. Usually, these involve increasing the quadrat size until you stop finding new species. For simple field studies, the number of samples you take (the sample size or *n* value) will be determined largely by the resources and time that you have available to collect and analyze your data. It is usually best to take as many samples as you can, as this helps to account for any natural variability present and will give you greater confidence in your data. For a summary of these aspects of study design as well as coverage of collecting methods see: *Jones, A. et al. (1998) Practical Skills in Biology* (or the earlier 1994 edition).

1. Explain the importance of each of the following in field studies:

    (a) Appropriate quadrat size (or any equivalent sampling unit): _____

    _____

    (b) Recognizing any assumptions that you are making: _____

    _____

    (c) Appropriate consideration of the environment: _____

    _____

    (d) Return of organisms to the same place after removal: _____

    _____

    (e) Appropriate size of total sampling area within which the sites are located: _____

    _____

2. Explain how you could test whether any given quadrat size was adequate to effectively sample the organism involved:

    _____

    _____

    _____

    _____

## YOUR CHECKLIST FOR FIELD STUDY DESIGN

The following provides a checklist for a field study. Check off the points when you are confident that you have satisfied the requirements in each case:

1. **Preliminary:**

    ☐ (a) Makes a hypothesis based on observation(s).

    ☐ (b) The hypothesis (and its predictions) are testable using the resources you have available (the study is feasible).

    ☐ (c) The organism you have chosen is suitable for the study and you have considered the ethics involved.

2. **Assumptions and site selection:**

    ☐ (a) You are aware of any assumptions that you are making in your study.

    ☐ (b) You have identified aspects of your field design that could present problems (such as time of year, biological rhythms of your test organism, difficulty in identifying suitable habitats etc.).

    ☐ (c) The study sites you have selected have the features necessary in order for you to answer the questions you have asked in your hypothesis.

3. **Data collection:**

    ☐ (a) You are happy with the way in which you are going to take your measurements or samples.

    ☐ (b) You have considered the size of your sampling unit and the number of samples you are going to take (and tested for these if necessary).

    ☐ (c) You have given consideration to how you will analyze the data you collect and made sure that your study design allows you to answer the questions you wish to answer.

# Monitoring Physical Factors

Most ecological studies require us to measure the physical factors (parameters) in the environment that may influence the abundance and distribution of organisms. In recent years there have been substantial advances in the development of portable, light-weight meters and dataloggers. These enable easy collection and storage of data in the field.

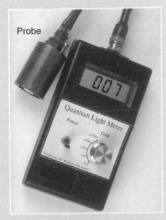

Quantum light meter: Measures light intensity levels. It is not capable of measuring light quality (wavelength).

Probe

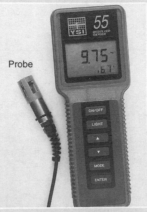

Dissolved oxygen meter: Measures the amount of oxygen dissolved in water (expressed as mgl⁻¹).

pH meter: Measures the acidity of water or soil, if it is first dissolved in pure water (pH scale 0 to 14).

Total dissolved solids (TDS) meter: Measures content of dissolved solids (as ions) in water in mgl⁻¹.

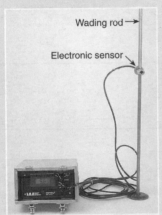

Current meter: The electronic sensor is positioned at set depths in a stream or river on the calibrated wading rod as current readings are taken.

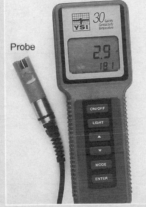

Multipurpose meter: This is a multi functional meter, which can measure salinity, conductivity and temperature simply by pushing the MODE button.

Secchi disc: This simple device is used to provide a crude measure of water clarity (the maximum depth at which the disc can just be seen).

Collecting a water sample: A Nansen bottle is used to collect water samples from a lake for lab analysis, testing for nutrients, oxygen and pH.

This photo JDG, Others, Campus photography, University of Waikato

Practical Ecology

## Dataloggers and Environmental Sensors

Dataloggers are electronic instruments that record measurements over time. They are equipped with a microprocessor, data storage facility, and sensor. Different sensors are employed to measure a range of variables in water (photos A and B) or air (photos C and D), as well as make physiological measurements. The datalogger is connected to a computer, and software is used to set the limits of operation (e.g. the sampling interval) and initiate the logger. The logger is then disconnected and used remotely to record and store data. When reconnected to the computer, the data are downloaded, viewed, and plotted. Dataloggers, such as those pictured here from PASCO, are being increasingly used in professional and school research. They make data collection quick and accurate, and they enable prompt data analysis.

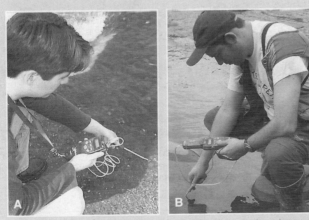
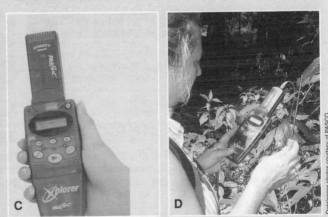

Datalogger photos courtesy of PASCO

Dataloggers are now widely used to monitor conditions in aquatic environments. Different variables such as pH, temperature, conductivity, and dissolved oxygen can be measured by changing the sensor attached to the logger.

Dataloggers fitted with sensors are portable and easy to use in a wide range of terrestrial environments. They are used to measure variables such as air temperature and pressure, relative humidity, light, and carbon dioxide gas.

1. The physical factors of an exposed rocky shore and a sheltered estuarine mudflat differ markedly. For each of the factors listed in the table below, briefly describe how they may differ (if at all):

| Environmental parameter | Exposed rocky coastline | Estuarine mudflat |
|---|---|---|
| Severity of wave action | | |
| Light intensity and quality | | |
| Salinity/ conductivity | | |
| Temperature change (diurnal) | | |
| Substrate/ sediment type | | |
| Oxygen concentration | | |
| Exposure time to air (tide out) | | |

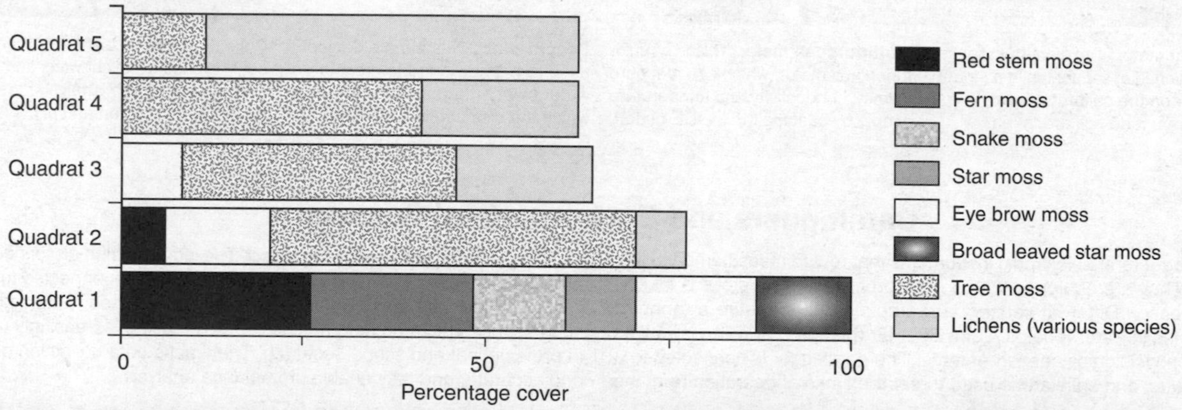

Legend:
- Red stem moss
- Fern moss
- Snake moss
- Star moss
- Eye brow moss
- Broad leaved star moss
- Tree moss
- Lichens (various species)

Quadrat 5, Quadrat 4, Quadrat 3, Quadrat 2, Quadrat 1

Percentage cover

| QUADRAT | 1 | 2 | 3 | 4 | 5 |
|---|---|---|---|---|---|
| Height (m) | 0.4 | 0.8 | 1.2 | 1.6 | 2.0 |
| Light (arbitrary units) | 40 | 56 | 68 | 72 | 72 |
| Humidity (percent) | 99 | 88 | 80 | 76 | 78 |
| Temperature (°C) | 12.1 | 12.2 | 13 | 14.3 | 14.2 |

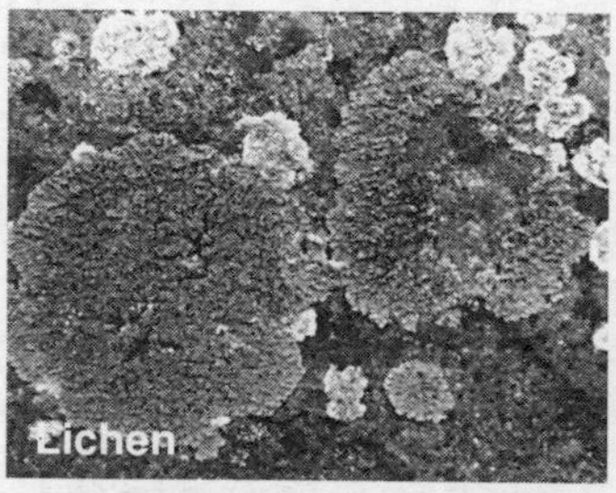

Lichen

Moss

2. The figure (above) shows the changes in vegetation cover along a 2 m vertical transect up the trunk of an oak tree (*Quercus*). Changes in the physical factors light, humidity, and temperature along the same transect were also recorded. From what you know about the ecology of mosses and lichens, account for the observed vegetation distribution:

# Indirect Sampling

If populations are small and easily recognized they may be monitored directly quite easily. However, direct measurement of elusive, easily disturbed, or widely dispersed populations is not always feasible. In these cases, **indirect methods** can be used to assess population abundance, provide information on habitat use and range, and enable biologists to link habitat quality to species presence or absence. Indirect sampling methods provide less reliable measures of abundance than direct sampling

methods, such as mark and recapture, but are widely used nevertheless. They rely on recording the signs of a species, e.g. scat, calls, tracks, and rubbings or markings on vegetation, and using these to assess population abundance. In Australia, the Environmental Protection Agency (EPA) provides a Frog Census Datasheet (below) on which volunteers record details about frog populations and habitat quality in their area. This program enables the EPA to gather information across Australia.

**INFORMATION NEEDED FOR THE FROG CENSUS**

- **Where** you recorded frogs calling: **When** you made the recordings, and **What** frogs you recorded (if possible).

Observers Name:
Contact Address:

Post Code:
Telephone Home: _____ Work / Mobile:

Do You Want to be involved next year?(Please Circle)

Location Description (Try to provide enough detail to enable us to find map.
Please use a separate datasheet for each site)

is location the same as in (CIRCLE)   1994   1995   1996   1997

Grid Reference of Location and Type of Map Used:
OR Street Directory Reference:   Year and Edition:
Page Number:   Grid Reference:
Nearest Town from Location (if known):

Date of Observation (e.g. 8 Sept 1998):
Time Range of Observation (e.g. 8.30-8.40 pm):

*Recording a date and accurate map reference is important*

*Population estimates are based on the number of frog calls recorded by the observer*

**HABITAT ASSESSMENT**
Habitat Type (please circle one):   pond   dam   stream   drain
reservoir   wetland   spring   swamp
Comments:

**WATER QUALITY and WEATHER**
CIRCLE to indicate the condition of the site (you can circle more than one choice).
Water Flow:   Still   Flowing Slowly   Flowing Quickly
Water Appearance:   Clear   Polluted   Frothy Oily   Muddy
Weather Conditions:   1. Windy / Still
2. Overcast / Recent Rains / Dry (indicate for 1 AND 2)

**FROGS HEARD CALLING**
Please indicate your estimate of how many frogs you heard calling
(NOTE it is very important to tell us if you heard no frogs)
Number of Calls Heard (circle):
None   One   Few (2-9)   Many (10-50)   Lots (>50)
If you want to test your frog knowledge write the species you heard calling:
Species of Frog(s) Identified: 1. ___   2. ___
3. ___   4. ___
Comments:

Now we need you to return your datasheet and tape in the **postage free post-pak** addressed to REPLY PAID 6360 Mr Peter Goonan Environment Protection Agency GPO Box 2607 ADELAIDE SA 5001. We will identify your frog calls and let you know the results of your recordings.

**Office use only. Please leave blank.**
**FROG SPECIES PRESENT.**

| Species Number | Species 1 | Species 2 | Species 3 | Species 4 | Species 5 |
|---|---|---|---|---|---|
| Species Name | | | | | |
| (2 - 9) | | | | | |
| (10 - 50) | | | | | |
| (>50) | | | | | |

**ENVIRONMENT PROTECTION AGENCY**
**DEPARTMENT FOR ENVIRONMENT HERITAGE AND ABORIGINAL AFFAIRS**

To sample nocturnal, highly mobile species, e.g. bats, electronic devices, such as the bat detector above, can be used to estimate population density. In this case, the detector is tuned to the particular frequency of the hunting clicks emitted by specific bat species. The number of calls recorded per unit time can be used to estimate numbers per area.

The analysis of animal tracks allows wildlife biologists to identify habitats in which animals live and to conduct population surveys. Interpreting tracks accurately requires considerable skill as tracks may vary in appearance even when from the same individual. Tracks are particularly useful as a way to determine habitat use and preference.

Wombat scat

All animals leave scats (feces) which are species specific and readily identifiable. Scats can be a valuable tool by which to gather data from elusive, nocturnal, easily disturbed, or highly mobile species. Fecal analyses can provide information on diet, movements, population density, sex ratios, age structure, and even genetic diversity.

**Practical Ecology**

1. Describe two kinds of indirect signs that could be used to detect the presence of frogs:

   (a) _____   (b) _____

2. Describe the kind of information that the EPA would gather from their Frog Census Datasheet: _____

3. Describe one other indirect method of population sampling and outline its advantages and drawbacks:

RA 1

# Sampling Populations

Information about the populations of rare organisms in isolated populations may, in some instances, be collected by direct measure (direct counts and measurements of all the individuals in the population). However, in most cases, populations are too large to be examined directly and they must be sampled in a way that still provides information about them. Most practical exercises in population ecology involve the collection or census of living organisms, with a view to identifying the species and quantifying their abundance and other population features of interest. Sampling techniques must be appropriate to the community being studied and the information you wish to obtain. Some of the common strategies used in ecological sampling, and the situations for which they are best suited, are outlined in the table below. It provides an overview of points to consider when choosing a sampling regime. One must always consider the time and equipment available, the organisms involved, and the impact of the sampling method on the environment. For example, if the organisms involved are very mobile, sampling frames are not appropriate. If it is important not to disturb the organisms, observation alone must be used to gain information.

| Method | Equipment and procedure | Information provided and considerations for use |
|---|---|---|
| **Point sampling**<br>Random   Systematic (grid) | Individual points are chosen on a map (using a grid reference or random numbers applied to a map grid) and the organisms are sampled at those points. Mobile organisms may be sampled using traps, nets etc. | **Useful for:** Determining species abundance and community composition. If samples are large enough, population characteristics (e.g. age structure, reproductive parameters) can be determined.<br><br>**Considerations:** Time efficient. Suitable for most organisms. Depending on method, environmental disturbance is minimal. Species occurring in low abundance may be missed. |
| **Transect sampling**<br><br>Environmental gradient<br>0.5 m | Lines are drawn across a map and organisms occurring along the line are sampled.<br><br>**Line transects:** Tape or rope marks the line. The species occurring on the line are recorded (all along the line or, more usually, at regular intervals). Lines can be chosen randomly (left) or may follow an environmental gradient.<br><br>**Belt transects:** A measured strip is located across the study area to highlight any transitions. Quadrats are used to sample the plants and animals at regular intervals along the belt. Plants and immobile animals are easily recorded. Mobile or cryptic animals need to be trapped or recorded using appropriate methods. | **Useful for:** Well suited to determining changes in community composition along an environmental gradient. When placed randomly, they provide a quick measure of species occurrence.<br><br>**Considerations for line transects:** Time efficient. Most suitable for plants and immobile or easily caught animals. Disturbance to the environment can be minimized. Species occurring in low abundance may be missed.<br><br>**Considerations for belt transects:** Time consuming to do well. Most suitable for plants and immobile or easily caught animals. Good chance of recording most or all species. Efforts should be made to minimize disturbance to the environment. |
| **Quadrat sampling** | Sampling units or quadrats are placed randomly or in a grid pattern on the sample area. The occurrence of organisms in these squares is noted. Plants and slow moving animals are easily recorded. Rapidly moving or cryptic animals need to be trapped or recorded using appropriate methods. | **Useful for:** Well suited to determining community composition and features of population abundance: species density, frequency of occurrence, percentage cover, and biomass (if harvested).<br><br>**Considerations:** Time consuming to do well. Most suitable for plants and immobile or easily caught animals. Quadrat size must be appropriate for the organisms being sampled and the information required. Disturbing if organisms are removed. |
| **Mark and recapture (capture-recapture)**<br>First sample: marked   Second sample: proportion recaptured | Animals are captured, marked, and then released. After a suitable time period, the population is resampled. The number of marked animals recaptured in a second sample is recorded as a proportion of the total. | **Useful for:** Determining total population density for highly mobile species in a certain area (e.g. butterflies). Movements of individuals in the population can be tracked (especially when used in conjunction with electronic tracking devices).<br><br>**Considerations:** Time consuming to do well. Not suitable for immobile species. Population should have a finite boundary. Period between samplings must allow for redistribution of marked animals in the population. Marking should present little disturbance and should not affect behavior. |

1. Explain why we **sample** populations: _____

_____

2. Describe a sampling technique that would be appropriate for determining each of the following:

(a) The percentage cover of a plant species in pasture: _____

(b) The density and age structure of a plankton population: _____

(c) Change in community composition from low to high altitude on a mountain: _____

**A 2**

**Related activities:** Quadrat Sampling, Transect Sampling, Mark and Recapture Sampling

# Quadrat Sampling

**Quadrat sampling** is a method by which organisms in a certain proportion (sample) of the habitat are counted directly. As with all sampling methods, it is used to estimate population parameters when the organisms present are too numerous to count in total. It can be used to estimate population **abundance** (number), **density**, **frequency of occurrence**, and **distribution**. Quadrats may be used without a transect when studying a relatively uniform habitat. In this case, the quadrat positions are chosen randomly using a random number table.

The general procedure is to count all the individuals (or estimate their percentage cover) in a number of quadrats of known size and to use this information to work out the abundance or percentage cover value for the whole area. The number of quadrats used and their size should be appropriate to the type of organism involved (e.g. grass vs tree).

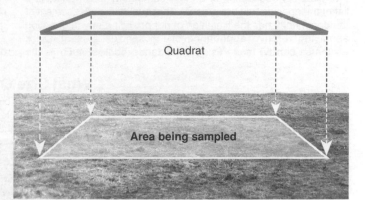
Quadrat

Area being sampled

$$\text{Estimated average density} = \frac{\text{Total number of individuals counted}}{\text{Number of quadrats} \times \text{area of each quadrat}}$$

## Guidelines for Quadrat Use:

1. The **area of each quadrat** must be known exactly and ideally quadrats should be the same shape. The quadrat does not have to be square (it may be rectangular, hexagonal etc.).

2. **Enough quadrat samples** must be taken to provide results that are representative of the total population.

3. The **population of each quadrat** must be known exactly. Species must be distinguishable from each other, even if they have to be identified at a later date. It has to be decided beforehand what the count procedure will be and how organisms over the quadrat boundary will be counted.

4. The size of the quadrat should be appropriate to the organisms and habitat, e.g. a large size quadrat for trees.

5. The quadrats must be **representative of the whole area**. This is usually achieved by **random sampling** (right).

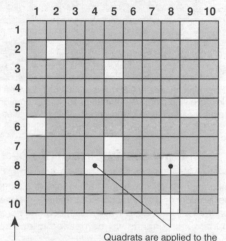

The area to be sampled is divided up into a grid pattern with indexed coordinates

Quadrats are applied to the predetermined grid on a random basis. This can be achieved by using a random number table.

## Sampling a centipede population

A researcher by the name of Lloyd (1967) carried out a sampling of centipedes in Wytham Woods, near Oxford in England. A total of 37 hexagon–shaped quadrats were used, with a diameter of 30 cm (see diagram on right). These were arranged in a pattern so that they were all touching each other. Use the data in the diagram to answer the following questions:

1. Determine the average number of centipedes captured per quadrat:

   _____

2. Calculate the estimated average density of centipedes per square meter (remember that each quadrat is 0.08 square meters in area):

   _____

3. Looking at the data for individual quadrats, describe in general terms the distribution of the centipedes in the sample area:

   _____

4. Describe one factor that might account for the distribution pattern:

   _____
   _____
   _____

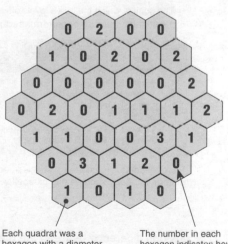

Each quadrat was a hexagon with a diameter of 30 cm and an area of 0.08 square meters.

The number in each hexagon indicates how many centipedes were caught in that quadrat.

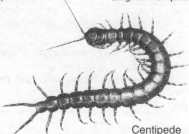
Centipede

**Related activities**: Density and Distribution, Sampling a Leaf Litter Population
**Web links**: Investigating Marine Life, Using Quadrats to Sample

DA 2

# Quadrat-Based Estimates

The simplest description of a plant community in a habitat is a list of the species that are present. This qualitative assessment of the community has the limitation of not providing any information about the **relative abundance** of the species present. Quick estimates can be made using **abundance scales**, such as the ACFOR scale described below. Estimates of percentage cover provide similar information. These methods require the use of **quadrats**. Quadrats are used extensively in plant ecology. This activity outlines some of the common considerations when using quadrats to sample plant communities.

## What Size Quadrat?

Quadrats are usually square, and cover 0.25 m² (0.5 m x 0.5 m) or 1 m², but they can be of any size or shape, even a single point. The quadrats used to sample plant communities are often 0.25 m². This size is ideal for low-growing vegetation, but quadrat size needs to be adjusted to habitat type. The quadrat must be large enough to be representative of the community, but not so large as to take a very long time to use.

A quadrat covering an area of 0.25 m² is suitable for most low growing plant communities, such as this alpine meadow, fields, and grasslands.

Larger quadrats (e.g. 1 m²) are needed for communities with shrubs and trees. Quadrats as large as 4 m x 4 m may be needed in woodlands.

Small quadrats ( 0.01 m² or 100 mm x 100 mm) are appropriate for lichens and mosses on rock faces and tree trunks.

## How Many Quadrats?

As well as deciding on a suitable quadrat size, the other consideration is how many quadrats to take (the sample size). In species-poor or very homogeneous habitats, a small number of quadrats will be sufficient. In species-rich or heterogeneous habitats, more quadrats will be needed to ensure that all species are represented adequately.

### Determining the number of quadrats needed

- Plot the cumulative number of species recorded (on the $y$ axis) against the number of quadrats already taken (on the $x$ axis).

- The point at which the curve levels off indicates the suitable number of quadrats required.

Fewer quadrats are needed in species-poor or very uniform habitats, such as this bluebell woodland.

## Describing Vegetation

Density (number of individuals per unit area) is a useful measure of abundance for animal populations, but can be problematic in plant communities where it can be difficult to determine where one plant ends and another begins. For this reason, plant abundance is often assessed using **percentage cover**. Here, the percentage of each quadrat covered by each species is recorded, either as a numerical value or using an abundance scale such as the ACFOR scale.

### The ACFOR Abundance Scale

**A** = Abundant (30% +)

**C** = Common (20-29%)

**F** = Frequent (10-19%)

**O** = Occasional (5-9%)

**R** = Rare (1-4%)

The AFCOR scale could be used to assess the abundance of species in this wildflower meadow. Abundance scales are subjective, but it is not difficult to determine which abundance category each species falls into.

1. Describe one difference between the methods used to assess species abundance in plant and in animal communities:

_____

2. Identify the main consideration when determining appropriate quadrat size: _____

3. Identify the main consideration when determining number of quadrats: _____

4. Explain two main disadvantages of using the ACFOR abundance scale to record information about a plant community:

(a) _____

(b) _____

# Sampling a Leaf Litter Population

The diagram on the following page represents an area of leaf litter from a forest floor with a resident population of organisms. The distribution of four animal species as well as the arrangement of leaf litter is illustrated. Leaf litter comprises leaves and debris that have dropped off trees to form a layer of detritus. This exercise is designed to practice the steps required in planning and carrying out a sampling of a natural population. It is desirable, but not essential, that students work in groups of 2–4.

### 1. Decide on the sampling method

For the purpose of this exercise, it has been decided that the populations to be investigated are too large to be counted directly and a quadrat sampling method is to be used to estimate the average density of the four animal species as well as that of the leaf litter.

### 2. Mark out a grid pattern

Use a ruler to mark out 3 cm intervals along each side of the sampling area (area of quadrat = 0.03 x 0.03 m). **Draw lines** between these marks to create a 6 x 6 grid pattern (total area = 0.18 x 0.18 m). This will provide a total of 36 quadrats that can be investigated.

### 3. Number the axes of the grid

Only a small proportion of the possible quadrat positions are going to be sampled. It is necessary to select the quadrats in a random manner. It is not sufficient to simply guess or choose your own on a 'gut feeling'. The best way to choose the quadrats randomly is to create a numbering system for the grid pattern and then select the quadrats from a random number table. Starting at the *top left hand corner*, **number the columns** and **rows** from 1 to 6 on each axis.

### 4. Choose quadrats randomly

To select the required number of quadrats randomly, use random numbers from a random number table. The random numbers are used as an index to the grid coordinates. Choose 6 quadrats from the total of 36 using table of random numbers provided for you at the bottom of the following page. Make a note of which column of random numbers you choose. Each member of your group should choose a different set of random numbers (i.e. different column: A–D) so that you can compare the effectiveness of the sampling method.

Column of random numbers chosen: _____

NOTE: Highlight the boundary of each selected quadrat with coloured pen/highlighter.

### 5. Decide on the counting criteria

Before the counting of the individuals for each species is carried out, the criteria for counting need to be established.

There may be some problems here. You must decide before sampling begins as to what to do about individuals that are only partly inside the quadrat. Possible answers include:

(a) Only counting individuals if they are completely inside the quadrat.

(b) Only counting individuals that have a clearly defined part of their body inside the quadrat (such as the head).

(c) Allowing for 'half individuals' in the data (e.g. 3.5 snails).

(d) Counting an individual that is inside the quadrat by half or more as one complete individual.

**Discuss the merits and problems** of the suggestions above with other members of the class (or group). You may even have counting criteria of your own. Think about other factors that could cause problems with your counting.

### 6. Carry out the sampling

Carefully examine each selected quadrat and **count the number of individuals** of each species present. Record your data in the spaces provided on the following page.

### 7. Calculate the population density

Use the combined data TOTALS for the sampled quadrats to estimate the average density for each species by using the formula:

**Density** =

$$\frac{\text{Total number in all quadrats sampled}}{\text{Number of quadrats sampled} \times \text{area of a quadrat}}$$

Remember that a total of 6 quadrats are sampled and each has an area of $0.0009 \text{ m}^2$. The density should be expressed as the number of individuals *per square meter* (no. m$^{-2}$).

Woodlouse: ☐  False scorpion: ☐

Centipede: ☐  Leaf: ☐

Springtail: ☐

8. (a) In this example the animals are not moving. Describe the problems associated with sampling moving organisms. Explain how you would cope with sampling these same animals if they were really alive and very active:

_____

_____

_____

(b) Carry out a direct count of all four animal species and the leaf litter for the whole sample area (all 36 quadrats). Apply the data from your direct count to the equation given in (7) above to calculate the actual population density (remember that the number of quadrats in this case = 36):

Woodlouse: ☐  Centipede: ☐  False scorpion: ☐  Springtail: ☐  Leaf: ☐

Compare your estimated population density to the actual population density for each species:

_____

_____

_____

**Related activities**: Quadrat Sampling, Mark and Recapture Sampling

**PDA 2**

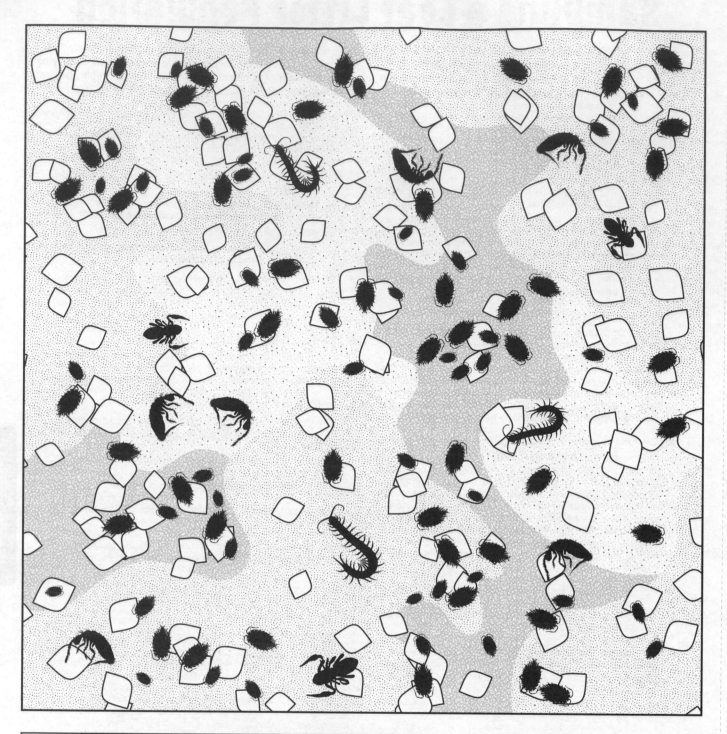

| Coordinates for each quadrat | Woodlouse | Centipede | False scorpion | Springtail | Leaf |
|---|---|---|---|---|---|
| 1: | | | | | |
| 2: | | | | | |
| 3: | | | | | |
| 4: | | | | | |
| 5: | | | | | |
| 6: | | | | | |
| TOTAL | | | | | |

### Table of random numbers

| A | B | C | D |
|---|---|---|---|
| 2 2 | 3 1 | 6 2 | 2 2 |
| 3 2 | 1 5 | 6 3 | 4 3 |
| 3 1 | 5 6 | 3 6 | 6 4 |
| 4 6 | 3 6 | 1 3 | 4 5 |
| 4 3 | 4 2 | 4 5 | 3 5 |
| 5 6 | 1 4 | 3 1 | 1 4 |

The table above has been adapted from a table of random numbers from a statistics book. Use this table to select quadrats randomly from the grid above. Choose one of the columns (A to D) and use the numbers in that column as an index to the grid. The first digit refers to the row number and the second digit refers to the column number. To locate each of the 6 quadrats, find where the row and column intersect, as shown below:

Example: | 5 2 | refers to the 5th row and the 2nd column

# Transect Sampling

A **transect** is a line placed across a community of organisms. Transects are usually carried out to provide information on the **distribution** of species in the community. This is of particular value in situations where environmental factors that change over the sampled distance. This change is called an **environmental gradient** (e.g. up a mountain or across a seashore). The usual practice for small transects is to stretch a string between two markers. The string is marked off in measured distance intervals, and the species at each marked point are noted. The sampling points along the transect may also be used for the siting of quadrats, so that changes in density and community composition can be recorded. Belt transects are essentially a form of continuous quadrat sampling. They provide more information on community composition but can be difficult to carry out. Some transects provide information on the vertical, as well as horizontal, distribution of species (e.g. tree canopies in a forest).

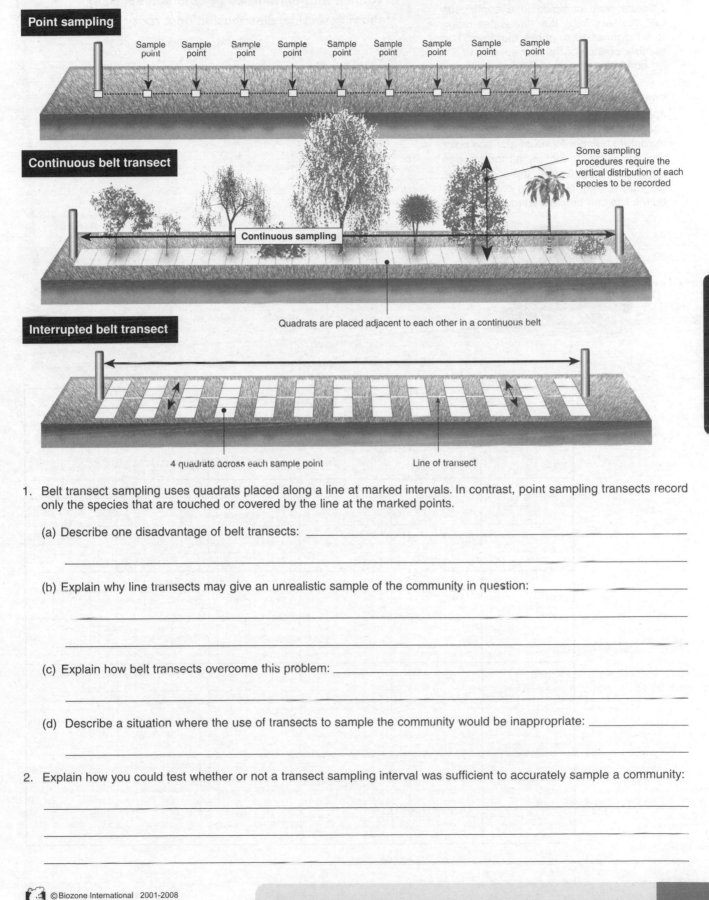

**Point sampling**

Sample point   Sample point   Sample point   Sample point   Sample point   Sample point   Sample point   Sample point   Sample point

**Continuous belt transect**

Some sampling procedures require the vertical distribution of each species to be recorded

Continuous sampling

Quadrats are placed adjacent to each other in a continuous belt

**Interrupted belt transect**

4 quadrats across each sample point          Line of transect

**Practical Ecology**

1. Belt transect sampling uses quadrats placed along a line at marked intervals. In contrast, point sampling transects record only the species that are touched or covered by the line at the marked points.

(a) Describe one disadvantage of belt transects: _____

_____

(b) Explain why line transects may give an unrealistic sample of the community in question: _____

_____

_____

(c) Explain how belt transects overcome this problem: _____

_____

(d) Describe a situation where the use of transects to sample the community would be inappropriate: _____

_____

2. Explain how you could test whether or not a transect sampling interval was sufficient to accurately sample a community:

_____

_____

_____

**Related activities**: Density and Distribution, Physical Factors and Gradients, Drawing Kite Graphs

DA 2

Kite graphs are an ideal way in which to present distributional data from a belt transect (e.g. abundance or percentage cover along an environmental gradient). Usually, they involve plots for more than one species. This makes them good for highlighting probable differences in habitat preference between species. Kite graphs may also be used to show changes in distribution with time (e.g. with daily or seasonal cycles).

3. The data on the right were collected from a rocky shore field trip. Periwinkles from four common species of the genus *Littorina* were sampled in a continuous belt transect from the low water mark, to a height of 10 m above that level. The number of each of the four species in a 1 m² quadrat was recorded.

Plot a **kite graph** of the data for all four species on the grid below. Be sure to choose a scale that takes account of the maximum number found at any one point and allows you to include all the species on the one plot. Include the scale on the diagram so that the number at each point on the kite can be calculated.

### Field data notebook
**Numbers of periwinkles (4 common species) showing vertical distribution on a rocky shore**

Periwinkle species:

| Height above low water (m) | L. littorea | L. saxatalis | L. neritoides | L. littoralis |
|---|---|---|---|---|
| 0-1 | 0 | 0 | 0 | 0 |
| 1-2 | 1 | 0 | 0 | 3 |
| 2-3 | 3 | 0 | 0 | 17 |
| 3-4 | 9 | 3 | 0 | 12 |
| 4-5 | 15 | 12 | 0 | 1 |
| 5-6 | 5 | 24 | 0 | 0 |
| 6-7 | 2 | 9 | 2 | 0 |
| 7-8 | 0 | 2 | 11 | 0 |
| 8-9 | 0 | 0 | 47 | 0 |
| 9-10 | 0 | 0 | 59 | 0 |

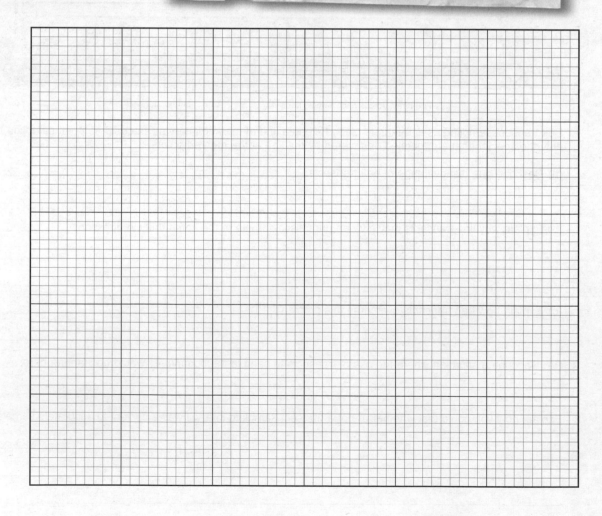

# Mark and Recapture Sampling

The mark and recapture method of estimating population size is used in the study of animal populations where individuals are highly mobile. It is of no value where animals do not move or move very little. The number of animals caught in each sample must be large enough to be valid. The technique is outlined in the diagram below.

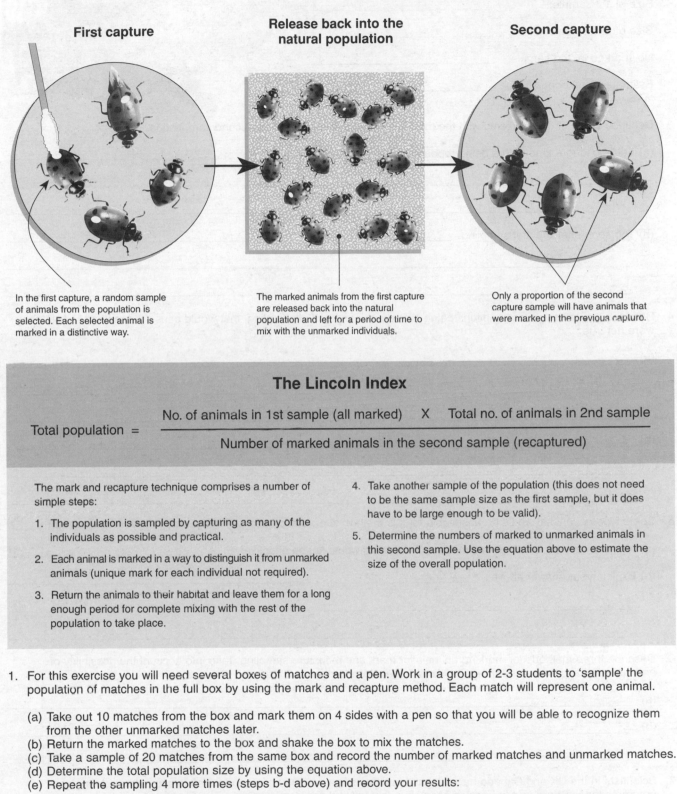

**First capture**

**Release back into the natural population**

**Second capture**

In the first capture, a random sample of animals from the population is selected. Each selected animal is marked in a distinctive way.

The marked animals from the first capture are released back into the natural population and left for a period of time to mix with the unmarked individuals.

Only a proportion of the second capture sample will have animals that were marked in the previous capture.

Practical Ecology

## The Lincoln Index

$$\text{Total population} = \frac{\text{No. of animals in 1st sample (all marked)} \quad X \quad \text{Total no. of animals in 2nd sample}}{\text{Number of marked animals in the second sample (recaptured)}}$$

The mark and recapture technique comprises a number of simple steps:

1. The population is sampled by capturing as many of the individuals as possible and practical.

2. Each animal is marked in a way to distinguish it from unmarked animals (unique mark for each individual not required).

3. Return the animals to their habitat and leave them for a long enough period for complete mixing with the rest of the population to take place.

4. Take another sample of the population (this does not need to be the same sample size as the first sample, but it does have to be large enough to be valid).

5. Determine the numbers of marked to unmarked animals in this second sample. Use the equation above to estimate the size of the overall population.

1. For this exercise you will need several boxes of matches and a pen. Work in a group of 2-3 students to 'sample' the population of matches in the full box by using the mark and recapture method. Each match will represent one animal.

   (a) Take out 10 matches from the box and mark them on 4 sides with a pen so that you will be able to recognize them from the other unmarked matches later.
   (b) Return the marked matches to the box and shake the box to mix the matches.
   (c) Take a sample of 20 matches from the same box and record the number of marked matches and unmarked matches.
   (d) Determine the total population size by using the equation above.
   (e) Repeat the sampling 4 more times (steps b-d above) and record your results:

| | Sample 1 | Sample 2 | Sample 3 | Sample 4 | Sample 5 |
|---|---|---|---|---|---|
| Estimated Population | | | | | |

   (f) Count the actual number of matches in the matchbox : _____

   (g) Compare the actual number to your estimates and state by how much it differs: _____

2. In 1919 a researcher by the name of Dahl wanted to estimate the number of trout in a Norwegian lake. The trout were subject to fishing so it was important to know how big the population was in order to manage the fish stock. He captured and marked 109 trout in his first sample. A few days later, he caught 177 trout in his second sample, of which 57 were marked. Use the **Lincoln index** (on the previous page) to estimate the total population size:

Size of 1st sample: _____

Size of 2nd sample: _____

No. marked in 2nd sample: _____

Estimated total population: _____

3. Describe some of the problems with the mark and recapture method if the second sampling is:

(a) Left too long a time before being repeated: _____

_____

_____

(b) Too soon after the first sampling: _____

_____

_____

4. Describe two important assumptions being made in this method of sampling, that would cause the method to fail if they were not true:

(a) _____

_____

_____

(b) _____

_____

_____

5. Some types of animal would be unsuitable for this method of population estimation (i.e. the method would not work).

(a) Name an animal for which this method of sampling would not be effective: _____

(b) Explain your answer above: _____

_____

_____

6. Describe three methods for marking animals for mark and recapture sampling. Take into account the possibility of animals shedding their skin, or being difficult to get close to again:

(a) _____

(b) _____

(c) _____

7. Scientists in the UK and Canada have, at various times since the 1950s, been involved in computerized tagging programs for Northern cod (a species once abundant in Northern Hemisphere waters but now severely depleted). Describe the type of information that could be obtained through such tagging programs:

_____

_____

_____

# Sampling Animal Populations

Unlike plants, most animals are highly mobile and present special challenges in terms of sampling them **quantitatively** to estimate their distribution and abundance. The equipment available for sampling animals ranges from various types of nets and traps (below), to more complex electronic devices, such as those used for radio-tracking large mobile species.

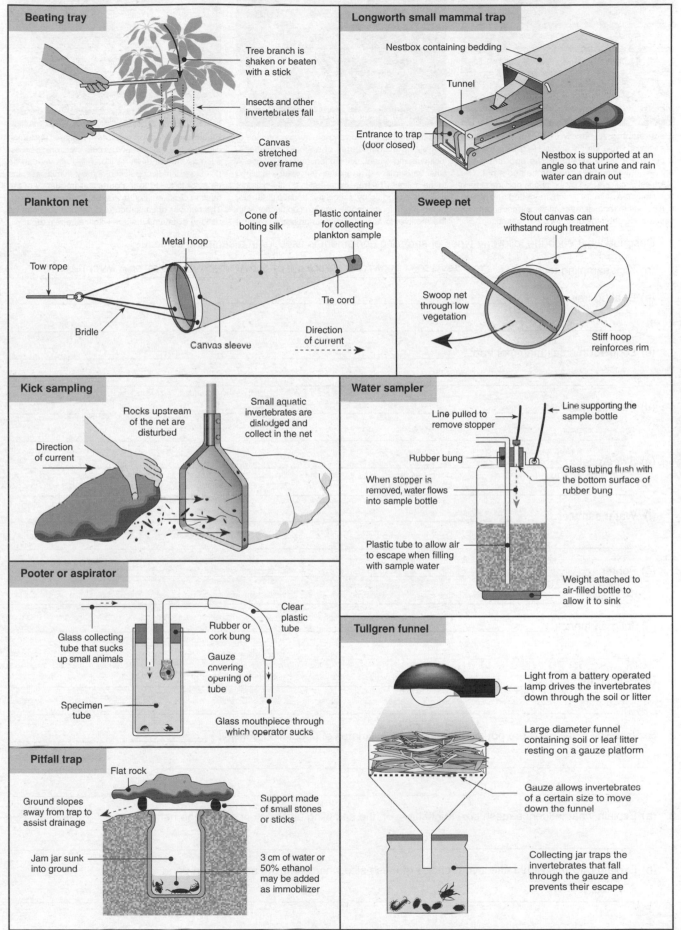

**Beating tray**

- Tree branch is shaken or beaten with a stick
- Insects and other invertebrates fall
- Canvas stretched over frame

**Longworth small mammal trap**

- Nestbox containing bedding
- Tunnel
- Entrance to trap (door closed)
- Nestbox is supported at an angle so that urine and rain water can drain out

**Plankton net**

- Cone of bolting silk
- Plastic container for collecting plankton sample
- Metal hoop
- Tow rope
- Tie cord
- Bridle
- Canvas sleeve
- Direction of current

**Sweep net**

- Stout canvas can withstand rough treatment
- Swoop net through low vegetation
- Stiff hoop reinforces rim

**Kick sampling**

- Rocks upstream of the net are disturbed
- Small aquatic invertebrates are dislodged and collect in the net
- Direction of current

**Water sampler**

- Line pulled to remove stopper
- Line supporting the sample bottle
- Rubber bung
- Glass tubing flush with the bottom surface of rubber bung
- When stopper is removed, water flows into sample bottle
- Plastic tube to allow air to escape when filling with sample water
- Weight attached to air-filled bottle to allow it to sink

**Pooter or aspirator**

- Clear plastic tube
- Rubber or cork bung
- Glass collecting tube that sucks up small animals
- Gauze covering opening of tube
- Specimen tube
- Glass mouthpiece through which operator sucks

**Tullgren funnel**

- Light from a battery operated lamp drives the invertebrates down through the soil or litter
- Large diameter funnel containing soil or leaf litter resting on a gauze platform
- Gauze allows invertebrates of a certain size to move down the funnel
- Collecting jar traps the invertebrates that fall through the gauze and prevents their escape

**Pitfall trap**

- Flat rock
- Ground slopes away from trap to assist drainage
- Support made of small stones or sticks
- Jam jar sunk into ground
- 3 cm of water or 50% ethanol may be added as immobilizer

*Practical Ecology*

**Related activities**: Density and Distribution

RA 2

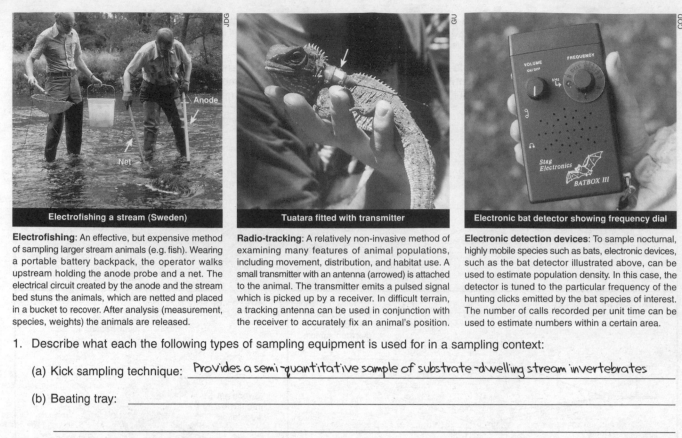

**Electrofishing a stream (Sweden)**

**Tuatara fitted with transmitter**

**Electronic bat detector showing frequency dial**

**Electrofishing**: An effective, but expensive method of sampling larger stream animals (e.g. fish). Wearing a portable battery backpack, the operator walks upstream holding the anode probe and a net. The electrical circuit created by the anode and the stream bed stuns the animals, which are netted and placed in a bucket to recover. After analysis (measurement, species, weights) the animals are released.

**Radio-tracking**: A relatively non-invasive method of examining many features of animal populations, including movement, distribution, and habitat use. A small transmitter with an antenna (arrowed) is attached to the animal. The transmitter emits a pulsed signal which is picked up by a receiver. In difficult terrain, a tracking antenna can be used in conjunction with the receiver to accurately fix an animal's position.

**Electronic detection devices**: To sample nocturnal, highly mobile species such as bats, electronic devices, such as the bat detector illustrated above, can be used to estimate population density. In this case, the detector is tuned to the particular frequency of the hunting clicks emitted by the bat species of interest. The number of calls recorded per unit time can be used to estimate numbers within a certain area.

1. Describe what each the following types of sampling equipment is used for in a sampling context:

    (a) Kick sampling technique: _Provides a semi-quantitative sample of substrate-dwelling stream invertebrates_

    (b) Beating tray: _____

    _____

    (c) Longworth small mammal trap: _____

    _____

    (d) Plankton net: _____

    _____

    (e) Sweep net: _____

    (f) Water sampler: _____

    (g) Pooter: _____

    _____

    (h) Tullgren funnel: _____

    _____

    (i) Pitfall trap: _____

    _____

2. Explain why pitfall traps are not recommended for estimates of population density: _____

    _____

    _____

3. (a) Explain what influence mesh size might have on the sampling efficiency of a plankton net: _____

    _____

    (b) Explain how this would affect your choice of mesh size when sampling animals in a pond: _____

    _____

    _____

# Human Impact and Conservation

| IB SL | IB HL | IB Options | AP Biology |
|---|---|---|---|
| Complete: 1-3, 17-18 | Complete: 1-3, 17-18 | Complete: Option G: SL/HL: 4, 6, 8-16 HL: 4, 22-25, 27 | Complete: 1-28 Some numbers extension as appropriate |

## Learning Objectives

☐ 1. Compile your own glossary from the **KEY WORDS** displayed in **bold type** in the learning objectives below.

### Humans and Ecosystems (pages 369-370, 374)

☐ 2. <u>Background</u>: Appreciate that the impact of humans on the global environment is the result of resource use, rapid population growth, large population size, and disproportionate distribution of resources.

☐ 3. Outline two local or global examples of human induced damage to an ecosystem. One example should be the enhanced greenhouse effect. In your examples:
   • Discuss the causes and effects of the human impact.
   • Describe measures for preventing or reducing the effects of the impact.

☐ 4. Explain the use of **diversity indices** in community ecology. Calculate and use a common **diversity index**, such as the **Simpson's diversity index**, to analyze and compare two local communities. If required, explain the use of **biotic indices** (including **indicator species**) in monitoring environmental change.

### Threats to Biodiversity (pages 379-382, 387-389)

☐ 5. Explain the relationship between **diversity** and ecosystem **stability**. Recognize the role of **keystone species** in ecosystem function and discuss the possible consequences of removing these species.

☐ 6. Identify regions of naturally-occurring high **biodiversity** and describe the importance of these regions to global ecology. Using **rainforests** as an example, discuss the ethical, ecological, economic, and esthetic reasons for the conservation of biodiversity.

☐ 7. Discuss the causes and effects of **deforestation**, emphasizing the impact on the **biodiversity** and stability of forest ecosystems, and on carbon and nitrogen cycling. Identify regions (globally or locally) where deforestation is a major problem.

☐ 8. Discuss the impact of **alien species** on ecosystems and suggest why alien species are also often **invasive species**. Include reference to the effects of interspecific competition, predation, and extinction of native species.

☐ 9. Describe examples where the introduction of an alien species has had a significant impact on ecosystem function. Include one example of **biological control**, and one accidental and one deliberate introduction.

### Methods of Pest Control (pages 387-388 and the TRC: Human Impact Supplement)

☐ 10. Describe one or more examples of **biological control** of invasive species. Understand the basic principles of biological control and recognize the precautions that should be taken to guard against the biological control agent itself becoming a problem. Cite examples where this has occurred.

☐ 11. Distinguish between **chemical pest control** and biological control (see #10). Appreciate the biological and ethical issues surrounding these two methods of pest control. Consider the efficacy of the control, the environmental risks, economic costs, long term sustainability, and availability of alternatives.

☐ 12. With respect to chemical pest control, understand the terms: **persistence**, **toxicity**, **bioaccumulation**, and **specificity** (to the pest). Using an example, explain the causes and consequences of bioaccumulation.

### Air Pollution (page 371 and the TRC)

☐ 13. Discuss causes of **atmospheric pollution**. For each, identify its effect on the environment. Recognize **acid rain**, **global warming**, and stratospheric **ozone depletion** as consequences of atmospheric pollution.

### Stratospheric ozone depletion (pages 377-378)

☐ 14. Describe the role of the atmospheric (strictly stratospheric) ozone in absorbing ultraviolet (UV) radiation. Outline the effects of UV radiation on living tissues and on biological productivity.

☐ 15. Explain what is meant by **stratospheric ozone depletion**. Identify the agents implicated in its destruction, including reference to the effect of **chlorine** on the ozone layer. Describe the likely long term environmental effects of stratospheric ozone depletion.

☐ 16. Discuss measures to reduce the rate of ozone depletion. Emphasize methods for reducing the manufacture and release of ozone-depleting chemicals.

### Global warming (pages 375-376)

☐ 17. Explain what is meant by the terms **greenhouse effect** and **global warming**. Outline the main causes of the increase in greenhouse gases and discuss the impact of rising global temperatures on ecosystems.

☐ 18. Outline the **precautionary principle** as it relates to the enhanced greenhouse effect. Discuss measures that could be taken to reduce global warming or its impact. Consider both short and long term measures and comment on the feasibility of these.

### Water Pollution (pages 371-372, 373-374)

☐ 19. Describe causes and effects of **water pollution**, distinguishing between point and diffuse sources for water pollutants. Describe the effects of **organic effluent** (e.g. sewage or milk) and **fertilizer run-off** (nitrates and phosphates) on aquatic ecosystems. Include reference to any of: water quality, **biochemical oxygen demand**, effects on biodiversity, **eutrophication** and algal blooms, spread of pathogens, and (toxic) nitrate load in the groundwater.

20. Discuss measures for preventing, reducing, or mitigating water pollution, e.g. sewage treatment.

21. Appreciate that country-specific legislation provides water quality standards for different water uses.

## Conservation of Biodiversity (pages 383-386)

22. Identify factors that cause species to become **endangered**. Describe an example of a locally or globally endangered species, describe its conservation status and management (see #25).

23. Recognize **extinction** as a possible consequence of a species reaching endangered status. Outline the features contributing to the extinction of one named animal species, e.g. dodo or passenger pigeon.

24. Outline the biogeographical features of nature reserves that contribute to the conservation of biodiversity.

25. Using examples, discuss the advantages and application of the following conservation measures:
   - *In-situ* conservation methods such as protection and restoration of parks and reserves.
   - **Active management** of nature reserves, including control of alien species, **habitat restoration**, control of human exploitation, and **species recovery plans**.

- *Ex-situ* conservation methods such as **captive breeding** (and release) of animals, **botanic gardens**, and **seed** and sperm (gene) **banks**.
- The actions of international agencies (CITES, WWF).

## Sustainability of Resources (pages 390-392 and the TRC: Human Impact Supplement)

26. Explain the importance of **conserving resources** for now and for the future. Using examples (#27-29), describe how resources can be managed for long term sustainability and minimal impact on ecosystems.

27. Discuss fishing as an example of harvesting from a natural ecosystem. Describing an example, identify key aspects of fisheries management, including the significance of **maximum sustainable yield** in conserving fish stocks. Recognize how **by-catch** threatens marine ecosystems and discuss international measures to promote the conservation of fish stocks.

28. Discuss the view of solid waste as a potential resource (in part) and describe methods for waste management, including reducing waste and recycling organic waste and valuable commodities such as paper and glass.

See the 'Textbook Reference Grid' on pages 8-9 for textbook page references relating to material in this topic.

### Supplementary Texts

See pages 5-6 for additional details of these texts:
- Adds, J. *et al.*, 2004. **Exchange & Transport, Energy & Ecosystems** (NelsonThornes), chpt. 8-9.
- Adds, J., *et al.*, 2004. **Genetics, Evolution and Biodiversity**, (NelsonThornes), chpt. 5 (UK).
- Miller G.T. Jr., 2007. **Essentials of Ecology** (Thomson Brooks/Cole), chpt. 1, 10-13.

See page 6 for details of publishers of periodicals:

### STUDENT'S REFERENCE

- **Global Warming** Time, special issue, 2007. *A special issue on global warming: the causes, perils, solutions, and actions. Comprehensive and well illustrated, this account provide up-to-date information at a readable level.*
- **The Big Thaw** National Geographic, Sept. 2004, pp. 12-75. *A significant part of a special issue providing an account of the state of global warming and climate change.*
- **Water Pressure** National Geographic, Sept. 2002, pp. 2-33. *The demand for freshwater for human consumption and hygiene and the problems associated with increased pressure on supplies.*
- **Biodiversity and Ecosystems** Biol. Sci. Rev., 11(4) March 1999, pp. 18-21. *The importance of biodiversity to ecosystem stability and sustainability.*
- **Unlocking the Climate Puzzle** National Geographic, 193(5) May 1998, pp. 38-71. *Earth's climate, including global warming & desertification.*
- **Biodiversity: Taking Stock of Life** National Geographic, 195(2) Feb. 1999 (entire issue). *Special issue exploring the Earth's biodiversity and what we can do to preserve it.*
- **The Greenhouse Effect** New Scientist, 13 July 1996 (Inside Science). *An excellent summary of the causes and effects of greenhouse gases.*

- **The Forest Decline Mystery: Is Acid Rain the Killer?** Biol. Sci. Rev., 13(2) Nov. 2000, pp. 10-14. *Acid rain in Europe: how it is formed and its impact.*
- **Tropical Rainforest Regeneration** Biol. Sci. Rev., 17(2) Nov. 2004, pp. 34-37. *Tropical rainforests: causes of and reasons for their destruction, and the role of the many complex biotic interactions in forest regeneration.*
- **Tropical Rainforests: Conservation or Preservation?** Biol. Sci. Rev., 20(2) Nov. 2007, pp. 34-37. *Protected areas may not be adequate to preserve tropical rainforests. The answer to preservation may lie instead in reduced impact logging and better systems of sustainable management for rainforests.*
- **In Search of Solutions** National Geographic, Feb. 1999, pp. 72-87. *The impact of deforestation and measures possible to restore the damage.*
- **Attack of the Alien Invaders** National Geographic, March 2005, pp. 92-117. *The 'blender effect' which occurs all over the world, i.e. animals and plants that have evolved somewhere else are turning up where they are not wanted.*
- **Still Waters: The Global Fish Crisis** National Geographic, April 2007, pp. 32-99. *Four feature articles examining the decline in world fish stocks. Current, relevant, readable and well illustrated.*

### TEACHER'S REFERENCE

- **Can Sustainable Management Save Tropical Rainforests?** Scientific American, April 1997, pp. 34-39. *The difficulties of sustainable management of rainforests and the implications for conservation.*
- **How Did Humans First Alter Global Climate?** Scientific American, March 2005, pp. 34-41. *A bold new hypothesis suggests that humans began altering the global climate thousands of years before their more recent use of fossil fuels.*
- **Tropical Forests for Sale!** The Am. Biology Teacher, 60(9), Nov. 1998, pp. 677-680. *A simulation to increase awareness of the difficulties of tropical rainforest conservation.*
- **The Impact of Habitat Fragmentation on Arthropod Biodiversity** The Am. Biology Teacher, 62(6), June 2000, pp. 414-420. *An account of experimental work to investigate the impact of human activity on arthropod populations.*
- **Time to Rethink Everything** New Scientist, 27 April-18 May 2002 (4 issues). *Globalization, the impact of humans, & the sustainability of our future.*
- **Abrupt Climate Change** Scientific American, Nov. 2004, pp. 40-47. *Slow, steady changes to ambient conditions may push major climate drivers, such as ocean currents, to a critical point, triggering sudden and dramatic shifts in climate.*

- **All Wrapped Up in Kudzu and Other Ecological Disasters** The Am. Biology Teacher, 61(1), Jan., 1999, pp. 42-46. *The impact of alien species: scenarios for students to analyze.*
- **The Last Menageries** New Scientist, 19 Jan. 2002, pp. 40-43. *The role of zoos today in conservation, education, and research.*
- **Counting the Last Fish** Scientific American, July 2003, pp. 34-39. *Overfishing has reduced the world's fish stocks to an all time low. There is an urgent need for effective, cooperative management.*
- **The Case of the Missing Anurans** The Am. Biology Teacher, 63(9), Nov. 2001, pp. 670-676. *The threat to the world's frog populations; an article investigating threatened species decline.*
- **Kicking the Habit** New Scientist, 25 Nov. 2000, pp. 34-42. *The pressing need for alternative fuels.*

See pages 10-11 for details of how to access **Bio Links** from our web site: **www.thebiozone.com** From Bio Links, access sites under the topics:

**BIODIVERSITY: Biodiversity:** • Ecology and biodiversity • What are biodiversity hotspots

**CONSERVATION: > Endangered Species:** • Endangered species • WWF Endangered species ... *and others* > **Habitat Loss:** • Causes of habitat loss and species endangerment • Rainforest Information Centre... *and others* > **Conservation Issues:** • CITES • WWF ... *and others*

**HUMAN IMPACT:** • Human alteration of the global nitrogen cycle ... *and others* > **Pollution:** • USEPA Student Center • Pollution online > **Global Warming:** • CO₂ information analysis center • The EPA global warming site ... *and others* > **Ozone depletion:** • Ozone depletion resource center ... *and others* > **RESOURCE MANAGEMENT & AGRICULTURE** > **Fisheries and Aquaculture:** • NOAA Fisheries

**Presentation MEDIA** to support this topic:
**ECOLOGY:**
- **Biodiversity & Conservation**
- **Human Impact**

# Human Impact on Resources

During the past 100 years, human impact on the natural world has increased dramatically as the scope and intensity of human activities have increased. Although there has been progress in solving pollution problems in some countries, many negative trends continue. Unresolved problems include the loss of tropical forests, the buildup of greenhouse gases, and the loss of biodiversity. The world population, now at 6.6 billion, is growing at the rate of about 80 million per year. This growth is slower than predicted but the world population is still expected to increase substantially before stabilizing. Projections put world population at between 8 and 12 billion in 2050, with nearly all of this growth expected in the developing world (below).

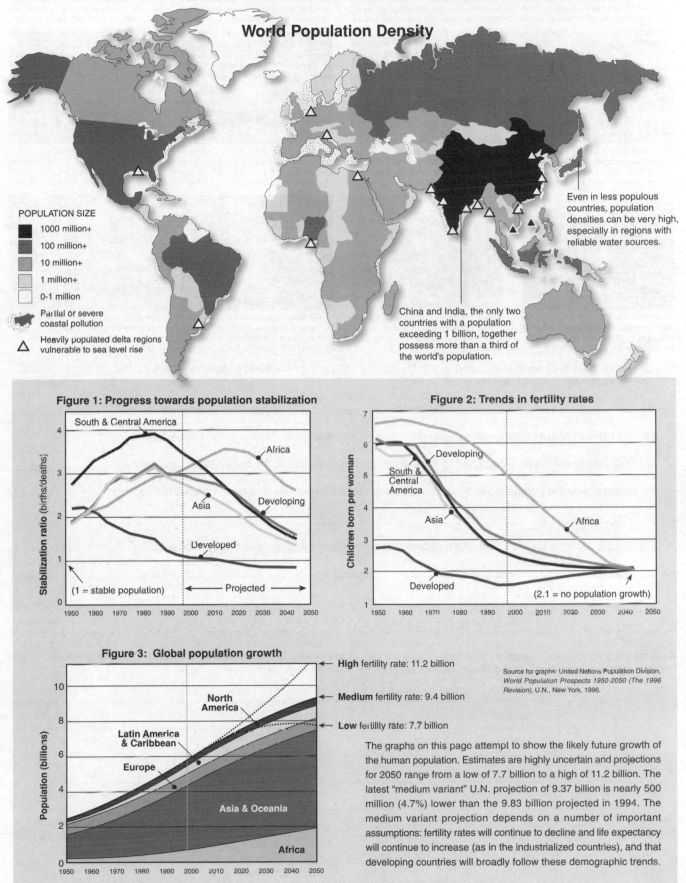

**World Population Density**

POPULATION SIZE
- 1000 million+
- 100 million+
- 10 million+
- 1 million+
- 0-1 million

Partial or severe coastal pollution

△ Heavily populated delta regions vulnerable to sea level rise

Even in less populous countries, population densities can be very high, especially in regions with reliable water sources.

China and India, the only two countries with a population exceeding 1 billion, together possess more than a third of the world's population.

**Figure 1: Progress towards population stabilization**

South & Central America, Africa, Asia, Developing, Developed

Stabilization ratio (births/deaths)

(1 = stable population)    ← Projected →

**Figure 2: Trends in fertility rates**

Children born per woman

Developing, South & Central America, Asia, Africa, Developed

(2.1 = no population growth)

**Figure 3: Global population growth**

Population (billions)

North America, Latin America & Caribbean, Europe, Asia & Oceania, Africa

← **High** fertility rate: 11.2 billion

← **Medium** fertility rate: 9.4 billion

← **Low** fertility rate: 7.7 billion

Source for graphs: United Nations Population Division, *World Population Prospects 1950-2050 (The 1996 Revision)*, U.N., New York, 1996.

The graphs on this page attempt to show the likely future growth of the human population. Estimates are highly uncertain and projections for 2050 range from a low of 7.7 billion to a high of 11.2 billion. The latest "medium variant" U.N. projection of 9.37 billion is nearly 500 million (4.7%) lower than the 9.83 billion projected in 1994. The medium variant projection depends on a number of important assumptions: fertility rates will continue to decline and life expectancy will continue to increase (as in the industrialized countries), and that developing countries will broadly follow these demographic trends.

Human Impact and Conservation

**Related activities**: Pollution, Global Warming, Loss of Biodiversity, Tropical Deforestation, Ecological Impacts of Fishing

RDA 2

Air pollution contributes to global warming, ozone depletion and acid rain, and is set to increase markedly in some third world countries in the next 30 years.

Global water consumption is rising rapidly. The availability of water is likely to become one of the most pressing resource issues of the 21st Century.

Combustion engine emissions, plaguing the West with pollution, are increasing rapidly in Asia as their economies develop and become more affluent.

Global energy use has increased by 70% since 1970 and will increase 2% annually over the next 15 years. Using fossil fuels will raise greenhouse gases by 50%.

Global climate change due to the greenhouse effect will cause a rise in sea level and threaten coastal populations such as those in Bangladesh (above).

In industrialized societies, a person consumes many tonnes of raw materials each year, which must be extracted, processed and disposed of as waste.

Aquatic environments such as coral reefs and freshwater habitats in lakes, rivers and wetlands are at risk (58% of the worlds reefs and 34% of all fish species).

Threats to biodiversity from all sources are quickly reaching a critical level. Current extinction rates are 100 to 1000 times higher than prehuman levels.

Consumption of natural resources by modern industrial economies remains very high, in the range of 45 to 85 tonnes per person annually.

Forest fires and logging continue to shrink world forests. Deforestation in the Amazon doubled from 1994 to 1995 before declining in 1996.

Overfishing of fish stocks to levels where they may not recover for many decades has occurred in many fishing grounds (e.g. cod fishing in the North Atlantic).

Although food production is generally adequate to meet human needs there are problems with distribution. Some 800 million people remain undernourished.

1. The future growth of world population is highly uncertain. State the estimated population levels for the year 2050, based on low, moderate and high fertility rates:

   (a) Low: _____ (b) Moderate: _____ (c) High: _____

2. Fertility rates of populations for all geographic regions are predicted to decline in the next 50 years.

   (a) State which continent is predicted to have the highest fertility rate at the beginning of next century: _____

   (b) Suggest why the population of this region is slower to achieve a low fertility rate than other regions: _____

   _____

3. Explain the reasons for high population densities in delta regions and discuss the problems associated with this:

   _____

   _____

   _____

4. Shrinking freshwater resources and lack of fuel are two of the most pressing resource issues for the 21st Century. Investigate one of these and discuss why it has become such an important issue:

   _____

   _____

   _____

   _____

   _____

   _____

   _____

   _____

# Pollution

Any addition to the air, water, soil, or food that threatens the survival, health, or activities of organisms is called **pollution**. **Pollutants** can enter the environment naturally (e.g. from volcanic eruptions) or through human activities. Most pollution from human activity occurs in or around urban and industrial areas and regions of industrialized agriculture. Pollutants may come from single identifiable **point sources**, such as power plants, or they may enter the environment from non-point or **diffuse sources**, such as through land runoff. While pollutants often contaminate the areas where they are produced, they can also be carried by wind or water to other areas. Commonly

recognized forms of pollution include air pollution, water pollution, and soil contamination, but other less obvious forms of pollution, including light and noise pollution, are also the result of concentrations of human activity. Some global phenomena, such as **global warming** and **ozone depletion** are the result of human pollution of the Earth's stratosphere. Toxic pollutants are also found accumulating within the human body. These include older chemicals such as DDT and PCBs, heavy metals and dioxins, newer pesticides and plastic ingredients, and flame-retarding substances called PBDEs, all of which contribute to the chemical 'body burden' that resides in all of us (see over page).

## Sources and Effects of Pollution

**Soil contamination** occurs via chemical spills, leaching, or leakage from underground storage. The runoff from open-caste mining operations can be loaded with heavy metals such as mercury, cadmium, and arsenic.

**Sewage:** Water containing human wastes, soaps and detergents, pathogens, and toxins are discharged into waterways and the sea. Most communities apply some level of waste water treatment at sewage treatment facilities.

Power plants and industrial emissions are a major source of air pollution. $SO_2$ and $NO_2$ from these primary sources mix with water vapor in the atmophere to form acids which may be deposited as rain, snow, or dry acid.

Fertilizers, herbicides, and pesticides are major contaminants of soil and water in areas where agriculture is industrialized. Fertilizer runoff and leaching adds large quantities of nitrogen and phosphorus to waterways and leads to accelerated **eutrophication**.

Mining and processing of radioactive metals may result in radioactive discharges into waterways. Accidents at nuclear power plants, such as at Chornobyl in 1986, (above) can cause widespread radioactive contamination which persists for long periods of time.

Automobiles are the single most important contributor of air pollutants in large cities, producing large amounts of carbon monoxide, hydrocarbons, and nitrous oxides. Ozone and smog are created as nitrogen oxides and hydrocarbons react to sunlight.

1. For each of the following forms of pollution, identify the source of the pollution and summarize its effects.

(a) Accelerated nutrient enrichment and eutrophication of waterways: _____

_____

(b) Acid deposition: _____

_____

(c) Smog and ozone: _____

_____

(d) Radioactive waste: _____

_____

(e) Heavy metals: _____

_____

**Related activities**: Monitoring Change in an Ecosystem, Global Warming, Stratospheric Ozone Depletion, Pest Control

**RA 2**

**Human Impact and Conservation**

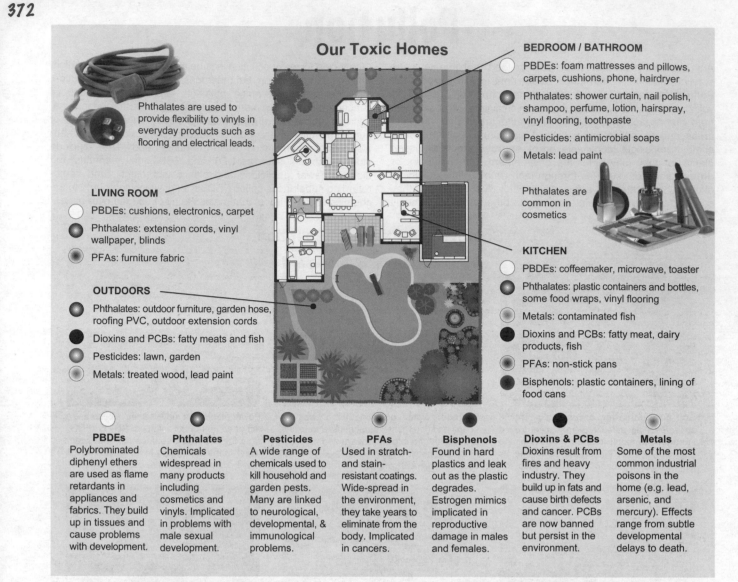

## Our Toxic Homes

Phthalates are used to provide flexibility to vinyls in everyday products such as flooring and electrical leads.

**BEDROOM / BATHROOM**
- PBDEs: foam mattresses and pillows, carpets, cushions, phone, hairdryer
- Phthalates: shower curtain, nail polish, shampoo, perfume, lotion, hairspray, vinyl flooring, toothpaste
- Pesticides: antimicrobial soaps
- Metals: lead paint

Phthalates are common in cosmetics

**LIVING ROOM**
- PBDEs: cushions, electronics, carpet
- Phthalates: extension cords, vinyl wallpaper, blinds
- PFAs: furniture fabric

**KITCHEN**
- PBDEs: coffeemaker, microwave, toaster
- Phthalates: plastic containers and bottles, some food wraps, vinyl flooring
- Metals: contaminated fish
- Dioxins and PCBs: fatty meat, dairy products, fish
- PFAs: non-stick pans
- Bisphenols: plastic containers, lining of food cans

**OUTDOORS**
- Phthalates: outdoor furniture, garden hose, roofing PVC, outdoor extension cords
- Dioxins and PCBs: fatty meats and fish
- Pesticides: lawn, garden
- Metals: treated wood, lead paint

**PBDEs**
Polybrominated diphenyl ethers are used as flame retardants in appliances and fabrics. They build up in tissues and cause problems with development.

**Phthalates**
Chemicals widespread in many products including cosmetics and vinyls. Implicated in problems with male sexual development.

**Pesticides**
A wide range of chemicals used to kill household and garden pests. Many are linked to neurological, developmental, & immunological problems.

**PFAs**
Used in stratch- and stain-resistant coatings. Wide-spread in the environment, they take years to eliminate from the body. Implicated in cancers.

**Bisphenols**
Found in hard plastics and leak out as the plastic degrades. Estrogen mimics implicated in reproductive damage in males and females.

**Dioxins & PCBs**
Dioxins result from fires and heavy industry. They build up in fats and cause birth defects and cancer. PCBs are now banned but persist in the environment.

**Metals**
Some of the most common industrial poisons in the home (e.g. lead, arsenic, and mercury). Effects range from subtle developmental delays to death.

2. Explain why pollution from non-point sources is more difficult to identify and control than pollution from point sources:

_____

_____

3. Summarize the main sources of pollution in your home and discuss measures that could be taken to protect against further human contamination:

_____

_____

_____

_____

_____

4. Identify one important source of environmental pollution in your region and discuss its causes and effects, as well as any measures to control the pollution or mitigate against environmental damage:

_____

_____

_____

_____

_____

_____

# Monitoring Change in an Ecosystem

Much of the importance we place on ecosystem change stems ultimately from what we want from that ecosystem. Ecosystems are monitored for changes in their status so that their usefulness can be maintained, whether that use is for agriculture, industry, recreation, or conservation. Never is this so apparent as in the monitoring of aquatic ecosystems. Aquatic environments of all types provide aesthetic pleasure, food, habitat for wildlife, water for industry and irrigation, and potable water. The different uses of aquatic environments demand different standards of **water quality**. For any water body, this is defined in terms of various chemical, physical, and biological characteristics. Together, these factors define the 'health' of the aquatic ecosystem and its suitability for various desirable uses. Water quality is determined by measurement or analysis on-site or in the laboratory. Other methods, involving the use of **indicator species**, can also be used to biologically assess the health of a water body.

## Techniques for Monitoring Water Quality

Some aspects of water quality, such as black disk clarity measurements (above), must be made in the field.

The collection of water samples allows many quality measurements to be carried out in the laboratory.

Telemetry stations transmit continuous measurements of the water level of a lake or river to a central control office.

Temperature and dissolved oxygen measurements must be carried out directly in the flowing water.

All Photos EW

## Water Quality Standards in Aquatic Ecosystems

| Water quality variable | Why measured | Standards applied: |
|---|---|---|
| **Dissolved oxygen** | • A requirement for most aquatic life<br>• Indicator of organic pollution<br>• Indicator of photosynthesis (plant growth) | More than 80% saturation **(F, FS, SG)**<br>More than 5 $gm^{-3}$ **(WS)** |
| **Temperature** | • Organisms have specific temperature needs<br>• Indicator of mixing processes<br>• Computer modeling examining the uptake and release of nutrients | Less than 25°C **(F)**<br>Less than 3°C change along **(AE, F,**<br>a stretch of river **FS, SG)** |
| **Conductivity** | • Indicator of total salts dissolved in water<br>• Indicator for geothermal input | |
| **pH (acidity)** | • Aquatic life protection<br>• Indicator of industrial discharges, mining | Between pH 6 - 9 **(WS)** |
| **Clarity** - turbidity<br>- black disk | • Aesthetic appearance<br>• Aquatic life protection<br>• Indicator of catchment condition, land use | Turbidity: 2 NTU<br>Black disk: more than 1.6 m **(AE, CR, A)** |
| **Color** - light absorption | • Aesthetic appearance<br>• Light availability for excessive plant growth<br>• Indicator of presence of organic matter | |
| **Nutrients**<br>(Nitrogen and phosphorus) | • Enrichment, excessive plant growth<br>• Limiting factor for plant and algal growth | DIN: less than 0.100 $gm^{-3}$<br>DRP: less than 0.030 $gm^{-3}$ **(AE, A)**<br>$NO_3^-$: less than 10 $gm^{-3}$ **(WS)** |
| **Major ions**<br>($Mg^{2+}$, $Ca^{2+}$, $Na^+$, $K^+$,<br>$Cl^-$, $HCO_3^-$, $SO_4^{2-}$) | • Baseline water quality characteristics<br>• Indicator for catchment soil types, geology<br>• Water hardness (magnesium/calcium)<br>• Buffering capacity for pH change ($HCO_3^-$) | |
| **Organic carbon** | • Indicator of organic pollution<br>• Catchment characteristics | BOD: less than 5 $gm^{-3}$ **(AE, CR, A)** |
| **Fecal bacteria** | • Indicator of pollution with fecal matter<br>• Disease risk for swimming etc. | ENT: less than 33 $cm^{-3}$ **(CR)**<br>FC: less than 200 $cm^{-3}$ |

Fly fishing is a pursuit which demands high water quality.

Spawning salmon require high oxygen levels for egg survival.

**Standards** refer to specified water uses: **AE** = aquatic ecosystem protection, **A** = aesthetic, **CR** = contact recreation, **SG** = shellfish gathering, **WS** = water supply, **F** = fishery, **FS** = fish spawning, **SW** = stock watering.

**Key to abbreviations:** NTU = a unit of measurement for turbidity, DIN = dissolved inorganic nitrogen, DRP = dissolved reactive phosphorus, BOD = biochemical oxygen demand, ENT = enterococci, FC = fecal coliform.

1. Explain why dissolved oxygen, temperature, and clarity measurements are made in the field rather than in the laboratory:

_____

_____

Human Impact and Conservation

**Related activities:** Monitoring Physical Factors, Ecosystem Stability

DA 2

## Calculation and Use of Diversity Indices

One of the best ways to determine the health of an ecosystem is to measure the variety (rather than the absolute number) of organisms living in it. Certain species, called **indicator species**, are typical of ecosystems in a particular state (e.g. polluted or pristine). An objective evaluation of an ecosystem's biodiversity can provide valuable insight into its status, particularly if the species assemblages have changed as a result of disturbance.

Diversity can be quantified using a **diversity index (DI)**. Diversity indices attempt to quantify the degree of diversity and identify indicators for environmental stress or degradation. Most indices of diversity are easy to use and they are widely used in ecological work, particularly for monitoring ecosystem change or pollution. One example, which is a derivation of **Simpson's index**, is described below. Other indices produce values ranging between 0 and almost 1. These are more easily interpreted because of the more limited range of values, but no single index offers the "best" measure of diversity: they are chosen on their suitability to different situations.

### Simpson's Index for finite populations

This diversity index (DI) is a commonly used inversion of Simpson's index, suitable for finite populations.

$$DI = \frac{N(N - 1)}{\Sigma n(n - 1)}$$

*After Smith and Smith as per IOB.*

Where:

$DI$ = Diversity index

$N$ = Total number of individuals (of all species) in the sample

$n$ = Number of individuals of each species in the sample

This index ranges between 1 (low diversity) and infinity. The higher the value, the greater the variety of living organisms. It can be difficult to evaluate objectively without reference to some standard ecosystem measure because the values calculated can, in theory, go to infinity.

## Example of species diversity in a stream

The example describes the results from a survey of stream invertebrates. The species have been identified, but this is not necessary in order to calculate diversity as long as the different species can be distinguished. Calculation of the DI using Simpson's index for finite populations is:

| Species | No. of individuals |
|---|---|
| A (Common backswimmer) | 12 |
| B (Stonefly larva) | 7 |
| C (Silver water beetle) | 2 |
| D (Caddis fly larva) | 6 |
| E (Water spider) | 5 |
| **Total number of individuals = 32** | |

$$DI = \frac{32 \times 31}{(12 \times 11) + (7 \times 6) + (2 \times 1) + (6 \times 5) + (5 \times 4)} = \frac{992}{226} = 4.39$$

A stream community with a high macroinvertebrate diversity (above) in contrast to a low diversity stream community (below).

Photos: Stephen Moore

2. Discuss the link between water quality and land use: _____

_____

_____

_____

3. Describe a situation where a species diversity index may provide useful information: _____

_____

_____

4. An area of forest floor was sampled and six invertebrate species were recorded, with counts of 7, 10, 11, 2, 4, and 3 individuals. Using Simpson's index for finite populations, calculate DI for this community:

(a) DI= _____     DI = _____

(b) Comment on the diversity of this community: _____

_____

_____

5. Explain how you could use indicator species to detect pollution in a stream: _____

_____

_____

# Global Warming

The Earth's atmosphere comprises a mixture of gases including nitrogen, oxygen, and water vapor. Also present are small quantities of carbon dioxide, methane, and a number of other trace gases. The **greenhouse effect** is a natural phenomenon caused by the release of **greenhouse gases**, which act as a thermal blanket in the atmosphere, letting in sunlight, but trapping the heat that would normally radiate back into space. About 75% of the natural greenhouse effect is due to water vapor. The next most significant contributor is carbon dioxide. In the past, our climate has shifted between periods of stable warm conditions to cycles of ice ages and 'interglacials'. The current period of warming is explained in part by recovery after the last

ice age 10 000 years ago. However there are many indications that climate warming is accelerating and that this acceleration is partly the result of human activity, in particular, the release of greenhouse gases into the atmosphere. Recent data from the UN Environment Programme, based on studies of glaciers across nine mountain ranges, indicates that average glacial shrinkage is accelerating. Moreover, the rates of summer melting of Arctic ice are exceeding early predictions, leading to new forecasts predicting an ice-free Arctic by as early as 2013. Ice sheet shrinkage has a feedback effect too, because ice increases the amount of heat reflected back from the Earth. The effect of global warming on the Earth' systems is likely to be considerable.

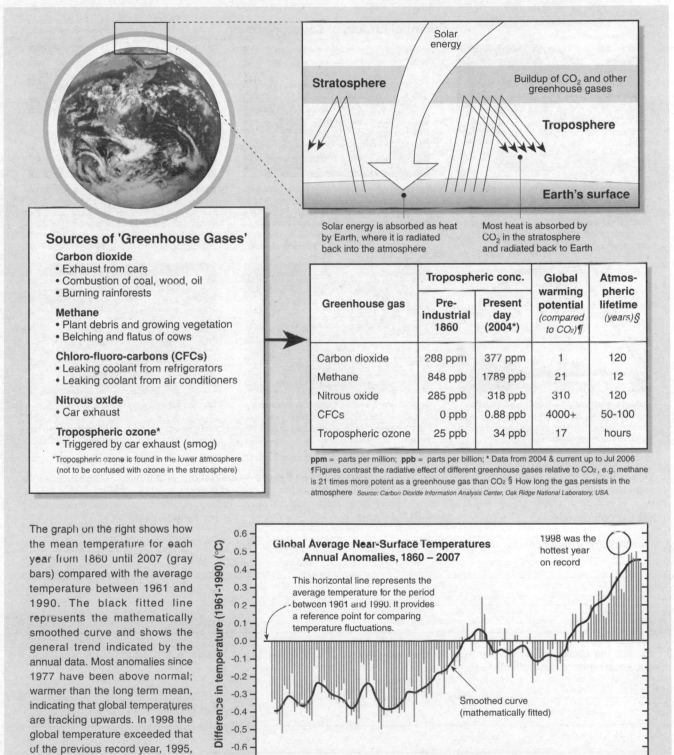

**Sources of 'Greenhouse Gases'**

**Carbon dioxide**
• Exhaust from cars
• Combustion of coal, wood, oil
• Burning rainforests

**Methane**
• Plant debris and growing vegetation
• Belching and flatus of cows

**Chloro-fluoro-carbons (CFCs)**
• Leaking coolant from refrigerators
• Leaking coolant from air conditioners

**Nitrous oxide**
• Car exhaust

**Tropospheric ozone\***
• Triggered by car exhaust (smog)

*\*Tropospheric ozone is found in the lower atmosphere (not to be confused with ozone in the stratosphere)*

Solar energy is absorbed as heat by Earth, where it is radiated back into the atmosphere

Most heat is absorbed by $CO_2$ in the stratosphere and radiated back to Earth

| Greenhouse gas | Tropospheric conc. | | Global warming potential (compared to $CO_2$)¶ | Atmos-pheric lifetime (years)§ |
|---|---|---|---|---|
| | Pre-industrial 1860 | Present day (2004\*) | | |
| Carbon dioxide | 288 ppm | 377 ppm | 1 | 120 |
| Methane | 848 ppb | 1789 ppb | 21 | 12 |
| Nitrous oxide | 285 ppb | 318 ppb | 310 | 120 |
| CFCs | 0 ppb | 0.88 ppb | 4000+ | 50-100 |
| Tropospheric ozone | 25 ppb | 34 ppb | 17 | hours |

**ppm** = parts per million; **ppb** = parts per billion; \* Data from 2004 & current up to Jul 2006 ¶Figures contrast the radiative effect of different greenhouse gases relative to $CO_2$, e.g. methane is 21 times more potent as a greenhouse gas than $CO_2$ § How long the gas persists in the atmosphere  *Source: Carbon Dioxide Information Analysis Center, Oak Ridge National Laboratory, USA.*

The graph on the right shows how the mean temperature for each year from 1860 until 2007 (gray bars) compared with the average temperature between 1961 and 1990. The black fitted line represents the mathematically smoothed curve and shows the general trend indicated by the annual data. Most anomalies since 1977 have been above normal; warmer than the long term mean, indicating that global temperatures are tracking upwards. In 1998 the global temperature exceeded that of the previous record year, 1995, by about 0.2°C.

Source: Hadley Center for Prediction and Research

**Global Average Near-Surface Temperatures Annual Anomalies, 1860 – 2007**

This horizontal line represents the average temperature for the period between 1961 and 1990. It provides a reference point for comparing temperature fluctuations.

1998 was the hottest year on record

Smoothed curve (mathematically fitted)

**Related activities**: Pollution
**Web links**: The Greenhouse Effect

DA 2

Human Impact and Conservation

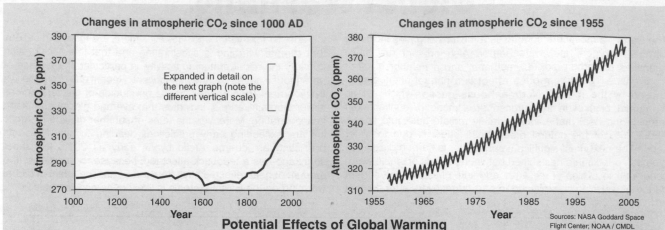

**Changes in atmospheric CO₂ since 1000 AD**

**Changes in atmospheric CO₂ since 1955**

Expanded in detail on the next graph (note the different vertical scale)

Sources: NASA Goddard Space Flight Center; NOAA / CMDL

## Potential Effects of Global Warming

**Sea levels** are expected to rise by 50 cm by the year 2100. This is the result of the thermal expansion of ocean water and melting of glaciers and ice shelves. Warming may also expand the habitat for many pests, e.g. mosquitoes, shifting the range of infectious diseases.

**Forests**: Higher temperatures and precipitation changes could increase forest susceptibility to fire, disease, and insect damage. Forest fires release more carbon into the atmosphere and reduces the size of carbon sinks. A richer CO₂ atmosphere will reduce transpiration in plants.

**Weather patterns**: Global warming may cause regional changes in weather patterns such as El Niño and La Nina, as well as affecting the intensity and frequency of storms. Driven by higher ocean surface temperatures, high intensity hurricanes now occur more frequently.

**Water resources**: Changes in precipitation and increased evaporation will affect water availability for irrigation, industrial use, drinking, and electricity generation.

**Agriculture**: Climate change may threaten the viability of important crop-growing regions. Paradoxically, climate change can cause both too much and too little rain.

**The ice-albedo effect**: Ice has a stabilizing effect on global climate, reflecting nearly all the sun's energy that hits it. As polar ice melts, more of that energy is absorbed by the Earth.

1. Calculate the increase (as a %) in the 'greenhouse gases' between the pre-industrial era and the 2004 measurements (use the data from the table, see previous page). **HINT**: The calculation for carbon dioxide is: (377 - 288) ÷ 288 x 100 =

   (a) Carbon dioxide: _____  (b) Methane: _____  (c) Nitrous oxide: _____

2. Describe the consequences of global temperature rise on Arctic ecosystems : _____

   _____

   _____

   _____

3. Explain the relationship between the rise in concentrations of atmospheric CO₂, methane and oxides of nitrogen, and the enhanced greenhouse effect:

   _____

   _____

   _____

   _____

4. Outline one international measure aimed at slowing the rate of global temperature rise: _____

   _____

# Stratospheric Ozone Depletion

In a band of the upper stratosphere, 17-26 km above the Earth's surface, exists a thin veil of renewable **ozone** ($O_3$). This ozone absorbs about 99% of the harmful incoming UV radiation from the sun and prevents it from reaching the Earth's surface. Apart from health problems, such as increasingly severe sunburns, increase in skin cancers, and more cataracts of the eye (in both humans and other animals), an increase in UV-B radiation is likely to cause immune system suppression in animals, lower crop yields, a decline in the productivity of forests and surface dwelling plankton, more smog, and changes in the global climate. Ozone is being depleted by a handful of human-produced chemicals (ozone depleting compounds or ODCs). The problem of **ozone depletion** was first detected in 1984. Researchers discovered that ozone in the upper stratosphere over Antarctica is destroyed during the Antarctic spring and early summer (September–December). Rather than a "hole", it is more a thinning, where ozone levels typically decrease by 50% to 100%. In 2000, the extent of the hole above Antarctica was the largest ever, but depletion levels were slightly less than 1999. Severe ozone loss has also been observed over the Arctic. During the winter of 1999-2000, Arctic ozone levels were depleted by 60% at an altitude of 18 km, up from around 45% in the previous winter. The primary cause for ozone depletion appears to be the increased use of chemicals such as chloro-fluoro-carbons (**CFCs**). Since 1987, nations have cut their consumption of ozone-depleting substances by 70%, although the phaseout is not complete and there is a significant black market in CFCs. **Free chlorine** in the stratosphere peaked around 1999 and is projected to decline for more than a century. Ozone loss is projected to diminish gradually until around 2050 when the polar ozone holes will return to 1975 levels. It will take another 100-200 years for full recovery to pre-1950 levels.

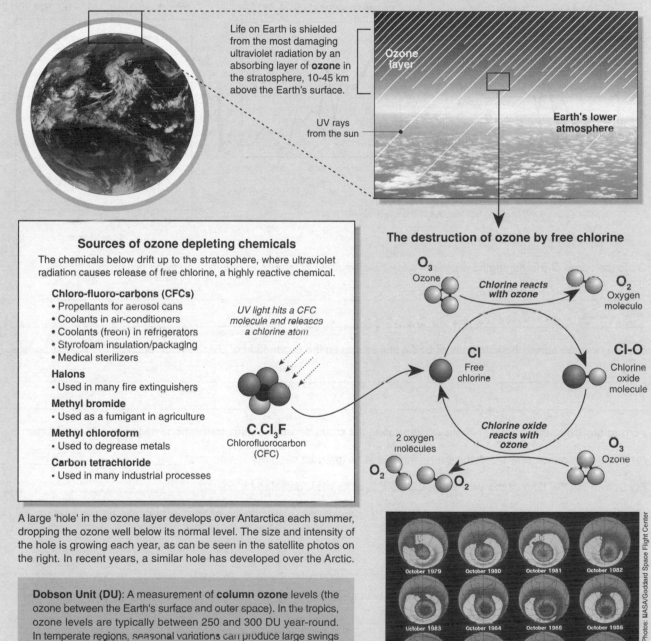

Life on Earth is shielded from the most damaging ultraviolet radiation by an absorbing layer of **ozone** in the stratosphere, 10-45 km above the Earth's surface.

Ozone layer

UV rays from the sun

**Earth's lower atmosphere**

## Sources of ozone depleting chemicals

The chemicals below drift up to the stratosphere, where ultraviolet radiation causes release of free chlorine, a highly reactive chemical.

**Chloro-fluoro-carbons (CFCs)**
- Propellants for aerosol cans
- Coolants in air-conditioners
- Coolants (freon) in refrigerators
- Styrofoam insulation/packaging
- Medical sterilizers

**Halons**
- Used in many fire extinguishers

**Methyl bromide**
- Used as a fumigant in agriculture

**Methyl chloroform**
- Used to degrease metals

**Carbon tetrachloride**
- Used in many industrial processes

*UV light hits a CFC molecule and releases a chlorine atom*

$C.Cl_3F$
Chlorofluorocarbon (CFC)

## The destruction of ozone by free chlorine

$O_3$ Ozone

*Chlorine reacts with ozone*

$O_2$ Oxygen molecule

**Cl** Free chlorine

**Cl-O** Chlorine oxide molecule

*Chlorine oxide reacts with ozone*

2 oxygen molecules

$O_2$   $O_2$

$O_3$ Ozone

A large 'hole' in the ozone layer develops over Antarctica each summer, dropping the ozone well below its normal level. The size and intensity of the hole is growing each year, as can be seen in the satellite photos on the right. In recent years, a similar hole has developed over the Arctic.

**Dobson Unit (DU):** A measurement of **column ozone** levels (the ozone between the Earth's surface and outer space). In the tropics, ozone levels are typically between 250 and 300 DU year-round. In temperate regions, seasonal variations can produce large swings in ozone levels. These variations occur even in the absence of ozone depletion. **Ozone depletion** refers to reductions in ozone below normal levels after accounting for seasonal cycles and other natural effects. For a graphical explanation, see NASA's TOMS site: *http://toms.gsfc.nasa.gov/teacher/basics/dobson.html*

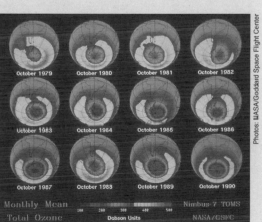

October 1979   October 1980   October 1981   October 1982
October 1983   October 1984   October 1985   October 1986
October 1987   October 1988   October 1989   October 1990

Monthly Mean Total Ozone          Nimbus-7 TOMS
                  Dobson Units     NASA/GSFC

Photos: IIASA/Goddard Space Flight Center

**Human Impact and Conservation**

Related activities: Mutagens   **RDA 2**

## Characteristics of the ozone 'hole'

The ozone 'hole' (stratospheric ozone depletion) can be characterized using several measures. The five graphs on this page show how the size and intensity of the hole varies through the course of a year, as well as how the phenomenon has progressed over the last two decades. An explanation of the unit used to measure ozone concentration (Dobson units) is given on the opposite page. Graphs 2 and 5 illustrate readings taken between the South Pole (90° south) and 40° latitude.

*Data supplied by NASA's Goddard Space Flight Center and the National Oceanic and Atmospheric Administration (NOAA) in the USA.*

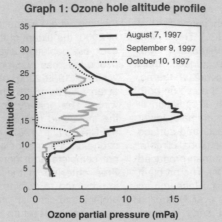

**Graph 1: Ozone hole altitude profile**

— August 7, 1997
— September 9, 1997
··· October 10, 1997

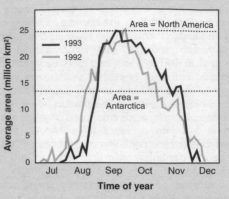

**Graph 2: Antarctic ozone hole area (<220 DU, 40° – 90° South)**

Area = North America

— 1993
— 1992

Area = Antarctica

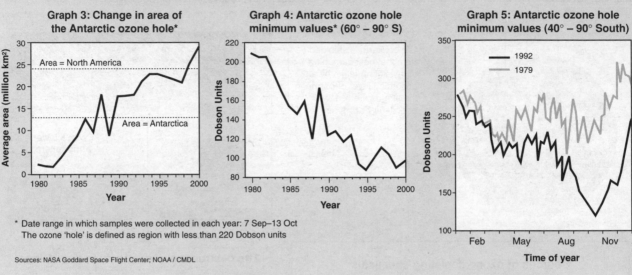

**Graph 3: Change in area of the Antarctic ozone hole***

Area = North America

Area = Antarctica

**Graph 4: Antarctic ozone hole minimum values* (60° – 90° S)**

**Graph 5: Antarctic ozone hole minimum values (40° – 90° South)**

— 1992
— 1979

\* Date range in which samples were collected in each year: 7 Sep–13 Oct
The ozone 'hole' is defined as region with less than 220 Dobson units

Sources: NASA Goddard Space Flight Center; NOAA / CMDL

---

1. Describe some of the damaging effects of excessive amounts of ultraviolet radiation on living organisms:

_____

_____

2. Explain how the atmospheric release of CFCs has increased the penetration of UV radiation reaching the Earth's surface:

_____

_____

3. With reference to the graphs (1-5 above) illustrating the characteristics of the stratospheric ozone depletion problem:

   (a) State the time of year when the ozone 'hole' is at its greatest geographic extent: _____

   (b) Determine the time of the year when the 'hole' is at its most depleted (thinnest): _____

   (c) Describe the trend over the last two decades of changes to the abundance of stratospheric ozone over Antarctica:

   _____

   _____

   (d) Describe the changes in stratospheric ozone with altitude between August and October 1997 in Graph 1 (above):

   _____

4. Discuss some of the political and commercial problems associated with reducing the use of ozone depleting chemicals:

_____

_____

_____

# Ecosystem Stability

Ecological theory suggests that all species in an ecosystem contribute in some way to ecosystem function. Therefore, species loss past a certain point is likely to have a detrimental effect on the functioning of the ecosystem and on its ability to resist change (its stability). Although many species still await discovery, we do know that the rate of species extinction is increasing. Scientists estimate that human destruction of natural habitats is implicated in the extinction of up to 100 000 species every year. This substantial loss of biodiversity has serious implications for the long term stability of many ecosystems.

## The Concept of Ecosystem Stability

The stability of an ecosystem refers to its apparently unchanging nature over time. Ecosystem stability has various components, including **inertia** (the ability to resist disturbance) and **resilience** (ability to recover from external disturbances). Ecosystem stability is closely linked to the biodiversity of the system, although it is difficult to predict which factors will stress an ecosystem beyond its range of tolerance. It was once thought that the most stable ecosystems were those with the greatest number of species, since these systems had the greatest number of biotic interactions operating to buffer them against change. This assumption is supported by experimental evidence but there is uncertainty over what level of biodiversity provides an insurance against catastrophe.

Monoculture | Natural grassland

Rainforest | Deforestation

Single species crops (monocultures), such as the soy bean crop (above, left), represent low diversity systems that can be vulnerable to disease, pests, and disturbance. In contrast, natural grasslands (above, right) may appear homogeneous, but contain many species which vary in their predominance seasonally. Although they may be easily disturbed (e.g. by burning) they are very resilient and usually recover quickly.

Tropical rainforests (above, left) represent the highest diversity systems on Earth. Whilst these ecosystems are generally resistant to disturbance, once degraded, (above, right) they have little ability to recover. The biodiversity of ecosystems at low latitudes is generally higher than that at high latitudes, where climates are harsher, niches are broader, and systems may be dependent on a small number of key species.

### Community Response to Environmental Change

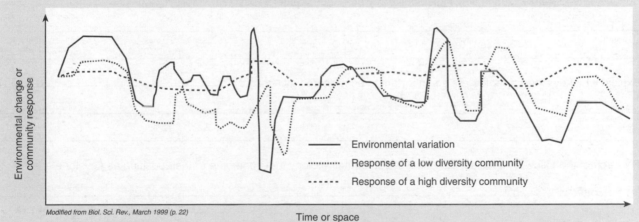

Environmental change or community response / Time or space

— Environmental variation
······ Response of a low diversity community
- - - Response of a high diversity community

Modified from Biol. Sci. Rev., March 1999 (p. 22)

In models of ecosystem function, higher species diversity increases the stability of ecosystem functions such as productivity and nutrient cycling. In the graph above, note how the low diversity system varies more consistently with the environmental variation, whereas the high diversity system is buffered against major fluctuations. In any one ecosystem, some species may be more influential than others in the stability of the system. Such **keystone (key) species** have a disproportionate effect on ecosystem function due to their pivotal role in some ecosystem function such as nutrient recycling or production of plant biomass.

Elephants can change the entire vegetation structure of areas into which they migrate. Their pattern of grazing on taller plant species promotes a predominance of lower growing grasses with small leaves.

Termites are amongst the few larger soil organisms able to break down plant cellulose. They shift large quantities of soil and plant matter and have a profound effect on the rates of nutrient processing in tropical environments.

The starfish *Pisaster* is found along the coasts of North America where it feeds on mussels. If it is removed, the mussels dominate, crowding out most algae and leading to a decrease in the number of herbivore species.

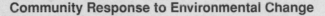

Human Impact and Conservation

**380**

## Keystone Species in North America

Gray wolf

Beaver, *Castor canadensis*

Sea otter, *Enhydra lutris*

Quaking aspen

**Gray** or **timber wolves** (*Canis lupus*) are a keystone predator and were once widespread in North American ecosystems. Historically, wolves were eliminated from Yellowstone National Park because of their perceived threat to humans and livestock. As a result, elk populations increased to the point that they adversely affected other flora and fauna. Wolves have since been reintroduced to the park and balance is returning to the ecosystem.

Two smaller mammals are also important keystone species in North America. **Beavers** (top) play a crucial role in biodiversity and many species, including 43% of North America's endangered species, depend partly or entirely on beaver ponds. **Sea otters** are also critical to ecosystem function. When their numbers were decimated by the fur trade, sea urchin populations exploded and the kelp forests, on which many species depend, were destroyed.

**Quaking aspen** (*Populus tremuloides*) is one of the most widely distributed tree species in North America, and aspen communities are among the most biologically diverse in the region, with a rich understorey flora supporting an abundance of wildlife. Moose, elk, deer, black bear, and snowshoe hare browse its bark, and aspen groves support up to 34 species of birds, including ruffed grouse, which depends heavily on aspen for its winter survival.

1. Suggest one probable reason why high biodiversity promotes greater ecosystem stability: _____

   _____

   _____

2. Explain why **keystone species** are so important to ecosystem function: _____

   _____

   _____

3. For each of the following species, discuss features of their biology that contribute to their position as keystone species:

   (a) Sea otter: _____

   _____

   (b) Beaver: _____

   _____

   (c) Gray wolf: _____

   _____

   (d) Quaking aspen: _____

   _____

4. Giving examples, explain how the actions of humans to remove a keystone species might result in ecosystem change:

   _____

   _____

   _____

   _____

# Loss of Biodiversity

The species is the basic unit by which we measure biological diversity or **biodiversity**. Biodiversity is not distributed evenly on Earth, being consistently richer in the tropics and concentrated more in some areas than in others. Conservation International recognizes 25 **biodiversity hotspots**. These are biologically diverse and ecologically distinct regions under the greatest threat of destruction. They are identified on the basis of the number of species present, the amount of **endemism**, and the extent to which the species are threatened. More than a third of the planet's known terrestrial plant and animal species are found in these 25 regions, which cover only 1.4% of the Earth's land area. Unfortunately, biodiversity hotspots often occur near areas of dense human habitation and rapid human population growth. Most are located in the tropics and most are forests. Loss of biodiversity reduces the stability and resilience of natural ecosystems and decreases the ability of their communities to adapt to changing environmental conditions. With increasing pressure on natural areas from urbanization, roading, and other human encroachment, maintaining species diversity is paramount and should concern us all today.

## Biodiversity Hotspots

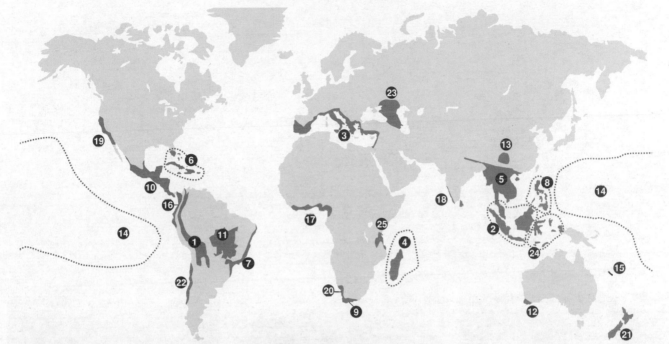

## Threats to Biodiversity

Rainforests in some of the most species-rich regions of the world are being destroyed at an alarming rate as world demand for tropical hardwoods increases and land is cleared for the establishment of agriculture.

Illegal trade in species (for food, body parts, or for the exotic pet trade) is pushing some species to the brink of extinction. Despite international bans on trade, illegal trade in primates, parrots, reptiles, and big cats (among others) continues.

Pollution and the pressure of human populations on natural habitats threatens biodiversity in many regions. Environmental pollutants may accumulate through food chains or cause harm directly, as with this bird trapped in oil.

**Human Impact and Conservation**

1. Use your research tools (e.g. textbook, internet, or encyclopaedia) to identify each of the 25 biodiversity hotspots illustrated in the diagram above. For each region, summarize the characteristics that have resulted in it being identified as a biodiversity hotspot. Present your summary as a short report and attach it to this page of your workbook.

2. Identify the threat to biodiversity that you perceive to be the most important and explain your choice:

_____
_____
_____

Related activities: Ecosystem Stability, Endangered Species, The Impact of Alien Species

**RA 3**

# Tropical Deforestation

Tropical rainforests prevail in places where the climate is very moist throughout the year (200 to 450 cm annual rainfall). Almost half of the world's rainforests are in just three countries: **Brazil** in South America, **Zaire** in Africa, and **Indonesia** in Southeast Asia. Much of the world's biodiversity resides in rainforests. Destruction of the forests will contribute towards global warming through a large reduction in photosynthesis. In the Amazon, 75% of deforestation has occurred within 50 km of Brazil's roads. Many potential drugs could still be discovered in rainforest plants, and loss of species through deforestation may mean they will never be found. Rainforests can provide economically sustain-able crops (rubber, coffee, nuts, fruits, and oils) for local people.

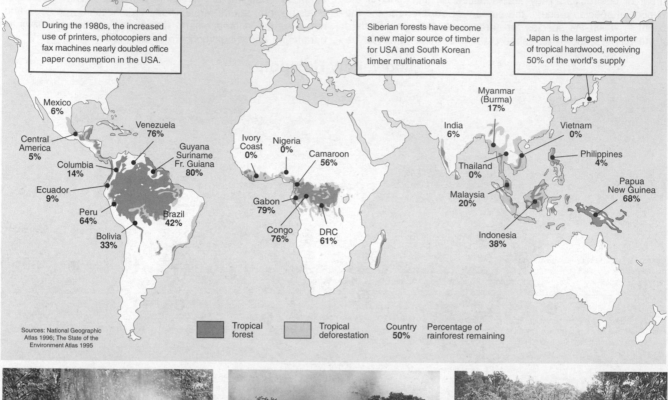

During the 1980s, the increased use of printers, photocopiers and fax machines nearly doubled office paper consumption in the USA.

Siberian forests have become a new major source of timber for USA and South Korean timber multinationals

Japan is the largest importer of tropical hardwood, receiving 50% of the world's supply

Mexico 6%
Central America 5%
Venezuela 76%
Guyana Suriname Fr. Guiana 80%
Columbia 14%
Ecuador 9%
Peru 64%
Bolivia 33%
Brazil 42%

Ivory Coast 0%
Nigeria 0%
Camaroon 56%
Gabon 79%
Congo 76%
DRC 61%

Myanmar (Burma) 17%
India 6%
Vietnam 0%
Thailand 0%
Philippines 4%
Malaysia 20%
Papua New Guinea 68%
Indonesia 38%

Sources: National Geographic Atlas 1996; The State of the Environment Atlas 1995

Tropical forest   Tropical deforestation   Country **50%**   Percentage of rainforest remaining

The felling of rainforest trees is taking place at an alarming rate as world demand for tropical hardwoods increases and land is cleared for the establishment of agriculture. The resulting farms and plantations often have shortlived productivity.

Huge forest fires have devastated large amounts of tropical rainforest in Indonesia and Brazil in 1997/98. The fires in Indonesia were started by people attempting to clear the forest areas for farming in a year of particularly low rainfall.

The building of new road networks into regions with tropical rainforests causes considerable environmental damage. In areas with very high rainfall there is an increased risk of erosion and loss of topsoil.

1. Describe three reasons why tropical rainforests should be conserved:

   (a) _____

   (b) _____

   (c) _____

2. Identify the three main human activities that cause tropical deforestation and discuss their detrimental effects:

   _____

   _____

   _____

**Related activities**: Loss of Biodiversity

# Endangered Species

Species under threat of severe population loss or extinction are classified as either **endangered** or threatened. An endangered species is one with so few individuals that it is at high risk of local extinction, while a threatened (or vulnerable) species is likely to become endangered in the near future. While **extinctions** are a natural phenomenon, the rapid increase in the rates of species extinction in recent decades is of major concern. It is estimated that every day up to 200 species become extinct as a result of human activity. Even if a species is preserved from extinction, remaining populations may be too small to be genetically viable. Human population growth, rising non-sustainable resource use, poverty, and lack of environmental accountability are the underlying causes of premature extinction of organisms. The two biggest direct causes are habitat loss, fragmentation, or degradation and the accidental or deliberate introduction of non-native species into ecosystems.

## Causes of Species Decline

Commercial and "scientific" whaling

### Hunting and Collecting

Species may be hunted or collected legally for commercial gain often because of poor control over the rate and scale of hunting. Some species are hunted because they interfere with human use of an area. Illegal trade and specimen collection threatens the population viability of some species.

Clear felling of native rainforest

### Habitat Destruction

Natural habitat can be lost through clearance for agriculture, urban development and land reclamation, or trampling and vegetation destruction by introduced pest plants and animals. Habitats potentially suitable for a threatened species may be too small and isolated to support a viable population.

Weasel with stolen egg

### Introduced Exotic Species

Introduced predators (e.g. rats, mustelids, and cats) prey on endangered birds and invertebrates. Introduced grazing and browsing animals (e.g. deer, goats) damage sensitive plants and trample vegetation. Weeds may out-compete endemic species.

Polluted discharge into waterway

### Pollution

Toxic substances released by humans into the environment, e.g. from industry, cause harm directly or accumulate in food chains. Estuaries, wetlands, river systems and coastal ecosystems near urban areas are particularly vulnerable.

### Case Study: Black Rhinoceros

Black rhinoceros *(Diceros bicornis)* were once plentiful throughout much of Africa. Now, only remnant populations remain. In Kenya, 98% of the population was lost in only 17 years.

Dehorning programs (above) carried out in Zimbabwe in 1991 have not halted the slaughter. Large numbers of dehorned rhinos are still being shot; conservationists suspect that a trader with a large stockpile of horn is trying to cause rhinoceros extinction in order to increase the horn's value.

1. Identify the factors that have contributed to the **extinction** of one named animal species: _____

_____

2. Describe two good reasons why any species should be preserved from extinction:

(a) _____

_____

(b) _____

_____

3. (a) Name an **endangered species** from your own country: _____

(b) Describe the probable cause of its decline: _____

_____

**Related activities**: Loss of Biodiversity, Conservation of African Elephants, Nature Reserves, The Impact of Alien Species

RA 2

Human Impact and Conservation

# Conservation of African Elephants

Both African and Asian elephant species are under threat of extinction. The International Union for the Conservation of Nature (**IUCN**) has rated the Asian elephant as endangered and the African elephant as vulnerable. In India, the human pressure on wild habitat has increased by 40% in the last 20 years. Where elephants live in close proximity to agricultural areas they raid crops and come into conflict with humans. The ivory trade represents the greatest threat to the African elephant. Elephant tusks have been sought after for centuries as a material for jewelry and artworks. In Africa, elephant numbers declined from 1.3 million to 600 000 during the 1980s. At this time, as many as 2000 elephants were killed for their tusks every week. By the late 1980s, elephant populations continued to fall in many countries, despite the investment of large amounts of money in fighting poaching. From 1975 to 1989 the ivory trade was regulated under CITES, and permits were required for international trading. Additional protection came in 1989, when the African elephant was placed on *Appendix I* of CITES, which imposed a ban on trade in elephant produce. In 1997 Botswana, Namibia, and Zimbabwe, together with South Africa in 2000, were allowed to transfer their elephant populations from Appendix I to Appendix II, allowing limited commercial trade in raw ivory. In 2002, CITES then approved the sale, to Japan, of legally stockpiled ivory by Namibia, South Africa, and Botswana. African countries have welcomed this decision, although there is still great concern that such a move may trigger the reemergence of a fashion for ivory goods and illegal trade.

Two subspecies of African elephant *Loxodonta africana* are currently recognized: the **savannah elephant** (*L. a. africana*) and the less common **forest elephant** (*L. a. cyclotis*). Recent evidence from mitochondrial DNA indicates that they may, in fact, be two distinct species.

In 1989 the Kenyan government publicly burned 12 tonnes of confiscated ivory. With the increased awareness, the United States and several European countries banned ivory imports. The photo above shows game wardens weighing confiscated ivory tusks and rhinoceros horns.

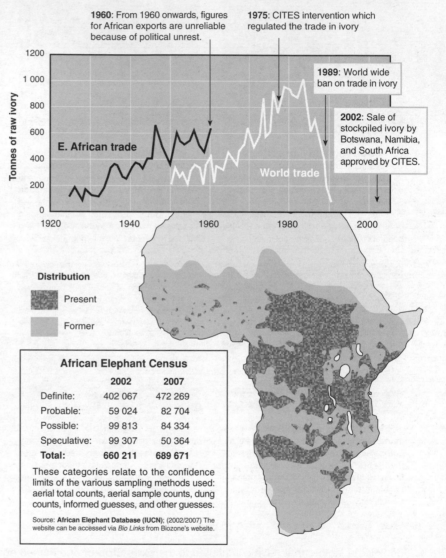

**1960**: From 1960 onwards, figures for African exports are unreliable because of political unrest.

**1975**: CITES intervention which regulated the trade in ivory

**1989**: World wide ban on trade in ivory

**2002**: Sale of stockpiled ivory by Botswana, Namibia, and South Africa approved by CITES.

E. African trade

World trade

Tonnes of raw ivory

### Distribution
■ Present
■ Former

### African Elephant Census

|  | 2002 | 2007 |
|---|---|---|
| Definite: | 402 067 | 472 269 |
| Probable: | 59 024 | 82 704 |
| Possible: | 99 813 | 84 334 |
| Speculative: | 99 307 | 50 364 |
| **Total:** | **660 211** | **689 671** |

These categories relate to the confidence limits of the various sampling methods used: aerial total counts, aerial sample counts, dung counts, informed guesses, and other guesses.

Source: **African Elephant Database (IUCN)**; (2002/2007) The website can be accessed via *Bio Links* from Biozone's website.

1. Outline the action taken in 1989 to try and stop the decline of the elephant populations in Africa: _____

_____

_____

2. In early 1999, Zimbabwe, Botswana and Namibia were allowed a one-off, CITES-approved, experimental sale of ivory to Japan. This involved the sale of 5,446 tusks (50 tonnes) and earned the governments approximately US$5 million.

　(a) Suggest why these countries are keen to resume ivory exports: _____

_____

　(b) Suggest two reasons why the legal trade in ivory is thought by some to put the remaining elephants at risk:

_____

_____

**Related activities**: Endangered Species

# Nature Reserves

**Conservation** on a national scale generally involves setting up reserves or protected areas to slow the loss of biodiversity. **Nature reserves** may be designated by government institutions in some countries or by private landowners. The different types of nature reserves, e.g. wildlife, scenic and scientific reserves, and National Parks, all have varying levels of protection depending upon country and local laws. Various management strategies (below) are proving successful in protecting species already at risk, and helping those on the verge of extinction to return to sustainable population sizes. Internationally, there are a number of agencies concerned with monitoring and managing

the loss of biodiversity. **The Nature Conservancy** is one such organization. The mission of the Conservancy is to preserve the plants, animals, and natural communities that represent the diversity of life on Earth, by protecting the lands and waters they need to survive. With donations from over a million members, the Conservancy has purchased 12 621 000 acres in the USA and a further 96 386 000 acres outside the USA (an area greater than the combined size of Costa Rica, Honduras and Panama). Larger nature reserves usually promote conservation of biodiversity more effectively than smaller ones, with **habitat corridors** for wildlife and **edge effects** also playing a part.

## Strategies for Managing Endangered Species

Puppet 'mother' feeds a takahe chick

Woodland-pond restoration (UK)

### Captive Breeding and Relocation

Individuals are captured and bred under protected conditions. If breeding programs are successful and there is suitable habitat available, captive individuals may be relocated to the wild where they can establish natural populations. Zoos now have an active role in captive breeding programs.

### Habitat Protection and Restoration

Most countries have a system of parks and reserves focused on whole ecosystem conservation. These areas aim to preserve habitats with special importance and they may be intensively managed through pest and weed control programs, revegetation, and reintroduction of threatened species.

Captive bred okapi (forest giraffe)

Orangutan (endangered species)

### Zoos and Gene Banks

Many zoos specialize in captive breeding programs, while botanical gardens raise endangered plant species. They also have a role in public education. Universities and government agencies participate by providing practical help and expertise. **Gene banks** around the world have a role in preserving the genetic diversity of species.

### CITES

The Convention on International Trade in Endangered Species (or CITES) is an international agreement between governments which aims to ensure that international trade in species of wild animals and plants does not threaten their survival. Unfortunately, even under CITES, species are not guaranteed safety from illegal trade.

## Mainland Island Management

A new strategy in conservation involves intensive management of species within a well defined area. These programs have a goal of comprehensive ecosystem restoration, with species recovery being an important consideration. In New Zealand, this strategy has been used very successfully to restore populations of the endangered wattled crow, kokako.

kokako

Kokako (above) are at risk through forest clearance and predation by introduced mammals, especially during the nesting season. Kokako recovery was implemented in a specified area of native forest which was large enough to sustain a viable population but small enough to implement long term pest control.

Chick survival is improved in a restored ecosystem

These "mainland island" projects as they are called, involve very intensive pest control programs and continued monitoring of both pest populations and the species under threat. Such programs are costly but effective; through intensive ecosystem management, the kokako population decline has been reversed and chicks (above) now survive to breed.

1. Discuss how the following *ex situ* conservation measures are used in the restoration of endangered species:

(a) Captive breeding of animals: _____

_____

(b) Botanic gardens and gene banks: _____

_____

2. Identify the advantages of *in situ* (in place) conservation measures, such as island reserves, in conserving biodiversity:

_____

_____

_____

**Related activities**: Endangered Species, Conservation of African Elephants, Loss of Biodiversity

RA 3

Human Impact and Conservation

**National parks** are usually located in places which have been largely undeveloped, and they often feature areas with exceptional ecosystems such as those with endangered species, high biodiversity, or unusual geological features. Canada's National Parks are a country-wide system of representative natural areas of Canadian significance. They are protected by law for public understanding, appreciation, and enjoyment, while being maintained for future generations. National parks have existed in Canada for well over a century. Some 83 million acres (11% of public lands) of the USA are in National Parks and Preserves, which protect natural resources, while allowing restricted activities. National wildlife refuges form a network across the USA, with at least one in every state. They provide habitat for endangered species, migratory birds, and big game.

## Parks and Reserves in North America

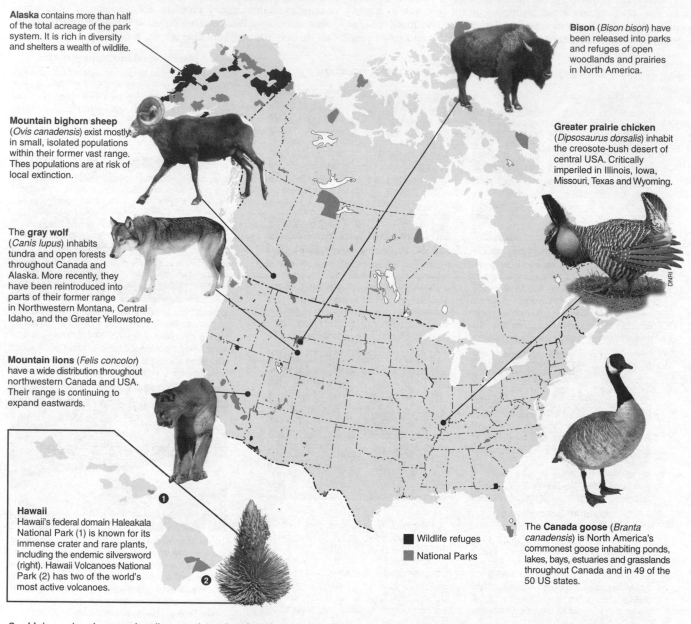

**Alaska** contains more than half of the total acreage of the park system. It is rich in diversity and shelters a wealth of wildlife.

**Mountain bighorn sheep** (*Ovis canadensis*) exist mostly in small, isolated populations within their former vast range. Thes populations are at risk of local extinction.

The **gray wolf** (*Canis lupus*) inhabits tundra and open forests throughout Canada and Alaska. More recently, they have been reintroduced into parts of their former range in Northwestern Montana, Central Idaho, and the Greater Yellowstone.

**Mountain lions** (*Felis concolor*) have a wide distribution throughout northwestern Canada and USA. Their range is continuing to expand eastwards.

**Hawaii**
Hawaii's federal domain Haleakala National Park (1) is known for its immense crater and rare plants, including the endemic silversword (right). Hawaii Volcanoes National Park (2) has two of the world's most active volcanoes.

**Bison** (*Bison bison*) have been released into parks and refuges of open woodlands and prairies in North America.

**Greater prairie chicken** (*Dipsosaurus dorsalis*) inhabit the creosote-bush desert of central USA. Critically imperiled in Illinois, Iowa, Missouri, Texas and Wyoming.

The **Canada goose** (*Branta canadensis*) is North America's commonest goose inhabiting ponds, lakes, bays, estuaries and grasslands throughout Canada and in 49 of the 50 US states.

■ Wildlife refuges

■ National Parks

3. Using a local example, discuss the role of **active management** strategies in conservation of an endangered species:

_____

4. Use your research tools (e.g. textbook, internet, or encyclopaedia) to identify a National park or wildlife refuge. Summarize the features that have resulted in it being identified as a protected area:

_____

_____

_____

_____

_____

_____

# Pest Control

**Pest control** refers to the regulation or management of a species defined as a pest because of perceived detrimental effects on other species, the environment, or the economy. Pests can be managed through **biological controls**, which exploit natural existing ecological relationships, and **chemical controls** (pesticides). Opponents of pesticide use believe that the harmful effects of pesticides outweigh the benefits, especially given an increasing resistance to pesticides by target organisms. When pesticide resistance develops, more frequent applications and larger doses are often recommended. This leads to a **pesticide** **treadmill**, where farmers pay more and more for a pest control program that becomes less and less effective. Newer, **integrated pest management** (IPM) programmes attempt to circumvent the pesticide treadmill by evaluating each crop and its pests as part of an ecological system and then developing a control programme that includes a sequence of crop management, and biological and chemical controls. The aim is not pest eradication but a reduction in crop damage to an economically tolerable level. Well managed IPM programs have outstanding success and are recognized as being economically and ecologically sound.

## Chemical Control

Pesticides, radioactive isotopes, heavy metals, and industrial chemicals such as PCBs can be taken up by organisms via their food or be absorbed from the surrounding medium. The **toxicity** of a chemical is a measure of how poisonous it is to both target and non-target organisms. Its **specificity** describes how selective it is in targeting a pest, while its **persistence** describes how long it stays in the environment. Many highly persistent pesticides show progressive concentration in food chain; an undesirable feature of their use called **bioaccumulation**.

| Pesticide type | Examples | Environmental persistence | Bioaccumulation |
|---|---|---|---|
| **Insecticides** | | | |
| Organochlorines | DDT*, dieldrin | 2-15 yrs | Yes |
| Organophosphates | Malathion | 1-2 weeks/years | No |
| Carbamates | Carbaryl | Days to weeks | No |
| Botanicals | Pyrethrum, camphor | Days to weeks | No |
| Microbials | Microorganisms | Days to weeks | No |
| **Fungicides** | | | |
| Various chemicals | Methyl bromide | Days | No |
| **Herbicides** | | | |
| Contact§ chemicals | Paraquat | Days to weeks | No |
| Systemic¶ chemicals | 2,4-D, 2,4,5-T, glyphosphate | Days to weeks | No |
| Soil sterilants | Butylate | Days | No |
| **Fumigants** | | | |
| Various chemicals | Methyl bromide | Years | Yes |

\* Now banned in most developed countries
¶ Systemic chemicals: Effective when absorbed into general circulation
§ Contact chemicals: Effective after contact with surface tissue

Source of data: Miller (2000) Living in the Environment, Brooks/Cole

### Bioaccumulation of DDT in an aquatic ecosystem

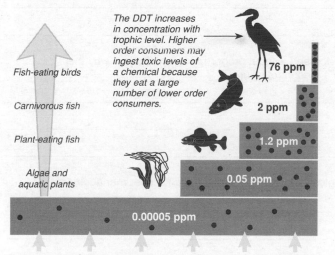

The DDT increases in concentration with trophic level. Higher order consumers may ingest toxic levels of a chemical because they eat a large number of lower order consumers.

Fish-eating birds — 76 ppm

Carnivorous fish — 2 ppm

Plant-eating fish — 1.2 ppm

Algae and aquatic plants — 0.05 ppm

0.00005 ppm

DDT enters the lake as runoff from farmland sprayed with the insecticide

## Biological Control

**Biological control** (biocontrol) is a management tool for controlling pests using parasites, predators, pathogens, and weed feeders. Some control agents with a botanical or microbial origin are called **biopesticides**. Others, such as pheromone traps, may also be classed as biocontrols. Biocontrol agents have the potential to become pests themselves so thorough investigation is required in order to predict the agent's behavior in the new environment. Biocontrol is an important alternative to conventional pesticide use and it is an important component of **integrated pest management**. A biological control program is unlikely to eliminate a pest; most aim only to maintain pest numbers at acceptably low levels.

### Biological Control of Greenhouse Whitefly (*Trialeurodes vaporariorum*)

Adult whiteflies resemble tiny moths. Their young appear as scales on the undersides of many glasshouse plants where they feed by sucking the sap. Whitefly can over-winter in a glasshouse on crops or weeds and the scales (the immobile nymph and pupal stages) can withstand occasional frosts. The young excrete a sticky "honeydew" on which sooty molds develop. The mold reduces the amount of light reaching the leaves, reducing photosynthetic rate and crop yield. Two biocontrol agents are in common use for whitefly. The ladybird *Delphastus* feeds voraciously on whitefly eggs and larvae, while the parasitic wasp, *Encarsia formosa*, parasitizes the whitefly scale and also feeds on them directly, further helping to reduce the whitefly numbers.

**Delphastus** *can consume up to 150 whitefly eggs in a day.*

**Adult whitefly** *produce 30-500 eggs in a 1-2 month life span.*

*Encarsia can parasitize up to 300 whitefly scales in 30 days.*

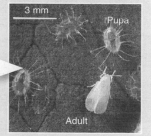

*Once the whitefly nymphs settle they become immobile.*

Photos: Dr. John Dale, Defenders Ltd

**Human Impact and Conservation**

**Related activities**: Pollution
**Web links**: Biocontrol Information Centre

**RA 2**

# Cane Toads: A Biocontrol Disaster

**Gray cane beetle, *Dermolepida albohirtum***

The introduction of cane toads to control the gray cane beetle was conducted without proper research and against the advice of scientists at the Australian Commonwealth Scientific and Research Organization (CSIRO). It was spectacularly unsuccessful; uncontrolled by the cane toad, the gray cane beetle continues to be a pest.

### The historical perspective
In 1935, 101 cane toads were deliberately introduced to Northern Queensland from South America to control the gray cane beetle, a pest of sugar cane crops in northern Australia.

### The ecological problem
Since their introduction, the toads have advanced through Queensland, the Northern Territory, and New South Wales. In the absence of natural predators and parasites, populations have reached ten times the densities found naturally in Venezuela. Their spread is continuing south and west at a rate of about 30 km per year, and they now threaten the ecologically important Kakadu National Park.

### Control options in the future
CSIRO aims to identify the genes involved in toad development and define a viral vector that could deliver a gene to disrupt metamorphosis.

**Cane toad, *Bufo marinus***

Cane toads have a voracious appetite for a wide variety of prey and compete vigourously with native species for food and habitat. All life stages, including the eggs, are highly toxic. As the toads invade a region, they threaten endemic fauna including reptiles, mammals, fish, and other amphibians. They are also harmful to domestic pests.

1. Define the following terms as they relate to the characteristics and use of pesticides:

    (a) Toxicity: _____

    (b) Specificity: _____

    (c) Biodegradable: _____

    (d) Bioaccumulation: _____

    (e) Contact chemical: _____

    (f) Systemic chemical: _____

2. Calculate the increase in DDT concentration between each step in the food chain:

    (a) Water to algae: _$0.05 \div 0.00005 = 1000$ times___

    (c) Herbivorous fish to carnivorous fish: _____

    (b) Algae to herbivorous fish: _____

    (d) Carnivorous fish to fish-eating birds: _____

3. Suggest why many insecticides fail to provide long term control of their target species: _____
   _____

4. Explain briefly why top consumers are most at risk from **bioaccumulation**: _____
   _____

5. Explain the general principle underlying the **biological control** of pests: _____
   _____
   _____

6. (a) The **cane toad** was introduced into Australia against advice and without proper research. Explain why the introduction of the cane toad to Australia has been such a biocontrol failure:
   _____
   _____
   _____

    (b) Describe the precautions now necessary before a biological control agent is released for pest management:
   _____
   _____
   _____

# The Impact of Alien Species

**Alien species** is a term used to describe those organisms that have evolved at one place in the world and have been transported by humans, either intentionally or inadvertently, to another region. Some of these alien species are beneficial, e.g. introduced agricultural plants and animals, and Japanese clams and oysters (the mainstays of global shellfish industries). **Invasive species** are those alien species that have a detrimental effect on the ecosystems into which they have been imported. They number in their hundreds with varying degrees of undesirability to humans. Humans have brought many exotic species into new environments for use as pets, food, ornamental specimens, or decoration, while others have hitched a ride with cargo shipments or in the ballast water of ships. Some have been deliberately introduced to control another pest species and have themselves become a problem. Some of the most destructive of all alien species are aggressive plants, e.g. mile-a-minute weed, a perennial vine from Central and South America, miconia, a South American tree invading Hawaii and Tahiti, and *Caulerpa* seaweed, the aquarium strain now found in the Mediterranean. Two animal aliens, one introduced unintentionally and other deliberately, are described below.

### Brushtail Possum

#### A deliberate introduction

The brushtail possum (*Trichosurus vulpecula*) was deliberately introduced to New Zealand from its native Australia in the 1800s to supply the fur trade. In the absence of natural predators and with an abundance of palatable food, possums have devastated New Zealand's flora and fauna. They are voracious omnivores where they selectively feed on the most vulnerable plant parts and eat the eggs and nestlings of birds, and compete with native species for food. There are now more than 70 million of them and they are widespread throughout the country. Possums also carry bovine tuberculosis and pose a risk to livestock in regions bordering farmed lands.

### Red Imported Fire Ant

#### An accidental invasion

Red fire ants (*Solenopsis invicta*) were accidentally introduced into the United States from South America in the 1920s and have spread north each year from their foothold in the Southeast. Red fire ants are now resident in 14 US states where they displace populations of native insects and ground-nesting wildlife. They also damage crops and are very aggressive, inflicting a nasty sting. The USDA estimates damage and control costs for red fire ants at more than $6 billion a year. Red fire ants lack natural control agents in North America and thrive in disturbed habitats such as agricultural lands, where they feed on cereal crops and build large mounded nests.

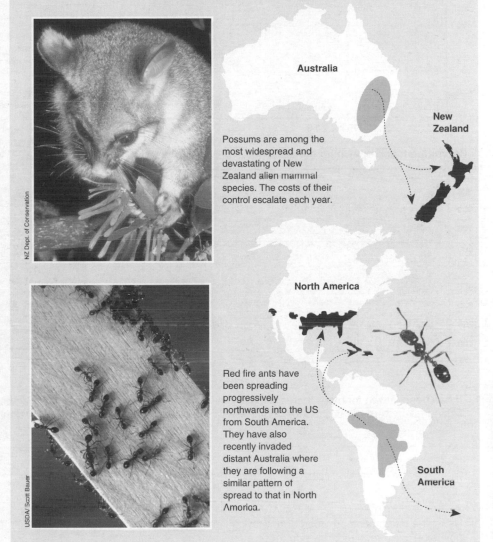

### The Spread of Alien Species

NZ Dept. of Conservation

USDA/ Scott Bauer

**Australia**

**New Zealand**

Possums are among the most widespread and devastating of New Zealand alien mammal species. The costs of their control escalate each year.

**North America**

Red fire ants have been spreading progressively northwards into the US from South America. They have also recently invaded distant Australia where they are following a similar pattern of spread to that in North America.

**South America**

Human Impact and Conservation

1. Give an example of an alien species and discuss the impact it has had on a named ecosystem:

_____

_____

_____

_____

2. Describe an example of biological control of an invasive species: _____

_____

_____

_____

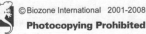 
**Related activities**: Interspecific Competition, Biological Control of Pests
**Web links**: Fire Ants Invade and Evolve

RA 2

# Fisheries Management

The stock of North Sea cod (*Gadus morhua*) is one of the world's six large populations of this economically important species. As one of the most intensively studied, monitored, and exploited fish stocks in the North Sea, it is considered a highly relevant indicator of how well sustainable fisheries policies are operating. Stocks of commercially fished species must be managed carefully to ensure that the catch (take) does not undermine the long term sustainability of the fishery. This requires close attention to **stock indicators**, such as catch per unit of fishing effort, stock recruitment rates, population age structure, and spawning biomass. Currently, the North Sea cod stock is below safe biological limits and stocks are also depleted in all waters adjacent to the North Sea, where the species is distributed. Recent emergency measures plan to arrest this decline.

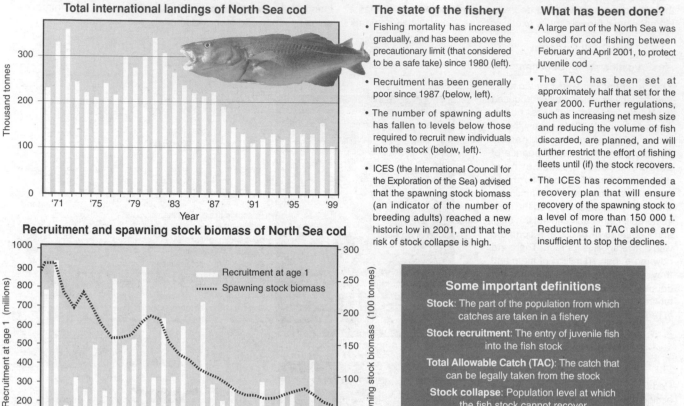

**Total international landings of North Sea cod**

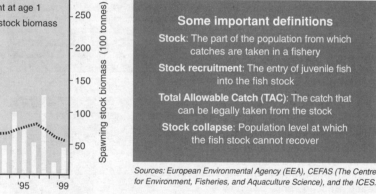

**Recruitment and spawning stock biomass of North Sea cod**

Recruitment at age 1
Spawning stock biomass

### The state of the fishery

- Fishing mortality has increased gradually, and has been above the precautionary limit (that considered to be a safe take) since 1980 (left).

- Recruitment has been generally poor since 1987 (below, left).

- The number of spawning adults has fallen to levels below those required to recruit new individuals into the stock (below, left).

- ICES (the International Council for the Exploration of the Sea) advised that the spawning stock biomass (an indicator of the number of breeding adults) reached a new historic low in 2001, and that the risk of stock collapse is high.

### What has been done?

- A large part of the North Sea was closed for cod fishing between February and April 2001, to protect juvenile cod .

- The TAC has been set at approximately half that set for the year 2000. Further regulations, such as increasing net mesh size and reducing the volume of fish discarded, are planned, and will further restrict the effort of fishing fleets until (if) the stock recovers.

- The ICES has recommended a recovery plan that will ensure recovery of the spawning stock to a level of more than 150 000 t. Reductions in TAC alone are insufficient to stop the declines.

### Some important definitions

**Stock**: The part of the population from which catches are taken in a fishery

**Stock recruitment**: The entry of juvenile fish into the fish stock

**Total Allowable Catch (TAC)**: The catch that can be legally taken from the stock

**Stock collapse**: Population level at which the fish stock cannot recover

*Sources: European Environmental Agency (EEA), CEFAS (The Centre for Environment, Fisheries, and Aquaculture Science), and the ICES.*

1. It has been known for more than a decade that the stock of cod in the North Sea has been declining drastically and that fishing takes were not sustainable. With reference to the data above, discuss the evidence to support this statement:

_____

_____

_____

2. Using the information provided above for guidance, describe the state the North Sea cod fishery, summarizing the main points below. If required, develop these as a separate report. Identify:

(a) The location of the fishery: _____

(b) The current state of the fishery (including stock status, catch rates, TAC, and quota): _____

_____

(c) Features of the biology of cod that are important in the management of the fishery (list): _____

_____

(d) Methods used to assess sustainability (list): _____

(e) Management options for the fishery (list): _____

_____

_____

# Ecological Impacts of Fishing

Fishing is a human tradition that not only satisfies a need for food, but is economically, socially, and culturally important. Today, fishing has grown to be a worldwide resource extraction industry. Decades of overfishing in all of the world's oceans has pushed commercially important species (such as cod) into steep decline. The UN's Food and Agriculture Organization (FAO) reports that almost seven out of ten of the ocean's commercially targeted marine fish stocks are either fully or heavily exploited (44%), over-exploited (16%), depleted (6%), or very slowly recovering from previous overfishing (3%). The **maximum sustainable yield** has been exceeded by too many fishing vessels catching too many fish, often using wasteful and destructive methods.

Lost fishing gear (particularly drift nets) threatens marine life. Comprehensive data on **ghost fishing** impacts is not available, but entanglement in, and or ingestion of, fishing debris has been reported for over 250 marine species.

Over-capitalization of the fishing industry has led to the build up of excessive fishing fleets, particularly of the large scale vessels. This has led to widespread overfishing (with many fish stocks at historic lows and fishing effort at unprecedented highs). Not only are the activities of these large vessels ecologically unsustainable in terms of fish stocks but, on average, for every calorie of fish caught, a fishing vessel uses 15 calories of fuel.

Bottom trawls and dredges cause large scale physical damage to the seafloor. Non-commercial, bottom-dwelling species in the path of the net can be uprooted, damaged, or killed, turning the seafloor into a barren, unproductive wasteland unable to sustain marine life. An area equal to half the world's continental shelves is now trawled every year. In other words, the world's seabed is being scraped 150 times faster than the world's forests are being clear-cut.

Due to the limited selectivity of fishing gear, millions of marine organisms are discarded for economic, legal, or personal reasons. Such organisms are defined as **by-catch** and include fish, invertebrates, protected marine mammals, sea turtles, and sea birds. Depending on the gear and handling techniques, some or all of the discarded animals die. A recent estimation of the worldwide by-catch is approximately 30 million tons per year, which is about one third of the estimated 85 million tons of catch that is retained each year.

Longline fishing (mainly for tuna) results in the death of 100 000 albatrosses and petrels every year in the southern Pacific alone. Six of the world's twenty albatross species are in serious decline and longline fishing is implicated in each case.

Over-harvesting of abundant species, or removal of too many reproductive individuals from a population, can have far reaching ecological effects. Modern boats, with their sophisticated fish-finding equipment, have the ability to catch entire schools of fish.

Fish farming, once thought to be the solution to the world's overfishing problems, actually accelerates the decline of wild fish stocks. Many farmed fish are fed meal made from wild fish, but it takes about one kilo of wild fish to grow 300 g of farmed fish. Some forms of fish farming destroy natural fish habitat and produce large scale effluent flows.

Human Impact and Conservation

1.  Explain the term **over-exploitation** in relation to commercial fisheries management: _____

    _____

2.  Explain what is meant by **by-catch**: _____

    _____

**Related activities**: Fisheries Management

## The Peruvian Anchovy Fishery: An Example of Over-Exploitation

Before 1950, fish in Peru were harvested mainly for human consumption. The total annual catch was 86 000 tonnes. In 1953, the first fish meal plants were developed. Within nine years, Peru became the number one fishing nation in the world by volume; 1700 purse seiners exploited a seven month fishing season and Peru's economy was buoyant.

In 1970, fearing a crash, a group of scientists in the Peruvian government issued a warning. They estimated that the sustainable yield was around 9.5 million tonnes, a number that was being surpassed. The government decided to ignore this; due to the collapse of the Norwegian and Icelandic herring fisheries the previous year, Peru was the dominant player in the lucrative anchovy market. In 1970, the government allowed a harvest of 12.4 million tonnes. In 1971, 10.5 million tonnes were harvested. In 1972, the combination of environmental changes (El Niño) and prolonged overfishing led to a complete collapse of the fishery, which has never recovered.

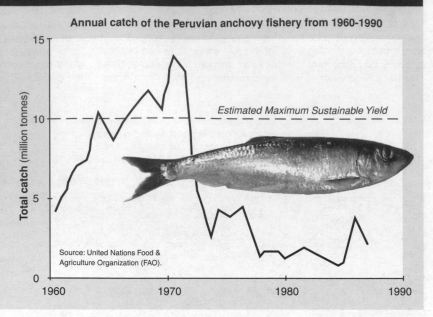

Annual catch of the Peruvian anchovy fishery from 1960-1990

Estimated Maximum Sustainable Yield

Source: United Nations Food & Agriculture Organization (FAO).

3. Using an example, explain why a catch over the **maximum sustainable yield** will result in the collapse of a fishery:

_____

_____

_____

4. Use the graph showing the relationship between age, biomass, and stock numbers in a commercially harvested fish population (below, right) to answer the following questions:

   (a) State the optimum age at which the animals should be harvested:

   _____

   (b) Identify the age range during which the greatest increase in biomass occurs:

   _____

   (c) Suggest what other life history data would be required by fisheries scientists when deciding on the management plan for this population:

   _____

   _____

   _____

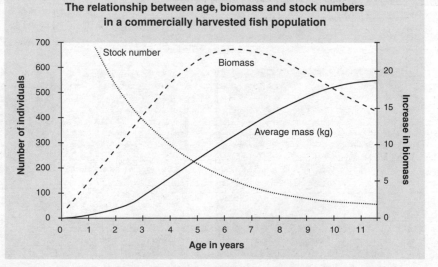

The relationship between age, biomass and stock numbers in a commercially harvested fish population

Stock number

Biomass

Average mass (kg)

5. Discuss three methods by which fish populations can be conserved: _____

_____

_____

_____

6. (a) Outline two advantages of marine fish farming: _____

   _____

   (b) Outline two disadvantages of marine fish farming: _____

   _____

# Index

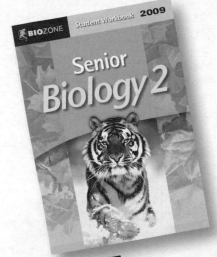

## Senior Biology 2

*A companion title to*
**Senior Biology 1**
*provides coverage of:*

- origin of life
- evolution
- population genetics
- pathogens & disease
- internal defense
- nutrition
- transport systems
- muscles & movement
- human evolution
- exercise physiology

- gas exchange
- homeostasis
- excretion
- reproduction
- nervous systems
- animal behavior
- plant adaptations
- plant responses
- microbiology
- biotechnology

## Model Answers

*Model Answers books are available for both
Senior Biology 1 and Senior Biology 2.
Each provides suggested answers to nearly
all of the activities in the workbook.*